CW00553464

BRITISH HOVERFLIES

AN ILLUSTRATED IDENTIFICATION GUIDE

BRITISH HOVERFLIES

AN ILLUSTRATED IDENTIFICATION GUIDE

Text and illustrated keys by
ALAN E. STUBBS

and

colour plates depicting *190* species by
STEVEN J. FALK

Revised and updated by
STUART G. BALL, ALAN E. STUBBS, IAN F.G. McLEAN,
ROGER K.A. MORRIS, STEVEN J. FALK and ROGER D. HAWKINS

British Entomological and
Natural History Society

November 2002

In memory of Cyril Oswald Hammond

Published by the British Entomological and Natural History Society,
The Pelham-Clinton Building, Dinton Pastures Country Park,
Hurst, Reading RG10 0TH.
Registered Charity Number 213149

First published 1983
Reprinted with supplement, 1986
Reprinted including supplement, 1993
Reprinted including first supplement, 1996
Second much enlarged and expanded supplement (issued separately), 1996
Reprinted including second supplement and an update, 2000
Second edition 2002

ISBN: 1-899935-05-3

Printed by Henry Ling Ltd., The Dorset Press, Dorchester, Dorset DT1 1HD.

British Hoverflies: an illustrated identification guide was first published in 1983, and rapidly gained an excellent reputation for enabling these attractive flies to be identified more easily and accurately than hitherto. The keys were prepared by Alan Stubbs after extensive testing by both beginners and experienced dipterists. The keys contain illustrations of the identification features alongside the couplets, which allows species to be recognised more readily than with previous publications. The text summarises an extensive body of information that was previously dispersed in many publications, as well as including numerous original observations based on many years of fieldwork. The colour plates by Steven Falk are widely acknowledged to be some of the finest painted for any group of British insects.

This second edition includes all 276 species that are known from Britain, compared with 256 in the first edition, and the keys and text have been revised extensively to take account of increased knowledge of hoverflies in Britain and continental Europe. Some European species that might be expected to occur in Britain are also described in the keys and species accounts. There are 17 new black and white plates to enable similar species to be identified more easily. In addition, the summaries of the distribution of species and their flight periods have been updated following the publication of the *Provisional Atlas of British Hoverflies* in 2000. This new edition will appeal both to experienced dipterists and to those starting to study flies for the first time.

The British Entomological and Natural History Society is a society for both amateur and professional entomologists. The Society was founded in 1872 as the South London Entomological and Natural History Society and since its inception has always included among its members many of the leading entomologists of the day. Over the years the membership of the Society has increased to include not only residents of the London area, but also people living all over the British Isles and abroad.

Indoor meetings are held monthly in central London and comprise lectures and discussions on a wide range of natural history subjects. In the autumn the Society holds its Annual Exhibition in London. Field meetings are held at weekends from late April to early October. The Society has a purpose-built headquarters, the Pelham-Clinton Building, situated near Reading, which houses the Society's library and collections and which acts as a focus for workshop meetings. The collections contain most orders of insects and include the H.W. Andrews and C.O. Hammond collections of Diptera, which have a good representation of the flies that are the subject of this book.

The Society publishes the quarterly *British Journal of Entomology and Natural History,* which frequently contains papers and observations on British and European Diptera. It also publishes key reference works, including *British Soldierflies and their allies*, *New British Beetles: species not in Joy's practical handbook*, and various reference works on macro and micro moths.

Affiliated to the BENHS is the Dipterists Forum, a society which runs the Diptera recording schemes and a programme of field, indoor and workshop meetings. It publishes the *Bulletin of the Dipterists Forum,* the journal *Dipterists Digest* and newsletters for the individual recording schemes.

Further details about the Society are available from the BENHS Secretary, c/o Dinton Pastures Country Park, Davis Street, Hurst, Reading, Berkshire RG10 0TH. News of current activities can be obtained via the website at: http//www.benhs.org.uk

The Authors

Alan Stubbs wrote *British Soldierflies and their allies* (with Martin Drake) published by BENHS, and is an Honorary Member and a past President of the Society. He was co-editor (with Peter Chandler) of *A Dipterist's Handbook* published by the Amateur Entomologists' Society in 1978. He is currently organiser of the Cranefly Recording Scheme, a member of Invertebrate Link (Joint Committee for the Conservation of British Invertebrates), and is a trustee of the newly-formed Buglife – The Invertebrate Conservation Trust. Until recently he was Secretary of the Dipterists Forum and a member of the National Trust Nature Conservation Panel. He represented Butterfly Conservation in the Biodiversity Challenge consortium of voluntary conservation organisations, which played a significant part in the development of the UK Biodiversity Action Plan. In the former Nature Conservancy he was Deputy Head of Geology and Physiography, and, on the basis of amateur entomological experience, in 1974 became Terrestrial Invertebrate Zoologist in the Chief Scientist's Team (later to become the Chief Scientist's Directorate) of the Nature Conservancy Council. On the split of NCC in 1991, he took early retirement.

Steven Falk developed a childhood interest in entomology, which rapidly came to focus on flies, bees and wasps. These became a theme of his artistic abilities and he was commissioned to illustrate *British Hoverflies* following a display of some hoverfly paintings at the AES exhibition in 1977. He has since illustrated a number of British and foreign insect guides, including the flies in the *Collins Guide to the Insects of Britain and Western Europe*. His career has mostly concentrated on nature conservation. Between 1985 and 1990 he authored reviews of both scarce and threatened Diptera and aculeate Hymenoptera while at the Nature Conservancy Council. He then spent ten years at Coventry Museum, initially as Keeper of Natural History and latterly as City Ecologist. In 2000, he took up the post of Senior Keeper of Natural History at Warwickshire Museums, where he is responsible for the extensive biological collections and for promoting natural history within the County.

CONTENTS

PLATES

TEXT FIGURES

PREFACE TO THIS SECOND EDITION

When the original book was published in 1983, it established a new style in user-friendly presentation. The hope was to inspire and encourage those who were drawn to find out more about these amazing insects. The number of reprints and updates that have followed is a measure of the extent to which it met a real need. Demand was high from the start and the original printing was sold out within three years, and total sales stand at 3,500 copies – not bad for a specialist work on flies. This much larger edition has become necessary largely due to the major increase in the number of people contributing their observations to the fund of knowledge about this popular family of flies.

Faced with a need to reprint the original volume once again, the British Entomological and Natural History Society's Publications Committee considered the options late in 2001 and decided that it was not satisfactory merely to reprint the book including supplements and update (especially as yet another update would be necessary!). Therefore this revision has been undertaken to reflect important advances in our knowledge of the British fauna. It incorporates the changes from the two supplements, additional species reported in the entomological press up until June 2002, and brings the names of species into line with the latest check list.

The original authors have contributed the lion's share of the material for the new edition. Alan Stubbs has refined his keys to cover the new species that have been discovered, and also adapted them to allow for other species, at present just across the Channel, which may eventually find their way here. Steven Falk has complemented his outstanding colour plates with detailed drawings of the male genitalia of the difficult genus *Cheilosia*. These are supplemented by Stuart Ball's drawings of the male genitalia of *Sphaerophoria*.

The species accounts have been updated to cover the additional species and to add information about habits and distribution previously published in supplements and elsewhere, including from our own *Provisional Atlas*. Whilst there has been some updating of information gleaned from the literature and unpublished sources, the deadline to which we have worked has not allowed for a comprehensive treatment.

The biggest task initially was to get the first edition into electronic form. It was scanned and transformed into word-processed text using optical character recognition software. Much of the checking that was necessary to ensure the original text was faithfully reproduced was done by Roger Morris. Alan Stubbs' original illustrations for the keys and text figures were scanned and the whole thing laid out afresh, the technical work being done by Stuart Ball. New text and illustrations from the main authors were then incorporated. Ian McLean undertook the time-consuming and painstaking job of collating references from the original text, supplements, update and new material and checking them for accuracy and consistency. Having carried out all this work, the great advantage is that it will now be much easier to keep the book up-to-date as knowledge advances.

The Society's continued support by keeping this book in print and encouraging this revision is very much appreciated. The help and support of Ian McLean (Chairman of BENHS Publications Committee) and Gavin Boyd (Sales Secretary) are equally valued, and we thank Malcolm Storey for much technical advice on the preparation of the text for publication.

Peter Chandler's diligence and care in revising the nomenclature of British Diptera is widely admired, including his efforts to stabilise historic usage and avoid some otherwise inappropriate name changes amongst the hoverflies.

This revision incorporates the observations and data from a huge number of dipterists, especially those that have contributed to the Hoverfly Recording Scheme; they deserve everyone's thanks. We urge all new recorders to become involved with the work of the Hoverfly Recording Scheme and to consider joining Dipterists Forum, which publishes a bulletin and journal (*Dipterists Digest*), as well as organising field meetings, training events and other indoor meetings. Additional opportunities to obtain assistance with identification can be had through meetings of the British Entomological and Natural History Society which runs workshops and open days at its headquarters at Dinton Pastures near Reading.

This revision would not have been possible without considerable assistance and advice from a number of individuals. We thank Dr Graham Rotheray, who provided continued advice on recent advances in hoverfly ecology and on the literature, and Peter Chandler, Jon Cole, David Iliff, Ivan Perry and Mike Pugh for their assistance in reading the text and testing the keys.

Finally, special thanks are extended to Roger Hawkins for his detailed and painstaking proof reading that has ensured that this volume attains the standard recently set by *British Soldierflies*.

Stuart Ball and Roger Morris.

PREFACE TO FIRST EDITION

Hoverflies are a popular and attractive group of insects. They are day flying and many of the 256 species are familiar to entomologists and natural history photographers. For anyone wishing to take up the study of insects, or to branch out from Lepidoptera, there are very few comprehensive and well illustrated identification guides. This book on hoverflies fills a major gap in British literature and will hopefully open the way to a wider understanding of the Diptera.

This is the first comprehensive work on any major part of the British insect fauna incorporating sketches within the body of the keys, entailing over 540 illustrations. It is a complete revision, with many new characters, incorporating species and taxa which have not previously been reported in Britain. There remain plenty of gaps in our knowledge of the taxonomy, biology and distribution of hoverflies; it is hoped that this publication will stimulate an advance in knowledge of our fauna and provide a basis on which the Hoverfly Recording Scheme can become fully effective.

The work is written for the amateur with no previous knowledge of hoverflies though it contains the basic essentials required for specialist study. The greatest barrier to the study of most insect groups is the need for a microscope. Thus great effort has been made to define simple characters which may be seen with a 10× hand lens, drawing upon microscopic characters only when these cannot be avoided.

The colour illustrations by Steven Falk, featuring 262 specimens belonging to 190 species, form a contribution of lasting value. Even if advances in our knowledge render the text outdated, these plates will faithfully portray the insects. We are very fortunate to have a talented artist available at the right time. It is the more remarkable that he started the plates at the age of sixteen while still at school. They were not illustrated in sequence, plate 7 being a fine example of his later work. Not only is great accuracy required, there is also the demanding task of portraying such varied flies ranging from furry ones to highly metallic insects.

The specimens illustrated are mostly those from our personal collections, which include some kindly given by Ivan Perry. We have been grateful to receive other specimens of critical value from Austin Brackenbury, Martin Drake and Iain MacGowan. On occasion we have had to turn elsewhere and we gratefully acknowledge the facility to study and illustrate specimens in the Natural History Museum and the Hope Department (Oxford University), whose respective Trustees we thank. The staff in the Diptera Section at the Natural History Museum have been most helpful throughout the long gestation of this book – Steven Falk and I wish to offer our warmest appreciation.

Sincere thanks are offered to all those who have given help, encouragement and support during the development of this book. Whilst remaining difficulties in the keys and text are fully the responsibility of the author, help has been given in testing various draft keys by a number of dipterists, including Austin Brackenbury, Ivan Perry, Mike Pugh and Derek Whiteley. The Field Studies Council (AIDGAP) took a helpful interest during the early stages.

Peter Chandler has acted as the Society's referee for the Publications Committee. His contribution during the final stages has been invaluable. He tested the keys on his and the

Society's collections, read the draft text, ensured reference to the Irish fauna was correct and advised on the thorny problem of the gender of specific names where affected by past and present moves between genera. Philip Entwistle, the Hoverfly Recording Scheme organiser, has also given much support and has commented on some of the distribution statements. Dr Ian McLean has helped in many ways, both with reading drafts and discussing the dilemmas which have arisen.

Dr F.C. Thompson of the USA has kindly twice paid visits to London to meet British dipterists and made available his ideas on revising the British check list. It has been helpful to know what may be eventually published and reference to personal communications from him are based on his views provided on these occasions. During the final stages in deciding on which species names to use in the book I have received magnificent support from Dr V.S. van der Goot of Amsterdam and through him advice from L. Verlinden, A. Barendregt, Dr C. Claussen, Dr J.A.W. Lucas and Dr E. Torp Pedersen.

Particular thanks are due to Dr Martin Speight, currently working in Ireland, who has done so much to keep the British list updated, with a string of important papers, as well as giving advice to many of us. Our geographical separation has made close liaison in the development of this book impractical, but I would like to record the friendly encouragement extended to me and the invaluable discussions and correspondence we have had over the years.

The original manuscript was typed at the Nature Conservancy Council, London and my sincere thanks are passed to Mrs Marina Palmer and her staff. Help with proof reading has kindly been given by Peter Chandler and Dr Ian McLean though any remaining errors must be the responsibility of myself and the printer. My wife Jane has assisted with the preparation of the index.

Members of the Society will not be surprised to learn of the close support of its Publications Committee, and of Council, and I would like to extend particular thanks to Ralph Tubbs and Rev. David Agassiz.

Cyril Hammond, to whom this book is dedicated, was an Honorary Member of the Society. As artist of *Flies of the British Isles* he set a standard of illustration, which together with the text by Colyer, did so much to stimulate interest in the Diptera. He provided great personal encouragement to a generation of dipterists and some of my happiest memories of him are our outings to Windsor Forest and other localities looking for hoverflies.

Alan E. Stubbs

CHAPTER 1

INTRODUCTION

This book was first published in 1983 and provides a guide to the identification of all the hoverfly species known to occur in the Britain and Ireland. Our fauna comprises 271 named species, but attention is drawn to the existence of a further 5 species and at least 11 forms whose name or taxonomic status is currently uncertain. There are also a number of species awaiting publication in Europe and attention is drawn to the need to retain specimens for species that are expected to be split.

Hoverflies form an attractive group of day-flying insects which includes many distinctive and familiar species. They are the friendly colourful sort of insects that many people enjoy seeing in the countryside and garden. Among their many interesting attributes is their famous precision at hovering. The American name is flower fly, referring to the habit of visiting flowers, and it is here that one learns to take a second look at what seems to be a bee or a wasp since some hoverflies are remarkable for their accomplished mimicry of such insects.

In these days of popularity of wildlife photography, and the ready availability of camera equipment suitable for close-up work, hoverflies are frequently found to be an ideal and often challenging subject.

There used to be just one over-riding problem. Here we had a popular group of insects but there was no readily available means of identifying them. Many people said that they started to take an interest in hoverflies but gave up because there was no suitable book. Even dipterists struggled with the available literature and it was poor encouragement to look at other Diptera if the favoured group of flies was difficult. In fact many dipterists used largely to ignore some of the hoverflies because they could not identify them with confidence – it just happens that hoverflies include some of the most difficult groups of Diptera. Also, the keys by Coe (1953a) were well out of date, only including 234 species. Thus by demand from fellow dipterists, a revised set of keys was embarked upon.

To write keys and descriptions for typical specimens would be a fairly manageable task. However, many hoverfly species are highly variable, a matter of interest in itself, but a problem when constructing keys. Some sections of the keys have been through numerous drafts in order to take account of variants which have been examined. Hopefully the majority of specimens will now cause no difficulty but, as more people look at hoverflies across Britain and Ireland, there are bound to be some further variants to consider. In 1983 the point had been reached where publication allowed a wider testing of ideas and promoted a continuing evolution of keys.

Whilst the Hoverfly Recording Scheme has considerably advanced our knowledge of the status and distribution of species, there is much still to be discovered.

This book offers a step towards an improved knowledge of hoverflies. At the outset there seemed to be reasonable stability in classification, but a fair number of new species have been recognised in the years since the book was first published (Stubbs, 1995b, 2000, 2001). Even so, it is likely to be some years before the present period of flux settles down. When this book reached the end of its last print run, the decision was taken to revise it so that the additions to the British fauna could be properly included in a single text. The opportunity has been taken to include in the keys some other European species that may yet be recognised as occurring in Britain, but time to do this has been short. In this exciting time in the development of knowledge of hoverflies, it would be a pity to stifle the study of our British fauna by letting this guide go out of print.

How to use this book

The contents pages give the structure of the book. Whilst the primary purpose of the book is identification, there are chapters which give an outline of how to study hoverflies.

There are several elements to identification.

— The colour plates will undoubtedly be the starting point for most readers. The great advantage of having so many species illustrated is that it is possible to become familiar with the different kinds of hoverfly even before being faced with a specimen to identify. The captions to the plates include brief comments which draw attention to significant points in the recognition of those species. With 190 species illustrated, including sexual dimorphism and other variation, it should often be possible to get close to an initial identification from the plates alone. They are equally important in providing a further check after having used the keys. [The sequence of species on the plates largely follows the order of the 1976 check list, a decision made in 1978, although an alphabetical sequence was adopted for the text.]

— The keys have some 580 illustrations to make them as easy to understand as possible. Notes on the use of keys are provided at the beginning of Chapter 7. The genera are arranged in alphabetical order within each subfamily.

— The text gives more information and helps to act as a check that identifications based on keys and plates are correct. Within each chapter covering a subfamily, the tribes, genera, subgenera and species are arranged alphabetically. The last paragraph on each species is concerned with distribution, habitat and time of occurrence. If everything does not match up, then particular caution is necessary. The organisers of the Recording Scheme will be glad to arrange for problem specimens to be examined.

— For some difficult groups, the male genitalia can provide useful confirmatory characters and, in a few cases, it is only possible to identify a species reliably from male specimens using such characters. Illustrations of the male genitalia of *Cheilosia* and *Sphaerophoria* are provided in Plates B–N and O–Q respectively, and some additional groups are illustrated in the keys and text figures. The text indicates cases where it is useful or essential to check the male genitalia.

There is a chapter on literature, comprising references and a bibliography. Often original papers contain more information than there is space for in this book. The handbook by Coe (1953a) is an important information source (unfortunately out of print) which has been taken for granted rather than acknowledged repetitively. Advances in our knowledge of the morphology and ecology of hoverfly larvae are covered by an excellent colour guide (Rotheray, 1993), and there is also a provisional atlas (Ball & Morris, 2000), which has improved our knowledge of hoverfly distribution on the British mainland considerably, and an up-to-date account of the ecology, distribution and status of the Irish fauna (Speight, 2000c). These works have been used to supplement the species accounts. Where appropriate, the headings of the species accounts include the page number for the map of that species in Ball & Morris (2000) and a reference to the colour plate of the larva in Rotheray (1993).

Attention is drawn to two books which give a great deal of broader background. A general introduction to the classification and habits of flies as a whole is provided by *Flies of the British Isles* (Colyer & Hammond, 1951, revised 1968). *A Dipterist's Handbook* (Stubbs & Chandler, 1978) is recommended as a source for techniques for the study of flies, their habitats and relationship to plants and other animals, as well as a key to families of larvae.

When Coe published his handbook in 1953, it seemed as if everyone settled back and accepted that hoverflies were well and truly sorted out, leaving little further to do. It would have been most disappointing if this book had the same effect; indeed, its intent was the exact opposite. There is so much more still to find out about our hoverfly fauna. No material was available for some species, even in the national collection at the Natural History Museum, and others are represented by only one or two specimens. We did not know the complete range of variation in many species. It is very difficult to construct reliable keys on this basis and in any case we were still turning up new species in the field. Although knowledge of the early stages has advanced considerably over the past two decades, the larvae of over half our species are still unknown and much remains to be discovered. There is also much still to find out about the habitat, distribution and seasonal occurrence of species. No doubt we will have missed snippets of useful information, but taken overall, there is nothing like preparing a book such as this to become very conscious that so much more remains to be discovered.

In the 19 years since this book was first published, much new information has emerged. This revised edition is a further stepping-stone towards consolidating knowledge and provides a better basis for further studies. The Hoverfly Recording Scheme remains the focus for gathering important ecological information and is actively working on projects that will further improve our knowledge.

The purpose of this book is to open up the study of hoverflies to a much wider audience, and hopefully open up the study of Diptera as a whole. Hoverflies are a fascinating group of insects, and they will be even more fascinating when we get to know more about them. What is particularly encouraging is that we are part of a growing wave of enthusiasm for hoverflies in Europe as a whole.

CHAPTER 2

OBSERVING, STUDYING AND PHOTOGRAPHING HOVERFLIES

These notes give some introductory advice, catering for those who like to look at hoverflies as well as those who wish to take the subject more seriously.

A good number of hoverflies are distinctive enough to recognise in the field without recourse to collecting. There is much to find out about such species. Plenty of hoverflies of interest can be found in the garden and on urban wasteland though naturally the scope is widened if habitats such as forests and marshes can be visited.

As with any group of insects, there are good days and poor days as regards success in finding hoverflies. Such fluctuations may depend on weather conditions and emergence peaks. There may be considerable variation from year to year, especially among the aphid-feeding genera since their prey also fluctuates in availability. However, many species have a long flight season and can be found with patience.

Flowers

One of the favourite habits of hoverflies is to visit flowers, providing opportunities for observation and photography. It does not take long to realise that different species of hoverfly tend to prefer different species of flower, or perhaps flowers of a certain colour and structural type. There are those which keep to flowers low on the ground and those which prefer large tall flowers. Time of day and weather conditions influence behaviour. The hoverflies may only be collecting nectar or they may be specifically after pollen (hoverflies are among the Diptera that can digest pollen) (Gilbert, 1981). Clearly hoverflies require plenty of fuel for their active life but flowers may also be used for other purposes.

Males may be visiting flowers as a likely place to find females. Thus males may be rushing from flower to flower (male solitary bees often do the same) or they may hover close by. Some species display a distinctive courtship behaviour at flowers. There is thus plenty to look out for and to record. We need to know far more about flower visiting and courtship displays.

Various types of mouthparts are found among hoverflies, some being adapted to take advantage of deep flowers while others are only suitable for flowers with easily accessible nectaries. Some species are attracted to honeydew (a sugary secretion of aphids on tree foliage) rather than flowers, perhaps accounting for the apparent rarity of some species.

On occasion hoverflies are abundant at flowers, yet at other times they are absent. During hot weather plants tend to develop water stress and this restricts nectar production to the morning – some composites close up for the afternoon anyway. If there is a long heat wave in midsummer there are often few flower visitors during 'normal' entomological hours, but one can never generalise since it is possible to have a hot day when hoverflies remain plentiful. The best days are usually typified by calm humid conditions when the sky is bright yet overcast or when there is a mixture of cloud and sunny intervals. If the air temperature is cool, the flies will disappear when the sun goes in, but under warm conditions hoverflies usually remain on the flowers. A sunny day after several dull ones, or after rain, tends to give the best results. Sheltered spots are always at a premium, especially on cold or windy days. The best one can say is that good hoverfly days are unpredictable no matter what factors are taken into account. Detailed studies in the early 1980s (Gilbert, 1985a) shed considerable light on this subject.

The obvious time to go looking for hoverflies is between 10am and 5pm when the sun is high and the conditions warm. However, some interesting observations may be missed. For instance it was thought that plantains were exclusively wind-pollinated, yet it has been noted that between 5am and 7am these flowers are visited by *Melanostoma* and *Platycheirus* (Stelleman, 1978). These genera also visit grasses and sedges for pollen so one should not restrict attention to flowers with petals. By late May, when day length is long, it seems that *Criorhina ranunculi* often visits hawthorn blossom in the evenings, and *Pocota* has also been seen at flowers in the evening. Hoverflies are obviously dividing their day between various activities, including the most important tasks of mating and egg laying, and probably resting as well.

When searching flowers it is as well not to become too mesmerised by the best and most obvious flowers, since a different hoverfly fauna may be present on less conspicuous ones. There is inadequate knowledge as to what pollinates much of our flora, but hoverflies must often play a valuable part. In the spring the best lures start with sallow in March, blackthorn following in April, and hawthorn in May or early June. Sycamore can also be very attractive. Umbellifer flowers provide a succession throughout the season, notably cow parsley, hogweed, water-dropworts, ground-elder, hedge-parsley, fool's water-cress, wild parsnip and angelica. Many of the composite flowers are of value, though the deep nectaries of the thistles can only be reached by the longer-tongued species. Devil's-bit scabious and water mint are also attractive to long-tongued species in late summer. Among the smaller flowers, heath bedstraw and tormentil are especially useful, as well as forget-me-nots and buttercups (notably lesser spearwort). In the autumn, ivy flowers in sheltered sunny spots are one of the few good attractions. Hoverflies also visit many garden flowers, and buddleia and Michaelmas daisies are well worth planting.

Interactions at flowers between hoverflies and other insects may also be revealing. For instance, to what extent are predatory wasps selective in the hoverflies they attempt to catch? Are some hoverfly species or other insects keeping other hoverflies away from choice flowers? Males of *Eristalis tenax* are said to be capable of aggressively keeping flowers clear of all other hoverfly species (Wellington & Fitzpatrick, 1981).

There is thus plenty of scope to record flower preferences and other aspects of flower visiting. To note the changes in fauna and activity at a patch of flowers during the day can be of interest, and also the way that a species with a long flight period may use different flowers as the season progresses. There are many observations on flower visitors scattered through the literature which need to be drawn together (possible taxonomic errors must be allowed for). Parmenter published details of flower visitors in many of his papers, his review of Bookham Common (1950b) and his paper on *Syritta pipiens* (1956b) being of particular value; see also other authors such as Chandler (1969), Morris (1998b) and Drabble & Drabble (1927). Flower preferences can also be assessed by means of species analysis of pollen adhering to hoverflies (Haslett & Entwistle, 1980).

The use of pollen sources is reviewed in a study in Germany (Ssymank & Gilbert, 1993). In the spring *Melanostoma* were found to use grasses and a sedge for about three-quarters of their diet.

Spring *Melangyna* were using catkins, especially alder, and herbs such as wood anemone. *Xylota* were obtaining pollen from leaf surfaces. At the study site, most of the pollen gained by *X. segnis* was from ramsons. However, *X. sylvarum* was exploiting a great range of wind-dispersed pollen, including that of nettles and wood dock.

The same study cites Imhof (1979) who reports *Lejops vittatus* and *Anasimyia transfuga* feeding on the pollen of bulrush. This is further evidence for the close ecological association of some *Anasimyia* with bulrush, but it is likely that the species referred to is *A. contracta* (the split from *A. transfuga* was not published until 1980 and the latter species is not particularly associated with this plant).

Drinking

During hot weather, hoverflies often seek moisture and possibly salts by drinking from mud or water at the edges of puddles, streams, ponds, etc. Some species, *e.g. Helophilus*, will alight on the floating leaves of water plants well away from the water's edge to drink. Alternative moisture sources include sap runs and even dung. A varied range of species have been noted doing this and Speight (2000a) includes a list.

Courtship

Reference has already been made to the use of flowers for courtship and to the behaviour which may be observed. We really know very little about the subject, especially where courtship occurs away from flowers. Males of some species display territorial behaviour, chasing off other males, as in the Eristalini; in *Eristalis tenax* individual males were found to maintain their own territory on a fairly permanent basis, carrying out all their activities within a home range (Wellington & Fitzpatrick, 1981). The males of *E. interruptus* may be seen hovering over settled females, often displaying a hovering jerky dance. Different species emit buzzing sounds of different pitch which may be relevant to the recognition of species and to courtship. It is rare to see paired hoverflies in many species so presumably they must retire somewhere inconspicuous.

To spur on further observations on this subject, we can do no better than quote R.C. Bradley's observations on *Anasimyia lineata* as given in Verrall (1901): "the female rests in a sitting position but with the wings slightly vibrating, while the male hovers a little above the female with its head bent wonderfully downwards and its wings vibrating so rapidly that they are almost invisible, and at the same time the body shakes just like a dog out of the water. Can there be any stridulation going on in which the peculiar shagreened patch of black bristles close to the base of the femora or the ribbed anal vein take a part?" It is the linkage between behaviour and use of body shape (and possibly of colour) with suggested function of structural features which is so revealing. Various other insects use stridulation (even *Drosophila* and leaf hoppers), so why not hoverflies? Over to the electronically minded.

Insight into this subject is growing, including a useful summary by Fitzpatrick & Wellington (1983; see also 1981). It is clear that time of day, time of year and prevailing weather patterns can induce varying behavioural responses. The activity/resting cycle has an important bearing.

In *Eumerus funeralis*, males stay in their adopted territory during both active and resting phases. Whilst active they face into their territory to intercept intruders, simply facing away towards the outer backdrop of vegetation during resting phases.

Eristalis tenax and *Merodon equestris* have large home ranges, navigating by polarised light, and hence are liable to get 'trapped' in one location if periods of cloud cover disrupt their movement patterns. These two species are very aggressive towards intruders. When off duty, they leave their patrol areas; they stay within a home range if numbers are low, but rest within their territories if harassed. The males only become aggressive after feeding to repletion in the morning (clearly they need a lot of fuel).

The behaviour of males of *E. tenax* varies according to the season. In midsummer the home range is about 5,000 m^2; the defended mating territory comprises 1 to 2 m^2 of vertical or horizontal space among flowers where females come for nectar. Their time is divided between defending this territory and, up to 15 m away, visiting neutral feeding stations and resting at preening stations. The males return daily to their own territory unless evicted (note that in some butterflies, as in *Pararge aegeria* (speckled wood), the holder of a territory apparently always wins when challenged by other males). In contrast, in the autumn generation, males do not hold territories but can be found feeding at flowers in large congregations. Males of the single-brooded *Merodon equestris* have a rather similar behaviour to *E. tenax* of the spring generation, though in this case defended territories are in situations where females come to oviposit rather than female nectaring areas.

Yet a further strategy is found in North American *Mallota* (plus *Spilomyia* and *Somula* which also breed in rotten wood). Here behaviour varies according to time of day. In the morning males patrol a territory of 10 to 20 flowering plants within 50 square metres or less of meadow. In the afternoon some males defend rot-hole breeding sites where females come to oviposit. The majority of eggs are fertilised by the last male to copulate with the female; there is plenty of scope for theory as to the pros and cons of such mixed strategies (Maier & Waldbauer, 1979).

Dual territorial behaviour related to courtship has also been observed in *Criorhina asilica*, males either hovering by potential oviposition sites or patrolling foliage of bushes for resting females; in this case both strategies occurred during late afternoon (Stubbs, 1989b).

One further aspect is that the eyes of male *Syritta pipiens* have enlarged facets for enhanced forward vision, an apparent adaptation to their stop-dart hovering behaviour when patrolling for females at flowers.

These and further notes will hopefully encourage a more critical look at what our British hoverflies are doing in the field. It is all too easy to be so involved with brief encounters with individual hoverflies that one fails to recognise the context of the underlying behaviour patterns.

Egg laying

There may be occasions when ovipositing females are observed. Such opportunities may occur by chance, but some good progress could be made by deliberately setting out to make observations on this subject (see Dixon, 1959). We could learn so much more about the ecology of hoverflies if egg-laying sites were better known. For example, observation of egg laying by females of genera such as *Cheilosia* and *Eumerus* has proved to be a good way of locating the larval food plant (Rotheray, 1993). Eggs may be laid at aphid colonies (or on the ground where root aphids may not be immediately obvious) or on other media such as pond-side mud, rotting vegetation or dead wood. *Rhingia* lays its eggs on grasses overhanging cow dung.

It would seem that the aggressive activity of male *Eristalis tenax* may prevent aphidophagous (and presumably certain other hoverflies) from egg laying in certain areas (Wellington & Fitzpatrick, 1981).

Migration

A number of species of hoverflies are migrants. This activity seems to be largely confined to Syrphini and may be an adaptation to exploit local fluctuations in abundance of aphids. There have been a number of observations of the sudden appearance of large numbers of hoverflies on the coast of England, sometimes with a strand-line littered with dead hoverflies that did not quite reach land (however, note that an offshore wind can result in such a phenomenon following a mass emergence in Britain). There are also inland observations of large-scale unidirectional movement of hoverflies across a broad front of countryside. Certain species that suddenly appear in enormous numbers in the garden may be migrants, or alternatively may represent a local mass emergence. The species most regularly associated with migration in Britain are *Episyrphus balteatus, Eupeodes corollae, E. luniger, Scaeva pyrastri, S. selenitica, Sphaerophoria scripta* and *Syrphus vitripennis*. A convenient table of known migratory species is given by Torp (1984) and his map of European observations would seem to imply that all observed movements are southwards (perhaps the numbers moving north in the spring are small and hence go unrecorded). A study of migration across an alpine pass (Aubert *et al.*, 1976) also included *Eristalis tenax, Melanostoma mellinum, Eupeodes lapponicus* and *Syrphus torvus*. They found that in *Episyrphus balteatus* the proportion of males to females varies between 1:1.9 and 1:2.7 in the period from July to September, but goes up to 1:10.6 in October, which may be the result of females living longer than males.

There must be greater movement going on than might be expected. The establishment of *Eupeodes* (*Lapposyrphus*) species A, *Eriozona syrphoides, Sphegina sibirica* and *Dasysyrphus friuliensis* in conifer plantations in the last few decades must have been via colonists from Europe (or introduction on imported trees, though usually it is seed that is imported). Here one should perhaps speak of dispersal leading to an extension of range (whereas migration is a seasonal movement which enables exploitation of transient breeding conditions beyond the range where the species can successfully survive throughout the year). It is often difficult to define exactly what is happening on the basis of few records. For instance, there are only a few British records of *Scaeva albomaculata* and just one of *S. mecogramma*, both species well outside their normal European range. Even the possibility of transport by ship must not be ruled out, though, if they had arrived by their own efforts, one would treat them as vagrants rather than imported species. *Eupeodes lundbecki* and *Helophilus affinis* are also recent additions to the British list which probably represent vagrant individuals. Not all examples of vagrants, migrants and dispersal concern aphid-feeders since, for instance, *Volucella zonaria* used to be regarded as a rare migrant or vagrant until its firm establishment in Britain in the 1940s; however the resident population may continue to be reinforced by migrants.

In Denmark it is considered that *Episyrphus balteatus* and *Scaeva pyrastri*, in common with *Eupeodes corollae*, do not overwinter as adults; in spring females arrive before the males. Only

Eristalis tenax is known to overwinter as an adult in Denmark. Adults of *E. balteatus* seem to overwinter in the milder parts of Britain, since they can be found on sunny days in midwinter together with *E. tenax*. Speight (1985) concluded that *S. pyrastri* is not resident in Ireland but is dependent on migration for its occurrence. Our recorders in Scotland have reached a similar conclusion and we need to re-evaluate the position in the mild southerly parts of England. It has been suggested that *Xanthandrus comtus* is also a migrant, with doubts expressed as to whether it can survive the winter in Britain (Shaw & Rotheray, 1990), although it has been observed at some localities over several consecutive seasons.

Overall there is growing evidence of movement by hoverflies, especially in urban areas. In Leicester a garden was monitored for 15 years, largely by means of Malaise traps (Owen, 1991). Over half the recorded species were casuals or strays for which there were no obvious breeding sites either in the garden or its immediate neighbourhood.

A method of garden monitoring by observation has reached comparable conclusions (Stubbs, 1991). This has revealed that the build up of numbers of such species as *Episyrphus balteatus* can be gradual or sudden and numbers can also fall off gradually or suddenly. It is unclear whether this involves local movement, following mass emergence from cereal fields, or long-distance migration.

In 1994 there were huge numbers of *E. balteatus* on the Norfolk coast coming onshore for two weeks and also large numbers in the sea, and on the coast of South Wales, but numbers were apparently not necessarily so exceptional inland. Observations have also been made of steady movement seawards on the south coast of England in the autumn.

Migration events are sometimes on a scale that is easy to recognise and far more observations are required. Lepidopterists have become quite refined in collating information on migration patterns, being able to recognise the movement of a migration front over a period of successive dates and analysing the weather patterns to interpret the origin of the insects concerned. Hoverflies would seem very suitable for similar studies since they are day-flying and the species involved are readily recognised and can occur in large numbers.

Whilst on the subject of distribution fluctuations, it is relevant to note that a number of British butterflies have changed, and are still changing, their distribution patterns. Some have undergone periods of expansion and contraction of range, such as the comma butterfly, *Polygonia c-album* (Asher *et al.*, 2001). It is almost certain that the same phenomenon is occurring amongst the hoverflies. When a species is regularly seen and then disappears for a number of years before being seen regularly again, has its range really changed, or has it simply declined within a district to such a small population that it is overlooked? With a national network of recording it should be possible to gain a better picture of what might be happening. Britain and Ireland are, of course, simply part of a broader European distribution which leads us back to species such as *Volucella zonaria* which appears to be expanding its range in southern and eastern England at the moment. Will this turn out to be a temporary phenomenon while conditions favour a periodic colonist, or will this spectacular species become more widely established with us?

Flight periods

The Provisional Atlas (Ball & Morris, 2000) includes phenology histograms that show the number of records for each species plotted at fortnightly intervals from 24 February to 16 November. These histograms are the basis of the statements about flight periods given in this book. However, taking combined national data obscures the fact that the pattern of emergence may vary between years by as much as four weeks according to weather conditions, and that considerable geographical variation may also occur. Thus, there may be two, three or more broods in some species, but only in some districts and in some years.

There have been an increasing number of studies involving regular sampling through the season. These can be made using traps, such as Malaise traps emptied daily or weekly (*e.g.* Owen, 1981) or by regular observations. It will become far more practical to make meaningful statements on seasonal occurrence and brood patterns once the results of enough such studies are available. For those interested in monitoring by observation, a transect method (*e.g.* Pollard, 1971 & 1977) with appropriate adaptation has been used with some success by Stubbs (1991) (see also Gilbert, 1981).

Flight period studies should also consider daily patterns in activity by hoverflies, though variations in light and temperature in the changeable British climate may produce rather a confused picture. However, there should be some partitioning of activity during the day between courtship, feeding, ovipositing and resting. On hot days some hoverflies may be active very early or very late, even as dusk approaches.

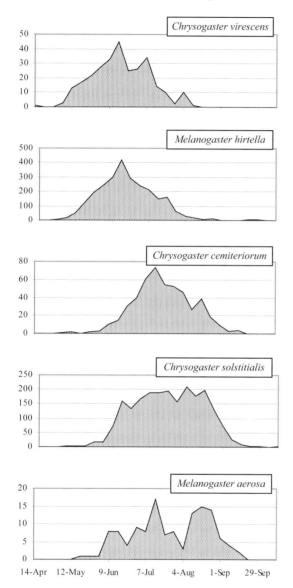

Text fig. 1. Flight periods of *Chrysogaster* and *Melanogaster* species.
The number of records each week is shown on the vertical axis.

Analysis of the emergence patterns of *Epistrophe eligans* (Ball & Morris, 1992) based on cumulative data from the recording scheme, has shown clearly that emergence is several weeks earlier in the south-west compared with northern England. This result is to be expected, but a firmer picture of regional differences is apparent. There is also some evidence that the flight period of *E. eligans* is shifting towards earlier emergence in southern England in response to warmer and earlier springs (Morris, 2000). It is hoped to develop analyses of this type for many more species.

In Fig. 1, records of *Melanogaster* and *Chrysogaster* species are grouped into weeks of occurrence, based upon observations collated by the Hoverfly Recording Scheme. The species are arranged in sequence by the average date of observation, from earliest to latest. The emergence periods of the closely related species *M. hirtella* and *M. aerosa* are clearly different, and *C. virescens* tends to be earlier than *C. cemiteriorum* and *C. solstitialis*. However, much of the detail is lost through combining data from many years and many localities; for instance, the small number of much later records of *M. hirtella* are from Scotland. This sort of analysis can easily be made from records of hoverflies seen in a garden, keeping each year's records separate so that differences between years can be considered.

A study by Gilbert (1985a) was based on transects across a site which revealed activity patterns related to time of day, temperature, humidity and sunshine. The larger species spent less time in flight and became active at lower temperatures than small species. Hoverflies were observed at temperatures of between 15° and 25°C, but a few were active as low as 8°C. During the early morning feeding was at pollen and this continued throughout the day, nectar feeding became more pronounced as the morning advanced and reached a peak near mid-day. Observations ceased at 3pm (British Summer Time) when activity had declined. Hoverflies became more likely to rest when the humidity rose, especially when above 80% relative humidity. Whilst feeding at flowers occurred more often in sunny situations, males flew equally in sun and shade, but females flew mainly in the shade. There was a certain amount of variation between species, and the paper has many interesting details. A point of particular note is that *Melanostoma* is active at low temperatures despite its small size (*M. mellinum* was seen at 8°C and was active at 13°C). It is noted that this genus feeds on grass pollen which is rich in starch and proline. It would seem that deriving energy from proline enables such species to fly with a lower body temperature than with an energy system based on sugars from nectar.

The above paper also reviewed reports of hoverflies at light traps and concluded that these are accidental visitors and do not indicate that night-time flight is normal!

The enemies of adult hoverflies

Little is recorded about the natural enemies of adult hoverflies. The fact that so many hoverflies display the warning colours or behaviour of bees and wasps suggests that predators with good sight, especially birds, are among the principal predators. The time of emergence may help reduce the chances of being eaten. For instance *Merodon* has its peak emergence before the main crop of new nestlings, so young birds are first likely to encounter bumblebees and, if they are forgetful in the following spring, they will have a refresher course on queen bumblebees that have hibernated before *Merodon* appears again (Conn, 1972). However, not all bumblebee mimics time their emergence in agreement with such a neat theory. Also some birds are content to eat bees and wasps, mimics and all.

Undoubtedly many hoverflies also fall prey to the great army of invertebrate predators. One of the most interesting relationships is the way that certain solitary wasps catch and paralyse Diptera in order to stock their nests with food for their larvae. Wasps of the genus *Ectemnius* often use hoverflies, as does *Crabro cribrarius*. Such wasps are frequently met with on umbellifer flowers and sometimes even occur in gardens. *Ectemnius* nests in old beetle borings, accounting for the mysterious packages of dead hoverflies that may sometimes be found on breaking open rotten wood. The wasp has brood parasites, so sometimes it is other flies, such as *Eustalomyia* (handsome black and grey anthomyiid flies) whose larvae consume the hoverflies. Social wasps are considerable predators of hoverflies, as are spiders. We need to know far more about which species of hoverfly are most susceptible to various species of predator.

Perhaps the most striking enemy of hoverflies is a fungus. It is not uncommon to find large numbers of *Melanostoma*, or sometimes other genera, dead on grass flowers or on foliage. Close examination will reveal that the abdomen is inflated, with the membranes having a rather granular appearance. These mummified flies have been attacked by the entomophagous (insect-eating) fungus *Entomophthora* (=*Empusa*) *muscae*. This fungus attacks a wide range of Diptera including various hoverflies, but some species are more susceptible than others.

Mimicry

Some species of hoverfly strongly resemble a bee or wasp to most people, but there are many more species where any suggestion of mimicry seems rather far fetched. Trials by Dittrich *et al.* (1994) indicated that pigeons responded along similar lines to these human perceptions. However, looking at an illustration or a museum specimen can give a very distorted perspective. In life the behaviour of the hoverfly, such as how it sits and its behaviour in flight, may transform an otherwise poor mimic into a good one. Colour patterns that seem irrelevant may in practice prove of value in creating deception. *Xylota sylvarum* is a good example because no one would describe it as a mimic of an *Ectemnius* wasp when pinned, but when alive, resting on foliage with its wings folded, it can be surprisingly convincing. Is the appearance and behaviour of suitable models similar to the mimics, or indeed do models actually occur on site? Better models may occur elsewhere within the range of a species, but not in Britain. Observations in this field are very much needed; see Howarth *et al.* (2000) for coverage of this topic.

Variation in body colour and form

The fact that butterflies vary in colour is well known. Such variation may for instance be related to geographic area, to difference between broods through the season, or to genetic aberrations. It has been shown experimentally that temperature can affect the amount of dark pigment laid down during pupal development.

Hoverflies show similar variation. In a number of bivoltine species of *Cheilosia* there are substantial differences between the two broods. The spring brood is often bigger, more hairy and has a virtually bare arista. This is most marked in *C. vulpina* and *C. proxima* which exhibit this tendency to the extent that, in the 1983 edition, the two broods of the latter were treated as separate species (spring = 'species E', summer = 'species D'). *C. pagana* and *C. vernalis* exhibit similar variation, but to a lesser extent. In *Eristalis pertinax* spring specimens are consistently hairier than summer and autumn specimens, with smaller and duller orange marks on the abdomen, and spring specimens of *Meliscaeva auricollis* are darker than summer specimens and are regarded as a named variety (var. *maculicornis*). In some cases it will only be by rearing that one can prove whether or not the different forms belong to the same species (*e.g. Cheilosia pagana*). Others, such as *Episyrphus balteatus*, show a range of colour forms from very light to very dark; observations suggest that pale forms are most often seen in hot summers and dark ones under colder conditions, as if temperature was playing a role. Dušek & Láska (1974) have shown that the temperature during pupal development does indeed affect the extent of dark markings in *E. balteatus* and other Syrphini.

Various species show two or more distinct colour forms. The genetic basis of such variation in *Volucella bombylans* is discussed by Keeler (1926). No doubt other examples, such as *Criorhina berberina* and its var. *oxyacanthae*, can be interpreted as genetically controlled. *Merodon* has a great range in colour forms (the subject of a study on genetics by Conn (1972) which includes a colour plate showing the various forms). Heal (1979a) carried out breeding experiments on *Eristalis tenax* to interpret the genetic basis of the variation in this species. In a second paper (1979b) he considered *E. intricarius* and found that temperature during pupal development could impose an effect on top of the genetic control in some cases. Heal's papers include a classification of colour forms.

Many butterflies display differences of colour and structure between the sexes. In some cases it is only one sex which produces colour variation. In the Syrphinae it would seem that genetically melanic (black) forms only occur in the females. In *Merodon*, var. *transversalis* is confined to the female (Conn, 1972).

Some variations are bizarre since they have a baffling mixture of male and female features. For instance, there is a specimen of *Platycheirus ambiguus* with male front legs, yet the frons is broad as in the female, whilst various other characters are not typical of either sex. The dark form of *Platycheirus granditarsus* is similarly a mixture. There are usually very small and non-functional male genitalia. Such examples are regarded as intersexes (a gynandromorph would be male on one side and female on the other). There is suspicion that *Cheilosia globulipes* is no more than an intersex of *C. urbana*, and an unusual form of the female of *Orthonevra nobilis* is interpreted in the same way.

Hoverflies may be found in which something has clearly gone wrong during their development. These are referred to as teratological specimens (their study has little merit). This condition is often found in the Syrphini where there are more spots or bars on one side of the abdomen than on the other – close examination will usually reveal that one of the tergites has only properly developed on one side of the body. Sometimes the face profile is distorted or legs are misshapen. Some families of flies are prone to develop curious wing venation though we have not yet seen a significant example among the Syrphidae.

Freshly emerged (teneral) adults have weak coloration on the body, legs and wings. It may take several days before markings gain their full strength.

It would be possible to waste much time and effort to no useful purpose by being over concerned with trivial variation. However, the discussion above will hopefully alert the keen observer and breeder of hoverflies to some of the possibilities worthy of further attention.

Hoverflies as pests and allies

Fortunately very few hoverflies are pests. The large bulb fly (*Merodon*) and lesser bulb flies (*Eumerus funeralis* and *E. strigatus*) attack bulbs in gardens, but under most circumstances there is little cause for concern. *Merodon* and *Eumerus* occur in most gardens and seem to cause little problem – the hoverflies are attractive and pleasing to see, so why worry at the inconspicuous loss of an occasional bulb? *Cheilosia antiqua* has been recorded as a pest of primroses but rarely occurs in gardens. With so many European plant species becoming serious weeds in the New World and Australasia, it is not surprising that biocontrol agencies look towards European insects as agents to suppress these plants. Within the Syrphidae, *Cheilosia* has come under close scrutiny, and Italian *C. grossa* has been introduced into parts of the USA to control musk thistle (Rizza *et al.*, 1988). At the time of writing this second edition, *C. urbana* and *psilophthalma* are about to be released into New Zealand to control hawkweeds.

The aphid-feeding hoverflies are allies of the gardener, farmer and forester, since hoverflies are among the insects that help keep the prodigious breeding capacity of aphids in check. Sometimes the aphids succeed in achieving a population explosion, the weather probably being one of the most significant factors in the complex equation of the relative success of aphids and their natural enemies. On agricultural crops it is obviously the hoverflies of open ground which are significant (Pollard, 1971); these include a number of the most common and mobile species, some of which are migrants. Thus much depends on the weather and emergence peaks as to the significance of hoverflies in the control of aphids from one year to another.

A review by Schneider (1969) reached the general conclusion that hoverflies are fairly inefficient predators of aphids in most situations. This view used to be shared by many economic entomologists, at least for agricultural crops. However, there is surprisingly little research on this subject, especially in circumstances other than highly artificial habitats such as transient agricultural monocultures.

Recent work on the beneficial role of aphid-eating hoverfly larvae in cereal crops shows that *Episyrphus balteatus* can be important in some years (in southern England). Even at low densities, this species may swamp the effect of polyphagous predators (such as predatory beetles). Since larvae are mainly active at night, it is likely that their numbers have been underestimated (see Winder *et al.*, 1994).

Thus there remain many gaps in our knowledge and understanding. Even the distribution of aphid-feeding hoverfly species in your own garden leaves scope for an interesting study. We still don't fully understand the competitive relationships between hoverfly larvae, ladybirds and lacewings – why is it that some years hoverflies do well yet in other years it is ladybirds that are abundant?

Hoverflies are also important pollinators of flowers. On fruit trees and some other crops they play their part, especially when bees are scarce. However, it is probably their contribution to the pollination of garden flowers and wild plants that is of greatest value. The pollen loads adhering to the hairs of hoverflies can be almost as great as the loads collected by bees.

Population studies

It is possible to deploy standard techniques for estimating population size and longevity (length of life). Such a study using the 'mark and recapture' method has been described by Nielsen (1969) for populations of *Helophilus hybridus* and *Sericomyia silentis* in Norway. A study of *Merodon* (Conn, 1976a) revealed that the average life of the adult was between 3 and 11 days, in contrast to the findings of Hodson (1932b), of between 11 and 17 days. Such studies will produce meaningful results where populations keep within reasonably small blocks of habitat and individuals are easy to find and catch; interpretation of results becomes more difficult if species are too mobile and if the chances of recapturing elusive individuals are remote. It is necessary to have the time to pay daily repeat visits.

A population study of *Eristalis pertinax* at Reading showed what can be achieved within four weeks by simple means (Holloway & McCaffery, 1990). The same methods of mark and recapture, applied to a woodland glade about 45 metres square and divided into recording sectors, gave an insight into the huge numbers of hoverflies in such a small area. A total of 5,236 flies were captured and marked in the first 15 days. It was estimated that 1,150 flies marked in the first seven days disappeared during the 24 hours after marking. Although this suggested that there was substantial movement in and out of the glade, many individuals stayed within a range of only 20 to 30 m over a 5-day period, especially females close to the wood edge. Longevity of up to 17 days was recorded, the average for males being 4.2 days and possibly longer for females which would have left the study site to lay eggs.

Ecological studies

Ecology is sometimes equated with habitat, but it is really the summation of all aspects of the relationship between an individual (population/species) and its environment. Thus we are really speaking of many aspects of the natural history of hoverflies, including their habits, habitat and interactions with other species (both plant and animal). The whole of this chapter is relevant to ecology but some suggestions suitable for the amateur may be helpful.

One could select a species, or a group of related species in a genus or tribe, and record all one can about the habitat requirements, courtship, flower preferences, daily rhythm of activity, etc. Differences between closely related species should begin to emerge. Nielsen (1966) has described such a study of *Helophilus*.

There have been various recent studies on adult hoverflies, including those on garden monitoring (Owen, 1991; Stubbs, 1991). Alternatively one may record the entire hoverfly fauna of a locality and consider the habitat distribution of the various species within a site. One may go on to a comparison with other sites of similar habitat, or sites with differing habitat. In choosing sites, it is worth anticipating options which may give interesting results. For instance, woods of different sizes may support different numbers of species (large woods ought to contain a richer fauna). A site which has always been woodland is likely to contain species which are absent from younger secondary woodland; Stubbs (1982) discusses this situation and has devised a provisional list of ancient woodland indicator species of hoverflies. It would also be of interest to compare natural deciduous woodland with conifer plantations. Whilst woodland is a good example, the same principles apply to other habitat types.

Research studies on the rhythm of hoverfly activity, the structure of hoverfly communities and mouthpart adaptation to various flowers are considered in various papers by Gilbert (1985a; Gilbert *et al.*, 1985; Gilbert & Owen, 1990). A longer proboscis with a broader labellum (broad mopping-up flaps at the end of the proboscis), and also increased body size, is linked with the more frequent taking of nectar. The larger hoverflies tend to spend less time flying. A wide labellum and short proboscis is associated with feeding on pollen and honeydew from leaves, as in *Xylota*. It is suggested that the size and shape of males is adapted to ability to control body temperature (short broader wings, larger thorax and narrower abdomen) whilst females are more adapted to feeding (the labellum is larger). The structure of hoverfly communities in ancient forest shows a range of body size and proboscis length that minimises competition between species, whilst in the disturbed habitat conditions in urban areas there is no recognisable community structure.

These brief comments will hopefully set the mind thinking about many other options for ecological studies. If you cannot get out into the countryside there remain plenty of potential studies in gardens and urban waste ground.

Genetics

Torp (1984) reviews work on the chromosomes and genetics of hoverflies. This is a specialist topic that is remote from the field entomologist. However, it is worth at least recognising that genetic studies can lead to a better understanding of taxonomic problems.

Thus, whilst *Platycheirus* species have good chromosomal characteristics in common, *Criorhina asilica* is genetically very different from *C. berberina* (not of closely related stock, so the generic grouping may not be justified). Similarly chromosome numbers vary within *Cheilosia* (little surprise here!). Looking at *Sphaerophoria rueppellii*, the chromosome diagrams are different for specimens from Italy and the Netherlands, and even different between two parts of Italy, so some rather intriguing interpretations may yet emerge.

Photography

The photographer of hoverflies is able to capture the natural postures and behaviour of these insects and thus record a very different aspect of a species than seen in a museum collection. Understanding of breeding sites can be advanced by photographing such situations; these habitat shots can be invaluable, especially for the more local species.

There is a very great need to get good colour photos of the early stages of those hoverflies with aphidophagous larvae, since they often have colours and patterns which are lost in preserved material (see plates in Rotheray, 1993). A link up with those interested in rearing is desirable since it will be essential to gain accurate identification.

If there happen to be people with video equipment, they are in the best position to record behaviour, especially courtship. It is probable that some features of courtship display will only be recognised when analysed frame by frame or in slow motion, not to mention the methods by which hoverflies hover and manoeuvre.

Taxonomic studies

How do you define a species, or a genus, and how do you produce a hierarchical classification that best describes the relationship of the different species and genera? This is often one of the most fascinating aspects of studying groups such as hoverflies and it is a form of detective work that can draw on many aspects of a hoverfly's life, including the external morphology and internal anatomy of the adult and larva, plus the biology, distribution, ecology, genetics and behaviour. It is not always easy to know whether you are dealing with one species or a group of closely related ones. Sometimes the external appearance of a hoverfly fails to give reliable clues. You may find better characters in the male genitalia, and ecology and locality or date of capture may help. It is not just the preserve of professional entomologists to research these areas. The great army of amateur entomologists in Britain has enjoyed a long tradition of clarifying the understanding of difficult species, discovering new British species and even discovering new undescribed species.

CHAPTER 3

COLLECTING

Considerable basic advice is given in *A Dipterists' Handbook* (Stubbs & Chandler, 1978).

The identification of many species will require the capture of hoverflies in order to examine them more closely. Most of the key features can be seen with a hand lens, enabling identification in the field. However, in order to reach a confident level with identification, and certainly when dealing with the more difficult species, it will be necessary to collect specimens and to examine them under a low-power microscope. Establishing a reference collection is essential for anyone wishing to take up the recording of all hoverflies seriously.

Nets

Virtually any kind of insect net will suffice. A black muslin net as used for Lepidoptera is suitable for netting single specimens. However, dipterists usually prefer a white net since flies tend to be swept up in numbers and it is easier to see them inside the net against a white background. Home-made nets can be used, with fine-mesh terylene netting and hard-wearing material on the rim. A net designed by dipterists is available from Marris House Nets, 54 Richmond Park Avenue, Queen's Park, Bournemouth, BH8 9DR. This consists of a 16 inch (40 cm) diameter frame (a fisherman's landing frame which folds into four, but is now an illegal size) on a detachable 1.2 m aluminium pole. Such a net is ideal for sweeping, catching from flowers, trapping on the ground and taking hovering insects out of the air. A long handle is not essential, but it helps when approaching wary hoverflies and when trying to reach hoverflies at height (*e.g.* on flowering shrubs in spring). It is also possible to buy poles with a telescopic extension (2 m landing net poles) from fishing shops, and most of these seem to have the right thread to accept entomological net frames. They are usually heavier and stronger than entomological poles, and the extra weight can assist with the sweeping action by improving the penetration of coarse vegetation. For flowers in awkward positions, as among brambles, a 15 cm diameter net (*e.g.* a frame of bent wire) can be useful.

When collecting at a patch of flowers, the small net can be used to select out chosen hoverflies without causing undue disturbance to everything else. Always approach slowly and avoid jerky movements. If the hoverflies seem reasonably tame, quickly scan all the flowers within disturbance range – the most noteworthy hoverfly may not be the one you first home in on. If using a large net it may be possible to line up on several required hoverflies and obtain them with one sweep, but the priorities need to be decided since disturbed hoverflies may not come back to give a second chance. Obviously one wishes to avoid damaging the plants as far as possible. There is often a constant interchange going on so it is worth revisiting a good patch of flowers or simply standing still for a while. Even if you think you've spotted all the interesting hoverflies, on leaving a locality it is sometimes worth sweeping through a patch of flowers with a large net since the smaller species are often overlooked.

Specimens hovering in the air above your head often seem slowest to react if the net comes up from underneath. For species hovering over open grassland, it is often important to get the net as close to the hovering fly as possible before you strike since they can react incredibly quickly. There is a problem if a hoverfly sits on a cylindrical surface such as a tree trunk – whatever you do will be wrong! For horizontal trunks a horizontal swipe is worth considering and for vertical trunks a stroke from below. When a hoverfly is sitting on thick herbage, a downward stroke will often cause the insect to dive downwards to escape. Thus such a stroke is only likely to be successful if the rim of the net reaches the ground so one can wait for the insect to walk up the net bag. If the rim will be obstructed before it reaches the ground, stick to a quick downward move, but hold the tip of the net bag with one hand so that a cage rather than a lump of muslin envelopes the hoverfly – there is then a good chance that the syrphid will fly up rather than down.

Another use of the net is sweeping. This entails walking along whilst sweeping the net through vegetation with alternate forehand and backhand strokes. When sweeping, it is best to walk into the sun or to stand in a position where your shadow is not falling across the place you want to sweep. Often large quantities of flies will be in the net so a pooter is especially useful for quick reactions on looking into the net (see comments under pooters). Sweeping is a useful technique when there are large quantities of small, low-growing flowers. It is also very useful for *Platycheirus* and *Sphaerophoria* in longish grass, etc., and for *Chamaesyrphus* on heather under pine; indeed in any type of open habitat it is worth trying for the smaller species. Sweeping sparse vegetation or low flowers along dry heathy paths may locate *Paragus* and *Sphaerophoria*. In open habitats, such as grassland and marshes (especially among sedges), it is practical to sweep under very dull conditions and even at dusk providing it is not too cold and windy – often a good range of species can be obtained, almost as good as under sunny conditions. This technique has certainly worked well in Scotland where hoverflies (and dipterists) may give up waiting for the sun. The short-handled canvas sweep-nets used by coleopterists are not really suitable for hoverfly recording. Sweeping very wet vegetation should also be avoided – it just produces a heap of soggy insects that are barely identifiable and unsalvageable as decent specimens.

Tubes and pooters

Having got a hoverfly into the net, the next problem is to get it out. If the fly is active, trap it in the end of the bag and if necessary hold it in a fold so it cannot move. A glass tube can then be inserted and the fly teased in, the opening of the tube being first closed by a finger from outside, muslin and all, and then the other hand is inserted into the net with a cork. Keep a small piece of soft tissue in your tube to prevent condensation from building up and damaging your specimen. Do not leave specimens in a tube for more than a few hours (unless you put them in the fridge), and ensure that damp tissue is allowed to dry out again.

An alternative is to use a pooter instead of a tube. These come in various sizes and can be made from glass or perspex (glass ones are prone to breakage, but perspex is dissolved by ethyl acetate). Barrels of around 40 mm diameter are best (smaller ones have limited capacity) and are obtainable from entomological suppliers. If the hoverflies are not too active, it may be possible to peer in through the mouth of the net and poot up anything worth retaining (the tip of the net bag must be orientated upwards and towards the sun or brightest part of the sky, your head creating a mainly dark closure to the net mouth). For small species where several specimens may be needed (*e.g. Neoascia* and *Sphaerophoria*), a pooter is by far the quickest approach. Pooters are not ideal for larger more active species as these can damage other fragile specimens you have caught, and the largest hoverflies (*e.g.* big *Eristalis* and *Volucella*) do not fit down (or get stuck in!) the entry tube anyway. Do not leave specimens in a pooter for more than a couple of hours at a time as they desiccate quickly and can damage themselves, and remember to block the entrance tube between usage (otherwise you will get escapes!). A suitably sized twig or a bundle of grass stalks makes a good, improvised bung. Keeping the pooter in the shade makes a big difference; the flies inside will get very hot and perhaps die if exposed to the sun. Be careful what else you collect in your pooter; sawflies, soldier beetles and other predators will quickly dismember and consume flies.

Ethyl acetate is the preferred killing agent, introduced on a small twist of tissue (damp, not wet) into the tube or pooter. Remember to ensure that your pooter is clear of fumes before you use it again! A good way of dispensing this chemical in the field is to use a small dropper-bottle which has a nozzle that can be removed to allow replenishment. Alternatively a lepidopterist's killing bottle can be used. If hoverflies are required for a collection, it may be best to bring them home alive and keep them in a cool dark place for 24 hours so that they digest any nectar in the gut, and brush off any pollen on their body. Specimens full of nectar are liable to turn black and the abdomen becomes greasy (even gooey), but problems are rare providing hoverflies with their abdomen bloated with nectar are avoided. When keeping live specimens, or dead ones, in air-tight tubes, it is essential to include a small piece of tissue to absorb condensation and excreta.

The pooter can on occasion be used to take small hoverflies directly off flowers and this may be the only available technique in situations where use of a net is impracticable. This works best if the hoverfly is approached directly from behind, with the glass entry tube as far extended as possible. If this fails, try coming in slowly to one side and suddenly angle the end of the pooter across with a flick of the wrist and suck at the same time – with luck the hoverfly will be sucked in just as it takes off.

If specimens are to be retained for a collection, it is as well to bear in mind that at the beginning of an emergence period most individuals will be teneral. This means that markings may be weak and that on drying, the legs, and possibly the body and head, may collapse and distort. Specimens obtained in the middle of a flight period are in the best condition if that option is available. Fortunately the problem rarely arises to any serious degree.

Mounting and curation

On arriving home, there may not be time to deal with the day's catch immediately. The priority is to ensure the hoverflies remain fresh and that no condensation is occurring in the tubes. Tubes with live or dead hoverflies, with a bit of tissue in each tube, and enclosed in a cardboard box, may be placed in the fridge till the following day, indeed dead hoverflies can be kept in this way for 5 or 6 days. This procedure allows dead hoverflies to become relaxed and hence easier to set (if you are likely to deal with the catch immediately on reaching home, then it is best to kill the required hoverflies in the field so that they will have had a couple of hours to relax). If dead and somewhat dried hoverflies need to be relaxed, then chopped young cherry laurel leaves in a tube or jar will do the job – small specimens only need a few hours. It is also possible to put hoverflies in the freezer (rather than the fridge) if you want them to stay fresh for a long period.

The idea of keeping and pinning a hoverfly is to be able to examine the features required for identification. It is thus sufficient to use a long pin through the thorax, extend the legs downwards with fine tweezers and to prop the wings slightly apart with other long pins (if necessary) until the insect is dry. The alternative is to set specimens in the same fashion as is traditional with Lepidoptera (the plates illustrate such a format, with the middle legs forwards). Lepidoptera setting boards can be used, though the groove tends to be so deep that the legs cannot be arranged neatly. Thin sheets of balsa wood are used by some Microlepidopterists, impressing a groove suitable for the insect concerned – this seems a useful approach for small hoverflies. Setting boards get the wings flat, but they take up room and a day's catch may be dispersed through a whole series of boards of different sizes.

A quick, compact method of mounting used by many dipterists is to micro-pin onto a flat surface. plastazote in shallow 120 × 78 × 22 mm plastic boxes is ideal (obtain the "crystal boxes" and plastazote in large sheets from various entomological suppliers). On a flat surface the legs are easily extended and the wings are gently anchored by a shallowly oblique pin across the wing.

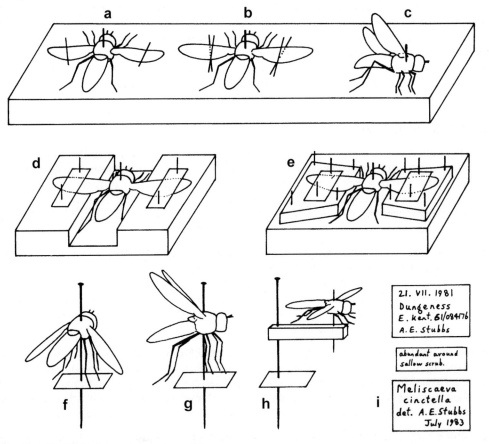

Text fig. 2. Methods of pinning hoverflies.
a - one pressure anchor per wing; **b** - under and upper pressure anchor per wing; **c** - side pinning (easier to examine legs); **d** – lepidopterists' setting board with transparent tape holding wings; **e** - use of small strips of plastazote (or cork) to suit a particular fly; **f** - macro pinning; **g** - macro pinning, with wings somewhat raised (much easier to view legs); **h** - method of staging a micro-pinned specimen; **i** - locality label, with supplementary labels for habitat (habits) and determination.

This results in the wing being a little distorted. A modification which reduces the distortion is to use two pins per wing, one underneath as a prop and the other above as a pressure anchor on the first, so the wing tip does not touch the surface (this procedure takes longer and still results in some distortion). One can also use thin strips or triangles of plastazote under the wings as miniature setting boards. Many dipterists pin flies from the side, this being very quick, and for hoverflies it is useful to have some specimens mounted in this fashion. *Cheilosia*, for instance, have features which are most easily compared in side view and with *Platycheirus* the legs are much more easy to examine than in a specimen pinned from above. Side-pinning also makes it far easier to pull out and anchor the male genitalia as the specimen is drying (essential on *Sphaerophoria*, but recommended as good practice for all male specimens). Micro-pinned specimens will need staging.

Clear labelling with date, locality, vice-county and collector is required, together with grid reference if possible. Supplementary labels can be used for extra information, such as flower species visited and determination (especially if a third party has done this for you). Storage and care of the collection is similar to that for other groups of pinned insects, and you should be careful not to expose collections to damp (which can lead to mould). Pests such as carpet beetles (*Anthrenus*) or booklice can also cause problems. Entomological cabinets and store-boxes are specifically designed for storing pinned insects, but air-tight boxes of polythene or polystyrene lined with plastazote can be just as effective.

Other collecting methods

The use of traps is becoming popular as their potential for recording becomes more widely recognised. Traps often add substantially to a faunal list, especially when time available for field work is limited, and they can provide a basis for replicable sampling (important when making strictly comparative surveys). However, they do not allow the building up of important observational information. They may not be suitable on sites with many visitors or with grazing animals.

The simplest trap is the water tray. This is a shallow dish partially filled with water and with some detergent (a drop of washing-up liquid) added to reduce surface tension. Flies settle on the dish and are trapped. The colour of the dish affects the results, some colours such as yellow attracting hoverflies. In tall vegetation the dish should be placed on top of a pole about level with the average top height of the vegetation. Disney *et al.* (1982) discuss the use of water traps and compare the results with other techniques.

Another simple approach, a lure rather than a trap, is a bunch of flowers. There may be the perfect spot for hoverflies, but no flowers. A pole is stuck in the ground, topped by about 15 cm of hose pipe which, given a small amount of water, acts as a flower vase. Flowers are picked from elsewhere and put in the vase (the "Brackenbury Lure", after its designer). This technique can be very successful, but why stop here? Flower pots of suitable flowers could be used.

The Malaise trap (a sort of muslin tent obtainable from Marris House Nets, address above) has been of very great value in the study of flies. Ninety-one species of hoverflies were caught in a Leicestershire garden (Owen, 1991) and very good results have been obtained in many studies. Species which are not normally seen manage to appear in the trap and some quite remarkable records have been made this way. The positioning of a Malaise trap is critical, needing to be on a flight line used by hoverflies, usually the edge of a fence, hedge, wood, forest ride, etc. It should be noted that a well positioned Malaise trap run during good weather at the height of the season can catch very large quantities of insects of many orders. Sorting and identifying the quantity of material involved can be challenging, time-consuming and also expensive (in terms of the cost of storage tubes and preservatives). There is also a moral obligation not to waste all the non-hoverfly specimens which may be obtained. These should be offered to the relevant specialists and recording schemes.

Field craft

Many of the above comments relate to field craft, but there are some general points to be added. With the use of maps and advice from other naturalists it should be possible to plan ahead and make the best use of your time in the field. It is largely a question of arriving at the right place at the right time and in this regard the next chapter on habitats and seasons will help.

Whenever a locality is visited, it is helpful to recognise the most rewarding spots as rapidly as possible. Usually it is the most sheltered and sunny parts that will suit hoverflies best, especially if suitable flowers are available. If the sun is off a nice patch of flowers, then assess when conditions may be more favourable later in the day. The same applies to dead wood – a clearing with a fallen tree may only be in the sun for an hour or two. It's as well to learn to recognise useful plants when they are not flowering, even dead stems in midwinter, since each visit should be viewed as a reconnaissance that may pay off on a future visit. It is often possible to recognise potential for a different time of year, whether for adults or larvae.

Success in finding a good range of species will depend on flexibility of approach. Conspicuous hoverfly flowers may produce a reasonable list, but it may be less obvious flowers which have a different and important fauna. On a sunny day it is even worth looking at flowers in the shade, with plants such as sanicle attracting *Sphegina*. But remember to be patient, for you cannot force all the hoverflies at a site to assemble simultaneously on a convenient batch of flowers just for your benefit!

Perhaps some species will not be on flowers at all. Some may be sitting on bare ground (*e.g.* *Parasyrphus* on forest tracks) or flying obscurely over bare patches and among sparse vegetation (*e.g.* female *Heringia* (*Neocnemodon*), *Paragus*, *Pipizella*). Many species sunbathe on foliage (*e.g.* most Syrphini, some *Cheilosia*, *Pipiza*) and a few hardly ever visit flowers but seem to get all sustenance off leaf surfaces (*e.g.* most *Xylota*). Leaves covered with honeydew (secretion of aphids) are often very attractive. In hot weather, some species are best looked for at the edges of water, including puddles, where they come to drink. Various species are only found about dead wood. Different situations with dead wood may yield different species; the habitat may not be obvious at all, such as small cavities about the roots which give access to a rotten centre in a live tree. A sharp eye is required to spot sap runs, which may support *Brachyopa*, or, with luck, a tree supporting the wood-boring caterpillars of goat moth, *Cossus cossus*, from whose burrows sap flows copiously and attracts many other insects including hoverflies. Many of the dead-wood hoverflies mimic bees, as do various other hoverflies to some degree. Thus it is necessary to examine carefully anything that could be a mimic, especially a 'bee' that is in the wrong habitat: a 'bumblebee' showing an interest in tree trunks for example. Some mimics are exceptionally good, notably *Pocota personata* and *Volucella zonaria* which mimic bumblebees and the hornet respectively, and it is often not until you see them at close quarters that you realise that they are flies.

It is tempting to look down at the ground and at flowers when the unusual fly may be hovering above you. In shafts of sunlight in forest, adjacent to bushes, or simply 'in space', there will be common hoverflies, but it is a case of recognising the opportunities when something interesting is involved. Some of our rare species may not be so rare, but may be up in the tree canopy (one of those street-light inspection lorries driven along a forest ride could be a revelation! – or could suspended aerial Malaise traps work with hoverflies?).

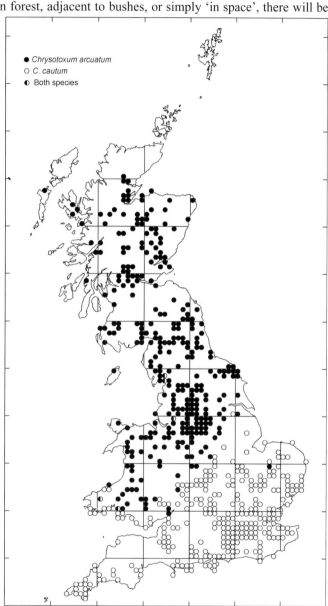

Recording

As is clear in the introduction and elsewhere, this book is not a complete statement on the British hoverfly fauna. These pages are no more than a stepping stone to an improved knowledge of the subject.

The Hoverfly Recording Scheme, run by Stuart Ball and Roger Morris, now holds some 375,000 records from Great Britain. It was used to produce the *Provisional Atlas* (Ball & Morris, 2000) and is being maintained towards the production of a "final" atlas in due course. However, this is not the only possible output from a large amount of reliable data. New contributors to the Scheme are most welcome and assistance will be given to inexperienced recorders who need the identity of a specimen confirmed (contact details for the Scheme can be obtained

Text fig. 3. Distribution map of *Chrysotoxum arcuatum* and *C. cautum*.

from the Biological Records Centre – address below).

As an example, fig. 3 shows those 10km squares of the National Grid for Great Britain from which two *Chrysotoxum* species have been reported. They show almost mutually exclusive distributions: *C. arcuatum* occurs in Scotland, northern England and Wales, except for the coast of South Wales, and has an outlier in the East Anglian Brecks. In contrast, *C. cautum* occurs in the Midlands, south and east England, with an outlying population in north-west England (*n.b.* these squares were not included in the published atlas, but the records have subsequently been confirmed (Birkett, 2000)). Out of a total of 598 squares from which one or other species has been reported to the Recording Scheme, both have been found in only five!

Since publication of the *Provisional Atlas*, data from the Recording Scheme have been used to investigate a number of aspects of hoverfly biology. In particular there are opportunities to investigate the impact of climate change on hoverfly phenology (flight times), demonstrating the process of expansion in range of some species, and examining the effects of weather patterns on populations of others. It has also been used to evaluate the status of hoverflies and to determine whether the frequency of any species is increasing or declining. A series of papers are emerging that show how the data can be used, or might be used in future. All observations, including regular recording from a garden, will be useful even though they may not add dots to distribution maps.

All recorders can make a useful contribution to hoverfly recording. When you are planning your recording, take account of the following dos and don'ts to make the most of your contribution:

DO

- Give a full date for all records. If you are operating a trap, give the start and end date for the period it was set.

- List all species recorded from a particular site visit on a separate sheet or card. Ideally, make separate lists for each distinct area within a site you have visited.

- Give the location in one of the widely recognised co-ordinate systems (OS grid reference systems for Great Britain or Ireland; latitude and longitude) and be as precise as the recording method and available maps or other tools allow. If you are using 1:50,000 maps, a six-figure reference (*e.g.* TQ271754) is ideal, but if you have walked round an area generally, a four-figure reference (*e.g.* TQ2775) may be more appropriate.

- If you know you are on a designated site of some sort, *e.g.* Nature Reserve, Site of Special Scientific Interest (SSSI), give its name and the organisation that is responsible for it (*e.g.* Wicken Fen, NT).

- Give a description of the situation and habitat in which an observation was made, but be specific ("on a flowering hawthorn in an open glade in mixed woodland"). A general list of all the habitats in the area ("woods, hedges, ponds") is of little value.

- Record flower visits and other useful biological information.

- Give the altitude at which the observation was made, if known.

DO NOT

- Just give the year, or range of years, for a record (*e.g.* 1994 to 1997).

- Only list what you consider to be the "interesting" species or rarities.

- Lump records from a number of disparate locations within the same grid square, unless they are from within a contiguous site.

- Give just the ten-kilometre grid reference (*e.g.* TQ27).

- Give the central grid reference (the six-figure grid reference sometimes given in reserve leaflets) for all the records you make anywhere on a site.

This advice applies only to new records. If you already have information, or are extracting data from existing collections or paper records, you will have to make the most of whatever information is available. Such historic data may still have value, even if they are incomplete by today's standards.

Recording cards for hoverflies are obtainable free from the Biological Records Centre at Monks Wood (CEH, Monks Wood, Abbots Ripton, Huntingdon, PE28 2LS). The card RA33 is the preferred version and should be used to record data for just one site visit because the use of a card for numerous visits is difficult to transcribe and results in errors in data entry. Data recorded on standard databases and biological recording packages can also be incorporated in machine-readable form (contact the Scheme for advice on the preferred format) and will be readily accepted.

Producing county atlases or setting up county-based recording groups is rewarding if you have the time and enthusiasm. They produce new information on local habitat associations (which can vary across a range of a species or be linked to local geology and land use) and can contribute to the national Recording Scheme. What is more, well-managed county datasets can be invaluable for promoting nature conservation locally and Local Biodiversity Action Plans.

Conservation

The collection of a few voucher specimens is unlikely to do any harm to hoverfly populations, especially if care is taken with rare species with very restricted breeding sites. Insect faunas are at far greater risk through not knowing which sites are important and not appreciating the management needs of those sites. All of the relevant conservation agencies (Countryside Council for Wales, English Nature, Scottish Natural Heritage and the Joint Nature Conservation Committee) have specialists in invertebrate conservation who make use of the data from recording schemes in providing advice to Government and the wider conservation community.

Conservation through ecological studies

Hoverflies occur in a wide range of habitats and their larvae utilise a broad spectrum of niches (see Rotheray, 1993). This means that they can be used to assist in the process of site assessment and management planning, especially if rare or otherwise unusual species are present. The adults of many species are very mobile so that their inclusion in a site list does not necessarily mean that they breed there, so you have to be careful how you present and interpret a hoverfly list for a site. Various attempts have been made to compile lists of possible habitat indicators (Stubbs, 1982; Whiteley, 1987; Morris, 1998b). A significant number of species are indicators of habitat quality, and the dead-wood fauna is particularly useful. We need to gain a much more thorough knowledge of the true status and habitat requirements of the species, via the Recording Scheme, before hoverflies can be used with confidence for site evaluation. An interactive computer programme *Syrph the Net on CD* (Speight *et al.*, 2001) has been published and provides a first attempt to allow recorders to predict the assemblage that might be found on a particular site. This package is a major advance, but needs to be refined further by testing against observations.

A Red Data Book listing 56 hoverflies (10 "Endangered", 17 "Vulnerable" and 29 "Rare") was published by Shirt (1987), and a first list of scarce and threatened hoverflies was given in Falk (1991b). These are now somewhat out of date and the Recording Scheme organisers hope to be able to undertake a full revision in the near future. Ball & Morris (2000) include a table listing the various conservation statuses that have been applied to hoverflies.

The value of hoverflies as a popular and attractive group of day-flying insects is now well established. They have been used particularly to highlight the plight of ancient trees and decaying timber and are well represented in current Biodiversity Action Plans. The Priority Species for which action plans have been published (UK Biodiversity Group, 1998) are *Blera fallax*, *Callicera spinolae*, *Chrysotoxum octomaculatum*, *Doros profuges*, *Eristalis cryptarum*, *Hammerschmidtia ferruginea* and *Myolepta potens*.

Some of the most remarkable examples of conservation practice involving hoverflies have been in the Scottish Highlands, where some of our great rarities occur. Surveys of *Hammerschmidtia ferruginea* and *Blera fallax* have revealed that these species (especially the latter) are confined to very few sites. Conservation action plans have been prepared and are being put into effect. Another such example is *Callicera rufa*, a spectacular species of Caledonian pine forests which has been recorded only rarely as an adult but has proved much more widespread through surveys of the easily recognised larvae and puparia in water-filled rot-holes. Moreover, a technique was developed to carve out artificial rot-holes (MacGowan, 1994b), thus aiding survival where suitable natural rot-holes are sparse, and giving controlled conditions in which to study the life-cycle. This and other exciting advances are due to the activities of the Malloch Society, a group of active dipterists based in Scotland who demonstrate what can be achieved when relatively few people team up for targeted projects.

A recent and, as yet, unpublished project by Alain Maibach involved the use of artificial rot-holes in the New Forest. Plastic bottles with a side opening were filled with wet sawdust and strapped at various heights to tree trunks facing four compass aspects. Results were encouraging. One aim was to understand the ecology of hoverflies that use this often inaccessible habitat, as well as to gain larval material for taxonomic study. However, the technique may also offer an excellent means of providing continuity of hoverfly populations where natural rot-holes are scarce and where a gap in the age structure of trees may result in a temporary loss of habitat. If one can provide nest boxes for birds, dormice and bats, why not breeding bottles for hoverflies?

Many other advances are also relevant to conservation. Field craft for locating the breeding sites of many hoverflies has advanced over the last decade, together with the means of identifying larvae (Rotheray, 1993). In particular, major advances have been made with saproxylic hoverflies (associated with sap runs and with dead and dying wood), so that knowledge of conservation management and site evaluation is considerably improved. We are much closer to understanding the needs of such little-known species as *Parasyrphus nigritarsis* which is now known to be associated with sallow and alder scrub by rivers and in wetlands where the larvae feed on larvae of chrysomelid beetles (Falk, 1992; MacGowan & Watt, 1994). Two species which were feared to be extinct have been rediscovered: *Eristalis cryptarum* which had disappeared from most of its former haunts has been found in a small area of Dartmoor (Levy & Levy, 1994); and larvae of *Myolepta potens* have been found in Herefordshire (A. Godfrey), 40 years after the last record from its former haunts in Somerset.

It is not possible to conclude this conservation review without reference to one of the historic firsts. The Council for Europe not only published a review of the conservation needs of saproxylic insects in Europe (Speight, 1989b), but the Committee of Ministers published a Recommendation [No R (88) 10] which sets out a policy requiring specific measures. If member states do what they are supposed to do, then there ought to be significant improvements, but it requires all of us to keep this international Recommendation in mind and make sure that everyone knows about it. The conservation of habitat is the prime objective, but it is of interest to note which of our species of hoverflies are listed in the report as useful in identifying sites of international importance. These are: *Brachyopa bicolor, Caliprobola speciosa, Callicera aurata, C. rufa, C. spinolae, Chalcosyrphus eunotus, Ferdinandea ruficornis, Hammerschmidtia ferruginea, Myolepta potens, Pocota personata* and *Psilota anthracina*.

Hoverfly conservation in your patch

Traditionally, sites have been given protection on the basis of botanical and ornithological interests (*e.g.* SSSIs – Sites of Special Scientific Interest), but in recent years there has been a much greater effort to use a broad spectrum of plant and animal groups, with important invertebrate assemblages often helping to support designation. You can contribute to this process quite easily by collating good and reasonably comparable data for the sites in your patch, and feeding these data to your local biological records centre or local authority ecologist. Falk (1998) describes a relatively simple method for assessing the potential impact of a development on important insect species.

Another way in which you can promote hoverfly conservation in your area is by ensuring that your data are taken into account in site management plans. Most SSSIs, Local Nature Reserves, wildlife trust reserves and country parks have management plans, and although the quality of these may vary, most have built-in review dates which allow for new data and priorities to be added. But remember that hoverflies are just one of many types of wildlife at a site, and conserving the rarest plant may have to take priority over conserving an unusual but less critically rare hoverfly. Also remember that an unusual hoverfly recorded at your site may have been a non-breeding vagrant and that changing the management of a site for such a species is inappropriate; reasonable evidence for permanent establishment on a site carries weight!

The current trend for producing Local Biodiversity Action Plans (LBAPs) is providing unprecedented opportunities for the involvement of amateur entomologists. LBAPs contain habitat action plans and species action plans, in much the same manner as for the national process.

CHAPTER 4

HABITATS AND SEASONS

There is not space for an exhaustive treatment of this topic and in any case far more recording of habitat requirements and associations is needed. Attention is given here to some of the characteristic and special species to look for, acting as an index to the notes under each species. June and July form the peak period in most habitats.

Habitats

Mountains and moorland

Three special species occur at and above the tree line, July being the peak period: *Cheilosia sahlbergi*, *Melanostoma dubium* (plus *Melanostoma* form A) and *Platycheirus melanopsis*. In addition more widespread species of this habitat include *Trichopsomyia flavitarsis*, *P. nielseni* and confusing forms of *M. mellinum*. *P. ramsarensis* is associated with the boggy fringes of moorland streams. Species new to Britain are likely in this poorly recorded habitat.

Scottish Coast

Helophilus groenlandicus is known only from the coast of north-west Scotland and the Inner Hebrides in July and ought also to occur on the Outer Hebrides. *Cheilosia ahenea* is now known to occur on the machair grasslands of the Inner Hebrides. On the sea lochs of the west coast *Lejogaster tarsata* is found at iris beds along the shore in June (and July?).

Caledonian Forests

The pine and birch woods of the Scottish Highlands contain a number of special species. The dead-wood fauna includes *Callicera rufa* (pine), *Blera fallax* (pine), *Hammerschmidtia ferruginea* (aspen) and *Xylota jakutorum* (conifers). *Chamaesyrphus* species can be swept from heather under pine. The Syrphini include *Eupeodes nielseni*, *E. lapponicus*, *Didea intermedia* and *Eriozona erratica*.

Southern Deciduous Forest

A very rich fauna is involved with a long season. The fauna of dead wood and sap runs comprises *Brachypalpus*, *Brachypalpoides*, *Brachyopa*, *Chalcosyrphus*, *Caliprobola*, *Callicera*, *Criorhina*, *Myolepta*, *Mallota*, *Myathropa*, *Pocota*, *Xylota*, *Ferdinandea* and *Sphegina*. The Syrphini of woodland include *Eupeodes nitens*, *Epistrophe nitidicollis*, *Meligramma euchromum*, some *Dasysyrphus*, some *Leucozona*, *Melangyna*, *Parasyrphus punctulatus* and some *Sphaerophoria*. The woodland fauna also includes certain *Cheilosia* such as *carbonaria* and *nigripes*, *Eumerus ornatus*, *Merodon*, *Heringia*, *Pipiza*, *Portevinia*, *Psilota*, *Rhingia rostrata* and *Volucella inflata*. Spring-flowering shrubs such as sallow, hawthorn, blackthorn and wild cherry are important flowers in addition to those along rides. Later in the year umbellifers, brambles and thistles can be important. Ivy and Devil's-bit scabious can provide a finale in September and

October. Wet or humid deciduous woodland has a number of characteristic woodland species, including *Cheilosia impressa*, *Leucozona glaucia* and *laternaria*, *Chrysogaster solstitialis*, *Cheilosia chrysocoma*, *Xylota abiens*, *Orthonevra brevicornis* and *Arctophila*. Woodland streams and their fringing trees can support *Chalcosyrphus eunotus*, *Xylota florum*, *Parasyrphus nigritarsis* and, where butterbur is present, *Neoascia obliqua*.

Old Parkland

Old (veteran) trees are not necessarily found in woods, so many of their specialist species are just as likely to be encountered in the grounds of a National Trust site or an ancient deer park. Collections of very old trees produce certain habitats in a quantity that cannot be matched by stands of younger trees, such as rot-holes, heart rot and sap runs, and sites with these habitats may have had several hundred years in which to acquire their special fauna. The characteristic hoverflies include *Callicera aurata*, *C. spinolae*, *Mallota*, *Pocota*, *Volucella inflata*, *Brachyopa insensilis*, *Brachypalpus*, *Ferdinandea ruficornis*, *Psilota anthracina*, *Caliprobola*, *Myolepta* and *Criorhina* species. Many of these species are important at a European level, as veteran trees are rare in many parts of the continent.

Conifer Plantations

The widespread planting of conifers within deciduous woodland and elsewhere has caused many native species to extend their range, whilst other species are newly established in Britain and more may follow. Spruce and pines generate the most interesting hoverfly assemblages. The newcomers are *Eupeodes* (*Lapposyrphus*) species A, *Dasysyrphus friuliensis*, *Eriozona syrphoides* and *Sphegina sibirica*. Longer-established species extending their range within conifer plantations are principally the *Parasyrphus* species plus *Melangyna quadrimaculata*, *Didea intermedia*, *Eupeodes nielseni*, *Scaeva selenitica*, *Eriozona erratica* and *Xylota jakutorum*. Whilst planting of conifers may have added a number of species locally, this has often been at the expense of native habitats and their fauna.

Dry Grassland

Microdon devius in early June is the speciality on chalk grassland. Typical species on the Chalk include *Platycheirus manicatus*, *Paragus haemorrhous* and *Pipizella viduata*, whilst other types of dry grassland may also have *Platycheirus angustatus*, various *Sphaerophoria* species and a variety of *Cheilosia* (especially those associated with thistles, hawkweed-type composites or umbellifers). Sites with scrub and woodland edge may have *Doros*, various *Chrysotoxum*, *Pipizella virens* and *Xanthandrus*. The flowers of open grassland can draw species in from other habitats such as nearby woodland.

Lush Marsh and Fen

A large fauna may be present, much depending on the vegetation types, the presence of open water (considered separately) or seepages, and the presence of flowers (especially umbellifers). *Cheilosia pubera* is confined to fen, but *C. albipila* is less fussy. More widespread species are *Tropidia scita*, *Platycheirus fulviventris* (especially on sweet-grass), *Melanogaster hirtella*, *Orthonevra nobilis*, *O. geniculata*, *Lejogaster metallina*, *Neoascia* and *Riponnensia splendens*. Lush meadows with rushes in the southern counties may contain *Sphaerophoria taeniata*. Other

Syrphinae of this habitat include *Platycheirus scambus*, *P. occultus*, *P. granditarsus* and *Eupeodes latifasciatus*. The *Cheilosia* are out early but the rest of the fauna peaks in June and July.

Acid Marsh

This is taken to include less lush marshes, stands of sedges around acid basin mires, poor wet pasture and other situations which cannot be classified as bog. This is good *Platycheirus* country, in the north including *P. perpallidus*, *P. occultus* and *P. podagratus*. *Sericomyia silentis*, *Melanogaster aerosa*, *Lejogaster metallina* and *Trichopsomyia flavitarsis* may also be present, and more rarely *Microdon myrmicae*. June to July is a good period.

Bog

The wet nature of sites results in a number of aquatic species being characteristic. Examples are *Sericomyia silentis*, *S. lappona*, *Melanogaster aerosa*, *Orthonevra geniculata* and *Anasimyia lunulata*. *Trichopsomyia* tends to occur at the margins of bogs. *Platycheirus ramsarensis* occurs at boggy margins of upland streams. *Eristalis cryptarum* is associated with small boggy runnels (confined to Dartmoor). June to July is a suitable time.

Southern Heath

The four specialities are *Chrysotoxum octomaculatum*, *Pelecocera tricincta*, *Paragus tibialis* and *Microdon analis*. Other species include *Paragus haemorrhous*, *Sphaerophoria philanthus*, *S. virgata* and *Trichopsomyia flavitarsis*. Most occupy very dry heath though *Pelecocera* and *Trichopsomyia* seem to prefer damp heath. Catkins of creeping willow in April and May are worth searching for such species as *Cheilosia urbana*.

Coastal Habitats

Western sand dunes have *Eumerus sabulonum* and *Cheilosia mutabilis*. Catkins of creeping willow (in May) are especially useful in this habitat. *Eristalinus aeneus* likes rocky coasts and salt marshes. Dry grassy flood embankments tend to have *Sphaerophoria rueppellii*, possibly also *Paragus albifrons*. Brackish marsh, often behind such embankments, is the place to look for *Lejops vittatus* on sea club-rush and *Sphaerophoria loewi* on sea club-rush or common reed. High on tidal marsh, in estuaries or on sheltered coasts, *Platycheirus immarginatus* should be searched for. *Lejogaster tarsata* is another brackish-marsh species, sometimes with *Neoascia interrupta*. *Eristalis abusivus* can be abundant near the coast. In south-west England *Chrysotoxum elegans* occurs on cliff-top grassland, another habitat for *Eumerus sabulonum* which is most frequently seen along the margins of bare paths.

Ditches, Pond and Lake Margins

The fauna present depends on the nature of marshy margins, whether lush or not, so that some of the species previously discussed may occur. The aquatic fauna comprises, in particular, the Eristalini, *Chrysogaster*, and its allies. The presence of bulrush is important for *Parhelophilus* and some *Anasimyia*, also possibly *Helophilus hybridus*, whilst bur-reeds are preferred by *A.*

transfuga. Various *Helophilus* and *Eristalis* are normally present, often *Eristalinus sepulchralis* as well. Tiny *Neoascia* are often abundant.

Farm Yards

A small but distinctive fauna breeds in compost, manure and silage, including putrefying liquid emerging from such materials. Polluted ditches around a farm yard may be an ideal breeding site for the Eristalini, as well as pools and ponds polluted with dung by visiting cattle. The principal species are *Eristalis tenax*, *E. pertinax*, *E. interruptus*, *E. arbustorum* (plus *E. intricarius* to some extent), *Eristalinus sepulchralis* and *Helophilus pendulus*. In non-aquatic situations, *Syritta pipiens* and *Neoascia podagrica* may be abundant.

Parks and gardens

A large fauna can occur, attracted to no small extent by the vast quantity of flowers available for much of the year. Some of the commoner species tend to be *Baccha*, *Melanostoma scalare*, *Episyrphus balteatus*, *Meliscaeva cinctella*, *Eupeodes corollae*, *E. luniger*, *Platycheirus albimanus*, *Scaeva pyrastri*, *Sphaerophoria scripta*, *Syrphus*, *Eumerus funeralis*, *E. strigatus*, *Helophilus pendulus*, *Merodon*, *Myathropa*, *Neoascia podagrica*, *Pipiza noctiluca*, *Syritta* (for which the garden compost heap provides ideal breeding conditions) and *Xylota segnis*. *Volucella pellucens* and *V. bombylans* may occur around woodland remnants, but in London *V. inanis* and *V. zonaria* are regularly reported in August, even in gardens. Some *Heringia* species may prove to belong to the urban fringe, exploiting the high densities of poplars, such as Lombardy poplar. The mature trees associated with urban parks, old churchyards and other formal grounds can be very valuable, supporting something approaching an ancient parkland fauna. The sap runs on urban horse-chestnuts frequently harbour colonies of *Brachyopa*, especially *B. insensilis*, whilst rot-holes can produce urban records of rarities such as *Callicera aurata* and *Mallota cimbiciformis*, plus *Criorhina* species. It should not be long before an urban *Pocota* population is discovered.

Brown-field sites

These can include urban waste ground, old quarries or gravel workings, and disused railways. They can acquire many of the habitats described above (often as a complicated habitat mosaic), though it is the predominance of flowery 'ruderal' ground, with much bare ground between plants, that often gives such sites their character. *Triglyphus primus* is most often found on wasteland due to its reliance on mugwort. Species with the bulk of their population on brown-field sites in areas such as the Midlands, include *Paragus haemorrhous*, *Chrysotoxum verralli*, *Sphaerophoria rueppellii*, *Cheilosia bergenstammi*, *C. latifrons*, *C. urbana* and *C. psilophthalma*. Some species of *Xanthogramma* and *Chrysotoxum* are also most easily found here.

Seasons

Winter

Mild sunny days even in midwinter can sometimes bring out hibernating hoverflies. However, the only real hope of seeing them is on winter-flowering shrubs in gardens and parks. Kew Gardens is a particularly favourable locality. The known hibernators are *Episyrphus balteatus*,

Meliscaeva auricollis and *Eristalis tenax*, but further observations may extend this list. It is worth noting whether both sexes or only females pass through the winter.

Spring

In addition to the hibernating hoverflies, there is a chance of finding the beginnings of a new emergence by mid February or early March. *Melangyna quadrimaculata* has even been seen when patches of snow remain on the ground. Warm sunny conditions in sheltered situations are best. A few species such as *M. quadrimaculata* may be feeding on pollen at catkins of hazel or alder. By mid to late March (in the south), sallow catkins (including those of goat willow and grey willow) can provide a good lure, followed shortly by blackthorn and wild cherry. These attract species such as *Melangyna arctica*, *M. barbifrons*, *M. lasiophthalma*, *M. quadrimaculata*, *Parasyrphus punctulatus*, *Platycheirus discimanus*, *P. ambiguus* (on blackthorn), *Syrphus torvus* and *Criorhina ranunculi*. Sunbathing is very important on cool spring mornings, so check the leaves of bramble and nettle and tufts of dead grass where these occur in sheltered spots near to blossom – you will often find as much here as on the blossom itself. Look for *Cheilosia grossa* and *C. albipila*, sunbathing and on sallow catkins, in localities with thistles; males may hover beside sallow bushes. Colt's-foot and butterbur tend to attract some early species, especially Eristalini, but marsh-marigold attracts a wider range of species. From early May onwards, in a warm spring in the south, there is a great increase in species so looking for hoverflies becomes much easier with buttercups and hawthorn becoming important flowers.

Summer

According to the records submitted to the Hoverfly Recording Scheme, the peak in the number of species reported per week occurs around mid June and declines only slowly until around the third week of August. High summer is the main season for the majority of species. Nevertheless, during periods of hot and dry weather hoverflies can be difficult to find and it may be necessary to be out early or later in the day when conditions are cooler. This is the time of year of the "hogweed fauna", a large suite of species that characteristically visit common, open-structured flowers exemplified by hogweed, but also other umbellifers, knapweeds, buddleia and many garden flowers. These species include *Melanostoma mellinum*, *M. scalare*, *Platycheirus*, *Syrphus*, *Eupeodes*, *Melangyna cincta*, *Meliscaeva cinctella*, *Episyrphus balteatus*, *Epistrophe grossulariae*, *Leucozona laternaria*, *L. glaucia*, *Chrysotoxum bicinctum*, *Sphaerophoria scripta*, *Eristalis arbustorum*, *E. interruptus*, *E. pertinax*, *E. tenax*, *E. horticola*, *Eristalinus sepulchralis*, *Myathropa florea*, *Helophilus pendulus*, *Volucella pellucens*, *V. inanis*, *V. zonaria*, *Cheilosia* (especially *barbata*, *illustrata*, *pagana*, *soror*, and *vulpina*), *Rhingia campestris*, *Pipiza*, *Chrysogaster solstitialis*, *Sericomyia silentis* and *Syritta pipiens*. Angelica tends to flower later than hogweed and, in late July to mid August, can attract good numbers of the second brood of several species. Some of the very mobile species such as *Episyrphus balteatus*, *Eupeodes corollae*, *Eristalis* and *Helophilus* can suddenly appear in enormous numbers in flowery localities such as gardens. It is hard to tell whether this represents an influx from far afield due to migration, or more local mass emergence (for example, large numbers of *Episyrphus balteatus* emerging more or less simultaneously from vast cereal fields). Massed occurrences of such species can often occur even in the more specialised habitats of grassland, wetland, dunes, heathland, etc., or sheltered edges around scrub and hedgerows. Substantial lists of species, perhaps exceeding 30 at a good site, can be assembled at this time of year by choosing a well-

40

frequented patch of flowers and recording diligently, retaining difficult taxa such as *Cheilosia* for subsequent identification. Apart from the umbellifers, especially good lures include water mint and common fleabane, but attention should also be paid to ruderal assemblages such as those comprising scentless mayweed, goosefoot and redshank which will often yield many species, especially of *Sphaerophoria*.

Autumn

Ivy on walls and trees in a sheltered sunny spot in the middle of the day attracts large numbers of common autumn species, including those which are due to hibernate such as *Eristalis tenax*. The best results will be in the vicinity of good hoverfly habitat, such as a wood edge. The most interesting species are *Callicera spinolae* (in East Anglia) and *Didea fasciata*, but others could occur on early flowers in September, peak flowering normally being in October. In late summer and autumn *Xanthandrus comtus* should be sought at flowers on scrub grassland and scrubby woodland edges. In damp meadows in the north and west, the flowers of Devil's-bit scabious can attract a rich variety of species of which the bumblebee mimic, *Arctophila superbiens* is a special feature. A number of other species show late-summer peaks, such as *Cheilosia latifrons*, *C. griseiventris*, *C. cynocephala*, *Syrphus torvus* and *Eristalis pertinax*.

Habitats of Early Stages

Dead wood

Trees with holes and heart rot support many species. Live trees with hollow trunks can be good, even where a superficially sound tree has only a small entrance into a hollow (*e.g.* in a fork between tree roots). Fallen timber is also suitable where larvae of a few species are found under the bark. It ought to be in the shade, partially submerged in water or only in direct sun for a few hours a day (otherwise heat desiccation can cause problems). Stumps can be used, those with heart rot underground in the roots being most suitable. Beech, elm and ash are the most productive trees, more rarely oak and lime. In Scotland native Scots pine is important, together with birch and aspen. Many species use rotting heartwood and roots once these attain the consistency of porridge.

Blera (pine), *Brachypalpoides*, *Brachypalpus*, *Caliprobola*, *Callicera*, *Chalcosyrphus*, *Criorhina*, *Hammerschmidtia*, *Mallota*, *Microdon analis* (black-ant colonies under the bark), *Myolepta*, *Pocota*, *Sphegina* and *Xylota*.

Sap runs

These occur sparsely on the trunks of live trees, either sporadically on a given tree or as a fairly permanent feature. Sap runs may develop at a wound, including those caused by the goat moth, *Cossus cossus*. Elm was particularly prone to develop sap runs, but most trees can produce them, especially horse-chestnut and yew. For example, horse-chestnuts in suburban areas have proved to be especially favoured by *Brachyopa insensilis*.

Brachyopa, *Ferdinandea*, *Psilota*, *Volucella inflata*, *Xylota tarda*.

Higher plant associations

The best-known plant associations are those of economic importance – the bulb flies (Fryer, 1914). *Merodon*, the Large Bulb Fly, attacks a great range of bulbs, daffodil being the one of main economic concern (however, it rarely attacks tulips). Squills and snowflakes are among the garden genera (Hodson, 1932b) which may act as potential hosts in the wild. The occurrence of *Merodon* in bluebell woods leads to the assumption that this is a major host in the countryside. The Lesser Bulb Flies, *Eumerus funeralis* and *E. strigatus*, also attack daffodils and there are records from iris and parsnip (Hodson, 1927, 1932a). There are also records from onions and potatoes (review in Coe, 1953a). Little is known about the host plants of *Eumerus* in the countryside, again bluebell being one likely candidate, but by no means accounting for the distribution and habitat of all four British species. *Eumerus sabulonum* has been observed to lay eggs on the rosettes of sheep's-bit in sand dunes.

Cheilosia and *Portevinia* also have larvae which feed on live plants. The following tabulation includes information from Rotheray (1993), Stuke (2002) and Smith (1989). The latter covers various literature sources which have been corrected to modern nomenclature, but some sources are ancient and there is a need to check some of these plant associations by further rearing. Observations on *C. fraterna* and *C. pagana* are given in Stubbs (1980a) and some additional information is given here. Only *C. antiqua*, on primulas, has been reported as a pest (Carpenter, 1913), but such circumstances would appear to be exceptional in recent years. Names in bold type indicate proven associations in Britain and Ireland.

Ranunculaceae	Meadow Buttercup	*Cheilosia albitarsis* [egg-laying female]
	Creeping Buttercup	**C. albitarsis**
Polygonaceae	Alpine Bistort	*C. sahlbergi*
	Scottish Dock	*C. gigantea* (? species B)
	Northern Dock	*C. gigantea* (? species B)
Primulaceae	Cultivated Primulas, Primrose, Oxlip	**C. antiqua**
Crassulaceae	Orpine	**C. semifasciata**
	Navelwort	**C. semifasciata**
Rosaceae	Lady's Mantle	*C. vicina*
	Water Avens	*C. pubera*
Apiaceae	Angelica	**C. chrysocoma** [egg-laying female], *C. illustrata*, *C. pagana*
	Cow Parsley	**C. pagana**
	Hogweed	**C. illustrata**, *C. pagana*
	Wild Parsnip	*C. illustrata*
	Cultivated Parsnip	*Eumerus strigatus*
Plantaginaceae	Ribwort Plantain	*C. lasiopa*
	Greater Plantain	*C. lasiopa* (eggs)
Scrophulariaceae	Water Figwort	**C. variabilis**
	Common Figwort	**C. variabilis**, *C. velutina*
	Hoary Mullein	*C. vernalis*? (puparium under decaying leaves, identification very questionable)

42

Campanulaceae	Sheep's-bit	***Eumerus sabulonum***
Asteraceae	Yarrow	***C. vernalis*** (from root gall of the tephritid *Dithryca guttularis*)
	Greater Burdock	*C. barbata, C. impressa, C. vulpina*
	Lesser Burdock	*C. vulpina*
	Welted Thistle	*C. albipila, C. cynocephala, C. fraterna, C. grossa, C. mutabilis, C. variabilis*
	Musk Thistle	***C. cynocephala***, *C. grossa, C. variabilis*
	Slender Thistle	*C. grossa*
	Creeping Thistle	*C. albipila, C. vulpina?*
	Woolly Thistle	*C. albipila, C. fraterna, C. grossa*
	Marsh Thistle	***C. albipila***, *C. cynocephala*, ***C. fraterna***, ***C. grossa***, ***C. proxima***, *C. vulpina*
	Cabbage Thistle	*C. fraterna, C. grossa*
	Spear Thistle	*C. albipila, C. cynocephala, C. fraterna*, ***C. grossa***, *C. variabilis, C. vulpina*
	Globe Artichoke	*C. vulpina*
	Mouse-ear Hawkweed	*C. psilophthalma, C. urbana*
	Autumn Hawkbit	*C. latifrons* [egg-laying female]
	Scented Mayweed	*C. vernalis*
	Scotch Thistle	*C. grossa*
	Smooth Sow-thistle	*C. vernalis*
	Goatsbeard	*C. vernalis*
	Common Ragwort	***C. bergenstammi***
	Hoary Ragwort	*C. bergenstammi* [egg-laying female]
Liliaceae	Ramsons	***Portevinia maculata***
	Onion	***Eumerus strigatus***
	garden Daffodil	***Eumerus strigatus, E. funeralis, Merodon equestris***
Iridaceae	garden Iris	***Eumerus strigatus, E. funeralis***

The associations with higher plants relate to larvae in roots and stem bases, with the exception of *C. semifasciata* mining the leaves of Crassulaceae, and *C. psilophthalma* feeding on the above-ground parts of hawkweeds. The dominance of the Asteraceae (= composites) is apparent. It is probable that some species will have a larger range of host plants than so far recognised. It is clear, for example, that many of the *Cheilosia* associated with thistles can utilise a range of species.

Fungi

Three closely related *Cheilosia* breed in fungi. They all belong to *Cheilosia* group E, although the only other member of this group, *C. pagana*, is associated with higher plants.

Cheilosia scutellata and *C. soror* have been reared from truffles. *C. scutellata* and *C. longula* breed in *Boletus* and its allies (*Leccinum*, *Suillus* and *Gyroporus*). This information is taken from Smith (1989), Rotheray (1993) and Stuke (2002).

There are a few records of *C. scutellata* having been reared from gill fungi: Chandler (1969) from an *Agaricus* (published as *Pholiota*) and Dely-Draskovits & Babos (1993) from *Russula vesca*.

Dung

Rhingia campestris has been reared from cow dung. It is unknown whether any other dung types are suitable, but the species can be abundant in areas where cattle are scarce or absent (*e.g.* in woods and gardens in the intensively cultivated areas of eastern England), so other media must be utilised. Nothing is known of the early stages of the woodland species, *R. rostrata*.

Decaying vegetable matter

This is said to be a breeding medium though it can be remarkably difficult to find any larvae. Compost heaps may support *Syritta*, but such large aggregations of material do not typify wild habitats. It is probable that the early months in the year are the best time to search (January to April) since soil and litter are then almost continuously moist.

Genera using this habitat are *Neoascia*, *Syritta*, *Tropidia* and some *Xylota*, but there is really a transition into genera of more aquatic habitats such as *Chrysogaster* and its allies and *Eristalis*. Accumulations of wet leaves in a dried-out puddle can contain larvae of Eristalini, for instance, whilst such accumulations in rot-holes and crevices in trees can support *Myathropa* and other rot-hole specialists.

Aquatic larvae

Most species require organically rich conditions. Thus there are many Eristalini which thrive where organic pollution affects ponds and ditches, including putrefying run-off from manure heaps, silage clamps, and cattle dung in wet mud. However, rotting vegetation beside water and in wet marshy and peaty soils can also provide suitable conditions. Thus many Eristalini, Sericomyiini, *Chrysogaster*, *Lejogaster*, *Melanogaster*, *Orthonevra*, *Riponnensia* and some *Neoascia* are adapted to a varying range of aquatic or semi-aquatic niches. The greatest specialisation is found in *Melanogaster* which can live permanently submerged by plugging their hind spiracles into air spaces in aquatic plants.

Bees and wasps

Most *Volucella* are scavengers or predators in the nests of social wasps (*Vespa*, *Vespula*), with *V. bombylans* also occurring in the nests of bumblebees (*Bombus*). However *V. inanis* is solely a predator of the host's larvae.

Ants

Microdon larvae are predatory on ant larvae. Some Syrphinae, in particular *Chrysotoxum* and *Xanthogramma*, have underground larvae which feed on root aphids attended by ants (Rotheray *et al.*, 1996), but it is unknown whether the presence of the ants is essential.

Aphids

The introductory text to the Syrphinae and the Pipizini discusses the predation by hoverfly larvae on aphids. Such habits concern about half the British hoverfly fauna. It is unclear to what extent aphids form the sole diet or whether in some species any type of small prey is acceptable.

Caterpillars

Xanthandrus is recorded as a predator of small moth caterpillars. *Parasyrphus nigritarsis* feeds on the caterpillar-like larvae of chrysomelid leaf beetles on alder and sallow. There are also some reports of sawfly caterpillars being adopted as prey. Little is recorded on this subject.

CHAPTER 5

THE EARLY STAGES

This book is primarily concerned with the identification of adults, so comments here on the early stages are only concerned with giving a lead into follow-up studies on the subject. However, such superficial treatment should not be interpreted as reflecting the irrelevance of the subject since the early stages require vigorous new studies in their own right.

Whilst the basic outline of life-histories is reasonably well established, there remains a huge gulf in knowledge, even over the description of early stages. It is probable that some inaccurate or misleading statements have become entrenched in the literature, including those based on misidentifications, so verification of the facts is often required. Coe (1953a) gave a good lead into the literature of the time, notably in his comments under genera, but it is now out of date and out of print. This work was updated by Smith (1989) in his Handbook on immature stages. Rotheray (1993) provides an extensive introduction to the morphology and ecology of hoverfly larvae, together with an excellent series of colour photographs.

Flies have a complete life-cycle comprising egg, larva, pupa and adult.

Eggs

Female hoverflies apparently use both sight and smell in locating suitable egg-laying sites, probably supplemented by other senses such as touch. The antennae, for instance, tend to have various specialised structures of unknown function, many hoverflies having various pits on the third antennal segment (obvious in some *Brachyopa*, for instance, but also visible as multiple pits in some *Cheilosia*). Anyone with access to an electron microscope could have an interesting time on this subject.

Eggs are normally cigar-shaped and often slightly curved. The surface is sculptured with a reticulate or longitudinal pattern of pits or ridges. Chandler (1968c) describes and illustrates the sculpture in a number of species of Syrphinae. He even went so far as to identify eggs found in the field, certainly a good way of contributing to knowledge of the ecology of species, but a technique open to misidentifications when the characters of the egg in many species remain unknown. There is worthwhile work in extending studies of this type, and checking earlier identifications. Mature eggs may be dissected out of gravid females or the female may be encouraged to lay eggs within a container or cage (containing aphid-infested shoots and either suitable flowers or cotton wool soaked in a sugar solution).

The Syrphinae often lay their eggs singly, but in *Platycheirus* have been recorded as laying small batches of eggs. *Pipizella viduata* was found to lay its eggs near the base of the stem of umbellifers, its larval prey being root aphids. Though eggs are often laid close to an aphid colony, eggs may also be laid speculatively in places where aphids may colonise, the point being that aphids may come and go so quickly that both strategies have their advantages and disadvantages (see Chandler, 1968a, 1968b).

Hoverflies with other breeding sites usually lay their eggs on or in close proximity to the larval food. In the case of *Rhingia campestris*, eggs were found to be laid on vegetation overhanging the cow-pat breeding sites (Coe, 1942). *Microdon* is said to enter ants' nests to lay its eggs, presumably without challenge. In most cases there is no knowledge on this subject, yet simple field observations could readily advance our understanding of the breeding sites adopted by hoverflies.

Larvae

The larvae are maggot-like, lacking legs though sometimes having crochets (hooks) and prolegs, like caterpillars. Fleshy outgrowths also occur on the sides or dorsally in some species, as with *Rhingia campestris* where the surrounding medium is attached to the larva as a form of camouflage. The larvae of *Microdon* are hemispherical and lack obvious segments – it is perhaps not surprising that on several occasions between 1824 and 1907 some authors attempted to classify them as molluscs (Donisthorpe, 1927). Larvae moult their skins several times during growth and there may be some differences between the instars; it is as well to retain shed skins if possible.

The distinctive feature of hoverfly larvae is the presence of fused posterior breathing tubes projecting at the hind end of the larva. This projection is usually short, but can be very elongate in species which live in water. The extreme condition is found with the rat-tailed maggots belonging to the Eristalini, where the telescopic breathing tube can extend to 27 cm in some species. This enables the body of the larva to live hidden within detritus at the bottom of a pool while still being able to breathe air. *Melanogaster hirtella* has been even more cunning, since its posterior spiracles are designed to pierce underwater plants, such as sweet-grass, to tap the large air spaces which give the plant buoyancy.

Aphidophagous (aphid-eating) larvae characterise the Syrphinae and also the Pipizini. Syrphinae larvae are unusual in the Diptera in that many of them are active mobile predators on the foliage of trees and herbs, not what one would expect of blind and legless maggots. They have colour patterns, which in some cases act as a ready means of identification. Such larvae are often nocturnal, hiding away by day in curled leaves and other crannies, occasionally leaving black tar-like excreta within an aphid colony which betray their presence. Larvae may be found by careful searching on or at the base of herbaceous plants or by beating the foliage of trees and bushes. Some species specialise on root aphids so require diligent search and it is suspected that a few (*e.g. Chrysotoxum*) may have an association with ants' nests.

The location of larvae requires searching in the breeding media used by hoverflies. They can be very elusive, but perseverance often leads to success. Breeding media include mud, fungi, rotting vegetation (including compost heaps), dung (including manure heaps), inside stems and leaves of herbaceous plants, and dead wood. There may be plenty of dead wood or other suitable habitat, but larvae are often concentrated in discrete locations and may be absent from much of the medium. It is essential not to tear dead wood to bits since this will destroy the habitat for other insects, so a more gentle approach is needed. Dead-wood larvae can sometimes be located with good effect by digging up the soil just at the base of the trunk, even of a live tree where the bark is locally unsound. Rotheray (1993) gives methods for finding larvae in each of the main types of habitat.

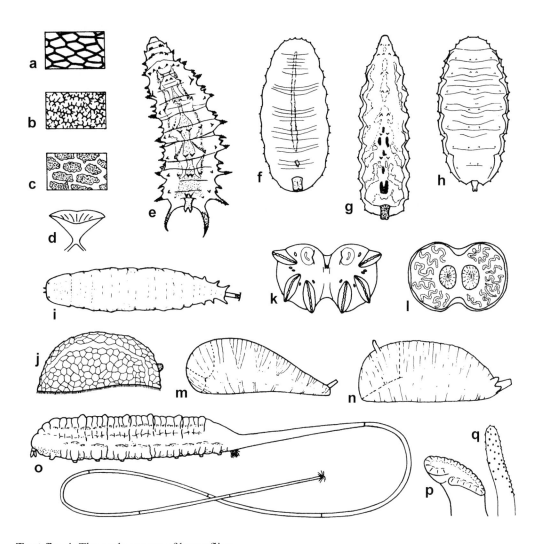

Text fig. 4. The early stages of hoverflies.

a-c Egg sculpture (**a** - *Pipizella viduata*, **b** - *Meligramma trianguliferum*, **c** - *Eupeodes corollae*); **d** - Egg chorionic projection (*Syrphus vitripennis*); **e-j** Larvae (**e** - *Dasysyrphus albostriatus*, **f** - *Epistrophe eligans*, **g** - *Meligramma trianguliferum*, **h** - *Pipizella viduata*, **i** - *Xylota segnis*, **j** - *Microdon analis*); **k-l** Posterior spiracular plates at end of siphon; larvae illustrated, but puparia similar (**k** - *Eupeodes luniger*, **l** - *Volucella inanis*); **m-n** Puparia, posterior siphon at right hand end (**m** - *Epistrophe eligans* showing typical tapering side view of Syrphinae, **n** - *Cheilosia pagana* showing more oval side view of Milesiinae, including anterior spiracular horn). **o-q** *Eristalis tenax* (**o** - rat-tailed maggot larva, **p** - anterior spiracle of larva, **q** - anterior spiracular horn of puparium). Re-drawn from Chandler (1968c), Dixon (1960), Hartley (1961), Brauns (1954) and van der Goot (1981), plus original.

In order to rear larvae it is often sufficient to put some of the medium, such as dead wood or rotting vegetation, into a polythene bag. Leave a small opening for air, without causing the contents to dry out, and place the bag in a larger container such as a seed propagator. A plant root with *Cheilosia* larvae can be potted up with soil, and the pot placed in a polythene bag and thence in a propagator. The emerging fly will come out into the propagator where it is easily seen and will not go mouldy. *Eristalis* cultures can be established in manure soup (Heal, 1979a), but it is a very smelly occupation (ensuring your rapid ejection from the family home!). Aphid-feeding larvae grow rapidly and can be kept in a lepidopterist's breeding cage with infested plant shoots in water (plug the entrance to the water bottle), or an air-tight plastic box may be sufficient. Always keep breeding containers in the shade – sweating and condensation lead to moulds and diseases. A method of rearing *Merodon* is described by Conn (1976c), no doubt being adaptable for *Eumerus*. Rotheray (1993) describes rearing methods for the various types of larvae.

Most hoverflies hibernate in the larval stage. This can cause a problem if an aphid-feeding larva is mature in June and has to be kept alive till the following May before it pupates. Such larvae can be found in woodland leaf litter during the winter, so the answer is probably to mimic these conditions by putting soil and leaf litter in a flower pot covered with muslin, which is then kept shaded and moist in the garden. The easiest species to rear are multiple-brooded ones where early larvae will quickly produce adults. An alternative strategy is to search in March and April so that larvae and puparia will not have to be tended for long. The easiest way to gain identifiable larvae for description is probably to rear from eggs of known parentage, either from eggs seen laid in the field or from caged gravid females, but note that larval colours may be atypical under artificial conditions. See Rotheray (1993) for preservation methods and also hints on examining both living and preserved larvae.

Useful publications are as follows: Dixon (1960) covered all types of aphidophagous larvae then known, and Goeldlin de Tiefenau (1974) is also invaluable for this group. For hoverfly larvae other than Syrphinae, Hartley (1961) provides an important review with excellent illustrations and Dolezil (1972) considers the Eristalini. Coe (1953a) illustrates the early stages of *Rhingia* (see also Coe, 1942) and the larvae of *Callicera* and *Xylota*. Larval mouthparts are described by Hartley (1963) and Roberts (1970). *A Dipterist's Handbook* (Stubbs & Chandler, 1978) includes a key (by A. Brindle and K.G.V. Smith) to families of Diptera larvae, advice on preservation of larvae, and information on rearing, biology and other aspects of the study of larvae, including a list of larvae described by Dixon and Goeldlin de Tiefenau. Smith (1989) gives a key to subfamilies and tribes and summarises the available literature, and a generic key by Thompson & Rotheray (1998) is given in the Palaearctic Manual. Rotheray (1993) summarises the information then known and includes keys, descriptions and colour photographs. Phylogenetic relationships are reviewed by Rotheray & Gilbert (1999).

Puparia

The pupa is formed inside the shrunken and hardened larval skin so outwardly one is looking at a puparium (as in many other Diptera). This means that many of the features of the last larval instar are preserved in the puparium, even if grossly modified, so retention of the puparium is essential when hoverflies are reared.

The posterior respiratory process retains a characteristic pattern on the end (the spiracular plates of the larva). The pupal spiracles near the front end are invaluable in describing puparia of Milesiinae (Hartley, 1961). The surface of the puparium may have a fine microscopic sculpture. For identification and other purposes it is very important to retain the bits of the puparium that may become detached when the adult fly emerges.

Puparia of Syrphinae can often be found on leaves near to aphid colonies and these will usually produce adults within a week or a matter of days. Puparia from over-wintering larvae are often more hidden and may be found when searching leaf litter for larvae, especially in the spring. Puparia of other groups of hoverflies are either in or close to the larval habitat.

Enemies of early stages

The early stages suffer from predation by many types of animals. However, a more specialised relationship has developed with the parasitic wasps. The exposed eggs, larvae and puparia of the Syrphinae are particularly vulnerable, but the early stages of the rest of the hoverflies are not immune. Minute egg parasites belonging to the Proctotrupoidea attack hoverfly eggs. Among the larger parasites, the Diplazontinae seem entirely specialised to aphidophagous hoverflies. The parasite lays its egg in the hoverfly egg or larva, and the parasite emerges from the host puparium. These parasitic wasps are among the commonest ichneumonids and may be looked for around aphid colonies (see Rotheray, 1979b, 1981 and Fitton & Rotheray, 1982). Some other groups of parasitic wasps also attack hoverflies, for instance *Dendrocerus puparum* (Ceraphronoidea) is recorded from *Syrphus ribesii* and *Episyrphus balteatus* (Fergusson, 1980).

A Dipterist's Handbook discusses the subject in further detail and mentions examples within the Pteromalidae, Encyrtidae, Aspicerinae (Figitidae), Phygadeuontinae (Ichneumonidae) and the Ceraphronoidea. Rotheray (1993) lists parasitoids of hoverfly larvae and pupae.

CHAPTER 6

THE CHARACTERS OF ADULT HOVERFLIES

The Distinctive Features of Hoverflies

Though extremely varied in size, shape and colour, it is fairly easy to become accustomed to recognising hoverflies. Behaviour of the flies is often as important as their physical features. However, confusion can arise from mimicry, and some of the less boldly marked species are not readily distinguished as hoverflies.

Two wings

Hoverflies belong to the group of insects called Diptera, the literal translation of the word meaning "two-winged". Virtually all other insects have four wings. Thus bees and wasps, for instance, have four wings though the hind pair are small and at times may be covered by the larger front pair. The hind pair of wings in the Diptera have become reduced to tiny drumsticks called halteres.

Robust flies with legs of moderate length.

One large group of flies, the Nematocera, usually have very long legs. These are craneflies, mosquitoes and gnats of various types, which are elongate in build and have very long legs so are unlikely to be confused with hoverflies. The hoverfly *Baccha* is very elongate but its legs are not nearly as long as those of a cranefly. Nematocera also have thread-like antennae with many segments, quite unlike the antennae of a hoverfly.

Thorax without bristles on top.

Many Diptera are in the same range of size and shape as hoverflies, but have a set pattern of stout bristles on the thorax (for instance the housefly). Hoverflies only have fine hairs on top of the thorax (there are a few with stout bristles confined to the margins of the thoracic dorsum). This is a very good initial field character, but it is also necessary to check the wing venation since there are some other groups of flies which also lack bristles.

Wing with a spurious vein (= false vein).

Hoverflies are the only Diptera to have a *vena spuria*. However, this vein is not always obvious in the smaller species.

Wing with two outer cross-veins.

Hoverflies have two outer cross-veins, both fairly near the wing margin. Many other Diptera have only one outer cross-vein or none at all. However, those other flies with two cross-veins are unlikely to cause confusion since rarely are both these veins close to the wing margin and, if they are close, then usually there are bristles on the thorax.

52

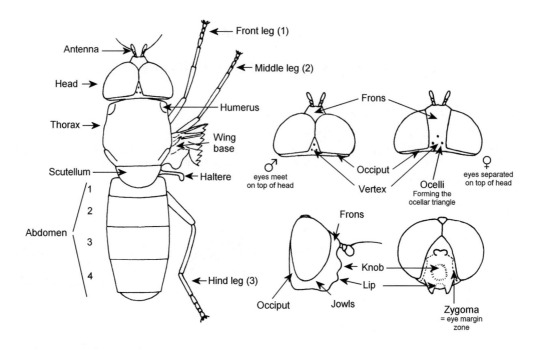

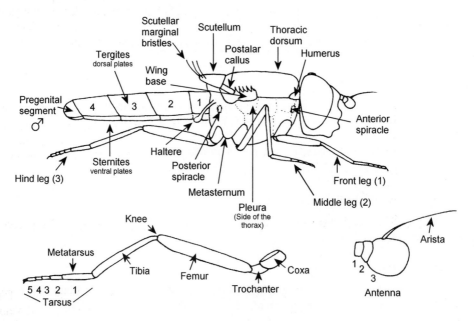

Text fig. 5. Hoverfly body and legs (of a male *Cheilosia albitarsis*).

Thorax

The dorsal surface is called the THORACIC DORSUM, defined at its margins by a slight ridge or other structure. At the front corners there are swellings called the HUMERI (= shoulders); at the posterior corners there are elongate swellings called the *postalar calli*. Behind the dorsum there is a semicircular projection called the SCUTELLUM which often bears along its hind rim some *scutellar bristles*. The sides of the thorax consist of several units (separated from each other by furrows, or sutures) which are collectively referred to as the PLEURA (cf. pleural cavity of thorax in a vertebrate). The pleura have small openings to the internal breathing tubes (tracheae), consisting of an *anterior spiracle* and a *posterior spiracle* on each side. In some cases it is necessary to note the presence or absence of hairs on the *metasternum*, which is on the underside of the thorax between the bases of the middle and hind legs.

Legs

The LEGS consist of five main units. The COXA (at the base), the TROCHANTER (a small unit), the FEMUR (often the most powerful unit of the leg), the TIBIA (another long unit) and the TARSUS (which consists of five small segments). The basal segment of the tarsus is the stoutest and is called the METATARSUS. The joint at the junction of the femur and the tibia is termed the *knee*. The legs will only fold up in one plane; thus it is easy to define the ventral surfaces as those which will fold up against each other, with the dorsal surfaces opposite to them, and so in turn defining the sides of the leg. The anterior surface faces forwards and the posterior surface faces backwards. In some of the diagrams in the keys, 'behind' means 90° (approximately) round the hind surface of the leg from true ventral. A set specimen with its legs splayed out, as in many of the colour plates, generally shows the legs from above – and hence in approximately dorsal view.

Wings

The WINGS consist of a membrane supported by thin thread-like struts called VEINS (when the newly emerged fly expands its wings, the veins are pumped full of fluid which then hardens to

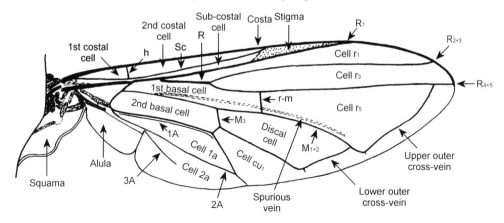

Text fig. 6. Hoverfly wing (of *Cheilosia albitarsis*).

give semi-rigid support for the wing). Though at first sight looking complex, the wing venation has a basically simple pattern of veins radiating from the wing base with cross connections called CROSS-VEINS. Areas of the wing between the veins are referred to as CELLS.

Though it looks complicated, there is a logical sequence of veins and vein numbers, based on radial veins (R), median veins (M), cubital veins (Cu) and anal veins (A). Vein R_{4+5} is often referred to in the Keys. The cells are mostly named after the vein immediately above. The special feature of a hoverfly wing, the spurious (or false) vein is shown. Note the inner cross-vein r-m (connecting radial and median veins) above the discal cell. The upper and lower outer cross-veins are important features. The stigma is conspicuous in many species because it is coloured (though in some cases it is transparent and not so apparent). The costal vein runs as a thickened front margin to the wing, reaching as far as the wing tip at vein R_{4+5}. The squama and alula are membranous flaps which are sometimes referred to in the Keys.

For the most part hoverflies can be identified by reference to relatively few wing features, and the sketches in the keys should make any prior knowledge of wing venation unnecessary. The most commonly used characters are as follows:

The STIGMA lies on the front margin of the wing, between the first two long veins to reach the margin; frequently the membrane of the stigma is tinged with some darker coloration compared with adjacent areas of the wing. VEIN R_{4+5} is the fourth long vein to reach the margin and is the vein nearest the wing tip; it is this vein which is important as being straight, curved (dipped) or looped before the wing tip. Below the wing tip there is the UPPER OUTER CROSS-VEIN, running almost parallel with the wing margin (but various bends aid identification in some species) and it is this vein which closes CELL r_5. In the lower centre of the wing lies the DISCAL CELL, closed on the outer side by the LOWER OUTER CROSS-VEIN. An inner cross-vein, r-m, meets the front margin of the discal cell, the position of this junction being important in recognising some groups of hoverflies. Towards the base of the wing, on the hind margin, there is a membranous flap called the *alula*. Where the hind margin of the wing meets the thorax there is a membranous flange called the SQUAMA (the certain identification of the genus *Syrphus* depends on the recognition of hairs on top of the squama). Thus knowledge of relatively few wing features is sufficient to follow most of the key. The only other important feature, unique to hoverflies and therefore aiding their recognition, is the SPURIOUS VEIN (or false vein, sometimes also called the *vena spuria*) which is a faint vein running along the central axis of the wing through vein r-m but not connected at either end.

For advanced studies on hoverflies, and in particular in those cases where critical identification depends on use of the microscope, reference to a greater range of wing characters will on occasions be necessary. This is particularly the case where the distribution of MICROTRICHIA (microscopic hairs) on the wing membrane is significant. Here the recognition of the *basal cells* is important.

There is a pair of HALTERES consisting of small drumstick-like processes behind the wings. These represent the hind wings. Each haltere consists of a slender *stalk* and a swollen *club* (= knob in some books) at the apex.

Abdomen

The ABDOMEN is segmented, the number of visible segments depending on the subfamily, the sex and, in the females, on the degree to which the terminal segments are extended or retracted. The segments each consist of two units. The top surfaces are referred to as TERGITES (think of T for top) and underneath there are separate units, called STERNITES (cf. sternum of a vertebrate). A membrane connects tergites and sternites, this sometimes being obvious, especially when the female abdomen is bloated with eggs. In the *male* the last segments curve underneath the abdomen in a twisted U-turn; this leaves a somewhat rounded or bulbous surface at the end of the abdomen called the *pre-genital segment* whilst the *genitalia* at the end of the abdomen are often tucked firmly underneath and may be largely obscured by the last conspicuous sternite. The *female* has a gently tapering end to the abdomen with the last segments very small and usually contracted out of sight.

In some species the abdomen has a pattern of coloured markings which are fairly constant in some species, but very variable in others. The most distinctive types of markings in the Syrphinae are illustrated (p. 62) together with the descriptive names adopted in this book. The colour and length of hairs, together with areas of surface dusting in some species, are used as further characters on the abdomen, as on other parts of the fly.

The male genitalia can be used for identification, more easily in some genera than others. They are divided into two main parts, which are articulated (see Plate A). The *epandrium* (a highly modified tergite 9) bears the cerci and paired claspers called *surstyli* (= *paralobes*) which can provide a useful character through their varied shape. Joined to the base of the *epandrium* is the *hypandrium* (a highly modified sternite 9) which consist of a membranous body often termed the *theca*, which gives rise to another smaller pair of clasping organs called the *parameres* or *superior lobes* which flank the *aedeagus*. The *aedeagus* has a long *apodeme* that passes back into the *theca* and acts as a muscle attachment. The *hypandrium* can be particularly useful for identification. Male genitalia have only been referred to where essential, as in *Sphaerophoria*, *Cheilosia* and the Pipizini. The dissected male genitalia of *Cheilosia* are illustrated in Plates B – N and those of *Sphaerophoria* in Plates O – Q.

CHAPTER 7

KEYS

Hints on the Use of Keys

The following hints will help reduce errors in the use of the keys, which are designed for use with a hand lens.

Use of Keys

Keys aid a methodical approach to identification. The most common errors result from rushing, and in particular through jumping to a different line from the one intended.

— Do not force a specimen if the characters do not entirely fit. Read the text to a species as a double check and look at the plates.

— It is better to name a few specimens accurately than to name numerous specimens incorrectly. Put a question mark on your identification if there is doubt. Incorrect records are infinitely more trouble than they are worth.

— If you cannot name a specimen to start with, put it on one side and come back to it with a fresh mind on another day. As you gain experience and become familiar with the key, initial uncertainties should tend to evaporate away.

— Keys ought to work with typical specimens, but there will always be a small percentage of abnormal specimens which cause difficulty. Hoverflies are highly variable and also new species may be discovered. It is only by drawing attention to problem specimens that keys can evolve to a higher plane of accuracy.

— Retain problem specimens and refer them to the recording scheme specialists for advice.

— Species in some genera are not easy to identify. A voucher collection is essential for comparing specimens and vouchers should be retained for all difficult and rarer species. This enables identifications to be checked and confirmed by specialists later.

— Take care with teneral (freshly emerged) specimens. Dark markings on the body, legs and wings may be very faint and assumed to be absent. The body surface (chitin) is soft and, even if apparently hardened, the legs and antennae may lose their three-dimensional shape on drying. The face may collapse, with the mouth margin becoming abnormally narrow (thus the face width or face profile can be distorted).

— All illustrations are orientated as in text figs. 5 and 6 in Chapter 6 unless otherwise stated.

Use of a Lens

— Hold the lens close to your eye in order to get clearest views. A lens of 10× should suffice in the field, but 15× or 20× may be needed to see the smaller details at home.

— When examining a specimen, good lighting is essential.

— When looking for the presence or absence of hairs, or the colour of hairs, look against both light and dark backgrounds. Remember that pale hairs in silhouette will seem to be black and that at certain angles black hairs may reflect light and seem to be pale. It is necessary to adjust the angle of view.

— Dust spots and other surface features may only be visible from certain angles.

— In a few cases the keys have had to include microscope characters. These are prefixed with M and placed in square brackets. All such features used here should be visible at 25× or 30× with a stereoscopic binocular microscope. Hair colours show up best under general lighting (*e.g.* an Anglepoise lamp) rather than an intense spotlight.

Examining Live Specimens

— It is not always necessary to kill hoverflies in order to identify them. There are many species which are easy to identify alive. However, it is necessary to recognise that some species are difficult to identify and can only be considered if retained in a collection.

— If your specimen may be retained for the collection, do not risk damage by grasping it with your fingers.

— Should you wish to examine large species by hand, then gently hold the thorax between finger and thumb. The fly will settle down if its legs can rest on a finger. Only hold a wing if the legs are offered a finger to grasp – otherwise the fly will whir round until the wing is torn off. Remember that even gentle handling may mutilate the fly.

— Live specimens for field identification should be placed in narrow glass tubes so that they cannot run round too rapidly. A fly will usually quieten down if kept in the dark for a few minutes. The container must not be deeper than the depth of focus of your hand lens. There is, however, a problem since the wings will be folded over the abdomen, thus making critical examination of markings difficult.

— It is possible to gently anaesthetise a hoverfly, examine it and allow it to recover before release.

Key to Tribes

1. Humeri bare [SYRPHINAE].
   Head deeply concave so usually sits over and
   masks the humeri.

14

— Humeri hairy [MILESIINAE +
   MICRODONTINAE]. Head naturally sits
   well forward so that the humeri are clearly
   visible. **If in doubt, key from here.**

2

2. Upper outer cross-vein re-entrant (*i.e.* the upper
   outer cross-vein bends inwards before it
   meets R_{4+5} at an angle of less than 90°,
   looking from the direction of the wing tip).

3

— Upper outer cross-vein not re-entrant. (If the
   upper outer cross-vein meets R_{4+5} at right-
   angles, as in *Neoascia*, then it is NOT
   considered re-entrant).

5

3. Antennae porrect (long, cylindrical, projecting
   straight in front of head).

MICRODONTINAE
p. 163

— Antennae short.
4

4. Arista plumose.

VOLUCELLINI
p. 158

— Arista bare. Furry bee-like species or with a
   flat hairy face and swollen hind femur (if not
   of this description, continue to couplet 5).
MERODONTINI
p. 147

5. Wing with R_{4+5} strongly looped. (Lower and
   upper outer cross-veins form an almost
   continuous vein parallel with wing margin).

ERISTALINI
p. 138

— Wing with R_{4+5} shallowly dipped or more
   nearly straight. (If R_{4+5} is somewhat dipped,
   the outer cross-veins are stepped rather than
   being continuous).
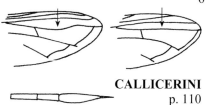
6

6. Antennae porrect (long cylindrical) with
   terminal arista.
CALLICERINI
p. 110

— Antennae not of this type (if porrect, the arista
   is dorsal).
7

7. Very large broadly built hoverflies with plumose arista.

SERICOMYIINI
p. 157

— Hoverflies without plumose arista (an exception, *Hammerschmidtia*, is not broadly built and is entirely orange-brown).

8

8. Face flat and entirely covered in long drooping shaggy hairs.

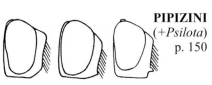

PIPIZINI
(+*Psilota*)
p. 150

— Face not of this type (either not flat or if flat then without an entire covering of shaggy hairs; facial knob often present).

9

9. Wing with inner cross-vein (r-m) before middle of discal cell. (*Ferdinandea*, with bristles on lateral margin of thoracic dorsum, belongs here).

10

— Wing with inner cross-vein (r-m) at or beyond middle of discal cell. (*Syritta*, with densely grey dusted pleura, belongs here).

XYLOTINI
p. 158

10. Face concave, without central prominence, but may have a 'lip' just above the mouth edge.

CHRYSOGASTRINI
(Part)
p. 127

— Face with central prominence (as well as a 'lip' just above the mouth edge) or entire lower part of face projecting forwards.

11

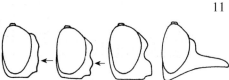

11. Small species (up to 6 mm long) with face projecting forwards in lower half. Arista shorter than third antennal segment.

PELECOCERINI p. 149

— Face not this shape, or if so then a larger species with arista much longer than third antennal segment.

12

12. Top of abdomen flat at least on tergite 2 and entirely dull on top or with large orange side patches.

CHRYSOGASTRINI (Part) p. 127

— Abdomen without above features.

13

13. Face with sharply defined and distinct eye margin zone for most of height. Humeri hairy. (The majority of species lack a colour pattern of spots or bars).

CHEILOSIINI p. 111

— Face without distinct eye margins, or such a zone only present on lower part of face. Humeri bare. (The majority of species have a distinct colour pattern of spots or bars).

14 **[SYRPHINAE]**

14. Face entirely yellow or at least yellow at the sides (only entirely black in some *Melangyna*, especially *M. quadrimaculata*, which belong in Syrphini).

15

— Face entirely black.

BACCHINI p. 65

15. Antennal third segment modestly elongate. Very small species (up to 5 mm body length).

PARAGINI p. 80

— Antennal third segment more compact or extremely elongate. Rarely so small.

SYRPHINI p. 81

Subfamily SYRPHINAE

Some Types of Markings in Syrphinae

SPOTS

	round spots	Tergite 2: *Xanthandrus comtus*, *Platycheirus* (*e.g. clypeatus, angustatus*); Tergite 3: *Platycheirus podagratus*
	oval spots	Tergite 2: *Dasysyrphus* Tergites 3 & 4: *Melangyna* (*e.g. arctica*)
	square spots (less than twice as wide as long)	Tergite 2: *Leucozona* (incl. *Ischyrosyrphus*) Tergites 3 & 4: *Melangyna*, *Sphaerophoria*, *Platycheirus*
	oblique spots	*Meligramma euchromum*
	elongate spots (elongate with axis of body)	*Melanostoma*, *Platycheirus*
	triangular spots (outer facing)	*Melanostoma* (females), *Platycheirus podagratus*
	triangular spots (inner facing)	*Meliscaeva auricollis*, *Meligramma trianguliferum*, *Didea*
	triangular spots (upper facing)	Tergite 2: *Melangyna cincta*, *Epistrophe eligans*
	hemispherical spots	*Parasyrphus punctulatus*, *Xanthandrus comtus*
	golf-club-shaped spots	Tergite 2 only: *Syrphus*, *Eupeodes*, *Parasyrphus*, *Didea* (often more broadly developed than shown)
	commas (upward facing)	*Eupeodes*, *Scaeva*
	crescents (downward facing)	Tergite 2: *Meliscaeva auricollis* Tergites 3 & 4: *Chrysotoxum*

BARS

bars (twice as wide as long or more) — *Dasysyrphus, Leucozona (Ischyrosyrphus), Melangyna, Xanthogramma*

hooked bars — *Dasysyrphus pinastri*

oblique bars — *Dasysyrphus albostriatus*

wedges(narrow triangles) — Tergite 2: *Xanthogramma citrofasciatum*
Tergites 3 & 4: *Epistrophe eligans*

BANDS

band — *Epistrophe, Melangyna cincta, Meliscaeva cinctella, Sphaerophoria*

double band — *Episyrphus balteatus*

band with tapered margin — *Epistrophe diaphana, Eupeodes latifasciatus, Parasyrphus nigritarsis*

undulating band — *Parasyrphus*

undulating band with tapered margins = moustache — *Syrphus, Eupeodes, Parasyrphus*

fused spots = spectacle — *Eupeodes, Xanthandrus comtus*

fused triangles — *Melangyna cincta, Meliscaeva cinctella, Didea*

Black Female Syrphinae and Similar Hoverflies

Melanic females could potentially occur in many species among the Syrphinae. However, there are certain species which seem prone to melanism and these known melanics are included in the following key. The main objective is to give a lead as to the likely genus or species involved and to separate melanic Syrphinae from rather similar members of the Milesiinae. It is advisable to compare melanics with typical specimens in order to see if such features as the frons shape and the frons pattern correspond. This key will no doubt need refinement as more specimens become available for study.

1.	Scutellum entirely yellow on top.	2
—	Scutellum black or only yellow posteriorly.	4
2.	Frons almost entirely yellow (large species).	**Scaeva (pyrastri)** p. 224
—	Frons black, with median band (or bars) of dusting.	3
3.	Hairs on top of scutellum black.	**Parasyrphus punctulatus** p. 222
—	Hairs on top of scutellum pale.	**Melangyna lasiophthalma** p. 215
4.	Eyes hairy, even if only weakly so.	5
—	Eyes bare.	6
5.	Eye margin zone (zygoma, see p. 52) confined to lower part of face.	**Melangyna quadrimaculata** p. 216
—	Eye margin zone (zygoma) extends far up sides of face.	**Cheilosia** p. 112
6.	Face concave. Legs entirely black.	**Chrysogaster** p. 131
—	Face with knob. Legs usually partly yellow.	7
7.	Scutellum with black marginal bristles.	8
—	Scutellum with fine hairs on hind margin.	9
8.	Scutellum yellow at apex.	**Cheilosia longula/scutellata** p. 253/258
—	Scutellum entirely black.	**Cheilosia** p. 112

9.   Metasternum winged. (The median plate between   **Platycheirus** (esp. **clypeatus**)
      the bases of the mid and hind legs).   p. 68

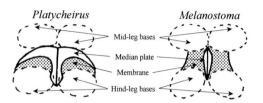

—   Metasternum reduced to a narrow median plate,   **Melanostoma**
      flanked by a large membranous area either side.   p. 66
      (The metasternum is visible if the mid legs are
      directed forwards and the hind legs
      backwards).

Tribe BACCHINI

All species of the subfamily Syrphinae with an *entirely* black scutellum are likely to belong to this tribe of four genera. The only exceptions are *Paragus* which is very distinctive, and some specimens of *Melangyna arctica* which is included in the next tribe, the Syrphini. There is generally a pattern on the abdomen consisting of pairs of coloured spots of grey, yellow or orange. Among the Milesiinae with such a pattern, plus a black scutellum, the most similar hoverflies are *Chamaesyrphus* (with a subapical arista; Scotland only), *Portevinia* and male *Cheilosia semifasciata*.

Key to genera

Note that specimens with an entirely black abdomen are considered in a separate key (p. 64).

1.   Body very elongate, slender and waisted.      **Baccha elongata**
                                                                                p. 168

—   Body more compact.   2

2. Large oval-bodied species. Tergite 2 with small round spots. Tergites 3 and 4 with hemi-spherical spots in male, square spots in female. Wing length 8.75–11 mm.

Xanthandrus comtus
p. 186

[A broad species with large yellow markings. Easily mistaken for a member of the Syrphini, but for the black scutellum.]

—   Smaller species with elliptical or parallel-sided abdomen. Wing length 5–8 mm.   3

3. Males (eyes touching on top of head).   4

—   Females (eyes separated on top of head).   5

4. Front tibia and tarsus cylindrical; abdomen with orange spots on at least two tergites.   ♂ **Melanostoma**
p. 66

—   Front tibia and/or tarsus partly flattened and inflated (only exceptions have grey spots on abdomen, or a pair of yellow spots on tergite 3).   ♂ **Platycheirus**
p. 68

5. Tergites 3 and 4 with roughly triangular spots pointing outwards towards sides. Front tarsus cylindrical.   ♀ **Melanostoma**
p. 66

—   Tergites with a different pattern. Front tarsus flattened (seems cylindrical from above, but in side view it is only half as thick).   ♀ **Platycheirus**
p. 74

Genus MELANOSTOMA

Confusion is most likely with *Platycheirus*. Considerable care is necessary with melanic females (see separate key, p. 64). A revision of this genus is in progress and is likely to result in additional species being split from both *mellinum* and *scalare* (at least two segregates of *scalare* and up to five of *mellinum* are rumoured to occur in Britain) so it is important to retain specimens (especially of males) pending publication.

1. Males (eyes meet on top of head).   2

—   Females (eyes separated).   5

2. Tergites 2 and 3 elongate, at least 1½ times as long as wide.

♂ **scalare**
p. 170

—   Tergites 2 and 3 usually about as long as wide.

3

3. Frons angle not more than 90°, frons shining. Face narrow. Abdomen strongly widening posteriorly, sternites extensively pale. Third antennal segment longer; arista longer and narrower.

♂ **mellinum**
p. 169

—   Frons angle more than 100°, frons often dusted. Face wider. Abdomen parallel-sided, sternites predominantly or completely dark. Third antennal segment short; arista short, swollen at base.

4

4. Thoracic dorsum and scutellum black.

♂ **dubium**
p. 169

—   Thoracic dorsum and scutellum greenish black, contrasting with black of abdomen.

♂ **form A**
p. 170

5. Frons with narrow dust spots (leaving the central half of the frons free of dusting).

♀ **mellinum**
p. 169

—   Frons with much more extensive dust spots.

6

6. Frons with sharply defined triangular dust spots. Face narrow (narrower than the eye width, narrower than high).

♀ **scalare**
p. 170

—   Frons with much more extensive dust spots, broadly connected in centre with some dusting in front. Face very wide (much wider than eye width, much wider than high).

7

7.   Thorax and scutellum black, similar to tergite colour.   ♀ **dubium**
                                                                                    p. 169

—   Thorax and scutellum a brassy or greenish black,   ♀ **form A**
        contrasting with pure black colour on tergites.   p. 170

Genus PLATYCHEIRUS

There are three subgenera, *Platycheirus*, *Pyrophaena* and *Pachysphyria* which are keyed together, being small species with spots normally present on segments 2, 3 and 4 (or bands in female *Pachysphyria*). *Pachysphyria* is represented by a single species, *ambiguus*. *Pyrophaena* is represented by two species, *granditarsus* and *rosarum*, and was considered a separate genus in previous editions of this key. The term metatarsus is used for the basal tarsal segment and there are references to various orientations in which legs need to be viewed. See the section on the legs (p. 53) in Chapter 6 for an explanation. The key includes two European species allied to *peltatus* which could occur in Britain. It has also been suggested that *P. immaculatus* might occur in Britain. This is only known from females, which are entirely black. In that antennal segments 2 and 3 are yellow beneath, the species would appear to be allied to the *albimanus/peltatus* group. Overall this is a narrow-bodied species with tergites 2 and 4 one and a quarter times as long as wide; tergite 3 is square. The frons has strong dust spots. Illustrations are provided by Choi & Han (1999).

Key to males (eyes meet on top of head)

1.   Abdomen extensively orange, or distinctive   2
        yellow spots on tergite 3 only (rarely black
        with an orange median stripe).

—   Abdomen with a different pattern.   3

2.   Tergites 2 to 4 with a large continuous area of   ♂ **granditarsus**
        reddish-orange coloration. [Intersex has a   p. 185
        black abdomen with a narrow median orange
        stripe.]

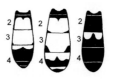

—   Tergite 3 with a band or pair of yellowish spots,   ♂ **rosarum**
        abdomen otherwise extensively dark.   p. 185

3.   Abdomen with silver or bronze spots.   4

—   Abdomen with yellow or orange spots.   7

4.	Front tarsus partly inflated.	5
—	Front tarsus cylindrical.	6
5.	Front tibia broadened at apex.	♂ **albimanus** p. 174
—	Front tibia almost cylindrical.	♂ **discimanus** p. 177
6.	Front femur without a curled hair.	♂ **sticticus** p. 184
—	Front femur with a curled hair behind at apex.	♂ **ambiguus** p. 171
7.	Front tibia almost cylindrical (except at extreme tip).	8
	Front tibia distinctly broadened or more obviously widening towards apex.	10
8.	Front tarsal segments 1 and 2 taper into 3.	♂ **melanopsis** p. 179
—	Front tarsal segment 3 abruptly narrower than 2.	9
9.	Top of thorax dull. Spots on tergite 2 reach close to hind margin.	♂ **manicatus** p. 179
—	Top of thorax shining. Spots on tergite 2 stop well short of hind margin.	♂ **tarsalis** p. 184
10.	Antennae with third antennal segment pale beneath and/or clumps of tangled hairs at base of front femur posteriorly.	11
—	Antennae black. Never with clumps of tangled hairs behind front femur.	19

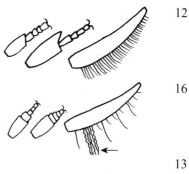

11. Front metatarsus large and asymmetrical. Front
    femur with dense fringe of black hairs.   12

—   Front metatarsus smaller and almost symmetrical.
    Front femur with tangled hairs at base
    posteriorly.   16

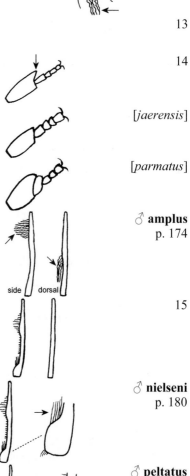

12. Basal segment of front tarsus without a triangular
    extension (illustrations in couplet 13).   13

—   Basal segment of front tarsus with a pronounced
    triangular extension.   14

13. Front tarsus with basal segment rather narrow.   [*jaerensis*]

—   Front tarsus with basal segment broad (as
    peltatus), second segment much broader than
    the third (unlike *peltatus*).   [*parmatus*]

14. Middle tibia slender throughout in side view, with
    inner long flag of hairs near base; in dorsal
    view posterior surface has long hairs directed
    towards apex.   ♂ **amplus**
                                                              p. 174

    side   dorsal

—   Middle tibia, in side view, more swollen near
    apex and also swollen close to small inner flag
    of hairs; in dorsal view without especially long
    hairs on posterior surface.   15

15. Middle tibia in side view, strongly swollen at
    apex, with a tuft of longish hairs directed
    upwards parallel with the shaft. Narrow
    species, tergites 2 to 4 almost square (*amplus*
    also narrow).   ♂ **nielseni**
                                                              p. 180

—   Middle tibia more gently swollen, without
    upwardly directed hairs. Typically a robust
    species with tergites 2 to 4 distinctly transverse
    (occasionally narrow).   ♂ **peltatus**
                                                              p. 181

16.   Front metatarsus 3 times as long as second
        segment. Abdominal spots vague and vary in
        colour depending on angle of view.

♂ **albimanus**
p. 174

—   Front metatarsus 6 times as long as second
        segment. Abdomen with spots often (but not
        always) yellow and distinct from all angles of
        view.

17

17.   Frons greyish dusted. Front tarsus with basal
        segment more elongate and tapering. Mid tibia
        in side view bent one third from apex and
        ventrally with only short hairs. Tergite 4
        elongate, about 1¼ times as long as wide. [M.
        Basal cells partly free of microtrichia at base.]

4

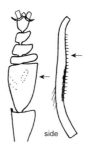

side

♂ **scutatus**
p. 183

—   Frons dull black. Front tarsus with basal segment
        more squat. Mid tibia in side view bent in
        middle or near apex and ventrally with some
        very long hairs. Tergite 4 square, or nearly so.
        [M. Basal cells covered in microtrichia.]

4

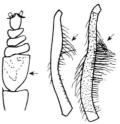

18

18.   Tergites 2 to 4 square; tergite 2 with strong spots.
        Front tarsus with segment 4 about twice as
        wide as long and highly asymmetrical. Mid
        tibia in side view bent in middle, rather swollen
        in basal half; anterior surface with long hairs at
        base only.

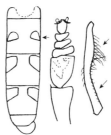

♂ **splendidus**
p. 183

—   Tergites 2 to 4 slightly elongate; tergite 2 with at
        most vague spots. Front tarsus with segment 4
        over twice as wide as long and reasonably
        symmetrical. Mid tibia in side view bent near
        apex, narrowest in basal half; anterior surface
        with long hairs in middle; apical third with
        erect hairs often well developed.

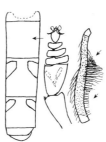

♂ **aurolateralis**
p. 176

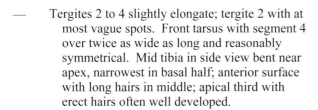

19.   Abdomen with very large spots (black at hind
       edge of tergite 4 narrower than width of hind
       tibia, or absent). Tergite 5 extensively yellow.   20

—   Abdomen with large spots, but black at hind edge
       at least as wide as hind tibia, especially on
       tergite 4. Tergite 5 largely or completely black
       (except in some *scambus*).   22

20.   Front tibia strongly broadened for most of length.   ♂ **fulviventris**
                                                                                              p. 178

—   Front tibia gradually widening towards apex.   21

21.   Front femur with a row of about 6 isolated long
       black hairs behind, normally on a dark stripe;
       hairs below short, pale and not in the same
       plane.   ♂ **immarginatus**
                                                                                              p. 178

—   Front femur entirely yellow with some less
       dominant black hairs closely underlain with
       longish hairs (usually mixed black and pale).   ♂ **perpallidus**
                                                                                              p. 181

22.   Front tibia abruptly broadening beyond middle.   ♂ **podagratus**
                                                                                              p. 182

—   Front tibia gradually broadening towards apex.   **23**

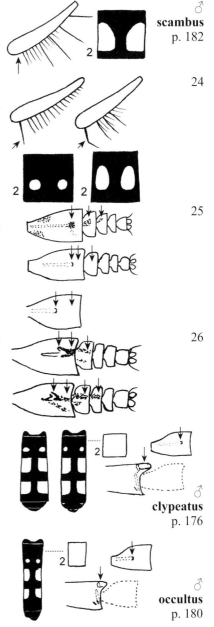

23. Front femur without a long white bristle at base; some long black bristles in apical half (rather like *immarginatus*). Tergite 2 with large spots more than half length of segment.   ♂ **scambus** p. 182

— Front femur with long white bristle at base behind; only fine hairs in apical half. Tergite 2 with elongate-oval or round spots, well clear of side margin.   24

24. Front metatarsus beneath with a rounded pit (at the end of a groove); any dark mark beyond not reaching apex of segment. Front tarsal segments 2 and 3 unmarked beneath or with only a single dark mark.   25

— Front metatarsus beneath with a tick-like or acute-angled pit; dark area beyond normally reaches apex of segment. Second and sometimes third segment with paired stripe-like markings. Front tarsal segment 2, and often 3, usually with a distinct dark stripe.   26

25. Front metatarsus more elongate, beneath with faint pit well beyond halfway. Front tibia with apical posterior spur much longer than wide (view from below). Abdomen often wider, with tergite 2 usually slightly transverse, but can be as narrow as next species with slightly elongate tergite 2.   ♂ **clypeatus** p. 176

— Front metatarsus less elongate, beneath with faint pit just before centre. Front tibia with apical posterior spur no longer than wide. Tergite 2 longer than wide; abdomen fairly narrow.   ♂ **occultus** p. 180

26. Front femur with posterior hairs confined to basal half. Front metatarsus beneath with acute-angled pit very near apex. Front tibia with apical posterior spur angled off to a point. Hind metatarsus swollen, much thicker than hind tibia. Tergite spots rounded. Tergite 2 squarish or slightly elongate.

♂ **ramsarensis**
p. 182

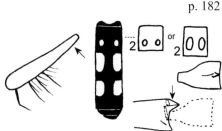

— Front femur with posterior hairs extending to near apex. Front metatarsus beneath with tick-like pit. Front tibia with apical posterior spur bluntly rounded. Hind metatarsus slender, nearly width of hind tibia. Tergite 2 rather more elongate.

27

27. Side of top of thorax and side of thorax in front of wing shining, like top of thorax. Front metatarsus beneath with tick-like pit near apex; dark markings poorly developed. Front tarsal segment 2 with any dark markings clear of axis; segment 3 with or without faint marking. Alula on wing narrow. Small slender species, wing length about 5 mm.

♂ **angustatus**
p. 175

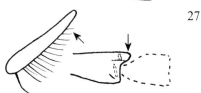

— Side of top of thorax and side of thorax in front of wing dulled with dust, contrasting with shining top of thorax. Front metatarsus beneath with tick-like pit well before apex; extra, strong markings extend onto segments 2 and 3 (as *ramsarensis*). Alula broader. Typically larger, wing length about 7 mm.

♂ **europaeus**
p. 177

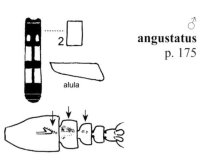

Key to females (eyes separated on top of head)

1. Abdomen extensively orange or with distinctive yellow spots on tergite 3 only (rarely black with an orange median stripe).

2

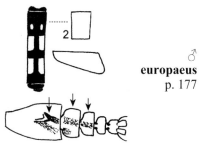

— Abdomen with a different pattern.

3

2.   Tergites 2 to 4 with a large continuous area of reddish-orange. [Intersex has a black abdomen with a narrow median orange stripe.]   ♀ **granditarsus** p. 185

—   Tergite 3 with a band or pair of yellowish spots, abdomen otherwise extensively dark.   ♀ **rosarum** p. 185

3.   Tergites with silver spots or bands.   4

—   Tergites with at least partly yellow or orange spots.   7

4.   Tergite 3 with a faint silver band (view from in front or behind).   ♀ **ambiguus** p. 171

—   Tergite 3 with spots.   5

5.   Tergite 2 elongate, 3 almost square.   ♀ **sticticus** p. 184

—   Tergites 2 and 3 transverse.   6

6.   Front and mid femora normally orange; frons with small but obvious dust spots.   ♀ **albimanus** p. 174

—   Front and mid femora black; frons without distinct dust spots.   ♀ **discimanus** p. 177

7.   Front femur strongly black in at least basal half. Face extended, lip reaches beyond knob.   8

—   Front femur completely yellow or only small areas of black. Face compact, lip no further forward than knob.   10

8.   Most of frons shining, dust confined to margins. Tergite 2 transverse, with bar markings.   ♀ **melanopsis** p. 179

—   Frons extensively dusted.   9

9. Dorsal surface of thorax heavily dull-dusted, usually striped. Frons mostly dull-dusted, extending to either side of ocellar triangle. Tergite 2 transverse, with anteriorly rounded spots.

♀ **manicatus** p. 179

— Dorsal surface of thorax shining. Frons with triangular dust spots that can be fused (as shown), but no dust on either side of ocellar triangle. Tergite 2 with spots angular into anterior corners, far removed from posterior margin.

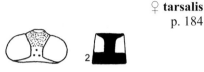

♀ **tarsalis** p. 184

10. Third antennal segment normally yellow beneath (may be very obscure; other segments may also have yellow). Face with very pronounced lip, projecting as much as strong knob. (If head missing, note that spots on tergites 3 and 4 are oblique on the front margin and the hind tarsus is entirely black).

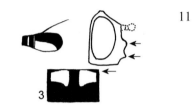

11

— Antennae entirely black. Face vertical below small knob. (Lacking this combination of tergite spots and hind tarsus colour).

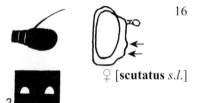

16

11. Tergite 2 with small median spots, hemispherical with hind margin not oblique.

♀ [**scutatus** *s.l.*]

[It is not currently possible to distinguish between females of *scutatus* (p. 183), *splendidus* (p. 183) and *aurolateralis* (p. 176) in which the female is not yet known. Some *amplus* may also key out here.]

— Tergite 2 with spots placed well forwards, hind margin oblique (spots yellow, rarely as grey dust only). [M. Second basal cell bare in basal half.]

12

12. Basal antennal segments yellow.

[*parmatus*]

— Basal antennal segments black or at least darkened.

13

13. Frons with dust spots faint or ill-defined.

[*jaerensis*]

— Dust spots strong and sharply defined.

14

14. Tergites strongly transverse, tergite 3 almost
     twice as wide as long.   ♀
                                                                              peltatus
                                                                                p. 181

—   Tergites less strongly transverse.   15

15. Frons, in side view, with large area above the   ♀ **nielseni**
     base of antennae bare of dusting. Tergite 2   p. 180
     with spots at least half the length of the tergite.

—   Frons, in side view, with more general dusting   ♀ **amplus**
     and with any bare area above the antennae   p. 174
     more restricted. Tergite 2 with much smaller
     spots.

16. Tergite 6 extensively yellow. Tergite 5 with   17
     entire side margins yellow or almost so
     (yellow broadens rapidly to margins; at most
     black narrowly reaching margin).

—   Tergite 6 black. Tergite 5 with any yellow at   20
     sides confined to anterior part (yellow, if
     present, normally as semi-rectangular spots).

17. Hind femur and tibia lacking distinct dark   18
     markings. Tergites 3 and 4 with spots broadly
     reaching lateral margin and posterior black
     strip thinner than hind tibia at posterior
     corners of tergites (view from side).

—   Hind femur and/or hind tibia normally with a   19
     distinct dark band or extensively black.
     Tergites 2 to 4 with spots often not reaching
     sides and always with black behind spots
     wider than hind tibia even at hind corners of
     tergites (view from side).

18. Third antennal segment wider than jowls (view   ♀
     head obliquely from below). Frons with inner   **fulviventris**
     margin of dust spots deeply hooked, boundary   p. 178
     sharp.

—   Third antennal segment about as wide as jowls.   ♀
     Frons with dust spots only slightly hooked,   **perpallidus**
     boundary often diffuse.   p. 181

19.   Front femur at base without a long white bristle
      behind. Tergite 2 with large spots. Tergites 2
      to 4 with hind margin of spots parallel with
      hind margin of tergites; at least some spots
      reaching lateral margin. Sternites 2 to 5
      shining, dust-free.

♀ **scambus**
p. 182

—   Front femur at base with a long white bristle
      behind. Tergites 2 to 4 with hind margin of
      spots oblique towards posterior corners of
      tergites; all spots stop well before lateral
      margin. Sternites 2 to 5 dulled with dust
      (view highly obliquely from side).

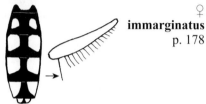

♀
immarginatus
p. 178

20.   Slender abdomen, tergites elongate. Top of
      thorax at sides and side of thorax in front of
      wing shining, as top of thorax. Frons spots
      small.

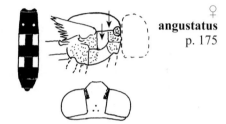

♀
angustatus
p. 175

—   Abdomen broader, tergites usually square or
      transverse. Top of thorax at sides and most of
      side of thorax dusted, in contrast to shining
      top of thorax (try different angles of light
      until dust shows). Frons spots large,
      extending well towards centre.

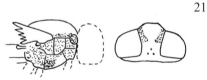

21

21.   Hind femur black at base or only very narrowly
      yellow (at most equal to width of femur).

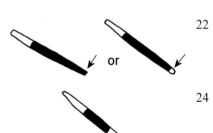

22

24

—   Hind femur with a median dark ring, at least
      basal fifth yellow.

22. Front femur with posterior hairs absent in apical half. Tergite 2 transverse. Front and mid tarsi with several apical segments dark.

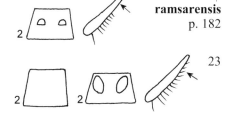

♀
ramsarensis
p. 182

— Front femur with posterior hairs extending to near apex. Tergite 2 square (rarely transverse, but then may have oblique oval spots). Front and mid tarsi entirely orange.

23

23. Tergite 2 almost square with hemispherical spots. Tergite 3 almost square with rectangular spots. Frons spots larger, leaving central quarter clear. Hind tarsus with segment 2 normally dusky yellow.

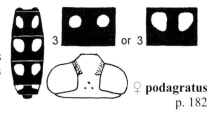

♀ **europaeus**
p. 177

— Tergites 2 to 4 with rounded spots, 3 and 4 often with outer posterior corners angled off (rather as in *Melanostoma* which has spots flush with the front margin of the segments). Frons spots smaller, leaving central half clear. Hind tarsus entirely black.

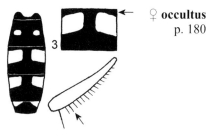

♀ **podagratus**
p. 182

24. Front femur without a well developed fan (basal hairs shorter than width of femur). Spots on tergite 3 normally more rounded at corners, outwardly oblique in front, not or only partly touching front margin. Head immediately behind ocelli shining, sharply separate from dusted zone behind eyes.

♀ **occultus**
p. 180

— Front femur with a fan of hairs behind grading from long to short (basal hairs as long as width of femur). Tergites 3 and 4 with rectangular spots which are flush with the front margins. Head immediately behind ocelli dusted (dust belt continuous from behind eyes).

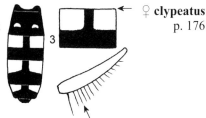

♀ **clypeatus**
p. 176

Tribe PARAGINI

Very small species, often black with contrasting orange legs and partly yellowish face. Some specimens have some reddish coloration on the centre of the abdomen, more extensively so in *albifrons*. Males of *tibialis* and *constrictus* can be separated on the shape of the outer lobes of the genitalia (equivalent to those of *Sphaerophoria* and visible when the genitalia are hinged out in the same way); the females cannot currently be separated.

Genus PARAGUS

1. Eyes with vertical stripes of white hairs, alternating with either stripes of brown hairs or bare areas. Abdomen parallel-sided and with broad segments (subgenus **Paragus**).   **albifrons** p. 188

—   Eyes more or less uniformly covered in white hairs. Abdomen slightly constricted and with narrower segments. (subgenus **Pandasyopthalmus).**   2

2. Males (eyes meet on top of head).   3

—   Females (eyes separated).   5

3. Abdomen seen from beneath with sternite 4 about ⅔ length of sternite 3. Pre-genital segment much shorter than sternite 4.   ♂ **haemorrhous** p. 187

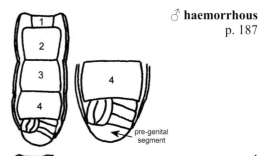

—   Abdomen with sternite 4 only about ⅓ as long as sternite 3. Pre-genital segment much longer than sternite 4 at its centre.   4

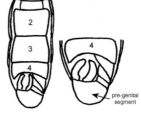

4	Outer lobe of the male genitalia bulbous at outer basal corner.	♂ **tibialis** p. 187
—	Outer lobe of the male genitalia with truncate outer basal corner.	♂ **constrictus** p. 187
5	Tergites 2 and 3 with a broad band of black hairs on posterior margin.	♀ **haemorrhous** p. 187
—	Tergites 2 and 3 with entirely pale hairs (or only a few black hairs at posterior corners).	♀ **constrictus / tibialis** p. 187

[It is not currently possible to separate females of *constrictus* and *tibialis*.]

Tribe SYRPHINI

This key runs to subgenera for specimens with markings. For *Melangyna quadrimaculata* females and melanic varieties of other species, see the separate key to entirely black-bodied hoverflies (page 64).

Key to genera and subgenera

1.	Thoracic pleura with clear yellow markings (can be dusted in *Doros*, which has wings with chocolate front edge).	2
—	Thoracic pleura entirely dark or pale areas obscured by dust.	5
2.	Antennae at least as long as head.	**Chrysotoxum** p. 86

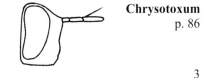

—	Antennae otherwise.	3
3.	Large slender species (body 15 to 20 mm) with chocolate-brown front margin to wing. Abdomen waisted.	**Doros profuges** p. 199

[A large black fly with a waisted abdomen displaying narrow yellow bands and conspicuously darkened wings.]

—	Smaller species without this combination of characters.	4

4.   Wings partly darkened along front margin; robust   **Xanthogramma**
     species with broad body.   p. 109

—   Wings clear; small narrow species.   **Sphaerophoria**
                                                                        p. 104

5.   Squama with long hairs on dorsal surface (as well   **Syrphus**
     as on hind margin).   p. 108

—   Squama without such hairs (if doubtful, continue   6
     here).

6.   Wing vein R_{4+5} strongly dipped, thus basal half of   7
     cell r_5 is parallel-sided.

—   Wing vein R_{4+5} more gently curved, thus cell r_5 9
     widens in basal half (*i.e.* cell r_5 is narrower at
     the base than halfway along).

7.   Basal joint of hind tarsus pale (or almost so).   8

—   Hind tarsus entirely black.   **Didea**
                                                                         p. 88

8.   Strong black facial stripe almost reaches   **Eriozona**
     antennae. Sternites with broad black bands for   **erratica**
     full width.   p. 203

     [A yellow- and black-banded species easily mistaken for a large *Syrphus*. However,
     the thorax is shiny and the markings more orange.]

—   Face with at most a weak stripe extending   g. **Eupeodes**
     upwards no further than the knob. Sternites   s.g. **Lapposyrphus**
     with central black spots.   p. 91

9.   Eyes distinctly hairy, at least in front (view from   10
     above against both a dark and a pale
     background). [Continue here if any hairs are
     visible, key works on either choice if only a
     few hairs.]

—   Eyes bare or with only a few scattered weak   15
     indiscernible hairs (at ×10 magnification).

10. Wing cloud below stigma. 11

— Wing membrane lacking a dark area below stigma. 12

11. Stigma pale. Hairy bee mimic with red tip to abdomen. **Eriozona syrphoides** p. 203

— Stigma dark. Tip of abdomen not red. g.&s.g. **Leucozona** p. 96

12. Tergite 2 with markings much larger and wider than the narrow bars on tergites 3 and 4 (markings usually pale, but sometimes only seen as greyish dusting or reflections). **Leucozona** s.g. **Ischyrosyrphus** p. 96

— Markings otherwise. 13

13. Hind legs almost completely black, at most narrowly pale on knees. **Melangyna** p. 97

— Hind legs partly yellow, including basal quarter of hind tibia. 14

14. Strong black or deep yellow facial stripe extending up into depression above knob. Tergites 3 and 4 with lateral margins bearing at least some pale hairs. Frons not inflated.

Dasysyrphus p. 87

— Face with a weak stripe not extending above knob. Tergites 3 and 4 with hairs on lateral margins entirely black. Frons inflated (except in *mecogramma*).

Scaeva p. 103

15. Tergites 3 and 4 with double black bands, sometimes reduced. **Episyrphus balteatus** p. 202

[This is the only genus with double black bands on tergites 3 and 4.]

extremely dark   typical   extremely light

— Markings otherwise. 16

16.   Hairs on side margins of tergites 3 to 5 entirely
      black.

      g. & s.g.
Eupeodes
p. 91

—   Hairs on side margins of tergites 3 to 5 partly
      pale.

17

17.   Tergite 4 without distinct markings or with
      wedges or bands which are much narrower than
      those on tergite 3.

**Epistrophe
eligans**
p. 200

—   Tergites 3 and 4 with markings of nearly equal
      size.

18

18.   Tergites 3 and 4 with bands.

19

—   Tergites 3 and 4 with spots.

23

19.   Tergite 2 with golf-club spots; tergites 3 and 4
      with moustache bands.

20

—   Markings otherwise.

21

20.   Face entirely yellow. Hairs on centre of
      scutellum shorter (1 to 1½ times as long as
      width of third antennal segment). Squamae
      with hairs on dorsal surface.

Syrphus
p. 108

—   Face usually with black knob, sometimes yellow.
      Hairs on centre of scutellum longer (2 or more
      times as long as width of third antennal
      segment). Squamae lacking hairs on dorsal
      surface.

Parasyrphus
p. 101

21.   Tergite 2 broad and with markings occupying
      most of lateral margin.

Epistrophe
p. 89

—   Tergite 2 narrower (even if markings similar) or
      if broad then markings are small. [Illustrations
      in next couplet.]

22

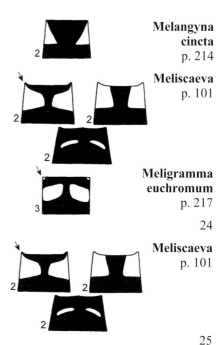

22.   Tergite 2 with sharply triangular spots.   **Melangyna cincta** p. 214

—   Tergite 2 with blunt spots or oblique crescent bars.   **Meliscaeva** p. 101

23.   Tergites 3 and 4 with slightly oblique squarish spots or rectangular bars, often with a yellow spot at front corners.   **Meligramma euchromum** p. 217

—   Markings otherwise.   24

24.   Tergite 2 with spots broadly reaching side margins (including the front corners of the tergite) or with oblique crescent bars.   **Meliscaeva** p. 101

—   Markings otherwise.   25

25.   Face knob yellow. (Narrow species with sides of thoracic dorsum yellow or tergites with triangular spots). (Rare *Syrphus* with divided bands have a yellow face, but other characters differ).   **Meligramma** p. 97

—   Face knob dark (and lacking above characters).   26

26.   Tergites 3 and 4 with spots which do not reach upper corners.      **Melangyna** p. 97

—   Tergites 3 and 4 with spots which reach upper corners.   **Parasyrphus punctulatus** p. 222

Genus CHRYSOTOXUM

Yellow and black species, often resembling a rather dumpy social wasp (*Vespula*), with exceptionally long antennae projecting straight out in front of head.

1. Abdomen with marginal beading continuously black (*i.e.* markings do not reach margin of segment); oblique yellow bars on tergites 2 to 5 (also in some forms of *elegans*). 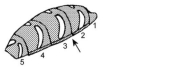 2

— Abdomen with marginal beading partly yellow because yellow markings extend right across beading. 3

2. Legs completely yellow and orange (or front and mid femora only very narrowly black at base). Bars on abdomen usually with distinct elbow bend. 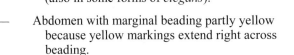 **festivum** p. 192

— Legs with front and mid femora broadly black at base. Bars on abdomen almost straight. 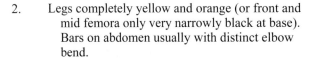 **vernale** p. 193

3. Anterior edge of wing chocolate-brown near tip. Tergites 2 and 4 with oblique bars, markings absent or reduced on segment 3. 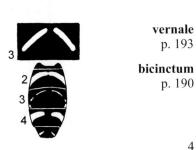 **bicinctum** p. 190

— Anterior edge of wing orange, yellowish or clear. Abdomen with different markings. 4

4. Antennal segment 3 much longer than 1 plus 2. Eyes above with dense dark hairs.  **arcuatum** p. 190

— Antennae with segment 3 as long as or slightly shorter than 1 plus 2. Eye hairs pale and inconspicuous. 5

5. Antennal segment 1 about ⅔ as long as 2. Male genitalia very large. Female thoracic dorsum with long dense hairs (quite as long as width of third antennal segment). **cautum** p. 190

— Antennal segment 1 as long as or longer than 2. Male genitalia smaller. Female thoracic dorsum with shorter hairs. 6

6. Tergites 3, 4 and 5 with front black band
    interrupted before side margin on at least one
    segment. Female thoracic dorsum with all
    hairs very short (no longer than maximum
    thickness of the arista). Male genitalia very
    small (as in *verralli*).
                                                        octomaculatum
                                                        p. 192

—   Tergites 3, 4 and 5 all with front black band
    continuous to side margin or stopping before
    margin. No tergite with *octomaculatum*
    pattern.
                                                        7

7. Tergite 2 with front black band narrow and
    parallel with front edge of segment for
    practically entire width. Female with all hairs
    on scutellum black.
                                                        verralli
                                                        p. 193

—   Tergite 2 with front black band curved back
    towards the side margins. Female with some
    pale hairs on scutellum.
                                                        elegans
                                                        p. 191

Genus DASYSYRPHUS

A distinctive group of hoverflies, often (but not always) having a black stigma. Tergite markings
unusual. The key takes into account the European species *nigricornis* Verrall which resembles
pinastri; it may yet be found in conifer plantations in Britain.

1. Yellow bars on tergite 3 much wider than those
    on tergites 2 and 4 (markings on tergite 2 may
    be absent).
                                                        tricinctus
                                                        p. 196

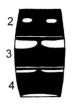

—   Tergites with different markings, those on 3 and 4
    of almost equal width.
                                                        2

2. Tergites 3 and 4 with oblique bars (which may
    join to form a band as shown).
                                                        albostriatus
                                                        p. 194

—   Markings otherwise.
                                                        3

3. Tergites 3 and 4 with hooked bars which do not
    reach side margin (inspect carefully).
                                                        4

—   Tergites 3 and 4 with pale areas reaching side
    margins.
                                                        5

4. Hind tarsus entirely black. Face hairs yellow. **pinastri** p. 195

— Hind tarsus with first three segments yellowish. Face hairs black. [*nigricornis*]

5. Antennae entirely dusky, third antennal segment very dark without any orange. Tergites 3 and 4 with bars having upper edge deeply undulating, even dividing the bars to create 4 spots per tergite. **friuliensis** p. 194

— Antennae mainly orange, third antennal segment at most ⅔ dusky. Tergites 3 and 4 with bars of fairly uniform width. 6

6. Face with knob darkened. [See text for additional characters.] **venustus** p. 196

— Face with knob yellow. [**hilaris**] p. 194

The status of '*hilaris*' remains far from clear (see text) and any specimen that appears to relate to this species should be retained and submitted for expert examination.

Genus DIDEA

Wings with R$_{4+5}$ strongly dipped. Tergites with oblique bars or wedges.

1. Halteres with orange club. Scutellum with rim mainly yellow. **fasciata** p. 197

— Halteres with dark club. Scutellum with rim black. 2

2. Males (eyes meet on top of head). 3

— Females (eyes separated). 4

3. Tergite 4 with front margin of wedge-shaped bars mostly flush with front edge of segment. ♂ **intermedia** p. 198

— Tergite 4 with front margin of wedge-shaped bars clearly separated from the front margin of the segment by black throughout or only touching front of segment about centre line. ♂ **alneti** p. 197

4. Tergite 5 with small orange wedge-shaped
    markings, hairs on lateral margin black.

♀ **intermedia**
p. 198

—   Tergite 5 entirely black, lateral margin with long
    white hairs in addition to a fringe of black
    hairs.

♀ **alneti**
p. 197

Genus EPISTROPHE

Doczkal & Schmid (1994) describe three further species of this group from Germany and provide a new key to the Western European species of *Epistrophe*. The additional species have the thorax more dusted and less strongly shining.

1. Tergites 3 and 4 with rectangular spots or bars
    which are slightly oblique.

**Meligramma
euchromum**
p. 217

—   Tergites 3 and 4 with a different pattern.   2

2. Tergites 3 and 4 with pale markings absent or
    narrower than those on tergite 2.

eligans
p. 200

—   Tergites 3 and 4 with well developed bands, as
    wide as markings on tergite 2.   3

3. Antennae predominantly orange.   4

—   Antennae entirely or predominantly black.   10

4. Scutellum with hairs all or mostly black.   5

—   Scutellum with entirely yellow hairs (but with a
    few black ones in *cryptica*).   6

5. Tarsi mainly yellow (compared with the species
    in couplet 6, the male frons has its eye angle
    less than 90°, female frons has strong side
    dusting leaving a strong, black T-shaped area
    between).

nitidicollis
p. 201

—   Tarsi black.

**Parasyrphus
nigritarsis**
p. 221

6.   Face entirely yellow or almost so.   7

—   Face with black fringe around mouth.   8

7.   Frons in front with a black mark, lightly dusted   [*flava*]
        behind.

—   Frons without black mark in front; in male,   **ochrostoma**
        dusting confined to posterior part; in female,   p. 202
        median pale dust band with anterior margin
        curved on either side to meet at a point.

8.   Frons yellow with a black mark in front backed   **melanostoma**
        by pale dust in both sexes.   p. 201

—   Frons without any major yellow areas (apart from   9
        lunules immediately above the antennae).

9.   Frontal lunule (immediately above antennae)   [*obscuripes*]
        much darker than rest of frons and well
        defined.

—   Frons fairly uniform, without contrasting darker   [*cryptica*]
        lunules.

10. Front femur narrowly black at base; tergites 3 and 4 with yellow bands sweeping back at margins. 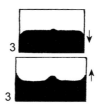 **grossulariae** p. 201

— Front femur entirely yellow; tergites 3 and 4 with black area sweeping forwards at margins. **diaphana** p. 200

Genus EUPEODES

Key to subgenera

1. Wing with vein R_{4+5} distinctly dipped (cell r_5 parallel-sided in basal half). 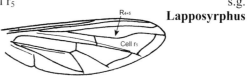 s.g. **Lapposyrphus**

— Wing with vein R_{4+5} only slightly dipped (cell r_5 gradually widening from base). 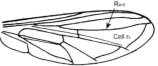 s.g. **Eupeodes**

Subgenus LAPPOSYRPHUS

1. Mouth margin with a continuous black belt. [M. First basal cell microtrichia: in male continuous belt in lower half of cell; in female small patch at base of cell.]  **lapponicus** p. 205

— Mouth margin partly yellow, but not always obvious (see text). [M. First basal cell microtrichia: in male absent for much of basal half of cell; in female absent from base of cell.]  **species A** p. 205

Subgenus EUPEODES

Key to males (eyes meet on top of head)

Males of species C are not available.

1.	Front femur on basal half with black hairs behind. Sternites with black bands across virtually entire width.	2
—	Front femur on basal half with mainly pale hairs behind, occasionally black. Sternites with central oval black patches or extending virtually full width.	3

2. Tergites normally with bands, occasionally spots. [M. Second basal cell completely covered in microtrichia, or almost so.]

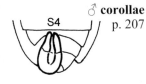

♂ **nitens**
p. 209

— Tergites always with spots. [M. Second basal cell at least half bare of microtrichia.]

♂ **nielseni**
p. 209

3. Tergites 3 and 4 with over 50% of lateral margins yellow. Genitalia large, almost reaching forward to sternite 4 (view from below).

S4

♂ **corollae**
p. 207

— Tergites 3 and 4 with lateral margins entirely black or only up to 25% yellow. Genitalia small, not nearly reaching sternite 4.

S4

4

4. Occiput broad, grey hairless zone only tapering to ⅔ width above (view obliquely from behind). [M. Second basal cell almost entirely covered in microtrichia: but see *bucculatus* form X which has about 75% cover (couplet 8).]

♂ **latifasciatus**
p. 207

— Occiput narrower, grey hairless zone tapering to ⅓ width above (view obliquely from behind). [M. Second basal cell at least 50% bare of microtrichia, except *bucculatus* form X.]

5

5.   Frons with angle between eyes about 70°.   ♂ **luniger**
                                                                                p. 208

—   Frons with angle between eyes 90° or more.   6
        [Take great care, see text.]

6.   Frons inflated (convex in side view); hairs absent   ♂ **lundbecki**
        in anterior third. Wing length about 12 mm.   p. 208

—   Frons almost flat in side view, with hairs in   7
        anterior third. Wing length about 7–9 mm.

7.   Face width one and a half times an eye width.   ♂ **species B**
        Tergite markings huge. Large species, wing   p. 210
        length about 9 mm.

—   Face width about as wide as an eye width.   8
        Tergite markings modest. Moderate-sized   (♂ **bucculatus
        species, wing length 7-8 mm.   agg.**)

8.   Third antennal segment more rounded, sloping   ♂ **bucculatus
        immediately beyond arista. Tergite 5 with a   form X**
        black band across virtually full width.   p. 206
        Scutellum on top with mixed pale and black
        hairs. [M. Second basal cell with c.75% cover
        of microtrichia; note that *latifasciatus* generally
        has almost complete cover of microtrichia, but
        tergite 5 as in *bucculatus* form Y.]

—   Third antennal segment more elongate. Tergite 5   ♂ **bucculatus
        with a restricted median black band. Scutellum   form Y**
        on top with black hairs only (apical margin   p. 206
        with pale ones). [M. Second basal cell with
        only c.30% cover of microtrichia.]

Key to females (eyes separated on top of head)

1. Front femur with black hairs on posterior surface. Black area on frons reaching far forwards as a broad bilobed extension.

    2

—   Front femur with pale hairs behind. Black area on frons of a different shape or placed much further back.

    3

2. Hind femur entirely or mostly yellow (rarely half black). [M. Alula entirely covered in microtrichia.]

    ♀ **nitens**
    p. 209

—   Hind femur extensively black (usually at least the basal half black). [M. Alula bare in front for about a quarter of total area.]

    ♀ **nielseni**
    p. 209

3. Frons without dust spots, front half yellow, hind half black (black area in front of ocellar triangle much longer than length of triangle).

    ♀ **latifasciatus**
    p. 207

—   Frons with dust spots at sides, black for full width only in hind quarter (equivalent to length of ocellar triangle).

    4

4. Tergites 3 and 4 normally with bands. Frons as in *luniger*.

    5

—   Tergites 3 and 4 with pairs of lunulate spots.

    7

5. Large species, wing length about 9 mm. Frons broad, with wide wedge-shaped strips of dust at the sides almost reaching the centre, and with only a small black spot between them.

    ♀ **species B**
    p. 210

3

—   Modest-sized species, wing length 7.5-8 mm. Frons narrow, with narrow dust strips and with a fairly large bilobed black spot between them.

    6
    (♀ **bucculatus**
    agg.)

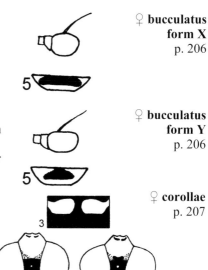

6.   Third antennal segment more rounded, sloping
      immediately beyond arista. Tergite 5 with a   ♀ **bucculatus**
      black band across virtually full width.   **form X**
      Scutellum on top with mixed pale and black   p. 206
      hairs. Hind femur with basal three quarters
      black.

—   Third antennal segment more elongate. Tergite 5   ♀ **bucculatus**
      with a restricted median black band. Scutellum   **form Y**
      on top with black hairs only (apical margin   p. 206
      with pale hairs). Hind femur with basal quarter
      black.

7.   Tergites 3 and 4 with lunulate spots reaching   ♀ **corollae**
      lateral margin. Scutellum with entirely yellow   p. 207
      hairs. Black area on frons without a forward
      extension (or sometimes with a short broad
      bilobed extension).

—   Tergites 3 and 4 with lunulate spots which do not   8
      reach lateral margin. Scutellum usually with at
      least half of the hairs black. Black area on
      frons often more extended forwards.

8.   Tergite 3 with front edge of spots strongly dipped.
      Frons somewhat inflated (side view). Frons
      with a broad bilobed black extension between
      the side dust strips. [M. Second basal cell, and   ♀ **lundbecki**
      much of basal half of wing, free of   p. 208
      microtrichia.]

—   Tergite 3 with front edge of spots less dipped.   9
      Frons depressed in hind half (side view). Frons
      with a narrower bilobed black extension. [M.
      Second basal cell with at least 30% cover of
      microtrichia.]

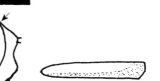

9.   Large species, wing length about 9 mm. Frons
        broad, with wide wedge-shaped strips of dust
        almost reaching the centre, and only a small
        black spot between them.

♀ **species B**
p. 210

—   Modest-sized species, wing length 7.5-8 mm.
        Frons narrow, black marking often extended as
        a bilobed process (rarely reduced to a central
        black spot).

10

10.   Black area on frons with a narrow Y-shaped
        extension, sometimes reduced to basal stem of
        Y. [M. Apex of second basal cell with a patch
        free of microtrichia.]

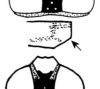

♀ **luniger**
p. 208

—   Black area on frons broadly bilobed. [M. Apex of
        second basal cell entirely covered in
        microtrichia.]

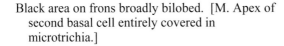

♀ **species C**
p. 210

Genus LEUCOZONA

The very large markings on the second abdominal segment, which are considerably larger than those on succeeding segments, are only otherwise characteristic of *Epistrophe eligans* which lacks a dark stigma. Recent studies in Europe have revealed the presence of *L. inopinata* Doczkal, which is common in parts of the Netherlands and could occur in Britain, especially in warm areas with sandy soils.

1.   Wing with a black cloud behind the stigma.

s.g. **Leucozona** 2

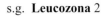

—   Wing clear apart from black stigma.

s.g. **Ischyrosyrphus**
3

2. Tergite 4 with pale hairs at the lateral margins and extending partly or entirely over whole dorsal surface.

lucorum p. 211

— Tergite 4 with entirely black hairs, even at lateral margins. [An indicative rather than definitive character: see text, p. 211.]

[*inopinata*]

3. Front legs mainly yellow, including tarsus; scutellum entirely yellow.

glaucia p. 211

— Front legs extensively black, including tarsus; scutellum black except for apex.

laternaria p. 211

Genera MELIGRAMMA and MELANGYNA

The hind legs are often almost completely black, as in some *Parasyrphus*. The genus *Meligramma* has long narrow wings (see comments under *Meliscaeva*). The key includes *Melangyna coei* and *lucifera*, both potential additions to the British fauna.

1. Narrow species. Knob on face yellow or tergite 2 with sharply triangular spots.

2

— Broader species. Facial knob black. Tergite 2 with spots of different shape.

5

2. Tergites 3 and 4 with bands.

Melangyna cincta p. 214

— Tergites 3 and 4 with rounded spots or triangular spots.

3

3. Tergites 3 and 4 with slightly oblique squarish spots or rectangular bars, often with a yellow spot at front corners.

Meligramma euchromum p. 217

— Markings otherwise.

4

4. Antennae black. Tergites 3 and 4 with rather   **Meligramma**
    small rounded spots well removed from the   **guttatum**
    front of the tergites.   p. 218

    3   3
    ♂   ♀

—   Antennae partly yellowish. Tergites 3 and 4 with   **Meligramma**
    triangular spots reaching or virtually reaching   **trianguliferum**
    the front of the tergites.   p. 218

    3   3
    ♂   ♀

5. Males (eyes meet on top of head).   6

—   Females (eyes widely separated).   15

6. Tergite 2 without spots.   7

—   Tergite 2 with spots, even if small.   8

7. Hairs on top of thorax and scutellum pale; eyes   ♂ **Melangyna**
    hairy.   **quadrimaculata**
                                                            p. 216

—   Hairs on top of thorax and scutellum mainly   ♂ **Melangyna**
    black; eyes bare or virtually so.   **barbifrons**
                                                            p. 213

8. Thoracic dorsum with black hairs dominant over   9
    at least hind half (view from side).

—   Thoracic dorsum with pale hairs (view from side).   11

9. Scutellum with a small black spot at base on each   [♂ *Melangyna*
    side. Frons shining (only thin dust).   *coei*]

—   Scutellum with a wedge-shaped black spot on   10
    each side. Frons well dusted.

10. Frons dark dusted, much darker than face dust.   ♂ **Melangyna**
    Halteres blackish.   **arctica**
                                                            p. 213

—   Frons pale dusted, as face. Halteres yellowish.   ♂ **Melangyna**
                                                          ericarum
                                                            p. 215

11. Scutellum with black wedge on each side, often
extending as thin black line around apex of
scutellum (view from side). Tergite 2 with
spots behind centre or very reduced.   12

— Scutellum with a small black spot at base of each
side, rim otherwise yellow (view from side).
Tergite 2 with spots well forwards.   13

12. Tergite 2 with spots behind middle, extending far
inwards. Eyes meet at about 90°.   ♂ **Melangyna**
lasiophthalma
p. 215

— Tergite 2 with small round spots very close to
sides, situated further forward. Eyes meet at
about 120°.   [♂ *Melangyna*
lucifera]

13. Thoracic dorsum shining black. Eyes bare. [M.
Second basal cell at least half bare of
microtrichia.]   ♂ **Melangyna**
umbellatarum
p. 217

— Thoracic dorsum dull. Eyes slightly hairy (hairs
pale and indistinct). [M. Second basal cell
completely covered in microtrichia or virtually
so.]   14

14. Eyes weakly hairy.   ♂ **Melangyna**
labiatarum
p. 215

— Eyes very feebly hairy, almost bare. [Distinction
not always certain.]   ♂ **Melangyna**
compositarum
p. 214

15. Frons with dust spots minute or absent.   16

— Frons with dust spots across ⅔ or more of width
or entirely dusted.   17

16. Tergites entirely black.   ♀ **Melangyna**
quadrimaculata
p. 216

— Tergites with pale spots.   ♀ **Melangyna**
barbifrons
p. 213

17.   Scutellum with a black wedge-shaped spot on
        each side, sometimes vague and dusky (view
        from side).   18

—   Scutellum with a sharply defined small black spot
        at base on each side, otherwise clear yellow
        (view from side).   21

18.   Frons with dust spots well forwards, boundaries   ♀ **Melangyna**
        often diffuse.   **arctica**
                                                                                            p. 213

—   Frons with dust spots forming a median band,
        boundaries usually sharp.   19

19.   Frons with broad dust spots. Eyes bare.   ♀ **Melangyna**
                                                                                       ericarum
                                                                                            p. 215

—   Frons with dust spots narrow. Eyes weakly hairy.   20
        [Note resemblance to *Parasyrphus*
        punctulatus.]

20.   Front and mid tibiae mostly black in apical half.   ♀ **Melangyna**
                                                                                  lasiophthalma
                                                                                            p. 215

—   Front and mid tibiae completely yellow on at least   [♀ *Melangyna*
        anterior and posterior sides.   *lucifera*]

21.   Frons with fairly narrow dust bars, narrowly   [♀ *Melangyna*
        separated in the middle; an extensive black area   *coei*]
        in front and behind.

—   Frons with very wide dust bars that merge in the   22
        middle; entirely dusted or leaving a narrow
        black area in front.

22.   Thoracic dorsum shining black. Frons dust band   ♀ **Melangyna**
        not so broad. [M. Second basal cell bare of   **umbellatarum**
        microtrichia.]   p. 217

—   Thoracic dorsum dusted, dull or only weakly   ♀ **Melangyna**
        shining. Frons dust band broader. [M. Second   **labiatarum**
        basal cell completely covered in microtrichia.]   / **compositarum**
                                                                                         p. 214 /215

[The frons character used in the first edition proved very unreliable. The separation of
compositarum and *labiatarum* remains a problem.]

Genus MELISCAEVA

Note that *Meliscaeva cinctella* is very similar to *Melangyna cincta* except that the spots on tergite 2 are blunt at their inner corners in *cinctella* rather than sharply pointed as in *cincta*.

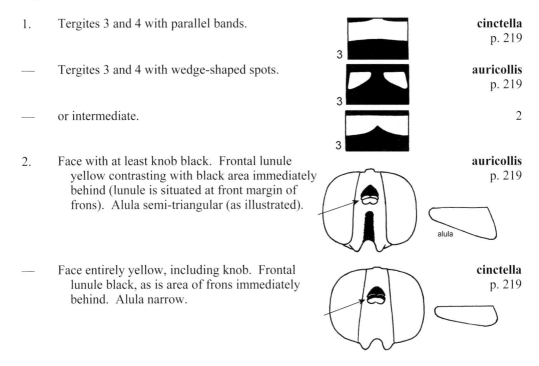

1.   Tergites 3 and 4 with parallel bands.   **cinctella**
                                                                              p. 219

—   Tergites 3 and 4 with wedge-shaped spots.   **auricollis**
                                                                              p. 219

—   or intermediate.   2

2.   Face with at least knob black. Frontal lunule   **auricollis**
     yellow contrasting with black area immediately   p. 219
     behind (lunule is situated at front margin of
     frons). Alula semi-triangular (as illustrated).

—   Face entirely yellow, including knob. Frontal   **cinctella**
     lunule black, as is area of frons immediately   p. 219
     behind. Alula narrow.

Genus PARASYRPHUS

The hind legs are almost entirely black (except in *nigritarsis*), a character shared with *Melangyna*. The body patterns of the two genera differ: *Parasyrphus* has moustache bands (as in *Syrphus*), or spots or bars that sweep forwards at the front corners. On the continent there are species resembling *punctulatus* which should be looked out for in Britain: *macularis* Zetterstedt, *tarsatus* (Zetterstedt) and *dryadis* (Holmgren) which are included in the key. *Syrphus nitidifrons* Becker is also included; it looks like *punctulatus* but most of the face is yellow and, although the squama does have the usual dorsal hairs that characterise the genus, they are usually sparse and fine and are easily overlooked.

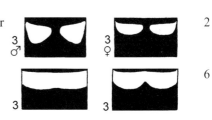

1.   Tergites 3 and 4 with a pair of spots, semicircular   2
     in the male, narrowly oval in the female (hind
     legs black, as in *lineola*).

—   Tergites 3 and 4 with parallel yellow bands or   6
     moustache bands.

2.   Frons entirely shining black.   [*Syrphus nitidifrons*]

—   Frons partly or completely dusted.   3

3.   Hind tibia mainly black.   4

—   Hind tibia yellow or with only a narrow median   5
      dark ring.

4.   Front and mid tarsi greyish-yellow (rarely dark).   **punctulatus**
      Male eye hairs sparse, few as long as front   p. 222
      ocellus.

—   Front and mid tarsi greyish-yellow (rarely dark).   [*macularis*]
      Male eye hairs dense, almost twice as long as
      front ocellus. [A rather larger species of
      conifer woods.]

5.   Face, just below antennae, twice as wide as an eye   [*dryadis*]
      (view from in front).

—   Face one and a half times as wide as an eye.   [*tarsatus*]

6.   Face entirely yellow. Antennae almost entirely   **nigritarsis**
      yellow. Tergites 3 and 4 with broad bands.   p. 221
      Hind femur and tibia yellow in female (may be
      partly black in male).

—   Face normally with black median stripe   7
      (sometimes all yellow in *vittiger*). Tergites
      with narrow bands. Hind legs more
      extensively black.

7.   Hind legs entirely black (or only very narrowly   **lineola**
      pale at knees).   p. 221

—   Hind legs with distinct yellow bands.   8

8.   Hind tibia black-ringed, broadly yellow at both   **vittiger**
      ends.   p. 223

—   Hind tibia black in distal half, only yellow at   9
      base.

9.   Male with front and mid tarsi yellow. Female      **annulatus**
        with base of hind femur yellow (and either   p. 220
        yellow or black at apex, as shown).

—   Male with front and mid tarsi dark above. Female   **malinellus**
        with base of hind femur black. The hind tibia   p. 221
        can be as much as half yellow (*i.e.* more
        extensively yellow than illustrated).

Genus SCAEVA

These are relatively large species with the frons inflated. In most species the tergites have distinctive lunules. The wings have vein R_{4+5} rather bowed and microtrichia are extensively absent. The key includes *dignota* (Rondani), one of the most likely European species to occur as a vagrant to Britain.

1.   Tergites 3 and 4 with bands (or reduced to   **mecogramma**
        lunules).   p. 223

—   Tergites 3 and 4 with commas or oblique bars.   2

2.   Tergites 3 and 4 with broad oblique bars.   **albomaculata**
                                                                                   p. 223

—   Tergites 3 and 4 with commas or oblique hooked   3
        bars.

3.   Tergites 3 and 4 with hooked bars of almost equal   **pyrastri**
        width at each end and with outer end not   p. 224
        reaching as far forward as inner end. In life,
        markings whitish.

—   Tergites 3 and 4 with outer end of commas   4
        narrower than inner end and both ends equally
        near front edge of segment. In life, markings
        yellow.

4.   Frons in both sexes markedly inflated. Male   **selenitica**
        frons with incredibly wide eye angle.   p. 224

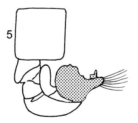

—   Frons only mildly inflated. Male frons with   [*dignota*]
        moderate eye angle.

Genus SPHAEROPHORIA

Small narrow-bodied flies with at least a partial yellow stripe at the sides of the thoracic dorsum. Identification of most species is only possible by reference to male genitalia (these may be hinged out as illustrated before the fresh specimen dries). The part which has been shaded in the diagram (of *scripta*) indicates the position of the lobes of the surstylus which are shown as enlargements against the species names. See also Plates O – Q. Examination under a microscope is necessary in order to accurately see the detailed features in most species.

1.   Thorax with yellow side-stripe interrupted above   2
        wing base (illustration is side view of top of
        thorax). Hairy lobe of genitalia very slender in
        side view, much of inner curve hairy. [Care is
        needed since some specimens of *fatarum* and
        virgata can have a broken thoracic stripe as in
        rueppellii.]

—   Thorax normally with a continuous yellow side-   3
        stripe. Hairy lobe thumb-like in side view.
        Inner curve not hairy (except species B which
        lacks indented curve).

2. Antennae completely black. Toothed lobe very slender. Hairy lobe, viewed from below, with beak-like inner apical projection.

♂ **loewi**
p. 227

— Antennae mainly yellow. Segment 3 usually darkened towards tip, but occasionally the antennae are entirely dark. Toothed lobe bulbous. Hairy lobe, viewed from below, without beak.

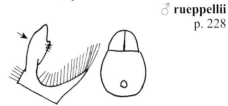

♂ **rueppellii**
p. 228

3. Abdomen extends well beyond wing tips. Genitalia, seen from below, elongate, the hairy lobes twice as long as wide. In side view surstylus very broad (as *philanthus* below). Inner process broad at base, abruptly slender to apex.

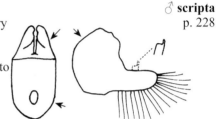

♂ **scripta**
p. 228

— Abdomen extends to about wing tips. Genitalia seen from below less elongate. Inner processes of more uniform width.

4

4. Toothed lobe in side view, broad. In ventral view hairy lobes about one and a half times as long as broad.

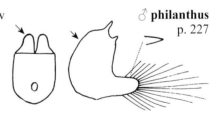

♂ **philanthus**
p. 227

— Toothed lobe less broad in side view. In ventral view hairy lobes at most as long as wide.

5

5.   Surstylus with smooth inner curve.   6

—   Surstylus with a tooth on the inner curve.   9

6.   Surstylus with curve scarcely developed. Hairy lobe very short, viewed from below, much wider than long.   ♂ **potentillae** p. 228

—   Surstylus with a well developed inner curve. Hairy lobes viewed from below, about as long as wide.   7

7.   Bulge at base of toothed lobe. Inner curve with angled straight section.   ♂ **batava** p. 226

—   No bulge at base of toothed lobe. Inner curve strongly developed.   8

8.   Toothed lobe with a long thick thumb-like apical tooth; no shoulder. Inner process blunt.   ♂ **interrupta** p. 227

—   Toothed lobe with a small apical tooth; very strong shoulder. Inner process slender-pointed.   ♂ **virgata** p. 229

9. Toothed lobe with bulge at base; strong shoulder   ♂ **bankowskae**
    towards apex. Inner process exceptionally   p. 226
    large. Femur black in basal quarter.

—   Toothed lobe without bulge at base; shoulder not   10
    so pronounced or absent. Femur normally pale
    at base.

10. Hairy lobe very short, with exceptionally short   ♂ **species B**
    hairs, much shorter than the lobe.   p. 230

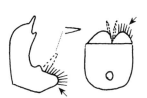

—   Hairy lobe not unduly short, with hairs much   11
    longer than lobe.

11. Toothed lobe with apical pair of teeth equally   ♂ **taeniata**
    developed. Inner curve with tooth in middle of   p. 229
    curve.

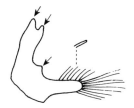

—   Toothed lobe with apical pair of teeth unequal.   12
    Inner curve with the tooth definitely on straight
    section of hairy lobe.

12. Toothed lobe broad, with wide shoulder on outer   ♂ **fatarum**
    side. Hairy lobe short and broad, shorter than   p. 226
    toothed lobe. Second basal cell almost entirely
    covered in microtrichia.

—   Toothed lobe more slender. Hairy lobe longer   13
    and narrower. Second basal cell with clear
    streak near base without microtrichia.

13.   Toothed lobe with well developed apical thumb.   ♂ **interrupta**
        (The tooth on the inner curve is very variable,   p. 227
        from a small pimple to a ridge with short hairs).

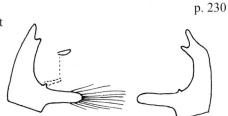

—   Toothed lobe with a less developed apical   ♂ **form A**
        process. Left and right lobes rather   p. 230
        asymmetrical (as in some other species). (It
        seems probable that this is a variant of
        interrupta).

Genus SYRPHUS

The hairs on the top surface of the lower lobe at the base of the wing (the squama) can only be seen if the wing is extended out from the body. Tergites 3 and 4 usually display moustache bands. Identification of species is not always easy and the discovery of *rectus*, which cannot apparently be distinguished from *vitripennis* in the male, further complicates matters. It is possible that *nitidifrons* Becker could yet be found in Britain. This species has lunulate spots and would thus resemble rare varieties of the familiar banded species. It occurs from April to June in the Netherlands. Since the squamal hairs are pale and sparse, they are easily overlooked, so it is more likely to run to *Parasyrphus* and is included in that key.

1.   Males (eyes meet on top of head).   2

—   Females (eyes widely separated).   4

2.   Eyes densely hairy.   ♂ **torvus**
                                                                               p. 233

—   Eyes bare.   3

3.   Hind femur yellow for at least apical third and   ♂ **ribesii**
       yellow area in front with tiny black hairs. [M.   p. 232
       Basal cells entirely covered in microtrichia.]

—   Hind femur with at most the apical quarter yellow   ♂ **vitripennis**
       and yellow area in front mainly with yellow   /**rectus**
       hairs. [M. Basal cells with areas bare of   p. 233/232
       microtrichia.]

4.   Hind femur entirely or almost entirely yellow.   5

—   Hind femur black in at least basal half.   6

5.   Hind femur with a weak dark strip anteriorly   ♀ **rectus**
       about halfway along. [M. Basal cells with   p. 232
       areas bare of microtrichia.]

—   Hind femur entirely yellow (or only a tiny dark   ♀ **ribesii**
       area ventrally at the base). [M. Basal cells   p. 232
       entirely covered in microtrichia.]

6.   Eyes weakly hairy, but hairs can be sparse and   ♀ **torvus**
       inconspicuous. Ocellar triangle broadest at   p. 233
       base. Front and mid femora with long black
       posterior hairs in apical quarter. [M. Second
       basal cell entirely covered in microtrichia.]

—   Eyes bare. Ocellar triangle narrowest at base.   ♀ **vitripennis**
       Front and mid femora with long pale posterior   p. 233
       hairs in apical quarter. [M. Second basal cell
       extensively bare of microtrichia.]

Genus XANTHOGRAMMA

Smart, robust species with a yellow stripe along the sides of the thoracic dorsum and the pleura with yellow markings. Coe (1953a) noted an extreme spotted form he called var. *flavipleura*. Recent studies by C. Kassebeer indicate that *X. pedissequum* will need to be split into three species, but unfortunately the details have not been published in time for inclusion here. Voucher specimens should be retained.

1.   Tergite 2 with narrow triangular yellow side   **citrofasciatum**
       markings. Hind femur and tibia entirely   p. 234
       yellow.

—   Tergite 2 with equilaterally triangular yellow side   **pedissequum**
       markings. Hind femur and tibia with preapical   p. 234
       dark bands.

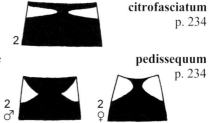

Subfamily MILESIINAE

Tribe CALLICERINI

Genus CALLICERA

There are three species known in Britain. Since additional species could occur, the key below includes all six species recognised in a revision of the European fauna (Speight, 1991b).

1. Femora entirely or mainly yellow-orange (some may have basal darkening).   2

—   Femora strongly black in at least basal half.   3

2. Abdomen mainly shining black. Thorax with reddish hairs. Only last two tarsal segments black. [Scotland, pine.]   **rufa** p. 239

—   Abdomen mainly shining brassy (as rest of genus). Thorax with yellowish hairs. Last three tarsal segments black (a common character in the genus). [East Anglia & south-east England.]   ♀ **spinolae** p. 239

3. Antennal segment 2 very short; thus segments 1+2 much shorter than length of 3 (as *rufa*).   4

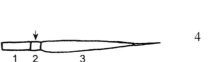

—   Antennal segment 2 elongate: thus segments 1+2 about equal to length of 3.   5

4. All tibiae partly black. Body hairs yellow-brown to grey-brown, relatively long and wavy, those on top of the scutellum all longer than the width of antennal segment 1. [April to mid July; has been found in the Netherlands and Belgium.]   [*fagesii*]

—   Front and mid tibiae entirely orange, or at least hind ones often brown or part black. Body hairs orange to whitish yellow, relatively short and straight, many of those on top of the scutellum shorter than the width of antennal segment 1. [Autumnal species of southern Europe.]   [*macquartii*]

5.   Top of thorax mainly shining (except anterior median dust stripes). Tarsi with last three segments black.   6

—   Top of thorax dulled by thin greyish dusting extending back to the scutellum (plus or minus some denser dust stripes). Tarsi entirely yellow or last segments only lightly greyish. [Peak in May/June, earlier than *aurata*, though records extend to September.]   [*aenea*]

6.   Black hairs on underside between front and mid legs; black hairs on coxae and posterior surface of front femur.   **aurata**
p. 238

—   Yellowish hairs on underside between front and mid legs; yellow hairs on coxae and posterior surface of front femur.   ♂ **spinolae**
p. 239

Tribe CHEILOSIINI

Key to genera

1.   Face greatly elongate. Abdomen extensively orange.   **Rhingia**
p. 127

—   Face not so elongate. Abdomen never partly orange.   2

2.   Thorax with grey stripes (not always distinct in *ruficornis*) and long side bristles. Hind legs yellow except for last 2 tarsal segments.   **Ferdinandea**
p. 127

—   Thorax without stripes (and side bristles less obvious or absent). Hind legs more extensively black.   3

3.   Face without distinct knob. Abdomen with grey spots.    **Portevinia maculata**
p. 267

—   Face normally with knob. Abdomen with or without grey spots.   **Cheilosia**
p. 112

Genus CHEILOSIA

Where species names are placed in square brackets this indicates that the species concerned does not belong to the species group as defined in the text.

Key to groups

1.	Wing with dark cloud in centre.	(A) ILLUSTRATA group p. 113
—	Wing without dark cloud (any slight darkening more diffuse and extensive).	2
2.	Face with erect projecting hairs. [*Melanogaster* commonly runs here if you go wrong in the key to tribes, so check the zygoma (see p. 52) and that the abdomen is not flat and dull on top.]	(B) VARIABILIS group p. 113
—	Face without projecting hairs, though a decumbent down may be present.	3
3.	Front tarsus has segments 2, 3 and 4 orange (even if dusky orange) contrasting with black segments 1 and 5. Legs otherwise entirely or mainly black.	(C) ALBITARSIS group p. 116
—	Legs without this combination.	4
4.	Eyes bare.	5
—	Eyes hairy (view against both light and dark backgrounds from various angles).	6
5.	Legs entirely black (rarely dull dusky orange at knees).	(D) ANTIQUA group p. 117
—	Legs partly yellow, conspicuously so, including the basal quarter or more of the tibiae.	(E) PAGANA group p. 119
6.	Legs entirely black.	(F) IMPRESSA group p. 120
—	Legs partly pale, including the base of the tibiae on at least one pair of legs.	7

7.   Hind tibia entirely yellow or only with an   (G) GROSSA
            indistinct and incomplete dark ring. Scutellum   group
            often without marginal bristles.   p. 121

—   Hind tibia with a strong dark ring or extensively   8
            dark. Scutellum always with marginal bristles
            even if weak.

8.   Sternites 2 to 4 obviously dusted, at least at sides   (H) PROXIMA
            (view obliquely from side).   group
                                                                            p. 123

—   Sternites partly or entirely glossy, at most with an   9
            inconspicuous dusting that does not become
            heavier at the sides.

9.   Antennae dark and hind tibiae half black or more.   (I) CARBONARIA
                                                                            group
                                                                            p. 124

—   Antennae orange or if dark then hind tibiae less   (J) BERGENSTAMMI
            than half black (*vernalis* is variable so repeated   group
            in both couplets).   p. 126

GROUP A – ILLUSTRATA GROUP

Furry bumblebee mimic with a strong dark cloud on the wing.

One species only: **illustrata** p. 251

GROUP B – VARIABILIS GROUP

Face with some erect hairs projecting at right angles. Note: *Chrysogaster* and *Melangyna quadrimaculata* also have face hairs of this type; thus check that the eye rims (zygomas) are of the *Cheilosia* type.

1.   Males (eyes meet on top of head).   2

—   Females (eyes separated).   7

2.   Scutellum with marginal bristles yellow or absent.   3

—   Scutellum with marginal bristles black, at least   4
            some distinct from hairs (view from side).

3.   Typically larger (wing length 8–9 mm), greyer and with a longer, narrower abdomen. Tergite 3 with triangular grey spots towards front corners (view from behind). Head in front view broader (width to height ratio of 5:4). Face and frons broader and more heavily dusted. Third antennal segment usually dark.   ♂ **griseiventris** p. 250

—   Typically smaller (wing length 7.5 mm) and more shining with a relatively compact build. Tergite 3 with grey spots nearly square or fused to form a band. Head in front view almost rounded (width to height ratio 10:9). Face and frons narrower and less heavily dusted. Third antennal segment usually largely reddish.   ♂ **latifrons** p. 252

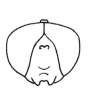

4.   Tergite 4 with all lateral hairs pale, short and of nearly even length (length about 1½ times width of hind tibia).   ♂ **lasiopa** p. 252

—   Tergite 4 with postero-lateral hairs black and long (length 2 to 3 times width of hind tibia).   5

5.   Third antennal segment reddish at base.   ♂ **barbata** p. 246

—   Third antennal segment black.   6

6.   Tergites 3 and 4 with very short black semi-adpressed hairs along median axis (view from side).   ♂ **variabilis** p. 262

—   Tergites 3 and 4 with a dense pile of long, more upright hairs (view from side).   ♂ **vulpina** p. 264

7.   Scutellar marginal bristles yellow or absent (at least indistinguishable from pile of hairs).   8

—   Scutellar marginal bristles black (distinct from hairs).   9

8.   Typically larger (wing length up to 7.5 mm but
      size more variable than male) and more
      narrowly built. Head in front view with
      width to height ratio of 4:3. Face in front
      view broader and more heavily dusted. Frons
      broader with conspicuous dusting at sides
      towards front. Top of scutellum with hairs at
      least as long as width of hind tibia and largely
      upright. Hind femur usually conspicuously
      yellow at base.

♀ **griseiventris**
p. 250

—   Smaller (wing length up to 6.5 mm) with more
      compact build. Head in front view with
      width to height ratio of 7:6. Face in front
      view narrower and less dusted. Frons
      narrower with only slight dusting at front
      corners. Top of scutellum with shorter hairs
      (about half width of hind tibia) and more
      inclined. Hind femur usually black at base or
      with pale patches at extreme base.

♀ **latifrons**
p. 252

9.   Scutellar dorsum with very long erect hairs, three
      times width of hind tibia.

[**Melangyna
quadrimaculata**]
p. 216

—   Scutellar dorsum with shorter hairs.

10

10.   Scutellar marginal bristles short, not half length of
      scutellum.

♀ **lasiopa**
p. 252

—   Scutellar marginal bristles with longest at least ⅔
      length of scutellum.

11

11.   Third antennal segment reddish at base below.

♀ **barbata**
p. 246

—   Third antennal segment black.

12

12.   Tergite 4 on extreme lateral margin with only
        very short hairs (view from side). Legs black,
        tibiae at most obscurely brownish at bases.
        Abdomen relatively narrow, tergite 2 about 1½
        times as wide as long. Occiput undusted and
        shining behind ocellar triangle and upper eye
        margins.    ♀ **variabilis**
                                                                          p. 262

—   Tergite 4 on extreme lateral margin usually with
        very long hairs, much longer than width of hind
        tibia (view from side). Legs with bases of
        tibiae and usually of mid tarsus yellow.
        Abdomen broader, tergite 2 twice as wide as
        long. Occiput dusted.   ♀ **vulpina**
                                                                          p. 264

GROUP C – ALBITARSIS GROUP

The legs are entirely black apart from the front tarsus having segments 2, 3 and 4 orange.
Sometimes this orange coloration is dusky or absent (*i.e.* entirely black), especially in female
albitarsis/ranunculi (repeated in Group D).

1.   Halteres orange (at least at tip). Body length 8   2
        mm or more. Female abdomen oval.

—   Halteres dark (at least at tip). Body length up to 7   **mutabilis**
        mm, narrow species in both sexes.   p. 254

2.   Apical segment of front tarsus with parallel sides    ♂ **albitarsis**
        when viewed from above. Tergite 2 at anterior   p. 245
        corners often with some black hairs. Third
        antennal segment almost round; as long as wide
        when viewed on inner face (all antennal
        segments usually blackish).

—   Apical segment of front tarsus clearly broadest at   ♂ **ranunculi**
        base when viewed from above. Tergite 2 at   p. 258
        anterior corners never with black hairs. Third
        antennal segment very short, not as long as
        wide when viewed on inner face (third antennal
        segment usually brownish).

        Females of *albitarsis* and *ranunculi* are not currently separable.

GROUP D – ANTIQUA GROUP

Legs entirely black (at most only knees narrowly pale). Eyes bare. Face lacking erect hairs. Allowance has been made for *impressa* (eyes may be very weakly hairy) and *albitarsis / ranunculi* (orange on front tarsus can be darkened; the female has bare eyes).

1.	Males (eyes meeting on top of head).	2
—	Females (eyes separated).	12
2	Tergite 2 with lateral hairs partly or entirely black (take care if hind leg is screening these hairs).	3
—	Tergite 2 with lateral hairs entirely pale.	7
3.	Thoracic dorsum with all hairs of almost uniform length in anterior half (view from side and front).	4
—	Thoracic dorsum with some hairs projecting above general pile in anterior half.	5
4.	Tergites 3 and 4 on top with inconspicuous very short semi-decumbent hairs (view from side).	♂ **antiqua** p. 245
—	Tergites 3 and 4 on top with obvious erect long pile of hairs (view from side).	[♂ **impressa**] p. 252
5.	Thoracic dorsum with main pile of hairs yellow-brown.	♂ **sahlbergi** p. 258
—	Thoracic dorsum with all hairs black.	6
6.	Frons dusted grey.	♂ **vicina** p. 264
—	Frons shining black.	♂ **nigripes** p. 255
7.	Thoracic dorsum with hairs pale yellowish.	8
—	Thoracic dorsum with hairs mainly black.	10
8.	Sternites 2, 3 and 4 glossy; sternite 1 lightly dusted (view from below).	♂ **antiqua** var. p. 245
—	Sternites 2, 3 and 4 heavily grey dusted, like sternite 1.	9

9.   Face extensively dusted, the knob at most only   ♂ **pubera**
        partly dust free, the dusting just above the knob   p. 257
        merging with the dust band below the antennae.
        Abdomen a dull brassy colour.

—   Face extensively free of dust, including much   ♂ **ahenea**
        more than the facial knob, with a sharply   p. 244
        defined dense white dust band immediately
        below the antennae. Abdomen shining black.

10.   Frons dusted grey.   ♂ **vicina**
                                                                            p. 264

—   Frons extensively without dust, shining.   11

11.   Thoracic dorsum with all hairs of almost uniform   ♂ **antiqua**
        length.   p. 245

—   Thoracic dorsum with some long hairs projecting   ♂ **nigripes**
        well above dense pile of hairs (illustrated in   p. 255
        couplet 3).

12.   Thoracic dorsum with strongly adpressed or   13
        inclined mainly black hairs (some may have
        pale reflection) (view from side).

—   Thoracic dorsum with entirely pale hairs forming   16
        a semi-erect short dense pile obviously rising
        above the surface (view from side).

13.   Wing strongly yellowish at the base (veins and   14
        membrane).

—   Wing not yellowish at base (veins brown or   15
        blackish, membrane clear or blackish).

14.   Wing veins and membrane yellowish over most of   [♀ **albitarsis** /
        wing. Large species (wing length 7–9.5 mm).   **ranunculi**]
                                                                      p. 245/p. 258

—   Wing veins and membrane yellowish only in   [♀ **impressa**]
        basal third of wing. Smaller species (wing   p. 252
        length 5.75–8 mm).

15.	Body about 7 mm long. Face profile very angular in upper part. Veins at base of wing brownish.		♀ **vicina** p. 264
—	Body about 8.5 mm long. Face profile often more sloping above knob. Veins at base of wing black (between basal cells and root of wing). [These distinctions are not reliable (see text for distribution and base records on males).]		♀ **nigripes** p. 255
16.	Thoracic dorsum with dense pile of hairs only, no long projecting hairs.		17
—	Thoracic dorsum with long hairs projecting well above dense pile of hairs (illustrated in couplet 3).		♀ **sahlbergi** p. 258
17.	Sternites 2, 3 and 4 dusted, as sternite 1.		18
—	Sternites 2, 3 and 4 glossy, in contrast to sternite 1.		♀ **antiqua** p. 245
18.	Frons with sides straight. Face extensively free of dust, including much more than the facial knob, with a sharply defined dense white dust band immediately below the antennae.		♀ **ahenea** p. 244
—	Frons with sides angled halfway along. Face extensively dusted, the knob at most only partly dust free, the dusting just above the knob merging with the dust band below the antennae.		♀ **pubera** p. 257

GROUP E – PAGANA GROUP

Eyes bare, legs partly yellow, face without erect hairs. If the front tarsus has segments 2, 3 and 4 orange (contrasting with black segments 1 and 5), then check Group C (*mutabilis*, especially females, may run here if the legs are pale).

1.	Scutellum without distinct black marginal bristles, all hairs pale (this species has erect facial hairs, but they are often difficult to see).	**[latifrons]** p. 252
—	Scutellum with distinct black marginal bristles.	2
2.	Antennal segment 3 bright orange, or with dark tip and orange at base.	3
—	Antennal segment 3 black or uniformly dull brown. Scutellum usually black with a brown tip.	4

3.   Arista densely pubescent at base (bare-eyed   **soror**
          bergenstammi would run here, but the arista is   p. 260
          bare).

—   Arista scarcely if at all pubescent.   **pagana**
                                                                         p. 255

4.   Facial knob viewed from above hemispherical,
          swelling abruptly close to eye. Third antennal
          segment usually with tip paler than base. Front
          and mid tarsi with first three segments clear   **scutellata**
          yellow. Male thoracic dorsum extensively   p. 258
          pale-haired and shining. Typically larger (wing
          length 7-8.5 mm).

—   Facial knob viewed from above semi-triangular,
          (the distinction is not always as clear as in
          these diagrams and some specimens are
          difficult to separate). Third antennal segment   **longula**
          uniformly blackish. Tarsi at most with basal   p. 253
          segments fuscous. Male thoracic dorsum
          dulled by dusting (best viewed from in front),
          mainly black-haired. Typically smaller (wing
          length 6-7 mm).

GROUP F – IMPRESSA GROUP

Legs black, eyes hairy, face without erect hairs. *C. impressa* is the only true member, but other
species can sometimes have entirely black legs.

1.   Face extended so that the mouth margin is as far   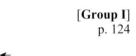   **[Group I]**
          forwards as the knob.   p. 124

—   Face short, mouth margin does not extend as far   2
          forwards as the knob.

2.   Apical segment of front tarsus squarish. Male:
      black lateral hairs confined to the front corners
      of tergite 2 (only black hairs illustrated) or all
      lateral hairs pale. [See Group C (p. 116) for
      separation of males, but females are bare-eyed
      and are keyed in Group D.]

      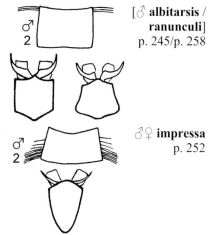

[♂ **albitarsis /**
ranunculi]
p. 245/p. 258

—   Apical segment of front tarsus slender at base and
      widening towards claws. Male and female
      with pale hairs at the front corners of tergite 2
      and black hairs confined to the hind corners in
      the male (the female has all lateral hairs pale) .

♂♀ **impressa**
p. 252

GROUP G – GROSSA GROUP

The group is centred on furry species with a yellow hind tibia and lacking marginal scutellar bristles. (The remaining species are more allied to *bergenstammi*, but are keyed here since the presence or absence of fine scutellar marginal bristles can be difficult to decide upon. *C. fraterna* is included here because it always has a yellow hind tibia. The key has only become complicated because allowance must be made for newly recognised rare species and a rare variety of *bergenstammi*, even though these are not related to *grossa*).

1.   Thoracic dorsum uniformly covered in dense erect   2
      pale hairs; ground surface brownish (compare
      with black of face). Tergite 1 dusted. Occiput
      dusted or dull in upper third.

—   Thoracic dorsum with some black hairs or, if   8
      entirely pale, the hairs are shorter than the
      thickness of the front metatarsus; ground
      surface black and shining. Tergite 1 glossy
      black or dusted. Occiput shining black behind
      top of eyes (easily seen in females).

2.   Scutellum with marginal bristles even if weak.   3
      Sternites heavily dusted or a small slender
      species with glossy sternites.

—   Scutellum without marginal bristles, fine hairs   5
      only. Sternites mostly glossy or faintly dusted.

3. Sternites heavily dusted. Male genitalia (Pl. M): superior lobe with a short stout dorsal process.

uviformis
p. 261

—   Sternites glossy black.   4

4. Male genitalia (Pl. L): dorsal process of superior lobe with a dorsal concavity and shaped like a long spine. Tarsal claws pale at base.

[urbana]
p. 260

—   Male genitalia (Pl. L): dorsal process of superior lobe with a convex outline, short and sloping downwards. Tarsal claws entirely black.

[psilophthalma]
p. 257

5. Third antennal segment black.

grossa
p. 251

—   Third antennal segment entirely or partly orange.   6

6. Body hairs bright foxy reddish-orange. Ground colour of thorax and abdomen of similar hue.

chrysocoma
p. 248

—   Body hairs mainly pale brown. Tergites with steely bluish-black reflections, contrasting with duller thoracic ground colour.   7

7. Large species with clear wings. Anteroventral surface of hind femur with some hairs much longer than maximum width (apparent in side view as illustrated). Female with hind femur entirely orange.

albipila
p. 244

—   Smaller species with dusky clouds on outer part of wings anteriorly. Anterior surface of hind femur with longest hairs about as long as its maximum width (apparent in side view as illustrated). Females with hind femur mainly black.

nebulosa
p. 254

8. Males (eyes meet on top of head).   9

—   Females (eyes separated).   10

9. Hind femur with some long posteroventral hairs in the basal half (as long as the width of the femur) in addition to long anteroventral hairs. Scutellum with some hairs and marginal bristles as long as the scutellum.

[♂ bergenstammi]
p. 246

—   Hind femur with any long hairs confined to the anteroventral position. Scutellum with shorter hairs and bristles.

♂ fraterna
p. 249

10.	Thoracic dorsum with closely adpressed golden hairs.	♀ **fraterna** p. 249
—	Thoracic dorsum with hairs inclined by at least 45°.	11
11.	Small slender species. Ventral surface of hind femur with few, if any, black spinules. [*psilophthalma*, with black claws, may key out here.]	[♀ **urbana**] p. 260
—	Larger robust species. Ventral surface of hind femur with short, but conspicuous black spinules for much of length.	[♀ **bergenstammi**] p. 246

GROUP H – PROXIMA GROUP

Eyes hairy, tibiae black and yellow, all sternites obviously dusted. A small slender species, *semifasciata*, might run here (the knob is very low on the face – see group I).

1.	Males (eyes meet on top of head).	2
—	Females (eyes separated).	6
2.	Face without mouth margin jutting forwards (lower part of face below knob almost vertical). Third antennal segment largely reddish.	3
—	Face with mouth margin jutting forwards as a distinct lip. Third antennal segment black or obscurely brownish.	4
3.	Frons only lightly dusted in middle. Mouth margin usually receding.	♂ **velutina** p. 262
—	Frons heavily grey dusted throughout. Mouth margin usually weakly projecting.	[♂ **uviformis**] p. 261
4.	Abdomen with hairs along axis pale (view from side). Thorax with hairs on axis (view from side) mainly pale, entirely pale in front quarter.	♂ **proxima** (spring) p. 256
—	Abdomen with some black hairs on axis of tergite 4, and sometimes 3 (view from side). Thorax with black hairs extensive, including some in front quarter (view from side).	5

5.   Hairs on top of thorax, scutellum and axis of   ♂ **species B**
        tergites 3 and 4 nearly all black; any pale hairs   p. 265
        at extreme front of thorax and on tergite 2 are
        whitish. Tergite 3 with erect hairs on axis,
        many of them longer than width of hind tibia.

—   Hairs often more extensively pale, these being   ♂ **proxima**
        yellow-brown. Tergite 3 with hairs on axis   (summer)
        inclined at 60° and no longer than width of hind   p. 256
        tibia.

6.   Thoracic dorsum with long pale hairs inclined at   ♀ **proxima**
        60° to 80° in centre (many hairs with length   (spring)
        equalling median width of hind tibia) (view   p. 256
        from side).

—   Thoracic dorsum with short hairs inclined at 45°   7
        (view from side).

7.   Face without mouth margin jutting forwards.   ♀ **velutina**
                                                                      p. 262

—   Face with mouth margin jutting forwards   ♀ **proxima**
        (separation of these two species is often   (summer)
        difficult).   p. 256

GROUP I – CARBONARIA GROUP

Eyes hairy, tibiae at least half black, sternites entirely or partly glossy, antennae usually dark.

1.   Males (eyes meet on top of head).   2

—   Females (eyes separated).   5

2.   Face profile with knob low. Abdomen with faint   ♂ **semifasciata**
        grey spots (view obliquely from in front).   p. 259

—   Face profile with knob high. Abdomen entirely   3
        black.

3. Abdomen elongate and parallel-sided; tergite 4   ♂ **carbonaria**
    with hairs on axis adpressed (view from side).   p. 247
    Femora with hairs almost entirely pale.

—   Abdomen less elongate and slightly oval; tergite 4   4
    with hairs often clearly seen as erect (view
    from side). Femora with hairs almost entirely
    black.

4. Pregenital segment lightly dusted compared with   ♂ **cynocephala**
    glossy tergite 4. Tergites 3 and 4 with lateral   p. 248
    marginal hairs entirely or predominantly black.

—   Pregenital segment not dusted, as glossy as tergite   ♂ **vernalis**
    4. Tergites 3 and 4 with lateral hairs pale or   p. 263
    only partly dark.

5. Abdomen pear-shaped, widest at posterior margin   ♀ **carbonaria**
    of tergite 3 (large species, body length about 9   p. 247
    mm).

—   Abdomen of different shape.   6

6. Tergite 4 with lateral hairs black and on axis at   ♀ **cynocephala**
    posterior end with long decumbent pale hairs.   p. 248
    Frons with a broad, strongly pitted eye margin
    zone (in most specimens).

—   Tergite 4 with pale lateral hairs and axis with   7
    adpressed short hairs throughout. Frons with a
    narrow eye margin zone, pitting indistinct.

7.   Abdomen broadly oval. Face profile with knob high.

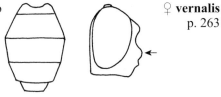

♀ **vernalis**
p. 263

—   Abdomen narrow. Face profile with knob low.

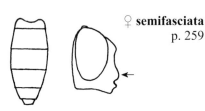

♀ **semifasciata**
p. 259

GROUP J – BERGENSTAMMI GROUP

Eyes hairy, tibiae at least half yellow, sternites entirely or partly glossy, antennae orange or dark.

1.   Large species (body length at least 8 mm). Hairs on abdomen orange-brown. Third antennal segment more or less rounded (as long as broad).

bergenstammi
p. 246

—   Smaller species (body length 7 mm or less). Any pale hairs on abdomen are pale brown.

2

2.   Compact build. Eye hairs very dark. Thorax and abdomen usually with extensive black hairs. Third antennal segment more or less rounded (as long as broad).

[vernalis]
p. 263

—   Slender species. Eye hairs very pale. Hairs on thorax and abdomen very pale. Third antennal segment distinctly longer than broad.

3

3.   [M. Claws yellow in basal half.] Male tergite 3 with more extensive grey markings, reaching further towards centre line or even fused.

urbana
p. 260

—   [M. Claws entirely black.] Male tergite 3 with smaller shining side spots (view obliquely from behind), separated by at least ⅓ width of tergite.

psilophthalma
p. 257

Genus FERDINANDEA

1. Abdomen mostly a shining brassy colour. Tibiae   **cuprea**
    with black bristles.   p. 266

—   Abdomen mostly shining bluish-black. Legs   **ruficornis**
    without black bristles (or exceptionally present   p. 266
    on hind tibia only).

Genus RHINGIA

The text to the genus mentions *borealis* Ringdahl which could have been overlooked in
mountainous areas in Britain. This has the tiny hairs on the arista slightly longer than in the
other two species, but this difference is not easy to see.

1. Orange abdomen with narrow black side margin   **campestris**
    (view from side).   p. 268

—   Orange abdomen lacking black margin (view   **rostrata**
    from side).   p. 268

Tribe CHRYSOGASTRINI

Key to genera

The main change from the first edition is the splitting of genera *Chrysogaster* (*Melanogaster*
new) and *Orthonevra* (*Riponnensia* new).

1. Abdomen waisted near base.   2

—   Abdomen not waisted near base (broadly-built   3
    species).

2. Wing with outer cross-veins bent at a sharp angle.      **Neoascia**
    Hind tibia with one black ring.   p. 134

—   Wing with outer cross-veins obliquely angled,   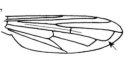   **Sphegina**
    upper cross-vein with very rounded angle.   p. 137
    Hind tibia with two black rings (upper one
    sometimes faint).

3. Abdomen partly or entirely pale coloured (red, orange or yellow). 4

— Abdomen entirely dark (blackish, metallic green or blue) or blackish-grey with faint grey spots. **(Chrysogaster** group) 6

4. Thorax shining black. Abdomen with reddish side patches. **Myolepta** p. 133

— Thorax grey or orange-brown. Abdomen entirely or almost entirely pale. 5

5. Wing with upper outer cross-vein strongly angled towards wing tip. Thorax grey (in known British species). **Brachyopa** p. 129

— Wing with upper outer cross-vein bent so as to meet vein R_{4+5} at right angles. Thorax orange. **Hammerschmidtia ferruginea** p. 273

[An orange brown fly; head profile characteristic including short-plumose arista.]

6. Tergites entirely metallic coloured, with green, bluish or reddish reflections. Male eyes separated (as female). **Lejogaster** p. 132

— Tergites dull (or semi-shining black) on dorsal surface. Male eyes meet on frons. 7

7. Tergite 1 with metallic margin as on other tergites. **Orthonevra / Riponnensia** p. 136

— Tergite 1 dull at margin, contrasting with metallic margins of other tergites. 8

8. Males (eyes meet on top of head). 9

— Females (eyes separated). 10

9.   Antennae with third segment completely black.   **Melanogaster**
        Hairs on sternite 2 as long as those on thoracic   p. 133
        dorsum.

—   Antennae with third segment partly or entirely   **Chrysogaster**
        reddish, rarely dark. Hairs on sternite 2 shorter   p. 131
        than those on thoracic dorsum.

10.   Thoracic dorsum with pale hairs. Antennae black.   **Melanogaster**
                                                                       p. 133

—   Thoracic dorsum virtually bald, with minute   **Chrysogaster**
        extremely short black hairs only. Antennae   p. 131
        often reddish but can be dark.

Genus BRACHYOPA

Only four species are recorded in Britain. However, the European fauna has a further eight species of which four are sufficiently widespread in western Europe that they might potentially occur here. The latter are included in the key in the hope that one or more may be found in Britain. *B. panzeri*, for instance, has been found at sap runs on horse-chestnut and sycamore (thus could be present among the known British species); *B. dorsata* is associated with spruce so potentially could become established in conifer plantations.

The four British species are best distinguished on antennal characters. Reliable identification usually requires a microscope. Considerable care is necessary if a hand lens is used since it is easy to misinterpret the shape of antennal pits and underestimate the extent of hairs on the arista. Note that the sensory pits are on the **inner** surface of the third antennal segment.

1.   Arista plumose. Top of thorax medium brown   2
        (with darker brown stripes).

—   Arista bare or pubescent. Top of thorax brown or   3
        with blackish ground colour.

2.   Unusually large species for this genus, wing
     length about 10 mm. Face very extended.
     Tergite 2 about one and a quarter times as wide
     as long at hind margin.   [*vittata*]

—   Usual size for the genus, wing length about 7 mm.
     Face less extended, head about as long as high.
     Tergite 2 about twice as wide as long at hind
     margin.   [*testacea*]

3.   Top of thorax brown, at least immediately in front
     of scutellum. (Arista almost bare).   4

—   Top of thorax dark with light grey dusting, even
     immediately in front of scutellum. (Arista
     almost bare or pubescent).   5

4.   Pit on antennal segment 3 tiny, separated from
     hind margin by its own width.   [*dorsata*]

—   Pit on antennal segment 3 somewhat larger, very
     close to hind margin.   [*panzeri*]

5.   Scutellum entirely yellow. Arista pubescent.   6

—   Scutellum grey-dusted, at least on the front edge.
     Arista almost bare.   7

6.   Humeri entirely yellow. Antennal pit kidney-
     shaped.   **scutellaris** p. 270

—   Humeri grey-dusted, strongly so above. Antennal
     pit circular.   **pilosa** p. 270

7.   Scutellum with front half grey-dusted. Antennal
     pit circular.   **bicolor** p. 269

—   Scutellum with only front fringe grey-dusted. No
     antennal pit.   **insensilis** p. 270

Genus CHRYSOGASTER

The males are rather more slender than the females, the latter usually having an exceptionally broad oval abdomen. The abdomen is normally dull on top but rather shining in some specimens, especially females. *Chrysogaster* has recently been split and some species placed here in earlier editions are now in *Melanogaster*. Confusion is most likely with *Cheilosia*, especially *Cheilosia vernalis* whose females have an abdomen of similar shape (but the legs are entirely black in *Chrysogaster*, unlike *Cheilosia vernalis*). The key includes *rondanii*, recently split from *virescens*, which may occur in Britain.

1.	Males (eyes meet on top of head).	2
—	Females (eyes separated).	5
2.	Side of thorax above front coxa (base of front leg) with extensive area strongly grey-dusted.	♂ **cemiteriorum** p. 271
—	Side of thorax above front coxa shining black (any grey dusting is in front of the coxa rather than above).	3
3.	Top of thorax matt black. Angle of frons where eyes meet not exceeding 90°.	♂ **solstitialis** p. 272
—	Top of the thorax shining. Angle of frons where eyes meet greater than 90°.	4
4.	Face with well developed knob. Top of thorax with most hairs inclined at about 45°.	♂ **virescens** p. 272
—	Face with knob less developed. Top of thorax with most hairs much more erect.	[♂ *rondanii*]
5.	Wings strongly blackish. Thoracic dorsum with purple reflections. Face narrow.	♀ **solstitialis** p. 272
—	Wings at most brownish in front. Thoracic dorsum black or greenish-black. Face wide.	6

6.   Pleura (sides of thorax) heavily grey-dusted above   ♀ **cemiteriorum**
      front coxae. Basal veins and often sub-costal   p. 271
      cell strongly yellow-tinged.

—   Pleura glossy black above front coxae. Basal   7
      veins and often sub-costal cell brownish.

7.   Top of thorax virtually bald (only minute black   ♀ **virescens**
      hairs). Scutellum bald (only a few minute   p. 272
      black hairs at margin). Sternite 1 with hairs
      shorter than width of hind femur.

—   Top of thorax with short pale hairs. Scutellum   [♀ *rondanii*]
      covered in pale hairs. Sternite 1 with hairs as
      long as width of hind femur.

Genus LEJOGASTER

1.   Males (eyes separated on top of head as in female;   2
      end of abdomen swollen beneath by genitalia).

—   Females (eyes separated on top of head as in   3
      male).

2.   Third antennal segment large, wider than long,   ♂ **metallina**
      black.   p. 273

—   Third antennal segment smaller, roundish, yellow   ♂ **tarsata**
      at base.   p. 274

3.   Third antennal segment about as broad as long,   ♀ **metallina**
      rounded.   p. 273

—   Third antennal segment longer than broad and   ♀ **tarsata**
      almost parallel-sided.   p. 274

Genus MELANOGASTER

This genus has recently been separated from *Chrysogaster*. The key includes *parumplicata*, recently split from *aerosa*, which may well be found in Britain.

1.	Males (eyes meet on top of head).	2
—	Females (eyes separated).	4
2.	Thoracic dorsum (viewed from in front) with hairs partly yellowish-brown.	♂ **hirtella** p. 275
—	Thoracic dorsum (viewed from in front) with hairs entirely black (easy to make a mistake so considerable caution is necessary here).	3
3.	Face with a very strong knob.	♂ **aerosa** p. 274
—	Face with knob only slightly developed.	[♂ *parumplicata*]
4.	Thoracic dorsum with hairs yellow (or greyish) and upstanding (view from side).	♀ **hirtella** p. 275
—	Thoracic dorsum with sparse golden hair lying almost flat on surface.	5
5.	Face profile strongly angled in middle and finishing at the lower end in a sharply angled lip.	♀ **aerosa** p. 274
—	Face profile gently curved. Lip not sharply angled.	[♀ *parumplicata*]

Genus MYOLEPTA

1.	Males (eyes meet on top of head).	2
—	Females (eyes separated).	3

2.   Face with black median stripe narrow.   ♂ **dubia**
                                                                                                                                            p. 276

—   Face with black median stripe broad, especially in
      upper part.   ♂ **potens**
                                                                                                                                            p. 276

3.   Tergite 2 with broad central black stripe of an
      hourglass shape.   ♀ **dubia**
                                                                                                                                            p. 276

—   Tergite 2 with narrow central black stripe,
      narrowed posteriorly but expanding as a broad
      line across the hind margin of the tergite.   ♀ **potens**
                                                                                                                                            p. 276

Genus NEOASCIA

Two subgenera have been proposed, separated by the presence or absence of a band of chitin across the rear of the thorax, above the hind coxae (below the base of the abdomen). This feature can be seen even with a hand lens by viewing the underside of the body obliquely from behind, but the legs are often in the way. The key to species avoids reliance on this character since it can be difficult to apply and is not always reliable in some species (*e.g. geniculata*).

Key to subgenera (not treated as such in the British list).

—   Bridge complete. Continuous band of chitin from
      one side of thorax to the other (view hind end
      of thorax from below). [*podagrica, tenur*]   subgenus
                                                                                                                                            Neoascia

—   Bridge incomplete. Chitin not continuous from
      one side of thorax to the other, only membrane
      present on centre line. [*geniculata, interrupta,
      meticulosa, obliqua*]   subgenus
                                                                                                                                            Neoasciella

Key to species

This key incorporates two European species, *annexa* and *unifasciata* which could occur in Britain. It is adapted from Barkemeyer & Claussen (1986), Speight (1988a) and in particular an unpublished version by C.W. Plant, and rearranged to avoid use of the bridge character.

1.   Upper and lower marginal cross-veins infuscated (wing darkened along these veins). Note that this can be faint in the common *podagrica* so check other characters.   2

—   These veins clear.   5

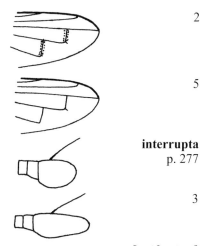

2.   Third antennal segment short. Tergite 4 normally with side spots.   **interrupta** p. 277

—   Third antennal segment elongate. Tergite 4 entirely black.   3

3.   Tergite 2 entirely black (except rarely in female). Female tergite 2 broad and squat, almost parallel-sided.   [*unifasciata*]

—   Tergite 2 with pale marking; in female narrower.   4

4.   Tergite 2 with transverse yellow band or bars as seen from above; from side the markings are only slightly slanted. [Male tergite 2 little more than twice as long as wide; in female very much wider on hind margin than front margin. Alula particularly narrow, width narrower than longest fringe hairs.]   **podagrica** p. 279

—   Tergite 2 with oblique bars as seen from above; from side the markings are strongly slanted. [Male tergite narrower, about three times as long as wide; in female less strongly widening to hind margin. Alula not as narrow, width wider than longest fringe hairs.]   **obliqua** p. 278

5.   Face projection blunt-ended. Front and mid   [*annexa*]
      femora and tibiae extensively or entirely
      yellow.

—   Face conical, apex pointed. Front and mid femora   6
      and tibiae often extensively dark, or with at
      least dark shading in the middle.

6.   Third antennal segment scarcely longer than   **geniculata**
      wide.   p. 277

—   Third antennal segment more elongate, almost   7
      twice as long as wide.

7.   Hind femur narrowly yellow at tip.   **meticulosa**
                                                                                          p. 278

—   Hind femur entirely black at tip.   **tenur**
                                                                                          p. 279

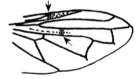

Genus ORTHONEVRA (including RIPONNENSIA)

1.   Legs partly yellow. [Wings with darkening at   **geniculata**
      inner end of stigma and around r-m. If these   p. 280
      markings are missing, check for other yellow-
      legged European species – see text.]

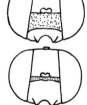

—   Legs entirely black.   2

2.   Broad white dust band across face.   **Riponnensia**
                                                                                       splendens
                                                                                          p. 281

—   Only a narrow strip of white dusting below   3
      antennae.

3.   Third antennal segment about as long as deep.   **brevicornis**
                                                                       p. 280

—   Third antennal segment twice as long as deep.   **nobilis**
                                                                       p. 281

Genus SPHEGINA

S. sibirica belongs to the subgenus *Asiosphegina*: the genitalia are asymmetrical and have a few long hairs on the main lobes (see below). All other British species are placed in subgenus *Sphegina* (Stubbs, 1994).

1.   Chitinous bridge behind hind coxae incomplete.   **sibirica**
     Sternopleuron shining in at least some   p. 282
     specimens (lower part of sides of thorax, above
     middle coxae). [Thorax colour, including
     humeri, very variable, ranging from
     completely yellow to completely dark, but
     many specimens have the thorax strikingly
     patterned with yellow and black making them
     instantly recognisable.]
     ♂
     genitalia

—   Chitinous bridge complete (as illustrated under   **2**
     Neoascia on p. 134).

2.   Thorax with anterior humeri clear yellow.   **elegans**
                                                                       p. 283

—   Thorax with anterior humeri darkened, at least on   **3**
     top.

3.   Face whitish-yellow in lower part. Wing with r-m   **clunipes**
     cross-vein well beyond end of Sc.   p. 282

—   Face entirely grey. Wing with r-m cross-vein   **verecunda**
     practically opposite Sc.   p. 283

Tribe ERISTALINI

The genera almost break down into two groups: the *Helophilus* group with a distinctly striped thorax (including *Anasimyia*, *Lejops* and *Parhelophilus*) and the remaining genera without stripes on the thorax. Unfortunately there are sufficient exceptions to make this subdivision unreliable, but it is a useful initial guide, noting in particular that *Eristalinus* commonly has stripes. *Merodon* is placed in this tribal key since it has a loop in radial vein R_{4+5}; it belongs to the tribe Merodontini.

Key to genera

1. Wing with the two anterior radial veins (R_1 and R_{2+3}) meeting to form a short stalk before reaching the wing margin.

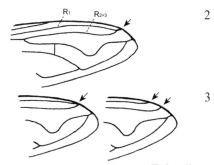

    2

— Wing with these veins only just meeting at the wing margin or widely separated.

    3

2. Scutellum black; eyes spotted even if indistinctly so.

    Eristalinus
    p. 141

— Scutellum not black; eyes never with a spotted pattern.

    Eristalis
    p. 141

3. Thoracic dorsum with characteristic black central patch partly bisected by pale bars.

    Myathropa
    florea
    p. 299

— Thoracic dorsum without *Myathropa* pattern.

    4

4. Upper outer cross-vein slightly re-entrant. Legs entirely black, hind femur with triangular projection.

    [Merodon
    equestris]
    p. 304

— Upper outer cross-vein directed continuously outwards. Hind femur without triangular projection.

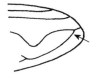

    5

5.   Large hive bee mimic without conspicuous   **Mallota**
     pattern of pale markings.   **cimbiciformis**
                                                                 p. 298

     [In western Europe there are additional species of *Mallota* which are furry bee mimics
     that might not immediately be recognised by British workers as belonging to this
     genus. However they should key through to this point without difficulty because of
     the wing venation. See text.]

—   More wasp-like species, abdomen with pale   6
     markings, thorax often with stripes.

6.   Hind tibia with two dark bands (sometimes faint),   7
     yellow in between.

—   Hind tibia with only one black band, not divided.   8

7.   Antennae black.   **Lejops vittatus**
                                                                 p. 297

—   Antennae reddish-orange, at least in part (sternites   **Anasimyia**
     densely grey-dusted, unlike *Parhelophilus*).   p. 139

8.   Antennae black.   **Helophilus**
                                                                 p. 143

—   Antennae mainly orange (sternites fairly shining,   **Parhelophilus**
     unlike *Anasimyia*).   p. 145

Genus ANASIMYIA

1.   Face strongly produced forwards into a point.   **lineata**
                                                                 p. 286

—   Face less produced and truncate.   2

2.   Tergites 2 and 3 with hook-shaped markings,   3
      occasionally reduced to spots.

—   Tergites 2 and 3 with triangular inwardly pointed   4
      markings, pointing towards centre.

3.   Tergite 2 with side margins angled inwards to   **contracta**
      form slight waist.   p. 284

—   Tergite 2 with almost straight side margins,   **transfuga**
      segment relatively broader.   p. 287

4.   Males (eyes separated, sides of frons parallel-   5
      sided in hind half). (End of abdomen swollen
      beneath by genitalia).

—   Females (eyes separated, sides of frons divergent   6
      throughout).

5.   Tergite 3 with pale markings elbowed on   ♂ **interpuncta**
      posterior edge so that black extends forwards   p. 286
      along lateral margin of tergite. Tergite 4 with
      black occupying over half the length of the
      front edge.

—   Tergite 3 with pale markings straight along   ♂ **lunulata**
      posterior edge so black does not extend   p. 286
      forwards along lateral margin of tergite.
      Tergite 4 with black occupying half the length
      of the front edge.

6. Face profile only bluntly extended. Tergites 3   ♀ **interpuncta**
    and 4 with slightly hooked markings, the grey   p. 286
    markings distinctly oblique on their inward
    portion.

—   Face profile more obviously extended. Tergites 3   ♀ **lunulata**
    and 4 with markings which are straight   p. 286
    (transverse) along their posterior edge.

Genus ERISTALINUS

1. Eyes entirely hairy. Abdomen often with distinct   **sepulchralis**
    dull patches along axis (usually distinct in   p. 288
    males, but can be absent in females).

—   Eyes not hairy below. Abdomen entirely glossy.   **aeneus**
                                                                p. 287

Genus ERISTALIS

There are other European species which could yet be found in Britain. Perhaps one of the most
likely is *E. anthophorinus* which is very similar to *intricarius* and is common in parts of the near
continent. There are also two species very similar to *E. rupium*, which occur in Belgium,
Denmark and the Netherlands which are difficult to identify and might easily be overlooked.
Brief mention is made in the appropriate couplets below, but differences are discussed in more
detail in the species accounts for *intricarius* and *rupium*.

1. Face with black central stripe very wide,   s.g. **Eristalis**
    maximum one third width.   **tenax**
                                                                p. 294

—   Face with central stripe narrower or absent.   s.g. **Eoseristalis**
                                                                   2

2. Front two pairs of legs with tarsi entirely yellow,   **pertinax**
    even on the last two segments.   p. 292

—   Front and mid tarsi partly or entirely dark.   3

3.	Sides of thorax and of femora strongly matt dull greyish dusted. Large size and elongate (as above species).	**similis** p. 293
—	Sides of thorax and of femora at most weakly dusted, semi-shining. Generally smaller and more compact species.	4
4.	Face entirely pale dusted, absolutely no trace of a central black stripe.	**arbustorum** p. 289
—	Face with a black stripe, even if vague (includes rubbed *arbustorum*).	5
5.	Furry species (bumblebee mimic). Sides of thorax below wings with black hairs. [*E. anthophorinus* has pale or dark hair on sides of thorax, but has pale squamae and basal third of arista with very short hairs – see text.]	**intricarius** p. 291
—	Less hairy species. Sides of thorax below wings with pale hairs.	6
6.	Hind tibia entirely orange.	**cryptarum** p. 289
—	Hind tibia at least partly black.	7
7.	Hind metatarsus (basal joint of tarsus) pale. [Two very similar species occur on the near continent, see text.]	**rupium** p. 292
—	Hind metatarsus with black ground colour.	8
8.	Mid tibia entirely yellowish or only obscurely darkened at apex. Arista short haired,	**abusivus** p. 289
—	Mid tibia strongly black at apex. Arista long haired.	9
9.	Stigma reduced to a small spot before tip of Sc.	**interruptus** p. 291
—	Stigma extends to or beyond tip of Sc, even if only as a pale brown extension to a dark spot.	10

10. Hind metatarsus inflated, about as thick as hind   **arbustorum**
     tibia. Face stripe usually poorly developed.   p. 289
     Wing membrane entirely clear apart from
     stigma.

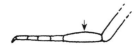

—   Hind metatarsus slender, thinner than hind tibia.   **horticola**
     Face stripe well developed. Wing with slight   p. 290
     darkening across below stigma.

Genus HELOPHILUS

The key includes a European species, *Mesembrius peregrinus*, which although in a different genus is very similar to the common *Helophilus* in general appearance. Although its range is in southern Europe, it has occurred in the nearby continent as a vagrant.

1.   Face entirely yellow (rarely reddish-brown, in   2
     which case check text).

—   Face with a black stripe.   3

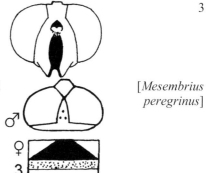

2.   Male eyes meet, female tergite 3 with a grey band   [*Mesembrius
     just beyond middle. Modest size and shape, as   peregrinus*]
     H. pendulus.

—   Eyes separated in both sexes, female tergite 3   **trivittatus**
     without grey dust band. Larger more elongate   p. 297
     shape.

3.   Hind margin of tergites black. Male genital   4
     segments shining black.

—   Hind margin of tergites narrowly yellow (black   5
     area stops short of hind margin). Male genital
     segments heavily grey-dusted.

4. Front tarsus yellow. Dusting on frons stops
    abruptly, well short of ocellar triangle.
    Markings on tergite 2 blunt-ended.

    affinis
    p. 295

—   Front tarsus black. Dusting on frons extends
    distinctly, though weakly, across ocellar
    triangle. Markings on tergite 2 sharp-pointed.

    groenlandicus
    p. 296

5. Males (eyes separated, sides of frons almost
    parallel-sided in hind half). End of abdomen
    swollen beneath by genitalia. Distinct partition
    across middle of frons.

    6

—   Females (eyes separated, sides of frons divergent
    throughout). No partition across middle of
    frons.

    7

6. Hind tibia with distal third black. Tergite 2 with a
    wide black band posteriorly, thus dividing the
    yellow area from that on tergite 3.

    ♂ **pendulus**
    p. 296

—   Hind tibia with distal half or more black. Tergites
    2 and 3 with lateral spots forming continuous
    yellow patch (occasionally with a slender
    partial black band on tergite 2).

    ♂ **hybridus**
    p. 296

7.   Hind tibia with distal third black. Dusting on
     frons stops abruptly, well in front of ocellar
     triangle. Tergite 5 with hairs on axis pale
     (view from side).

♀ **pendulus**
p. 296

—   Hind tibia with distal half or more black. Dusting
     on frons extends either side of ocellar triangle.
     Tergite 5 with hairs on axis black (view from
     side).

♀ **hybridus**
p. 296

Genus PARHELOPHILUS

The key includes *crococoronatus* Reemer, 2000, a recently described species from Portugal and
southern France, potentially of Lusitanian distribution which could therefore occur in south-
western parts of England and Ireland. Female characters are based on only a single specimen
(published illustration adjusted in comparison with British *frutetorum*).

1.   Males (eyes separated, frons narrow behind, sides
     sharply angled in front). (End of abdomen
     swollen beneath by genitalia).

2

—   Females (eyes separated, frons gradually
     widening, sides almost straight throughout).

5

2.   Hind femur with a ventral projection bearing a fan
     of black bristles.

3

—   Hind femur without a distinct ventral projection,
     even if hairs present.

4

3.   Hind femur with ventral projection extending as a
     distinct stalk, apically with a tuft of short black
     bristles of equal length.

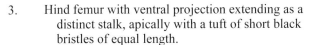

♂ **frutetorum**
p. 300

—   Hind femur with ventral projection very short;
     apical tuft of bristles includes some much
     longer ones that form a 'spine-like' projection.

[*crococoronatus*]

4.   Front tibia mainly yellow at apex as seen from   ♂ **versicolor**
      above. Hind femur postero-ventrally with a   p. 300
      brush of long golden hairs (view from beneath).
      Face less prominent than third antennal
      segment.

—   Front tibia black-tipped as seen from above. Hind   ♂ **consimilis**
      femur without a brush of long hairs postero-   p. 299
      ventrally. Face as prominent as tip of third
      antennal segment.

5.   Front tibia with a strong black patch on the dorsal   ♀ **consimilis**
      surface at the apex (obvious when viewed from   p. 299
      above). Face profile extends well forwards.

—   Front tibia without a dark dorsal patch, but   6
      usually with a ventral or anteroventral dark
      patch (not clearly seen from above). Face not
      so extended forwards.

6.   Hind margin of head with only yellow hairs near   ♀ **versicolor**
      the top corner of the eyes. Tergite 5 with black   p. 300
      hairs at posterior end. Tergite 4 with mainly
      semi-adpressed black hairs in the posterior
      quarter. Hind tarsus with basal segment more
      slender and longer than the remaining four
      segments combined.

—   Hind margin of head with a row of long black   7
      hairs (amidst many yellow ones) near the top
      corner of the eyes. Tergite 5 with all hairs
      yellow. Tergite 4 with erect black hairs in
      posterior quarter (view from side). Hind tarsus
      with basal segment equal in length to the
      remaining four segments combined.

7.   Tergite 3 with three separate pale dust spots.   ♀ **frutetorum**
                                                                     p. 300

      Tergite 3 with the central pair of dust spots   [*crococoronatus*]
      extended to join up with the median apical
      spot.

Tribe MERODONTINI

A group of three genera of very different appearance. All have a flattened shining band on tergite 1, though this is difficult to discern in *Psilota*.

Key to genera

1.   Upper outer cross-vein pointing outwards. Hind femur slender. — **Psilota anthracina** p. 305

—   Upper outer cross-vein mildly or strongly re-entrant. Hind femur swollen. — 2

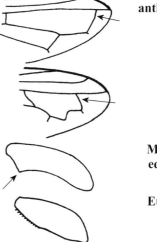

2.   Large furry bee-like species. Hind femur with triangular apical process beneath. — **Merodon equestris** p. 304

—   Small rather bald species. Hind femur without apical process. — **Eumerus** p. 147

Genus EUMERUS

Four species are known in Britain. Separation of the common *Eumerus strigatus* and *funeralis* requires some care and a further European species, *sogdianus*, could well occur. The latter is small and very similar to *funeralis*. There are characteristic processes on the male genitalia which are easily seen if the genitalia are hinged out as illustrated and can be used to confirm identification. The shape of the apical margin of sternite 4 also helps separate *sogdianus*.

surstylus

side   semi-ventral

strigatus   *funeralis*   *sogdianus*

surstylus

hind margin of sternite 4

1.   Abdomen with a reddish tinge.   **sabulonum**
                                                                                 p. 303

—   Abdomen without any reddish tinge visible from   2
      above.

2.   Ocelli well forward of hind margin of eyes. Male   **ornatus**
      genitalia with reddish lobes below.   p. 302

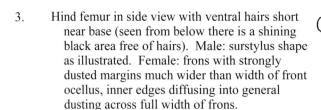

—   Ocelli nearer back of head (length of ocellar   3
      triangle much longer than distance from hind
      margin of eyes).

3.   Hind femur in side view with ventral hairs short   **funeralis**
      near base (seen from below there is a shining   p. 301
      black area free of hairs). Male: surstylus shape
      as illustrated. Female: frons with strongly
      dusted margins much wider than width of front
      ocellus, inner edges diffusing into general
      dusting across full width of frons.

—   Hind femur in side view with ventral hairs long   **strigatus**
      near base as well as near apex (seen from   p. 303
      below, entire ventral surface covered in hairs).
      Male: surstylus shape as illustrated. Female:
      frons with narrowly dusted margins, about
      equal to width of front ocellus, inner edges
      sharp, most of frons shining, dust-free.

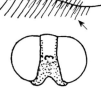

Tribe PELECOCERINI

Small species with a short thick arista which is no longer than the three antennal segments combined.

Key to genera

1. Upper outer cross-vein very oblique and with a rounded elbow bend. Arista dorsal, even if placed near apex.

    Chamaesyrphus p. 149

— Upper outer cross-vein less inclined and with sharp elbow bend. Arista apical. Antennae very characteristic.

    Pelecocera tricincta p. 307

Genus CHAMAESYRPHUS

1. Tergites with yellow spots, not dusted greyish. Long bristle at top of pleura, just in front of wing base (view from above as shown).

    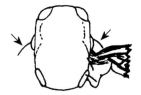

    scaevoides p. 307

— Tergites with yellow spots with greyish sheen or all grey. Pleura without a bristle.

    caledonicus p. 306

Tribe PIPIZINI

Face flat (with no trace of a knob) and completely covered in long drooping hairs. A rather similar genus, *Psilota*, is keyed here although it is currently regarded as a member of the tribe Merodontini.

Key to genera and subgenera

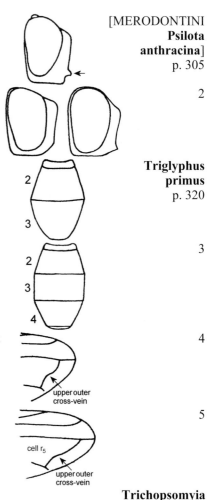

1.   Face in profile with a distinct projecting lip.   [MERODONTINI
     Wing strongly yellowish in front.   **Psilota
                                                              anthracina**]
                                                              p. 305

—   Face in profile without lip, absolutely flat or   2
     slightly advanced at mouth margin.

2.   Abdomen with only two fully developed tergites   **Triglyphus
     (tergites 2 and 3). Tergite 4 is minute or not   primus**
     visible. Rarely the females have a short tergite   p. 320
     4 visible.

—   Abdomen with three fully developed tergites   3
     (tergites 2, 3 and 4 are of equal length).

3.   Upper outer cross-vein with bend near centre, not   4
     steeply inclined in upper half.

—   Upper outer cross-vein with bend in lower third,   5
     steeply inclined in upper half, thus cell r_5 is
     greatly extended towards the wing tip.

4.   Hind tibia with long black hairs on anterior   **Trichopsomyia**
     surface. Female with a pair of orange spots on   p. 157
     tergite 2.

—   Hind tibia with entirely pale hairs on anterior   **Pipizella**
     surface. Female abdomen without spots.   p. 155

5.   Males (eyes meet on top of head).   6

—   Females (eyes separated).   8

6.   Hind leg with trochanter bearing a long   ♂ sg. **Neocnemodon**
      downwardly projecting spine (view from side).   p. 152

—   Hind trochanter without a spine.   7

7.   Head in profile with frons inflated, strongly   ♂ sg. **Heringia**
      curved and antennae inserted well below level   p. 151
      of top of frons.

—   Head in profile with frons fairly flat, top of frons   ♂ **Pipiza**
      not much higher than antennae.   p. 154

8.   Frons with triangular dust spots, sometimes fair^   ♀ **Pipiza**
      Antennae black. (Face projecting above and   p. 154
      usually curved in profile. Wings often with ʑ
      cloud. Abdomen often with spots).

—   Frons without dust spots or with narrow dust   9
      bars. Third antennal segment yellowish
      beneath, even if only obscurely so. (Face flat
      in profile. Wings clear. Abdomen entirely
      black).

9.   Frons with distinct narrow dust bars.   ♀ sg. **Heringia**
                                                                          p. 151

—   Frons entirely shining (at most with minute dust   ♀ sg. **Neocnemodon**
      spots the size of an ocellus).   p. 153

Genus HERINGIA

Subgenus HERINGIA

Subgenus *Heringia* differs from *Neocnemodon* in having the third antennal segment longer than wide (often with some orange at base beneath); the male mid and hind trochanters lack long spurs and the female frons has dust bars.

Key to males (females currently inseparable)

1. Hairs on head, base of abdomen and anterior side of hind tibia predominantly dark brown or black. Third antennal segment scarcely one and a half times as long as wide. Median plate of genitalia with three apical teeth.  ♂ **heringi** p. 308

—   Hairs on head (except frons), abdomen and anterior side of hind tibia white. Third antennal segment twice as long as wide. Median plate of genitalia truncate, without conspicuous apical teeth.  ♂ **senilis** p. 309

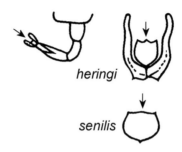

heringi

senilis

Subgenus NEOCNEMODON

The distinctive features of subgenus *Neocnemodon* include a rotund third antennal segment (note some yellow beneath: all black in *Pipiza*); the males have strongly developed spurs on the mid and hind trochanters and the female frons lacks dust spots. The key to males includes *fulvimanus* (Zetterstedt), a species looking like *pubescens* that occurs in neighbouring parts of the continent. See Speight & Smith (1975) for males, but separation of female *fulvimanus* remains uncertain.

Key to males (eyes meet on top of head)

1. Basal segment of front tarsus inflated or with a flap-like projection behind. 2

—   Basal segment of front tarsus slender, not thickened. 3

2. Basal segment of front tarsus with a flap-like projection behind (view from above). 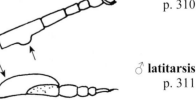 ♂ **brevidens** p. 310

—   Basal segment of front tarsus inflated to twice normal thickness (view from side). ♂ **latitarsis** p. 311

3.   Scutellum and sides of thorax with entirely black   4
       hairs, usually also the top of the thorax.

—   Scutellum and thorax with pale brown or whitish   5
       hairs.

4.   Sternite 3 without a median prominence.   ♂ **pubescens**
                                                                                      p. 311

—   Sternite 3 with a median prominence.   [♂ *fulvimanus*]

5.   Abdomen with hairs almost entirely pale on   ♂ **verrucula**
       tergites 2, 3 and 4.   p. 311

—   Abdomen with black hairs as well as pale ones on   ♂ **vitripennis**
       tergites 2, 3 and 4; tergite 4 covered in black   p. 311
       hairs as seen in side view.

Key to females (eyes separated on top of head)

1.   Hind tibia with virtually all anterior hairs shorter   2
       than width of tibia. Eye hairs dense and
       blackish or very sparse and pale. [M. Second
       basal cell almost entirely covered in
       microtrichia.]

—   Hind tibia with many anterior hairs as long as or   3
       longer than width of the tibia. Eye hairs fairly
       dense, pale. [M. Second basal cell with
       microtrichia absent from three-quarters of area.]

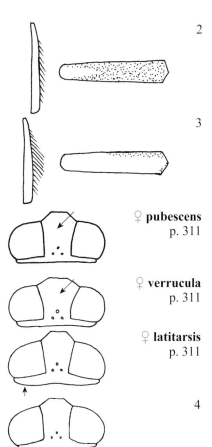

2.   Eye hairs dense, blackish or dark brown. Hairs on   ♀ **pubescens**
       occiput often dark, those below eyes usually   p. 311
       dark. Front of frons little wider than hind part
       (view head from above).

—   Eye hairs very sparse and inconspicuous, pale.   ♀ **verrucula**
       Hairs on occiput and below head entirely pale.   p. 311
       Front of frons much wider than hind part.

3.   Occiput wide; viewed from above, maximum   ♀ **latitarsis**
       width twice width of front tarsus. Frons with   p. 311
       nearly all hairs pale (a few dark hairs confined
       to front and hind margins) – view from side.

—   Occiput relatively narrow; viewed from above,   4
       only about width of front tarsus. Frons with far
       more dark hairs.

4.   Frons with nearly all hairs black, at most a narrow band of pale hairs in front of ocelli (view from side).

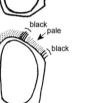

♀ **vitripennis**
p. 311

—   Frons with most hairs pale, the only black hairs in a narrow band in front and about ocelli.

♀ **brevidens**
p. 310

Genus PIPIZA

This is a difficult genus and entails uncertainties over the definition of some species. The key is still at the experimental stage; it should work on most specimens, but there will be a percentage which do not easily fit. Read the text to species and note that there is a discussion on forms of *noctiluca*. Vouchers should be retained, especially where the key does not work satisfactorily.

1.   Front and mid tarsi yellow (on at least all 4 distal segments), may be darker in female, but then all hairs on abdomen are pale.

luteitarsis
p. 315

—   Front and mid tarsi with at least some segments (including the most distal segment) dark. Female abdomen with some dark hairs.

2

2.   Hind femur very thickened distally (as a result of thickened ridges below, view from side).

austriaca
p. 313

—   Hind femur club-shaped.

3

3.   Males (eyes meet on top of head).

4

—   Females (eyes separated on top of head).

7

4.   Tergite 2 with lateral hairs entirely black (face hairs usually black).

5

—   Tergite 2 with lateral hairs pale on anterior half (face hairs always pale).

6

5.   Tarsi partly yellow. Slight darkening about veins across centre of wing.

♂ **noctiluca**
p. 315

—   Tarsi dark. Wings entirely clear apart from stigma.

♂ **bimaculata**
p. 313

6. Wing with very dark cloud strongly developed,   ♂ **lugubris**
    with sharp outer boundary. Tergite 1 with   p. 314
    lateral hairs pale.

—   Wing with less strong cloud, with diffuse outer   ♂ **fenestrata**
    boundary. Tergite 1 with lateral hairs black.   p. 314

7. Wing with very dark cloud strongly developed   ♀ **lugubris**
    and with sharp outer boundary. Tergites 4 and   p. 314
    5 entirely pale haired or, in some specimens,
    with black hairs extensive on top.

—   Wing with cloud less strong and with diffuse   8
    outer boundary or cloud absent. Tergites 4 and
    5 with some distinct zones of dark hairs (view
    from the side).

8. Tergite 4 on median axis (view from side) with   ♀ **fenestrata**
    very narrow zone of black hairs at front, rest   p. 314
    with yellowish hairs. Tergite 5 with black
    hairs (sketch shows distribution of black hairs
    only).

—   Tergite 4 with broader zone of black hairs and   9
    rest of hairs white, Tergite 5 with black hairs
    posteriorly. Alternatively all hairs are black or
    intermediate forms.

9. Scutellum with hairs on dorsal surface much   ♀ **noctiluca**
    longer than maximum width of front tibia   p. 315
    (view from side). Tarsi partly pale. Wings
    often with a slight cloud. [M. Second basal cell
    with basal ⅔ clear of microtrichia.]

—   Scutellum with hairs on dorsal surface as long as   ♀ **bimaculata**
    or shorter than maximum width of front tibia.   p. 313
    All tarsi dark. Wings clear. [M. Second basal
    cell entirely or almost entirely covered in
    microtrichia.]

Genus PIPIZELLA

1. Males (eyes meet on top of head).   2

—   Females (eyes separated).   4

2. Third antennal segment about twice as long as
   wide (view on outer side). Arista almost
   completely black. Genitalia elongate with a
   long 'neck' (view from below). Surstylus
   tear-drop-shaped in side view.

♂ **viduata**
p. 319

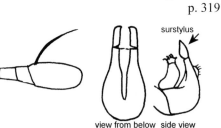

surstylus

view from below   side view

— Third antennal segment longer, arista yellow
   in thickened basal half. Genitalia compact.

3

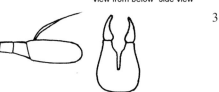

3. Body very black. Pale body hairs white. Eye
   hairs dark on upper half. Surstylus abruptly
   narrowing to a thick apical 'finger'.

♂ **maculipennis**
p. 318

— Body with slightly bronzy hue. Pale body
   hairs yellowish. Eye hairs entirely pale.
   Surstylus bulbous at base, tapering to a
   slender apical 'finger'.

♂ **virens**
p. 319

4. Third antennal segment twice as long as wide
   (view on outer side), arista dusky yellow at
   base. Anterior surface of hind tibia with
   hairs at most as long as width of tibia.
   Abdomen compact.

♀ **viduata**
p. 319

— Third antennal segment longer, arista clear
   yellow at base. Anterior surface of hind
   tibia with hairs much longer than width of
   tibia. Abdomen more elongate.

5

5. Third antennal segment at least 3 times as
    long as wide (view on outer side). Tergite 3
    usually with black hairs on axis (view from
    side; not easy to see).

    ♀ **maculipennis**
    p. 318

—   Third antennal segment a little shorter.
    Tergite 3 with pale hairs on axis.
    (Sometimes with black hairs in the apical
    fifth.)

    ♀ **virens**
    p. 319

Genus TRICHOPSOMYIA

Although only one species has been found in Britain and Ireland, there are now three species
known in Europe, including *lucida* which occurs as close as the Netherlands.

1. Wing relatively short, brownish clouded. Male
    thorax hairs entirely black. Female body
    surface relatively dull; tergite 2 with a pair of
    round reddish spots.

    flavitarsis
    p. 320

—   Wing long and narrow, hyaline. Male thorax
    hairs mixed black and white. Female body
    surface brightly shining; tergite 2 with a pair of
    square yellow spots.

    [*lucida*]

Tribe SERICOMYIINI

Key to genera

1. Hairy bumblebee mimic.

    **Arctophila
    superbiens**
    p. 321

—   Wasp mimics: abdomen black with yellow or
    white bars.

    Sericomyia
    p. 157

Genus SERICOMYIA

1. Tergites 2 to 4 with yellow bars strongly
    widening towards margin. Scutellum black, at
    least at anterior corners.

    silentis
    p. 322

—   Tergites 2 to 4 with white bars, only slightly
    widening towards margin. Scutellum entirely
    reddish.

    lappona
    p. 321

Tribe VOLUCELLINI
Genus VOLUCELLA

1.	Body very hairy, bumblebee mimic.	**bombylans** p. 323
—	Not a bumblebee mimic.	2
2.	Abdomen black with contrasting white or orange on tergite 2.	3
—	Abdomen with yellow and black bands.	4
3.	Spots on tergite 2 white or faintly yellowish. Scutellum with black hairs on top.	**pellucens** p. 324
—	Spots on tergite 2 strongly orange. Scutellum with pale hairs on top.	**inflata** p. 324
4.	Tergite 2 with markings dull chestnut-brown rather than yellow as on tergites 3 and 4. Sternite 2 black.	**zonaria** p. 324
—	Tergite 2 with bright clear yellow markings as on tergites 3 and 4. Sternite 2 yellow.	**inanis** p. 323

Tribe XYLOTINI

A very varied group, but containing some very distinctive genera. The text explains that the structure of the generic key relates to possible divisions within the tribe, which here includes the Milesiini of some authorities.

Key to genera

1.	Ground colour of face yellow.	2
—	Ground colour of face dark (though may be pale or yellow dusted).	3

2.	Large species with greenish abdomen and orange legs.	**Caliprobola speciosa** p. 327
—	Black species with end of abdomen red.	**Blera fallax** p. 325
3.	Face elongate below, with slight but distinct knob.	**Criorhina** p. 160
—	Face more compact, concave and without knob.	4
4.	Pleura densely dusted grey.	5
—	Pleura not like this.	6
5.	Hind femur strongly arched and with a triangular projection below. Sides of abdomen partly red.	**Tropidia** p. 160
—	Hind femur swollen in a compact manner, with small spines beneath apically. Small narrow fly.	**Syritta pipiens** p. 332
6.	Thoracic dorsum with distinct grey stripes and strong bristles along lateral margins.	[CHEILOSIINI **Ferdinandea**] p. 127
—	Thoracic dorsum otherwise.	7
7.	Hairy bumblebee mimic (with small head and slender hind femur).	**Pocota personata** p. 331
—	Not a good bumblebee mimic.	8
8.	Hive bee mimic. (Thorax with long hairs, but abdomen relatively bald. Tergite 1 densely dusted. Narrow brown shade across wing below stigma).	9
—	Not a hive bee mimic. (Thorax only short haired. Tergite 1 mostly shining. Wings clear).	**'Xylota'** p. 161

9. Metasternum hairy (between mid and hind coxae on the ventral centre line of the thorax). Male hind femur not arched.

Chalcosyrphus (Xylotodes) eunotus
p. 328

— Metasternum bald (hairs on coxae can cause confusion). Male hind femur strongly arched.

Brachypalpus laphriformis
p. 326

Genus CRIORHINA

1. Thoracic dorsum with entirely blackish hairs. Hind femur strongly swollen and arched.

ranunculi
p. 331

— Thoracic dorsum with pale hairs in front half or throughout. Hind femur slender.

2

2. Narrow-bodied species with grey or yellowish dusted bars on tergites 2 to 4. Hive bee mimic.

asilica
p. 329

— Broad-bodied bumblebee mimics without bar-shaped markings on the tergites.

3

3. Tergite 2 with distinct side tufts of long hairs; tergite 3 with hairs on axis (view from side) shorter than maximum width of hind tibia.

floccosa
p. 330

— Tergite 2 with side tufts not obvious since rest of abdomen very hairy; tergite 3 with hairs on axis (view from side) longer than maximum width of hind tibia.

berberina
p. 330

Genus TROPIDIA

The key includes *fasciata*, a species that occurs on the other side of the English Channel. It has been found by fen-edge pools in deciduous forest. For fuller details see Speight, 1988.

1. Hind femur with ventral surface having only short black bristles. Antennae black.

scita
p. 332

— Hind femur with ventral surface covered in pale hairs up to a third as long as the width of the femur. A larger species, often with orange antennae.

[*fasciata*]

Genus XYLOTA

The genus contains rather parallel-sided flies of distinctive appearance. There are three basic body patterns. *Brachypalpoides lentus* and *Chalcosyrphus* (*Xylotina*) *nemorum* are so like *Xylota* that it is easiest to treat them in the same key.

Key to Xylota and similar species.

1.	Abdomen with segments 2 and 3 entirely, or mostly, red or orange.	2
—	Abdomen with a different colour pattern.	4
2.	Legs entirely black. Tergites 2 and 3 blood-red in live specimen.	**Brachypalpoides lentus** p. 326
—	Legs partly pale.	3
3.	Reddish band on abdomen uniformly coloured except that a slight axial line may be present; abdomen parallel-sided. Male with long spurs on hind trochanter (view obliquely from below). Hind femur with two distinct rows of black spines below in apical third. [*ignava* has a similar continuous red band, but has the base of the hind tibia orange – see text.]	**Xylota segnis** p. 335
—	Reddish band on abdomen interrupted by faint dark fringe along hind edge of tergite 2; abdomen less parallel-sided, bulging towards hind end. Male with only a small projection on hind trochanter. Hind femur with random scatter of tiny black spines below in middle third.	**Xylota tarda** p. 336
4.	Tergite 4 partly or completely clothed in adpressed golden hairs.	5
—	Tergite 4 without such hairs, tergites 2 and 3 with spots.	6
5.	Hind tibia with distal half black (view from various angles until light is right).	**Xylota sylvarum** p. 336
—	Hind tibia entirely yellow from all points of view.	**Xylota xanthocnema** p. 336
6.	Hind tibia with basal third clear pale yellow.	7
—	Hind tibia with at most basal fifth pale.	10

The pair of anterior spiracles are widely separated near the front of the puparium, only piercing through the larval skin during pupation to become the active breathing tubes. The hind spiracles form a fused projection at the hind end, these being functional during the larval stage (when the skin is soft and flexible). Larvae and puparia look very similar, but the puparium can be recognised by the hardened skin and the projecting anterior spiracles. The puparium stage lasts only a few weeks at the most, so adults do not take long to emerge as rather feeble pallid flies; it can take some hours to expand the wings and harden up properly in the fresh air.

| 1. | Dorsal surface smooth, bald, reticular pattern confined to sides. | posterior spiracle | 2 |

| — | Dorsal surface entirely covered in reticular pattern of ridges. | | 3 |

| 2. | Anterior spiracle of puparium longer than width at base (take care with empty puparia that the spiracle is not partially depressed). Larva and puparium with very weakly defined reticulations at sides. [*Myrmica scabrinodis* nests in tussocks above saturated surroundings.] | | **myrmicae** p. 341 |

| — | Anterior spiracle of puparium shorter than width at base. Larva and puparium with strongly defined reticulations at sides. [*Formica lemani* nests under stones on dry ground.] | | **mutabilis** p. 340 |

| 3. | Very large reticulations. Ventral surface covered in fine hairs. [*Lasius flavus* nests, especially partially shaded.] | | **devius** p. 339 |

| — | Dense, tiny reticulations. Ventral surface bald, at least in *analis*. | | 4 |

4.   Anterior spiracle of puparium longer, twice as   **analis**
       long as width at base (take care with empty   p. 338
       puparia that the spiracle is not partially
       depressed). [*Lasius niger* nests, usually in
       stumps or lying dead wood on dry sites.]

—   Anterior spiracle of puparium short, only as long   [*miki*]
       as width at base. [No host information.]

CHAPTER 8

SUBFAMILY SYRPHINAE

One third of the British hoverfly fauna belong here. The subfamily is distinct in that the anterior humeri are bare. However, such a character is not easily seen since the head is deeply concave behind in the Syrphinae, thus sitting over the front of the thorax and masking the humeri. In a fresh specimen the head may be gently moved sideways to display the humeri, but only at the risk of the head falling off or becoming so weakly attached that it will easily fall off later. It is, however, convenient to note that the Milesiinae have the hind surface of the head only shallowly concave, flat or convex so that the hairy humeri are clearly visible. Thus as a general rule, if the head comes back over the humeri, the specimen is almost certainly a member of the Syrphinae.

In practice, most members of the Syrphinae look very different from members of other subfamilies so that reference to the plates will enable most specimens to be allocated to this subfamily with some confidence. The main difficulty will lie among specimens with an entirely black abdomen and here the key to black Syrphinae (p. 64) should readily sort out any uncertainties. It will be noticed in particular that the face has a knob and lacks a distinct eye-margin zone.

The Syrphinae are biologically distinct from most Milesiinae in that the larvae are predators, usually of aphids. Such aphids may be on the foliage of trees and shrubs, or on herbage or even underground on roots. Larvae of some species feed on prey other than aphids, entirely so in a few cases, and there are known instances of specialisation on particular kinds of prey. *Xanthandrus* seems to specialise on semi-gregarious micro-moth caterpillars, and *Parasyrphus nigritarsis* attacks the eggs and larvae of certain chrysomelid beetles. Other species may well feed on different categories of insect prey. The only other hoverfly group with aphid-feeding larvae is the tribe Pipizini which specialises on wax-secreting aphids which are largely avoided by the Syrphinae.

Tribe BACCHINI

The presence of a black scutellum distinguishes this tribe from the Syrphini (whose scutellum is yellow). Though a few exceptions in the Syrphini have a black scutellum, confusion is only likely to arise where melanic (black) female Bacchini resemble female *Melangyna quadrimaculata*.

Some authorities restrict the tribe Bacchini to the genus *Baccha* and place the remaining genera in a separate tribe, the Melanostomini.

Genus BACCHA

These very slender, long-waisted hoverflies are quite unmistakable. They are, however, easily overlooked because of their frequent habit of hovering low down among vegetation or, even if above vegetation, they are inconspicuous in dappled shade.

Baccha elongata (Fabricius, 1775)   Pl. 1, fig. 1
Baccha obscuripennis Meigen, 1822   Map: Ball & Morris p. 18
                                                                                              Larva: Rotheray Pl. 5d

This species formerly comprised *B. elongata* and *B. obscuripennis* that were separated on the
variation in dusting on the male frons and in some apparent differences in the male genitalia.
However, there have been persistent doubts about the validity of these differences and recent
revisions have synonymised the two under the name *B. elongata*. Wing length 4.5–8 mm.

This is a common hoverfly throughout Britain and Ireland. It should be found in most districts
by careful observation of sunny herbage along hedgerows or woodland margins, ride edges or in
shaded spots under trees where it will often be found in dappled light. Nettle beds in sheltered,
humid parts of woodland are particularly favoured by females and sweeping such areas will often
produce specimens. Occasionally it will be seen hovering among low branches of bushes or trees
and sometimes at flowers. The larvae are known to be predaceous upon a variety of ground-layer
aphids. April to November, peaking twice, in May and September.

Genus MELANOSTOMA

Members of this genus superficially resemble those of *Platycheirus*. However, the males have
cylindrical front legs without a specialised development of hairs, and the female front tarsus is
cylindrical rather than flattened. As alluded to in the key (p. 66), the females often have an
unusual pattern of triangular spots which are typically elongate with the outer posterior corners
obliquely truncated (*Platycheirus peltatus* and *P. podagratus* can have somewhat similar spots,
but these species are normally larger and the spots are not elongate). Female specimens with an
entirely black abdomen are frequent, but *Melanostoma* has the metasternum restricted to a
narrow plate on the mid-line (the underside of the thorax is mainly membranous between the mid
and hind coxae) whereas in *Platycheirus* the metasternum is winged laterally so that there is no
membranous area on either side. Andersson (1970a) illustrates differences between species in
the pre-genital segments of females. The genus was revised by Speight (1978d).

Verrall (1901) recognised three species (plus *ambiguus* which is now placed in *Platycheirus*).
His *dubium* Zetterstedt was wrongly interpreted by Coe (1953a), who did not consider that
Verrall's *dubium* was that of Zetterstedt but treated it as a variety of *mellinum*. However, Speight
(1978d) revised the genus, recognising that Verrall's description of *dubium* Zetterstedt was
correct, thus restoring the species to the British list. Speight left the reader to assume that Coe's
mellinum var. was the same as true *mellinum*. There remain considerable problems since some
specimens are neither clearly *dubium* nor *mellinum*, the dilemma of Coe. There is no option
other than to define a taxon which is here referred to as *Melanostoma* form A, this taxon covering
a range of variation that runs to *dubium* and *mellinum* in Speight's key. This form is close to
dubium, but its inclusion in that species would extend the definition beyond that previously
accepted. MacGowan *et al.* (1997) have again questioned whether *dubium* is a real species or
just the extreme end of clinal variation with altitude (in which "form A" may represent an
intermediate). See discussion under *dubium*.

Despite the abundance and wide distribution of adults, the larval stages are rarely found at aphid
colonies in natural situations. Rotheray (1993) suggested that they may be generalised predators
amongst leaf litter.

This genus is undergoing revision in Europe, but there are as yet no details of the reported new species (although it is said that segregates of both *mellinum* and *scalare* occur in Britain and Ireland). At this stage it is not possible to advise further, so specimens should be retained until new keys become available.

Melanostoma dubium (Zetterstedt, 1838)
M. dubium of Verrall (1901) and Speight   Map: Ball & Morris p. 89
(1988d), not Coe (1953a)

As outlined in the introductory remarks on the genus, the character and limits of this species have caused much confusion in the past and the majority of previous records must be discounted. Through the definition of a separate taxon, *Melanostoma* form A, it is hoped that a step has been made towards solving some of the problems, but the scarcity of material makes the definition of the species somewhat uncertain.

M. dubium is a small dark species. The male has a parallel-sided abdomen, with the markings yellowish or greyish, often rather vague or heavily dusted, and tergite 2 can be entirely black. The frons angle is well over 90°, and the frons and face obviously dusted. The abdomen is covered in pale hairs, even along the mid-line (as seen in side view), although a few black hairs may be present on the hind margin of tergite 4. Both sexes have entirely black antennae (or at most some yellow on the short third segment in the female). The female frons has broad dust spots extending well towards the centre, with diffuse dusting in the front third (*scalare* nearly always has the antennae partly yellow and its sternites have large paired yellow markings; sternites normally black in *dubium*). The female abdomen often seems shorter than in the other two species, and the legs in both sexes are typically almost entirely black apart from the tips of the femora and the bases of the tibiae. Comparative comments are made under *Melanostoma* form A which is considered after *scalare*. Wing length 5 mm.

MacGowan *et al.* (1997) examined material of *M. mellinum*, form A and *dubium* taken at different altitudes in Scotland and concluded that *dubium* is no more than the extreme end of an altitudinal cline in *mellinum* with "form A" representing an intermediate stage. These conclusions have not, so far, been accepted by other workers.

From what little is known of this species, it characteristically occurs on mountains between 500 and 1,000 m, especially on boggy ground near small streams. Thus small dark-legged *Melanostoma* are well worth checking when found in such situations. A specimen has also been taken on lower ground near a lake, but whether it was a stray or a resident in this habitat is unknown. Most records are from the Scottish Highlands, but it is also recorded from upland areas in north-west and south-west England, and North Wales. It is probable that a wide distribution in upland districts will become recognised. It has not been recorded from Ireland. June to August, peaking in June.

Melanostoma mellinum (Linnaeus, 1758)   Pl. 1, fig. 3
                                                          Map: Ball & Morris p. 89

The male is not unlike *Platycheirus clypeatus* (both often have the abdomen widening posteriorly) except that the spots on tergites 3 and 4 are broadly rounded at their hind outer corners and there is a substantial black margin laterally. Normally at least the basal antennal segments are entirely or partly darkened in both sexes. The female is readily distinguished from other *Melanostoma* and most *Platycheirus* since the frons is almost entirely shining black, with only a trace of dust spots (at greatest development there remains a gap of two-thirds the width of the frons). The sternites in the female are black or uniformly murky yellowish, although occasionally the sternites are yellow with a dusky median stripe (as can occur in *scalare*). This species is especially prone to producing melanic females (the frons provides a good lead to identification), although normally the abdomen has well developed spots of the typical *Melanostoma* triangular shape in this sex. However, there is considerable variation, including a form lacking spots on tergite 2. In upland districts some specimens closely resemble *dubium*. Wing length 4.75–7 mm.

This is one of the commonest hoverflies throughout Britain and Ireland. It is often abundant in grasslands, and extends up onto moorland and mountainsides. April to October, with two peaks, in late May to early June and again in July to August.

Melanostoma scalare (Fabricius, 1794)   Pl. 1, fig. 2
                                                                  Map: Ball & Morris p. 90

The elongate narrow body of the male is rather similar to that of *Platycheirus angustatus* but the front legs are cylindrical and the antennae extensively yellow, whereas in *P. angustatus* the front tibia and tarsus are broadened and the antennae are black. The female abdomen is not unduly elongate but the triangular spots indicate *Melanostoma*. The female frons has well developed and sharply defined triangular dust spots. A character separating *scalare* from most specimens of *mellinum* is the presence of well developed paired elongate orange spots on sternites 3 and 4. The female antennae are usually extensively yellow, including the basal segments, thus normally being paler than in typical *mellinum*. Wing length 5.5–8 mm.

M. scalare is another widespread species throughout Britain and Ireland. It is often common, preferring lush herbage in and beside scrub or woodland, but normally not extending onto moorland or mountainsides. April to November, with two peaks, in late May to early June and again in August.

Melanostoma form A   Map: Ball & Morris p. 90

The characters of this form are a confusing mixture of those found in other species, although superficially form A would be passed over as *mellinum*. The relevance of recognising this form arises in particular from the distinctive features of the female. It is the only taxon in which the thorax and scutellum are of a brassy greenish black, strongly contrasting with the black areas on the abdomen. The face is wide and often dusted, except for the knob (as in *dubium*). The female frons has well developed dust spots (unlike *mellinum*), either sharply defined (rather like *scalare*) or extended as a blurred area of dusting in front of and to the side of the antennae (as in *dubium*). The thickened arista in the male suggests a close affinity with *dubium*. MacGowan *et al.* (1997) suggest that "form A" may represent the intermediate condition in a clinal variation of *mellinum* with altitude, in which *dubium* represents the high-altitude extreme. See discussion under *dubium*.

In the female the tergites have spots, sometimes strongly reduced (unlike *dubium*), the reduced spots being rounded (rather as in *Platycheirus podagratus* but this has the front legs entirely yellow, unlike form A). The colour of the legs ranges from the dark condition of *dubium* to the paler tarsi and tibiae of *mellinum*, but the femora are black to varying degrees except at the apex. The male abdomen is parallel-sided (as in *dubium*, not *mellinum*). The frons angle is wide (as in *dubium*) and the frons and face are often dusted (as in *dubium*, not *mellinum*). Speight (1978d) used the presence of almost entirely pale hairs on the tergites as a key character for male *dubium*; form A can also be like this or transitional to the black-haired nature of *mellinum*. The sternites are black. The antennae in both sexes are black with segment 3 about one and a half times as long as segments 1 and 2 together. Separation of the male from *dubium* is not precise at present, but the relative length of the antennal segments seems the best character. Wing length 5 mm.

The above description is based on a series taken in the Cairngorms, collected along Glen Einich near and above the tree line. Most of the females were form A, but the males were a mixed series with *mellinum*. The Natural History Museum contains a few further specimens from the Scottish Highlands and there is one record from Lancashire. May to July, peaking in July.

Genus PLATYCHEIRUS

This is the largest genus within the subfamily Syrphinae (the only larger hoverfly genus is *Cheilosia*). As such there are a number of rather similar-looking species, but on the whole there are good characters for distinguishing the various species without too much difficulty.

There are three subgenera. Subgenus *Platycheirus* contains 22 species, *Pachysphyria* has one, and *Pyrophaena*, which was formerly treated as a separate genus, has two. With the exception of *P. rosarum*, all members of these subgenera have modified front legs in the male, with the tibia and/or the tarsus expanded and flattened in most species, and often ornamented with hair patterns (see Plate R). The middle pair of legs is also modified in some species.

This genus has a range of larval-feeding strategies, from generalised predators to specialists on just one or two aphid species.

Subgenus PACHYSPHYRIA

Because the front legs in the male are cylindrical, Coe (1953a) placed *ambiguus* within *Melanostoma*. However, the male front femur has long hairs along the posterior surface plus a curious curled hair near the apex, indicating a closer relationship to *Platycheirus* than to *Melanostoma*. There are related species in Scandinavia (Nielsen, 1974).

Platycheirus (Pachysphyria) ambiguus (Fallén, 1817)   Pl. R, fig. 16; Pl. 1, fig. 7
Melanostoma ambiguum of Coe (1953a)   Map: Ball & Morris p. 113

The general appearance resembles a somewhat small *P. albimanus* in that the abdomen has greyish markings, and is closely similar to *discimanus* and *sticticus* as regards size and the rather simple front legs in the male. The male has spots which change colour from dull bronze to grey according to angle of view, as in *albimanus*, but the curled hair on the femur is distinctive enough. The Scandinavian species *lundbecki* also has this hair (see notes under subgenus *Platycheirus* below). The females tend to be particularly small and the abdomen often appears to be black, with the faint grey markings only apparent from some viewpoints. Thus special care is necessary in identifying females since the complete grey band on tergites 3 and 4 is only visible with difficulty in some specimens (view obliquely from in front or behind). The beginner is well advised to rely on males to start with. The female frons has small but distinct dust spots (absent in *discimanus*) and tergite 3 is transverse (unlike *sticticus*) whilst *albimanus* always has a pair of grey spots on tergites 3 and 4. Wing length 4.5–7 mm.

P. ambiguus is very local but widespread, including Ireland. The best way of finding it is to visit large clumps of blackthorn in full blossom (usually the second half of April in the south), but beware of *Cheilosia urbana* which occurs in similar situations. If conditions are calm and sunny, the males will be seen hovering close to the bushes (easy to net) and both sexes at flowers (less easy to catch). In some localities this hoverfly is common in most years, especially where the blackthorn is at the sunny sheltered margin of a wood. It is less frequently found in other circumstances. April to September, peaking in May, with most late records referring to females.

Subgenus PLATYCHEIRUS

The first edition included 15 species in the subgenus *Platycheirus*. This edition includes 22 species within the original definition of the subgenus, and more additions may yet be made. Thus some explanation will be helpful.

For much of the 20th century the composition of the British fauna seemed well known and stable. There were a few more European species, but these were not thought to be relevant to the British fauna, although some revisionary work in Scandinavia in the 1970s should have been a warning. Since 1983, the situation has changed dramatically.

— In 1988, *amplus*, an ally of *peltatus*, was added to the Irish list (Speight & Vockeroth, 1988) and shortly afterwards Scottish specimens were recognised.

— Rumours that '*clypeatus*' was a species complex presaged the jolt in 1990 when three extra species were reported in Britain: *europaeus*, *occultus* and *ramsarensis*, all of them new to science (Goeldlin de Tiefenau, Maibach & Speight, 1990; Speight & Goeldlin de Tiefenau, 1990; Speight, 1990b).

— In the same year Vockeroth (1990) split *peltatus* through the description of *nielseni* ('Species A' of the 1986 supplement). Vockeroth's review of the North American and northern European fauna revealed that quite a number of species occurred on both sides of the Atlantic, with American species such as *amplus* being added to the fauna of north-western Europe. Thus there are now plenty more species to look out for, although some are apparently restricted to the boreal zone of northern Scandinavia.

— Still the splits continue, with *scutatus* being revealed as a complex including *splendidus* (Rotheray, 1998) and *aurolateralis* (Stubbs, 2002) discovered in Britain.

In the short time available for revising this book, it has not been practical to work out a key incorporating all the potential British species (as yet there is not even a key to the European species). However, it seems as well to offer some pointers, and to suggest that northern Britain offers good opportunities to discover additions to the British list. Only *jaerensis* and *parmatus* have been included in the key since these allies of *peltatus* are among the more likely extra species to occur here.

— *P. lundbecki* (Collin, 1931c) (ex *fjellbergi*), a species of northern Scandinavia, is very similar to *ambiguus*. The males share the characteristic curly hair at the apex of the front femur. In both sexes the third antennal segment is only a little longer than wide (significantly longer in *ambiguus*). The flight period is in late June to July so late records of *ambiguus* are worth checking. *P. hirtipes* (Kanervo, 1938) is in the same group, but the male lacks the curly hair.

— In *sticticus* and *discimanus* the front tibia is cylindrical or only very slightly widening towards the apex and the front tarsus is narrow or expanded. Whilst these two British species are very different, in Europe, especially in the north, there are a number of extra species with a range of differences in the combination and degree of expansion of front tibia and tarsus. Many have a grey-spotted abdomen.

— Two species close to *peltatus* (third antennal segment partly yellow, front femur with brush of black hairs along entire length) are amongst the more likely candidates:

    o   *jaerensis* Nielsen, 1971. Rather a large species resembling *peltatus*. The front tarsus has the basal segment much narrower than *peltatus*. Females have only ill-defined dust spots on the frons and the basal antennal segments are yellow. A species occurring in coastal lowland southern Norway in meadows with dandelions and buttercups close to woods.

    o   *parmatus* Rondani, 1857 (ex *ovalis* Becker) Resembles *jaerensis*. Male front tarsus with a broad basal segment as in *peltatus*, but the second segment is much broader than the third (*peltatus* with second segment almost as narrow as third). The female hind tibia is almost completely black. This species has been spreading its range in recent decades and occurs in the Netherlands and Belgium, so it could even turn up in southern Britain.

All the species of this subgenus have a narrow abdomen, rather parallel-sided in the male, with paired spots ranging from grey to orange. The only genus with a black scutellum likely to cause initial confusion is *Melanostoma* (already discussed); also perhaps *Chamaesyrphus* (or even the related *Pelecocera*), but the projecting lower half of the face and large third antennal segment with a thickened arista is quite unlike a *Platycheirus*. A few Syrphinae, notably some members of the genera *Melangyna* and *Meligramma*, look rather similar but have a yellow scutellum.

With 22 species in the subgenus, it is helpful to recognise the following species groups:

(a) *clypeatus* Group.

Hind legs with a fair amount of yellow, broadly so at apex of tibia and ringed with yellow at base of hind femur. Abdominal markings orange. Male front tibia gradually expanding towards apex or abruptly expanded near base. (*angustatus*, *clypeatus*, *europaeus*, *fulviventris*, *immarginatus*, *occultus*, *perpallidus*, *ramsarensis*, *scambus*).

All other groups have mainly black legs, knees usually only narrowly pale and femora only rarely yellow at extreme base in the female.

(b) *discimanus* Group

Abdominal markings grey and male front tarsus cylindrical, the female frons mainly without dusting. (*discimanus*, *sticticus*).

(c) *manicatus* Group

Abdominal markings orange. Male front tibia cylindrical, basal segments of tarsi abruptly broadened. Base of femora always black. (*manicatus*, *melanopsis* and *tarsalis*).

(d) *albimanus* Group

Markings grey, yellow or orange. Third antennal segment pale at base beneath. Male front tibia abruptly and broadly expanded near apex. Female sometimes with base of femora narrowly black or if entirely black, abdominal spots are grey (and face dusted) or spots are very rounded. (*albimanus*, *amplus*, *aurolateralis*, *nielseni*, *peltatus*, *podagratus*, *scutatus*, *splendidus*).

It is possible that further species occur in Britain, a matter deserving careful examination of British material.

Platycheirus (Platycheirus) albimanus (Fabricius, 1781)   Pl. R, fig. 6; Pl. 1, fig. 6
Platycheirus cyaneus (Walker, 1851)   Map: Ball & Morris p. 112

The most robust of the grey species, it is readily distinguished in the male since the front tibia abruptly expands near the apex. In the male, the spots on the tergites are usually dull bronze, changing to grey at some angles of view, or occasionally the spots are dull yellowish (but not clear yellow as in s*cutatus*). The front femur has a tuft of long crinkled hairs near the base on the posterior surface, as in *scutatus* (spots clear yellow in that species and the proportions of the tarsal segments are different). The female always has grey spots on the tergites and the face is faintly but distinctly dusted except for the knob (face extensively dust-free and shining in *discimanus* and *sticticus*; face dusted in *ambiguus*, but grey bands are present on tergites 3 and 4). Wing length 5–8 mm.

This is one of the most familiar hoverflies throughout Britain and Ireland. It likes woodland margins, hedgerows and gardens in particular and is especially conspicuous in May among the spring hoverflies. It is multi-brooded, with three broods even above 300 m in Wales. The larval stages are predaceous upon aphids on low-growing plants and bushes, and have also been found on fir, apple, and common reed. March to November, peaking twice, in May to early June, and again in July to August.

Platycheirus (Platycheirus) amplus Curran, 1927   Map: Ball & Morris p. 113

Rather small narrow specimens of the *peltatus*/*nielseni* type should be carefully checked for this recent addition to the British list. As in these species, the third antennal segment is yellowish beneath and the front femur has a posterior brush of black hairs for the entire length, although not so dense. Also, the males have a similar front tarsus, with a large basal segment which is very obliquely truncate at the apex, and with the following segments much narrower. The reliable way of recognising the males is to examine the middle tibia; in side view it is slender, with a ventral flag of black hairs situated close to the base, and in dorsal view the posterior surface has a fringe of long hairs which droop down towards the apex of the tibia. The female has been described (Steenis & Goeldlin de Tiefenau, 1998), but separation from other species was based on the shape of the markings on tergite 2 (small semicircular spots whose posterior margins are transverse rather than oblique, thus resembling *scutatus*) which may not be satisfactory (especially since *scutatus* has now been split and the females of the new species are not yet known). Hence, the key in this book focuses upon the front part of the frons (illustrated in the above paper) which would seem to have very broad dusting at the sides; all comparable British allies have only narrow dusting in this position. Wing length 7 mm.

Originally *amplus* was described as a North American species, but in 1988 its occurrence in several European countries was reported (Speight & Vockeroth, 1988). The records included a male which had been swept in a fen meadow on 21 June 1978 at Pollards Fen in County Kildare (eastern Ireland); since the capture, the site has been drained, burnt and then re-flooded. It remains a very little known species in Britain, but it has been found at several localities in the Scottish Highlands and also on the North York Moors (Grayson, 2002). Thus it could prove widespread in northern and western Britain, but its habitat would seem quite restricted. Records are confined to poor fen, including wet meadows and moorland flushes of comparable character. Adults have been observed to fly low down among sedges and other tall vegetation in the vicinity of water. June.

Platycheirus (Platycheirus) angustatus (Zetterstedt, 1843) Pl. R, fig. 9; Pl. 1, fig. 17
Map: Ball & Morris p. 114

The particularly slender abdomen and small size of this species is a good initial clue to its identity. The elongate tergite 2 and sternite 2 are characteristic of both sexes, but the range of variation tends towards *europaeus* in particular, some males being rather difficult to separate. In the male, the second basal cell can be partly bare of microtrichia but unfortunately some specimens have a complete covering as found in *clypeatus* (these are easily confused with *ramsarensis*). However, the pleura are less dusted than other members of the *clypeatus* complex, and shine as brightly as the mesonotum. Females are more easily separated, the frons having dust spots hugging the eye margin, whereas the dust spots are large and occupy two thirds of the width of the frons in related species. In the female the spots on the tergites can be reduced or absent, sometimes with well developed spots only present on tergites 2 and 3, or even just on 3. It is safest to rely on easily identifiable specimens, and catch several if necessary in order to obtain a female or a typical male. Wing length 5–7 mm.

The diagnostic features of this species have been significantly clarified with the separation of *ramsarensis* from the *clypeatus* complex, and the provision of additional characters for the male front femur and tarsus. In females the small size of the dust spots on the frons remains a valuable character, but the presence of an undusted area on the pleura in front of the wings is an obvious feature that helps to confirm its identity.

This is a frequent species over much of Britain and Ireland. It can be common in marshes and moist grassland and also occurs locally in dry grassland. The difference in ecology from *clypeatus* requires clarification. April to October, peaking in July, probably as two broods.

Platycheirus (Platycheirus) aurolateralis Stubbs, 2002

Superficially this species is similar to *scutatus*, or even more so to the recently described *splendidus*, and only the male is yet recognised. The most immediately obvious feature (in the available material) is that tergite 2 is entirely black or with only minute pale spots. The abdomen is intermediate in length between *scutatus* and *splendidus*, tergites 2 to 4 being a little longer than wide; the oblique spots on tergites 3 and 4 are relatively small. The frons is drab black and the front tarsus is also very like that of *splendidus*. The mid tibia is mainly black, but with yellow ends, and in side view there is a bend near the apex and the middle ventral section has particularly dense long hairs; the anterior surface has long hairs at the base and extending to the mid length. The side of the top of the thorax, running from the humerus back to above the wing base, has a golden reflection when viewed obliquely from behind (very weak in *splendidus*, absent in *scutatus*). Wing length 5 mm.

It is too soon to assess the distribution and status of this species. In the original 1983 edition of this book, the male specimen of '*scutatus*' without spots on tergite 2 belongs to this species: it was taken on 1 June 1975 in Windsor Forest. Two similar males were segregated by M. Parker in material from Delcombe Wood, Dorset, taken on 3 and 31 May 1997, confirming consistent characters. Examination of the Natural History Museum collections revealed material incorporated in fairly recent years: from Slough (18 May 1936), Bristol (1972 and 1985) and Watersmeet, Devon (28 April 1989). S. Falk has material from a garden in Wealdstone, Middlesex (1 June 1980), Holme Fen, Huntingdonshire (28 August 1992) and a site in Coventry (7 April 1998). Other collections need to be re-examined. Though evidently a scarce species, it seems likely that it will prove to be widespread in southern Britain. April to early June, and August.

Platycheirus (Platycheirus) clypeatus (Meigen, 1822)   Pl. R, fig. 10; Pl. 1, fig. 16
                                                                 Map: Ball & Morris p. 115

The splitting of *clypeatus* into several species sorts out some of the worrying variation that was evident in the past. True *clypeatus* is relatively broad-bodied compared with related species that may also be present on a site. The male front tarsus has the basal segment somewhat elongate, with a long median groove beneath which ends in a small circular pit well beyond halfway (not always obvious, but distinct when the pit is dark-rimmed). The female hind femur is broadly yellow at both ends, and the abdomen has strong rectangular spots on tergites 3 and 4 that reach the front margin (the difference from *occultus* can be overlooked, but the key gives additional characters). The spots on the female abdomen can be reduced, sometimes tergite 2, or even all tergites, being entirely black – in such examples the front tibia is distinctly broader than in black females of *Melanostoma*, and the broad dust spots on the frons and extensively yellow legs will indicate *clypeatus*. Wing length 5–7.5 mm

Most districts in Britain have suitable habitat since it has such a broad ecological range. It is often abundant on both dry grassland (including on chalk and limestone) and wet meadows and fens. Woodland rides can also be suitable if they contain well established grassland, but this is essentially a species of open habitats that avoids the shade. Moorland and upland grassland can support the species, especially in the vicinity of streams and longer herbage. A particular limitation is that is does not like heavy grazing (in common with many other hoverflies and other insects). It should be noted that closely related species also occupy these habitats, but tend to be more specific, so only overlap with *clypeatus* under particular conditions.

This is one of the commonest and most widespread hoverflies, occurring throughout Britain and Ireland. It is often abundant, although it has been reported to be rather local in Kent. April to October, peaking in July and August.

Platycheirus (Platycheirus) discimanus Loew, 1871   Pl. R, fig. 4; Pl. 1, fig. 10
                                                                        Map: Ball & Morris p. 115

This species closely resembles *albimanus* in having well developed grey spots in both sexes, but it is much smaller. The male has a narrow abdomen, the grey-dusted spots not changing colour according to view or only slightly so. The cylindrical front tibia and inflated basal tarsal segments are akin to the *manicatus* group (which never has grey spots). The female frons is without marginal dust spots, whereas these are small but distinct in *albimanus* and *sticticus*. Also the antennae are entirely black whereas the other two species have a small orange patch beneath the base of the third antennal segment. The female is noticeably squatter in build than other grey-marked species. Wing length 5.75–6.75 mm.

There are scattered records in England, Scotland and Ireland. Being a spring species and grey-spotted like *albimanus*, it is quite likely that this hoverfly has to some extent been overlooked. Several, but by no means all records are from heathy or forest localities. Searching blossom of blackthorn is one of the most practical ways of finding this species. April to June, peaking in late April and early May.

Platycheirus (Platycheirus) europaeus Goeldlin de Tiefenau,   Map: Ball & Morris p. 116
Maibach & Speight, 1990

Care is needed in separating this recently recognised member of the *clypeatus* group. The males have a narrow abdomen, and the underside of the basal segment of the front tarsus has a tick-shaped pit placed in the outer half. This description can also apply to *angustatus*, but that is a small delicate species whereas *europaeus* is quite large. *P. europaeus* has the side of the top of the thorax in front of the wing dulled by dusting (shining in *angustatus*) and the key gives further characters. The dust spots on the female frons project sharply inwards from the dust bands beside the eyes, unlike related species. The females often appear noticeably long-bodied with rounded spots on tergite 2 (usually hemispherical in *clypeatus*). Wing length 7 mm.

So far this species would appear to be largely absent from the southern counties of England, but it is proving fairly widespread in the Midlands and Wales, and also in Scotland as far north as the Central Highlands. It has not been recorded from Ireland. However, it is generally highly localised for reasons that are not yet understood. Scottish records are mainly from damp open situations within woodland, including pine woods. In the East Midlands the species occurs in woodland rides on clay, especially Boulder Clay, with a marked preference for sections with hairy sedge. In Suffolk it has been recorded from former calcareous heathland of the Breck, now planted with conifers, that most closely resemble its Scottish sites. At one of the Welsh sites, it was found in damp scrub on sand dunes. Adults are most easily found by sweeping low herbage or visiting the flowers of sedges and grasses. Early April to early September. May is a peak time in the East Midlands and there may be a later generation, but nationally the peak is in June and July.

Platycheirus (Platycheirus) fulviventris
(Macquart, 1829)

Pl. R, fig. 11; Pl. 1, fig. 18
Map: Ball & Morris p. 116
Larva: Rotheray Pl. 4c

Three members of the *clypeatus* group, *fulviventris*, *immarginatus* and *perpallidus*, have the abdomen very extensively orange, the black areas being exceptionally reduced, especially in the male. The male of *fulviventris* is readily recognised because the front tibia broadens near to the base. Female specimens are more of a problem and considerable care is necessary in identification. The hind tibia and tarsus are nearly always entirely yellow so confusion is most likely with *perpallidus*. The dust spots on the frons in *fulviventris* are sharply defined, even if there is a separate patch of dusting just above the antennae, whereas in *perpallidus* the dust spots have vague boundaries and merge into an area of light dusting above the antennae (some specimens will cause doubt). The front femur in the female has a downward-projecting fringe of hairs posteriorly, whereas in *perpallidus* hairs project on a wide radius on the posterior to postero-ventral surfaces (view along axis of femur). These characters, and the ratio between the width of the antennae and the depth of the jowls mentioned in the key, are best appreciated with comparative material. Wing length 6–7.75 mm.

Its distribution extends through much of Britain and Ireland, including Ireland, but is mainly southern. It is rare in Scotland. The larvae feed on the aphid *Hyalopterus pruni* on monocotyledonous plants in wetlands, and there is a strong association with lush open marsh, especially about stands of sweet-grass. The edges of ponds or sluggish rivers with a fringe of this habitat also support the species. It is regarded as distinctly local in many parts of Britain. Coastal districts and major river valleys provide the best prospects in some counties. April to September, peaking in June and July.

Platycheirus (Platycheirus) immarginatus
(Zetterstedt, 1849)

Pl. R, fig. 13; Pl. 1, fig. 20
Map: Ball & Morris p. 117

Though the abdomen in the male is predominantly orange, as in *fulviventris* and *perpallidus*, the hind legs are much darker, with at least half the tibia and often half the femur ringed in black. In fact, *scambus* is also rather similar, although the black at the hind margin of the tergites is rather wider. The males of *immarginatus* and *scambus* both have the front femur bearing a posterior row of about six long black isolated hairs, but *immarginatus* has a long white posterior hair at the base which is lacking in *scambus*. *P. immarginatus* usually has a dark stripe along the part of the front femur where the strong bristles arise (the front femur is entirely pale in *perpallidus* and *scambus*). Reference should be made to the description of *perpallidus* since these two species are often confused.

The female is much darker than *fulviventris* and *perpallidus*, there being a closer resemblance to *clypeatus*. On the basis of few available specimens it would seem that the markings of *immarginatus* are distinctive. Tergites 3 and 4 have spots which are strongly oblique on their hind margin, especially on tergite 4, so that the intervening black areas are forwardly directed triangles. On their lateral margins these spots are usually narrowly fringed in black (in *clypeatus* the spots are rectangular or not particularly oblique and they broadly reach the lateral margin).

Also, the entire lateral margins of tergites 5 and 6 are yellow in fresh specimens (dried specimens tend to darken so that distinction from the darker condition of *clypeatus* may be difficult). In the material examined the tergites are entirely covered in white hairs (whereas in *clypeatus* there are black hairs on the black areas, at least on the hind parts of tergites 4 and 5 about the axis) (view from side). The front femur has a posterior fringe of pale hairs, but even the longest hairs do not equal the width of the femur (in *clypeatus* the fringe is more fan-like, with the longest hairs as long as the femur width), but this distinction is not always easy. Wing length 5.5–7 mm.

This is a difficult species to identify and misidentifications are frequent in the literature and collections, thus confusing the picture. Based on records that are believed to be reliable, *immarginatus* appears to be widespread around the coast from southern England to northern Scotland, including Ireland. It is extremely local, but can be abundant where it occurs. The larvae feed on the aphid *Trichocallis cyperi* on sedges in wetlands, and there is a strong association with brackish marsh, either on the coast or along the tidal reaches of rivers. However, in Scotland and Ireland there are reliable records from some inland localities by lakes and rivers. May to September, peaking in June and July.

Platycheirus (Platycheirus) manicatus (Meigen, 1822)   Pl. R, fig. 2; Pl. 1, fig. 13
                                                                   Map: Ball & Morris p. 118

Typical specimens are relatively large and robust, with a particularly dull brownish thorax (shining in all other species), and the lower part of the face is extended (in side view the mouth margin extends well forwards of the knob; no other species shows this to such a marked degree except female *melanopsis*). The spots are elongate on tergite 2 and in the male the spots on tergites 3 and 4 are elongate with a very curved inner edge. As remarked under *tarsalis*, the male can occasionally have reduced yellow markings somewhat resembling that species, but in *manicatus* the front tarsus has the distal segment black and segment 2 is almost symmetrically placed relative to the joint with the third segment. The female is distinct in having the entire frons and vertex uniformly dull. Wing length 6.75–9 mm.

P. manicatus is a very widespread species throughout Britain and Ireland, even being recorded from Foula, a small island off the Shetlands. It is often common in dry open grassland, especially on calcareous or neutral soils, but can even appear in suburban gardens. April to November, peaking in June.

Platycheirus (Platycheirus) melanopsis Loew, 1856   Pl. R, fig. 1; Pl. 1, fig. 14
                                                               Map: Ball & Morris p. 118

The male front tarsus has the three whitish basal segments broadened and the abdomen is rather short by comparison with other species. The female has the base of the femora black, the mouth margin is produced beyond the knob as in *manicatus* (but the thorax is shining) and the frons is almost entirely shining black with dust spots restricted to a narrow rim by the eye margins. In the field, confusion is perhaps most likely with *clypeatus*, but the legs of *melanopsis* are predominantly dark. Wing length 6–7.25 mm.

Within the Central Highlands of Scotland it occurs on mountains and in open-structured pine forests at about 250–300 m. There are also old records from the Lake District. It has not been recorded from Ireland. Rotheray (1997b) suggests that the larvae feed on the scale insect

Arctorthezia cataphracta. The males tend to hover close to the ground over roads and bare tracks. June to August, peaking in July.

Platycheirus (Platycheirus) nielseni Vockeroth, 1990   Map: Ball & Morris p. 119
Platycheirus species A of Stubbs, 1986

Typically, specimens of *nielseni* are smaller and narrower than *peltatus* from which it was split. Males are readily separated from *peltatus* by a distinct tuft of long hairs emanating from the swollen apex of the middle tibia and lying parallel to the shaft. Females are somewhat more problematic because the separation is based on the degree to which the tergites are transverse, but usually the difference illustrated in the key is distinct. Wing length 6.5–8.5 mm.

There is considerable overlap between the distribution of *nielseni* and *peltatus*, but *nielseni* is largely confined to the north of a line between the Severn and the Humber. It is most frequently found in upland locations and is particularly widespread in Scotland, where it can be frequent in grassy areas. It is also recorded from Ireland where it is frequent in the west, but apparently absent from the lowlands of the east. Males have been noted hovering in loose swarms at a height of 0.5–1 m, in the vicinity of streams. May to October, peaking in late June and July.

Platycheirus (Platycheirus) occultus Goeldlin de Tiefenau,   Map: Ball & Morris p. 119
Maibach & Speight, 1990

This recently separated species is very similar to *clypeatus*. The male is narrower, notably tergite 2 being slightly longer than wide; the basal segment of the front tarsus is less elongate and the median furrow beneath it ends in a pit, halfway along, which is only easy to see if it is darkened (in *clypeatus* the furrow is longer so that the pit lies well beyond halfway). [Higher-altitude specimens should be checked for *P. angustipes* Goeldlin de Tiefenau, an alpine species with the pit in a similar position but with a dark area beyond it reaching to the front margin.] The female superficially resembles *clypeatus* but there are some subtle differences. The front margins of the spots on tergites 3 and 4 do not quite reach the front margin of the tergite, and are somewhat oblique so that the black front edge of the tergite gets wider towards the sides (in *clypeatus* the front margins of these spots are square-on so that the black front edge of the tergite is of even width). However, a more reliable character in the females is the much shorter fringe of hairs behind the front femur, while the area immediately behind the ocellar triangle is shining black (rather than dusted). Both sexes have a tendency for the wings to be brown-tinged which, taken together with the reduced abdominal markings, usually makes this species appear darker than *clypeatus* in the field. Wing length 5.5–6.5 mm.

Even within the short period since the recognition of this species, *occultus* has proved to be very widespread in Britain, and also in Ireland (Speight, 1990b). In particular it is associated with peaty wetlands, with a wide tolerance range including fens, poor fen, boggy areas on heathland in the lowlands, and extending up onto moorlands at fairly high altitude in the north and west. [Note that in the Alps *angustipes* replaces *occultus* at higher altitudes even within the tree-line; see above.] Sites supporting *occultus* generally have relatively lush herbage, and sweeping and searching flowers often reveals it to be abundant. However, the peak period on a site can be short and its occurrence can easily go undetected. Mid April to October, peaking in July.

Platycheirus (Platycheirus) peltatus   Pl. R, fig. 5; Pl. 1, fig. 12
(Meigen, 1822)   Map: Ball & Morris p. 120
                                                  Larva: Rotheray Pl. 4d

Many specimens are amongst the largest for this subgenus but there is substantial variation in size, so large size alone cannot be used to identify this species with certainty, especially now that further species, *amplus* and *nielseni*, have been recognised within the *peltatus* complex. Both males and females have distinctly broader abdomens than *amplus* and *nielseni*, and this is a feature that provides a first indication as to the specimen's identity. The sexes are very different in appearance. In the male, tergites 3 and 4 are squarish and tergite 2 has a pair of small centrally placed spots. The male front tarsus has the basal segment large and strongly asymmetrical at the apex, and the femur has dense black hairs on the posterior surface. The female has a relatively broad oval abdomen. Tergites 2, 3 and 4 have the spots placed well forwards and with hind margins oblique, those on tergites 3 and 4 being broadest on the inner edge – thus reminiscent of the condition found in female *Melanostoma*. The female frons has rather broad dust spots. Wing length 7–9 mm.

P. peltatus is widespread across Britain and Ireland but would appear to be more closely associated with lowlands and valley floors than the closely related *nielseni*, which shows affiliations with upland and northern locations. Speight (2000c) comments that it appears to be declining in Ireland and, judging from the number of records submitted each year, it may also be declining in frequency in Britain. April to November, peaking twice, in June and August.

Platycheirus (Platycheirus) perpallidus Verrall, 1901   Pl. R, fig. 12; Pl. 1, fig. 19
                                                                  Map: Ball & Morris p. 121

Among the extensively orange species, *perpallidus* has the hind femur and tibia wholly yellow or more typically with narrow dark rings no more than one quarter of their length. Thus there is a strong resemblance to *fulviventris* (but in this species the front tibia broadens gradually from the base in the male, and the dust spots on the female frons are of a different shape – see key, p. 68). The male front femur has short hairs on the posterior surface, often with some rather longer ones. However, the longest hairs are scarcely longer than the width of the femur and appear to be scattered among the other hairs, whereas in *immarginatus* and *scambus* (both with far more black on the hind legs) there are about six long thick hairs which are very distinct from the other hairs, and up to twice the width of the front femur in length (sometimes helpful to view along the axis of the femur). The angle between the eyes on the frons of the male is less than 90° in *perpallidus*, but greater in *angustatus* and *scambus* (take care that the face has not collapsed and reduced the eye angle). The female frons normally has rather diffuse dust spots, whereas in *fulviventris* and *scambus* the dust spots are sharply defined. Wing length 5.25–6.75 mm.

Whilst there are scattered records in England, Wales and Ireland, *perpallidus* is most frequent in the Scottish Highlands. The larvae feed on the aphid *Trichocallis cyperi* that lives on sedges in wetlands. Adults occur where sedges (*e.g.* bottle sedge) grow in wet poor fen, especially when this occurs at the margins of ponds and lakes. It also occurs on sedges by rivers. The emergence peaks are seemingly short which may contribute to its apparent rarity, but it can be abundant under favourable conditions. May to September, peaking in late June to early July.

Platycheirus (Platycheirus) podagratus   Pl. R, fig. 8; Pl. 1, fig. 11
(Zetterstedt, 1838)   Map: Ball & Morris p. 121
                                                         Larva: Rotheray Pl. 4f

In general appearance this species looks rather dark, with oval or rounded spots. The male has a rather narrow and often tapering abdomen with rather elongate oval spots. The shape of the male front tibia is distinctive, gently expanding from the base and then broadly expanded near the apex. The female frequently has the rounded spots largest on tergite 2, whilst those of tergites 3 and 4 have the posterior outer corners reduced obliquely (somewhat as in *Melanostoma* or *P. peltatus*). The sides of the female frons are dusted adjacent to the eyes but the dust spots scarcely extend inwards, thus leaving a gap of about half the width of the frons between the spots. It is clear that some past records of *podagratus* have been confused with *occultus* and specimens should therefore be re-checked. Wing length 5.25–7 mm.

Northern districts suit this species best, especially in Scotland and northern England, although even here it is only locally common. There are few, scattered records for Ireland. The few records for the south cannot be accepted without confirmation. Bogs and boggy ground provide the most favourable terrain, especially at low altitude, but it has been found at over 700 m in the Pennines. May to September, peaking in late June to early July.

Platycheirus (Platycheirus) ramsarensis Goeldlin de Tiefenau,   Map: Ball & Morris p. 122
Maibach & Speight, 1990

Previously unrecognised within the *clypeatus* complex, it is distinct because in both sexes the front femur has the posterior hair fringe confined to the basal half; thus the more easily seen apical half seems bald. In overall appearance it tends to be smaller and slightly narrower than *clypeatus*. The basal segment of the male front tarsus has an apical tick-like pit beneath (when such a mark is present in other species, it lies somewhat before the apex). The female is one of the species with the hind femur entirely or almost completely black at the base (unlike *clypeatus* and *occultus*). Wing length 5.5–7 mm.

When *ramsarensis* was first described, all the known material was from Ireland and Britain, except for one specimen from Norway. It was reported from mountainous parts of north west Ireland (the type locality is in Donegal) and from the Wicklow Mountains (eastern Ireland). The British records were from the Scottish Highlands, a site on Uist in the Outer Hebrides, and a single English site, Malham Tarn at 300 m on the western side of the Pennines. Subsequently the distribution has been found to be fairly widespread in upland and moorland districts throughout Britain, right down to the south west peninsula (Exmoor and Dartmoor). Typical habitat comprises wet patches of rushes beside moorland streams and in upland bogs where it can sometimes be found in abundance. Late May to early September, peaking in July.

Platycheirus (Platycheirus) scambus (Staeger, 1843)   Pl. R, fig. 14; Pl. 1, fig. 21
                                                         Map: Ball & Morris p. 123

Most specimens are relatively large with extensive bold orange markings, including spots which extend much of the length of tergite 2. The hind femur and tibia are each ringed with black for half their length. The last feature, and in the male the long black isolated bristles on the posterior edge of the front femur, cause a resemblance to *immarginatus*. However, *scambus* is distinct from all other members of the *clypeatus* group in the absence of a white bristle at the base of the front femur. Wing length 7.25–8.25 mm.

As with the last species, scambus can be locally common in northern districts. Records are very few south of the central midlands, but it has recently been recorded from a number of sites in North Devon. Although southerly records should be treated with extreme caution, they cannot be immediately discounted. It is widely distributed in Ireland. The preferred habitat is lush grass and marshy ground adjoining bushes and trees, although it can also be found in poor fen amongst stands of sweet-grass or reed canary-grass. May to October, peaking in late June and July.

Platycheirus (Platycheirus) scutatus (Meigen, 1822)　　　Pl. R, fig. 7; Pl. 1, fig. 8
　　　　　　　　　　　　　　　　　　　　　　　　　　　　Map: Ball & Morris p. 123
　　　　　　　　　　　　　　　　　　　　　　　　　　　　Larva: Rotheray Pl. 4e

The first edition of this book and its supplements drew attention to the variation in this species. Recent studies have concluded that it is a species complex, accounting for the differences in tergite 2 and the mid tibia that were previously mentioned. Thus *splendidus* and *aurolateralis* are now recognised as distinct species, separate from true *scutatus*. As now defined, male *scutatus* has a relatively elongate abdomen, with well developed pairs of greyish spots, those on tergites 3 and 4 having rather parallel front and hind margins. The basal segment of the front tarsus is about one and a quarter times as long as broad, and segment 4 is little wider than long and highly asymmetrical. The mid tibia is fairly uniformly slender in posterior view, curved in the apical third and ventrally with very short erect hairs (avoid confusion with long posterior hairs at some angles of view); in dorsal view it is rather sinuous and inflated in the middle, the anterior hairs reduced with only a few long ones near the base. A useful field character is that the frons is rather greyish dusted (black in related species), whilst under a microscope one may note that the wing membrane lacks microtrichia at the base of the basal cells and anal cell (complete coverage of microtrichia in the other two species). Female characters are far less certain at present. Wing length 5.5–7.5 mm.

The recognition of additional species within the *scutatus* complex has resolved some of the difficulties previously caused by its considerable variation. However, confusion remains possible and it is wise to retain voucher specimens as further species may yet be separated.

True *scutatus* occurs widely in Britain and Ireland and is multiple brooded so can be found through most of the field season. It is common and widespread in Ireland and occurs in Scotland. Wood margins provide the typical habitat. The ecology requires re-evaluation, but it is confirmed that larvae may be found both on herbaceous vegetation and shrubs. March to November, with at least two peaks, in June and again in August and September.

Platycheirus (Platycheirus) splendidus Rotheray, 1998　　　Map: Ball & Morris p. 124

As a recently described species, segregated from *scutatus* on rather subtle features, an understanding of the best characters to use in separating these two species is only gradually emerging. Initially, the size of the facial knob, the extent of adjacent dusting and the colour of the legs were drawn to attention. It emerges that a third segregate, *aurolateralis*, has also to be allowed for. Male *splendidus* have a rather short abdomen, tergites 2 to 4 being square or slightly elongate. The frons is drab black (as *aurolateralis*) and the front tarsus has the basal segment little longer than wide and segment 4 relatively wide (as *aurolateralis*). The mid tibia is distinctive in side view, being bent in the middle, somewhat inflated in the basal portion and dorsally with a narrow shining strip; anteriorly at the base there are some longish hairs (as *scutatus*, although rather longer; *aurolateralis* has much more extensive long hairs). Females are not distinguishable at present. Wing length 5 mm.

This species is widespread in Britain, but the pattern of relative abundance has still to be clarified. Present evidence is that it is more frequent than *scutatus* in Cornwall, and also in Warwickshire where 75% of '*scutatus*' specimens proved to be *splendidus*. However, initial re-assessment of collections revealed only one *splendidus* among '*scutatus*' from Middlesex, but more from the Wealden counties and East Anglia. In Scotland it is known from the Central Lowlands and penetrates the warmer valleys in south-central Perthshire. Irish specimens of *scutatus* have been checked, but *splendidus* has not so far been found. Adults have been bred from larvae found in leaf-curl galls on wych elm caused by the aphid *Schizoneura ulmi*, and it was also reared from among *Brachycaudus* aphids on red campion. The elm galls occupied by *splendidus* larvae were shaded, usually below 1.5 m, but absent from higher galls (up to 5 m). *P. scutatus* was absent in these galls, despite adults being present, in keeping with other observations that oviposition rarely occurs above 30 cm. This is predominantly a springtime species, occurring from mid April to early June in the south (May to June in the north); there is evidence of a partial second brood in Cornwall from mid July to August. April to June, exceptionally to August, peaking in June.

Platycheirus (Platycheirus) sticticus (Meigen, 1822)   Pl. R, fig. 15; Pl. 1, fig. 9
                                                                       Map: Ball & Morris p. 124

It would be easy to overlook this small dark species in the field. The spots are not obvious, being small. In the male the spots on tergite 2 are often absent and the tiny triangular spots on tergites 3 and 4 are often dull bronze with grey dusting that shows up at certain angles, or else these spots are grey or orange. The male is exceptional in having the front tarsus slender and the tibia scarcely expanded – thus there is a resemblance to *Platycheirus ambiguus* but the curly apical hair on the front femur is absent in *sticticus*, there being instead a few long isolated black bristles on the posterior surface. The female is small with poorly discernible spots on the tergites; confusion with *ambiguus* or *discimanus* is likely. However, in female *sticticus* tergites 2, 3, and 4 are all square or elongate, whereas in *ambiguus*, *albimanus* and *discimanus* these tergites are distinctly transverse, especially tergite 2. Wing length 4.25–6 mm.

Very little is known of this species. There are scattered records throughout Britain and Ireland, although there is only a single Irish record. It has been taken along a woodland edge and in rough grassland at 240 m, but there are few recorded observations of the habitat. April to September, with two peaks, in May and June and in August.

Platycheirus (Platycheirus) tarsalis (Schummel, 1836)   Pl. R, fig. 3; Pl. 1, fig. 15
                                                                       Map: Ball & Morris p. 125

In both sexes the abdomen has the yellow or orange-yellow markings broadly separated by the black ground colour. On tergites 3 and 4 the posterior third is black. On tergite 2 the spots are rather elongate and triangular with the hind edge parallel with the hind margin of the tergite, again leaving a third or a quarter of the tergite black. The most similar-looking species are *scutatus* (with spots on tergite 2 small and rounded) and *peltatus* (spots on tergite 2 with oblique hind margins). Rarely, male *manicatus* can resemble *tarsalis* so reference to the tarsal character is essential. The male front legs closely resemble those of *manicatus*, but the joint between the second and third tarsal segments is towards one side rather than central, and the last tarsal segment is whitish rather than black. The mid tarsus is more extensively pale, with the last segment always pale (black in *manicatus* in both sexes), and the thorax is shining (usually dull in *manicatus*). Wing length 7.5–8.75 mm.

P. tarsalis is widespread in England and can be locally abundant in some districts of the Midlands and the south-east. It is a very local species in much of Devon, Cornwall, northern England and Wales and something of a rarity in Scotland. It has not been recorded from Ireland. The typical habitat is a lush woodland edge where adults are particularly attracted to white cruciferous flowers such as garlic mustard. May to September, peaking in late May to early June.

Subgenus PYROPHAENA

In the first edition of this book, it was noted that suggestions had been made that *Pyrophaena* should be treated as a subgenus of *Platycheirus*. This placement was adopted in the most recent check list (Chandler, 1998) and by Thompson & Rotheray (1998).

Platycheirus (Pyrophaena) granditarsus (Forster, 1771)   Pl. 1, fig. 4
Pyrophaena granditarsa (Forster, 1771)   Map: Ball & Morris p. 117

The abdomen is extensively orange, in the male with a black band in front and behind, or in the female with a black band at the front and small black patches at the sides and posteriorly, making this a particularly distinctive hoverfly. The male front and mid tarsi have some expanded segments, the first segment of the front tarsus also having a thorn-like outgrowth beneath. The male markings resemble those of *Xylota segnis* (which has a simple front tarsus). Occasionally female specimens will be found with a black abdomen bearing a median orange stripe on tergites 3 and 4; these are interpreted as intersexes (developmental abnormalities with both male and female features). Wing length 5.25–8.5 mm.

P. granditarsus is often common in marshy meadows and in lush vegetation by ditches and lakes throughout much of Britain and Ireland. May to October, peaking between July and September.

Platycheirus (Pyrophaena) rosarum (Fabricius, 1787)   Pl. 1, fig. 5
Pyrophaena rosarum (Fabricius, 1787)   Map: Ball & Morris p. 122

The yellowish paired spots at the front margin of tergite 3, contrasting with an otherwise almost entirely black abdomen, make this hoverfly instantly recognisable. Tergite 4 usually has a pair of small faint bars and the tergites can have patches with steely blue reflections. The male front tarsus is simple. Wing length 5.25–7.75 mm.

P. rosarum is found in the same habitat as *granditarsus* and the two species often occur together, but in most districts *rosarum* is less abundant. It occurs widely throughout Britain and Ireland. May to October, peaking in June and July.

Genus XANTHANDRUS

Xanthandrus comtus (Harris, 1780)

Pl. 1, fig. 22
Map: Ball & Morris p. 146
Larva: Rotheray Pl. 4b

From the size, broad oval abdomen and bold yellow markings, one might assume this to be a member of the tribe Syrphini, but the black scutellum indicates that it belongs to the Bacchini. The abdomen has a distinctive pattern, tergite 2 having a pair of round spots, whilst tergites 3 and 4 have pairs of spots flush with the front margin, in the male these being large, hemispherical and at least partially fused whereas in the female these spots are square and well separated. The stigma is exceptionally long, being at least twice as long as the next section of the costal vein. Wing length 8.75–11.5 mm.

There are a reasonable number of specimens in old collections, but *X. comtus* apparently went through a period of great rarity until the last few years when records have become more frequent again. It occurs in meadows and by scrub and woodland edges. On the continent larvae have been found on the foliage of bushes where they were predatory on the caterpillars of micro moths (Chapman, 1906), including those of semi-gregarious tortricid moths (*e.g. Ancylis unculana* on buckthorn and alder buckthorn; *Acroclita subsequana* on spurges). This is predominantly a species of southern England, but records extend to North Wales, Scotland and Ireland. It appears to be strongly migratory with the British population boosted by an annual influx, as in Shetland in 2000 when ten were seen in the space of a few days with other migrants (Pennington, 2001). Only rarely are there observations from the same locality over several successive seasons. Although it has been found in the spring, the autumn is perhaps the most favourable period. March to October, peaking from July to September.

Tribe PARAGINI

Genus PARAGUS

These are minute hoverflies, only about 3.5–5 mm long. Usually they are entirely black, but sometimes the abdomen is partly red and in one species the scutellum is partly yellow. The legs are extensively yellow. The face is yellow with a black median stripe and the third antennal segment is somewhat elongated.

There is nothing that can be confused with *Paragus* although at a distance in the field it may be casually overlooked as one of the smaller Pipizini, such as *Neocnemodon*, or perhaps *Neoascia* (or as a member of the family Pipunculidae). However, most other tiny hoverflies have a black face. In common with many other small hoverflies, *Paragus* normally flies very close to the ground. The larvae of *Paragus* feed upon a range of ground-layer and arboreal aphids.

There are two subgenera, *Pandasyopthalmus* and *Paragus*, with three species recorded in Great Britain and a fourth from Ireland which could yet be found in Britain. There has been considerable review of the taxonomy of the genus in Europe. Speight (1978c) gives a key; van der Goot (1981) includes a further species, *flammeus* Goeldlin de Tiefenau.

Subgenus PANDASYOPTHALMUS

The eyes are uniformly covered in faint white hairs. The male abdomen is relatively narrow and slightly waisted. The females of the three known British species cannot yet be separated; there is a need to obtain pairs *in copula* so that a key can be devised. *P. tibialis* of Coe (1953a) included all species since he had not realised that more than one species was involved.

Paragus (Pandasyopthalmus) constrictus Šimić, 1986

This recently described species is very similar to *tibialis* and can only be distinguished at present by examination of the male genitalia. The difference in shape of the outer lobes is illustrated in the key (these are equivalent to those in *Sphaerophoria* and visible when the genital capsule is hinged out in a similar way). Wing length presumed to be similar to *tibialis*.

At the moment *constrictus* is known only from Ireland where it has been found to be widespread on the limestone pavements of the Burren (Speight & Chandler, 1995). A record from the Burren, attributed to *tibialis* in the first edition of this book, proved to be this species. It should be looked for on limestone pavement in the rest of Britain, those of the Morecambe Bay area being the most obvious possibility. Male specimens of *tibialis* in collections (especially from this habitat) should be re-examined. Late May to early September.

Paragus (Pandasyopthalmus) haemorrhous Meigen, 1822

Pl.1, fig. 24
Map: Ball & Morris p. 102
Larva: Rotheray Pl. 9e

The features given in the key (p. 80) need to be studied carefully and, although easier to see with a microscope, a hand lens should be sufficient to see the relative size of sternite 4 and of the genitalia. The abdomen is normally black, but occasionally part of tergite 3 or the tip of the abdomen is red. Wing length 3.5–4 mm.

This is by far the commonest *Paragus*, occurring in many districts throughout Britain and Ireland. However, the species is easily overlooked unless its habits are known. It can be found hovering a centimetre or two above bare patches of soil or where there is very sparse vegetation along tracks and banks. The presence of a relatively dry sunny situation is critical, but soil type is not too important since the grassy margins of sandy heaths, moorland, chalk grassland, coastal landslips and well drained commons on clay are among the typical habitats. *P. haemorrhous* can be found at very low-growing flowers such as tormentil. May to September, peaking in July.

Paragus (Pandasyopthalmus) tibialis (Fallén, 1817)

Map: Ball & Morris p. 102

The much larger pre-genital segment should be discernible with a 10× lens; comparison with specimens of *haemorrhous* should be made before confirming identification. Whilst this species is usually black, like *haemorrhous*, occasional specimens have some red on tergite 3 and at the tip of the abdomen. Wing length 3.5–4 mm.

P. tibialis is a rare and elusive species, even in favourable localities. Since it can be present among more numerous *haemorrhous* it is necessary to carefully check a number of specimens. So far *tibialis* has only been confirmed as occurring on heathland in southern England. Some old records for the Welsh coast must remain suspect and it should be borne in mind that all British *Paragus* other than *albifrons* used to be called *tibialis* until the revision by Speight (1978c). May to October, peaking in July.

Subgenus PARAGUS

The eyes have faint vertical stripes and are predominantly white-haired, but have stripes of brown hairs (or bare stripes). This feature can be difficult to see. However, the broad abdomen, wider than the thorax and with tergites 2 and 3 about three times as wide as long, causes this subgenus to appear distinctly more robust than *Pandasyopthalmus*. Also, there is no trace of a waist to the abdomen. The scutellum in this subgenus is usually yellow, at least at the tip.

Paragus (Paragus) albifrons (Fallén, 1817)   Pl. 1, fig. 23
Paragus bicolor of Coe (1953a).   Map: Ball & Morris p. 101

The abdomen is black, often with red marks on tergites 2 and 3. It should be noted that it is in this subgenus that additional British species could be found, but only males are identifiable. Thus if the abdomen is all red or partly red at the margins or with a red band right across, then another species is almost certainly involved. The non-British *P. majoranae* Rondani has narrow dust bars underneath the pale hairs on the abdomen, but is otherwise very similar to *P. albifrons*. All specimens should be checked by a specialist. Wing length 4–6 mm.

Very few specimens have been taken in Britain, all from the southern counties between Dorset and Essex, and mainly near the coast. Speight (1978c) states that it is a more secretive species of damper, more heavily vegetated sites, flying low among tall grass. The few recent records are all coastal and mostly from the Thames estuary in north Kent and south Essex, but also one from Hythe, Hampshire. June to September, peaking from late June to late August.

Tribe SYRPHINI

The yellow scutellum distinguishes this tribe from other hoverflies with Syrphinae-like spots, bars or bands. The face in most species is partially or completely yellow, unlike the Bacchini.

Some Syrphini have a partially black scutellum, as in *Leucozona laternaria* and *Chrysotoxum*, but there is normally at least a trace of yellow remaining. Difficulty is only likely to be experienced with female *Melangyna quadrimaculata* since the scutellum, abdomen and face are entirely black.

Occasionally, melanic specimens will be found in other species, the abdomen being black, but these are recognisable as Syrphini since the scutellum remains yellow. These genetic forms are confined to the female sex. Melanism is frequent in *Scaeva* and has been noted in a few other species such as *Melangyna lasiophthalma* and *Parasyrphus punctulatus*. Exceptionally dark markings, as found in some *Episyrphus balteatus*, can result from a physiological response to low temperatures during development of the pupae; in such cases both sexes may be affected. There is no ultimate means of knowing which species display melanics, especially when such examples are often passed over as unidentifiable. It is necessary to match up such specimens with typical ones using characters such as the frons pattern.

It should be noted that, among hoverflies with a black abdomen, the females of *Cheilosia longula*, *scutellata* and *soror* have a partially yellow scutellum and, moreover, the face of the first two is typically yellowish at the sides. However, in *Cheilosia* the humeri are hairy, the eye rims extend up to the level of the antennae, and the scutellum has short hairs on top and stout marginal bristles.

Over the years there have been many attempts at a generic classification within the Syrphini. One solution was to place most of the species in *Syrphus*, resulting in a cumbersome genus containing 42 species in Coe (1953a). More recent work (notably Vockeroth, 1969) has resulted in the clear definition of a number of separate genera and subgenera, which makes a lot of sense once one becomes familiar with the hoverflies concerned. Seven species in this group have been added to the British list since Coe's time and more could follow. For those wishing to pursue the taxonomy of the Syrphini in greater detail, Hippa (1968a) illustrated the genitalia of many European species but caution is necessary, since his work is based on material from a limited geographic range, and genitalia are variable.

A feature made use of by Coe (1953a) was the nature of the lateral margins of the tergites, a beaded rim being at least partially present in some species as opposed to margins which gently roll over at the sides. This character is of generic significance and would have been used in the keys here but for frequent complaints that the character is difficult to discern with confidence in some species. The main problem lies with *Epistrophe* which has at best very vague beading in most specimens, yet Coe (1953a) placed some species among the beaded group. For those who are content with this character, the genera of Syrphini with obvious beaded margins are *Chrysotoxum*, *Dasysyrphus*, *Didea*, *Eriozona*, *Eupeodes*, *Scaeva*, *Syrphus* and *Xanthogramma*, whilst those with rolled margins (lacking beading) are *Doros*, *Epistrophe*, *Episyrphus*, *Leucozona*, *Melangyna*, *Meligramma*, *Meliscaeva*, *Parasyrphus* (except *nigritarsis*) and *Sphaerophoria*.

Genus CHRYSOTOXUM

This is a particularly easy hoverfly genus to recognise because of the elongate antennae which project forwards (porrect); other British genera with such antennae lack bold yellow and black markings. The pleura are partially yellow. The thoracic dorsum has a complete or broken yellow stripe at the sides and a pair of grey stripes in the centre line in the front half. Wing vein R_{4+5} is dipped. The abdomen is black with yellow bars or bands, or yellow with characteristic black arcuate markings. The group with arcuate markings comprises species which are not easy to identify and many misidentifications have arisen in the past. Some authorities place *Chrysotoxum* in its own tribe, the Chrysotoxini.

In pattern and flight these are good wasp mimics, although easy to distinguish when they sit on flowers. Most species are associated with open habitat or woodland edge on dry soils, but much remains to be discovered about their biology. A larva of *bicinctum* was found in a compost heap, although the circumstances are not known in detail (Coe, 1953a) and that of *festivum* in an ant nest (Speight, 1976c). Larvae of *C. arcuatum* have been shown to feed on ant-attended, root-feeding aphids (Rotheray et al., 1996).

There are extra species in Europe. Some of the yellowish species have the front margin of the wing dusky, notably beyond the stigma to the end of vein R_{2+3}. This is true of *fasciolatum* De Geer and *intermedium* Meigen, both of which occur in Belgium.

The use of the name *festivum* of the British list has been confirmed as priority historic usage, thus overruling the confusing recent attempt to apply the name *arcuatum* to *festivum*, and *festivum* to *Xanthogramma citrofasciatum* (2001, *Bulletin of Zoological Nomenclature* **58** (3): 241. Opinion 1982 (Case 3090)).

Chrysotoxum arcuatum (Linnaeus, 1758)   Pl. 4, fig. 11
Chrysotoxum fasciatum (Müller) of some recent   Map: Ball & Morris p. 45
authors; substitution overruled

A small dumpy yellowish *Chrysotoxum*, this species is most readily distinguished by the presence of long dark brown hairs on the eyes. The antennae are also distinct among yellowish species in having segment 3 much longer than segments 1 and 2 together (see key, p. 86). Wing length 8–10.25 mm.

Whilst most *Chrysotoxum* species are southern, this is the exception in being essentially a northern and western species. With the exception of a single locality in Norfolk (which lies in an area known to support elements of a more northerly fauna), *arcuatum* occurs north and west of a line between the Severn and the Humber (see map, p. 29). It is typical of lightly wooded areas and moorland margins within upland districts of Britain and Ireland, being relatively frequent in such situations. The larvae feed on aphids associated with ant nests (Rotheray *et al.*, 1996). May to September, peaking in June.

Chrysotoxum bicinctum (Linnaeus, 1758)   Pl. 4, fig. 6
                                                                    Map: Ball & Morris p. 45

The name of this very distinctive species is derived from the two yellow bands on the abdomen. These dominant bands are on tergites 2 and 4, but there is sometimes also a weak minor band on tergite 3. The wings have a very strong dark chocolate-brown patch about the stigma. Wing length 7–10.25 mm.

In Ireland it is the commonest species of *Chrysotoxum*. Its status in the rest of Britain varies widely according to district, being frequent in some places, but scarcer in others and its wide distribution extends to the Scottish Highlands. It occurs in grassy situations, usually in sheltered places near scrub and trees. May to September, peaking from mid June to mid August.

Chrysotoxum cautum (Harris, 1776)   Pl. 4, fig. 9
                                                                    Map: Ball & Morris p. 46

The largest of the predominantly yellow *Chrysotoxum*, this species is most readily identified in the male because the genitalia are large and strongly asymmetrical (the genitalia reach forwards beneath the abdomen to a point equivalent to halfway along tergite 4). The female abdomen is particularly broad; it is easily distinguished from the other yellowish species in this sex since the dense hairs on top of the thorax are as long as the width of the antennae (shorter in other species).

The proportions of the antennae are also distinct (as given in the key, p. 86) but less easy to use as a field character. Wing length 10.25–13 mm.

This is one of the commoner yellowish *Chrysotoxum* species in southern and eastern England and the south coast of Wales (see map, p. 29). It has recently been added to the Irish list (Speight & Nash, 1993), although from a solitary specimen taken in 1919. *C. cautum* is most often found in grassland about wood or scrub edges. Females have been seen ovipositing on large sedges within clumps of trees on heathland (S.R. Miles). May to September, peaking in June.

Chrysotoxum elegans Loew, 1841   Pl. 4, fig. 10
Includes *latilimbatum* Collin of Coe (1953a).   Map: Ball & Morris p. 46

In general appearance this species is often not unlike *cautum* but is usually slightly smaller and distinctly narrower in build. In antennal characters it is most similar to *octomaculatum* and *verralli* (see key, p. 86). *C. elegans* is very variable in the extent of black markings, most specimens being extensively yellow but some are dark and approach the pattern of *festivum* (see that species for comment). The dark forms used to be classified as a separate species, *latilimbatum* Collin, 1940.

The main problems in identification concern the separation between *elegans* and the smaller *verralli*. The character traditionally used is the shape of the black front edge to tergite 2, this being curved and strongly broadening in *elegans* so that the lateral margin of the tergite is about half black, whereas in *verralli* the black band is narrow and its border with the yellow area is almost straight to the lateral margin, at most widening abruptly at the margin. However, confidence is lost when confronted with somewhat intermediate specimens. From the limited material available for these species, the following features seem usable in support. In the yellow forms of *elegans* the sternites have black markings centrally (in *verralli* there are narrow black bands curving forwards to reach or nearly reach the lateral margins of sternites 2, 3 and 4). Darker forms of *elegans* have sternites more similar to those of *verralli*. In both sexes of *elegans* the third antennal segment (as seen from below) is about as long as segments 1 and 2 together, whereas it is shorter in *verralli*. In female *elegans* the hairs on top of the thorax (view from side) are mixed long and short (latter equal to half the width of the first antennal segment), with the dense shorter hairs extensively orange-brown in the front half. If these hairs are more extensively black, there are pale hairs on the grey thoracic stripes (the very short dense hairs are virtually entirely black in female *verralli*, including the hairs on the grey stripes). The female of *elegans* has at least some yellow hairs on the yellow parts of the dorsal surface of the scutellum (all hairs on the scutellum are black in female *verralli*). The male genitalia are larger than in *octomaculatum* and *verralli* (requires comparative material). A few specimens have a fairly well developed orange spot on the wing behind the stigma, but these still seem to be referable to *elegans*. Wing length 9.5–12 mm.

C. elegans is a scarce hoverfly, although historically occurring widely in the southern half of England up to Norfolk and Worcester and westwards to Cornwall. Present indications are that it is declining, with few post-1980 records from the more northern and eastern parts of its former range. There appears to be a stronger association with woodland than in other *Chrysotoxum* species; several records apply to woodland glades and there is an observation of several females flying low over ivy on the ground in dense shade. However, in Cornwall it has been found on quite open ground along cliff tops. April to October, peaking twice, in June and July, and August to September.

Chrysotoxum festivum (Linnaeus, 1758)

Pl. 4, fig. 7

Chrysotoxum arcuatum (Linnaeus) of some
recent authors; substitution overruled

Map: Ball & Morris p. 47

In common with *vernale*, the abdominal pattern in *festivum* consists of three narrow yellow bars which stand out boldly against a black background on tergites 2, 3 and 4. The bars are distinctly and abruptly curved near their outer ends (almost straight in *vernale*). Either the legs are entirely orange-yellow (femora, tibiae and tarsi) or the front femur is only narrowly black at the base (in *vernale* the front and mid femora are black in at least the basal fifth). Both *festivum* and *vernale* have a distinct small dark patch on the wing behind the stigma, but in *festivum* the front half of the wing inwards from this patch is yellowish-brown (in *vernale* the veins in the hind half of the wing are margined by brownish coloration). These two species have the rims of tergites 2 to 4 entirely black since the yellow bars do not reach the edge of the tergites. This last feature is important since some dark varieties of *elegans* can look rather like *festivum*, except that in *elegans* the yellow markings reach the edge of the tergites and the wings lack distinctive coloration. Wing length 8.25–12 mm.

C. festivum is never abundant, but it is widespread in southern England and Wales extending up to north-west England. It is very scarce in north-east England and Scotland, but there are records as far north as Inverness. It also occurs at low-altitude sites in southern Ireland. Grassy places and heathland, usually near woods or scrub margins, provide typical habitats, and it can occur in gardens. Males sometimes hover in loose swarms at heights of 0.5–1 m and can be surprisingly difficult to catch. Coe (1953a) refers to a puparium being found under loose turf in a cultivated field in April. Speight (1976c) reared the same species from a larva found in March in the nest of the ant *Lasius niger* under a stone on damp grassland. May to September, peaking in July and August.

Chrysotoxum octomaculatum Curtis, 1837

Pl. 4, fig. 12
Map: Ball & Morris p. 47

This species is small like *arcuatum* but rather narrower. Normally the markings readily separate *octomaculatum*, the black anterior stripe on tergites 3 and 4 (or 5) being broken just before the lateral margin of the segment (see key, p. 86). However, this feature is not always constant but is usually present on at least one tergite; otherwise the black area reaches the margin of tergite 3 or the black marginal stripe is absent from tergite 4. The female is further distinct in that the hairs on the thoracic dorsum (view from the side) are mostly pale and exceedingly short, the length at most about the same as the greatest width of the arista (the hairs on the axis are pale although sometimes screened by dark hairs in the posterior half). The female scutellum has short pale hairs on most of the yellow area. The male third antennal segment is distinctly shorter than segments 1 and 2 together (as in *elegans*), but these are more nearly equal in the female. In both sexes tergite 2 has the front black zone similar to that of *elegans*. The sternites have black areas reaching or almost reaching their lateral margins (as in *verralli*). The male genitalia are small (as in *verralli*). Wing length 9–10.5 mm.

Nearly all records of this rarity come from the heathlands of east Dorset, the New Forest and Surrey. In this respect it is the southern equivalent of *arcuatum* as regards habitat. Recent records of *octomaculatum* are few, and its limited range appears to have contracted to just two small areas on the heaths of Dorset and Surrey. This is a Priority Species included on the UK Biodiversity Action Plan, and is the subject of further study to try to resolve its habitat requirements. Any additional records would be very welcome and should be accompanied by notes on the nature of the habitat from which it was taken, and any behavioural characteristics that might have been noted. June to September, peaking twice, in June and again in August.

Chrysotoxum vernale Loew, 1841   Pl. 4, fig. 8
                                                                Map: Ball & Morris p. 48

Confusion is most likely with *festivum*, the distinction between the two being discussed under the description of that species. Wing length 8–10.25 mm.

Little is known about this rarity of south-west England. Records, mostly old ones, extend from the New Forest and east Dorset to south Devon (near Plymouth) and Cornwall (Penzance). Thus this hoverfly is seemingly confined to the coast or extends inland only a short distance. Habitat information is sparse, but includes open woodland and scrub on well drained soils. May to August, peaking in June.

Chrysotoxum verralli Collin, 1940   Pl. 4, fig. 13
                                                                Map: Ball & Morris p. 48

Reference should be made to the description of *elegans* where the separation of these two very similar species is discussed. Wing length 8.25–10.5 mm.

C. verralli is largely confined to south-east England and the Midlands, with a few records from Merseyside and Lancashire. It has often been regarded as scarce, but in some parts of its range it can be the commonest *Chrysotoxum*, as in Kent, parts of the London fringe and parts of Warwickshire. However, judging by the number of records submitted in recent years, it seems to be declining. This is a grassland species, often occurring near trees and shrubs and on waste ground. There are records for heathland margins, and some locality records suggest a tolerance of marshy ground. This hoverfly is usually found sitting on foliage. June to October, peaking in July and early August.

Genus DASYSYRPHUS

The most distinctive feature of this genus is the occurrence of unusual types of abdominal markings. Thus oblique bars, curved bars, hooked bars, divided hooked bars and *tricinctus*-style bars are not found in other British Syrphinae except in a few cases which are unlikely to cause confusion. Some specimens of *Dasysyrphus* have a dark stigma, which is otherwise only found in *Didea*, *Leucozona* and some *Melangyna* among the Syrphinae.

This is a woodland genus which is most prevalent in the spring. The larvae are predaceous upon a variety of arboreal aphids and rest in the daytime on twigs and branches where they are superbly camouflaged by their colour patterns and spiky body shape (see plates in Rotheray, 1993).

Dasysyrphus albostriatus (Fallén, 1817)   Pl. 3, fig. 7
                                                                      Map: Ball & Morris p. 51

This is a very easily recognised hoverfly with its oblique bars on tergites 3 and 4. The bars are often fused in the centre line into an inverted V-shaped band, especially in the female of the summer brood. The front of the frons in the female is extensively orange or yellow (black in other *Dasysyrphus*). The stigma is nearly always dark. The front of the thorax has a pair of grey stripes (hence the species name; other species display very faint stripes when seen from some angles). In some respects this fly is like a small version of *Chrysotoxum festivum* (which has long antennae) or *Didea* (which has a very broad abdomen and a loop in vein R_{4+5}). A semi-melanic form of the female has been reported: tergite 2 has normal markings, tergite 3 has markings reduced to a small pair of spots and the rest of the abdomen is black. Wing length 6.25–9.5 mm.

In April and May this species is one of the characteristic heralds of the arrival of hot spring days. It is a woodland-edge species which is widespread through much of Great Britain and Ireland, extending north to Sutherland. April to November, peaking twice, in late May to early June, and again in late August to early September.

Dasysyrphus friuliensis van der Goot, 1960   Map: Ball & Morris p. 51

The bars on tergites 3 and 4 reach the lateral margins and are strongly hooked, the posterior edges of the bars being almost straight, but the anterior edges are deeply undulating so as to cause each bar to be waisted. This waist can be closed so that each bar is divided into two separate spots, resulting in an extraordinary line of four yellow spots across the tergite. The stigma is dark in the available specimens. This species somewhat resembles *venustus* but is normally about one third longer and the antennae are completely black. The hairs on the scutellum are always black. Wing length about 10 mm.

In 1979 the species was recognised as being new to Britain on the basis of a specimen from Yorkshire. It is now known to occur as far south as Warwickshire, but more widely in parts of Derbyshire and Yorkshire, and through northern England to southern Scotland. May to August, peaking in late May.

[Dasysyrphus hilaris (Zetterstedt, 1843)]   Map: Ball & Morris p. 52

D. hilaris most obviously differs from *venustus* in that the facial knob is yellow rather than darkened. Verrall draws attention to the name *hilaris* but does not treat it as a separate species. There are British specimens with the facial character of *hilaris* and it is undecided whether or not these are pale-faced varieties of *venustus*. Without currently accepting the validity of *D. hilaris* on the British list, the name is drawn to attention here, and in the key. Wing length 9–10 mm.

The species was noted as British in the world review by Vockeroth (1969) (it is understood, however, that Dr Vockeroth has not seen a definite British specimen) and as a consequence was included in the 1976 check list. Chandler (1998) however, notes the comment in Stubbs (1996a) that P. Entwistle found a specimen in northern Scotland which appears to have distinct male genitalia (Entwistle, 1995a). An examination of **females** of *hilaris* and *venustus* from various countries in Europe by Láska & Bičík (1996) led to the conclusion that there would appear to be two separate species, although hybridisation may account for intermediates; the character definitions for each species are tabulated here using the most clearly defined features. The variation in characters means that the most practical approach is to match a specimen against this table and find a best fit. Note that the table applies to females only.

Female characters	*venustus*	*hilaris*
Stripe on the face:	sharp, strong	vague or absent
Dusting of frons:	narrow, at sides	covers at least half width of frons
Colour of hind tibia:	entirely yellow	dark mark in middle
Shape of abdomen:	squat	elongate
Length of bars at sides of tergite 2:	about quarter length of tergite	almost half length of tergite
Shape of tergite 3:	width two and a half times length	width twice length
Markings on sternite 2:	strong black band	yellow or weakly dark

Specimens have been taken widely, extending from southern England to the Scottish Highlands and to Ireland, but with a preponderance of recent records from northern England. A series in the Verrall-Collin collection was taken before the modern expansion of conifer forest. April to July, peaking in June.

Dasysyrphus pinastri (De Geer, 1776)   Pl. 3, fig. 10
Dasysyrphus lunulatus (Meigen, 1822)   Map: Ball & Morris p. 52

On tergites 3 and 4 there are hooked bars which have the straight hind margin somewhat oblique. These markings do not reach the side margins, a condition similar to *albostriatus* (in the latter species the bars are straight and the hind margins of the markings on tergite 2 are strongly oblique). The stigma is usually dark or medium brown. The frons is shining black apart from grey dusted areas. A few species with somewhat similar tergite markings are found in other genera, notably *Scaeva pyrastri* (much larger species, frons entirely yellow) and *Eupeodes nielseni* (tergites with lateral marginal hairs entirely black from hind half of tergite 2; far fewer black hairs in *D. pinastri*). There have been various attempts to separate off additional species, but the variation between specimens is such that it is best to regard *D. pinastri* as a very variable species for the time being; *D. nigricornis* may be part of this complex. Consequently it would be wise to retain specimens. Wing length 6.5–8.5 mm.

Records suggest that *pinastri* is widely distributed, although it is likely to be commoner in northern and western Britain where conifer plantations are more extensive. There are a few widely scattered Irish records. It is usually found in woodland rides where it is a regular flower visitor. April to October, peaking in June.

Dasysyrphus tricinctus (Fallén, 1817)   Pl. 3, fig. 8
                                                                    Map: Ball & Morris p. 53
                                                                    Larva: Rotheray Pl. 8e

The distinctive type of triple markings makes this one of the easily recognised hoverflies. Whilst the front markings are small (small oval spots or narrow bars on tergite 2) and the hind markings are also small (narrow bars on tergite 4), the middle marking is much larger and dominant (wide bars on tergite 3). Occasionally markings are absent on tergite 2. Wing length 7.25–10.25 mm.

In May and June this is among the typical spring hoverflies, although rarely seen in any numbers. It is widespread, including Ireland. The margins of lowland woods provide the normal habitat. March to October, although records for March and early April are few. Peaking twice, in late May to early June, and again in late August to early September.

Dasysyrphus venustus (Meigen, 1822)   Pl. 3, fig. 9
                                                                    Map: Ball & Morris p. 53
                                                                    Larva: Rotheray Pl. 8f

The bars on tergites 3 and 4 reach the margins without narrowing. These markings have a slightly curved hind margin and are slightly inflated towards the inner end, thus giving a somewhat hooked appearance, although in the female the bars can be of uniform width or slightly waisted. The stigma is nearly always dark. The frons is almost entirely black, apart from areas of dusting. The antennae are partly yellow, including the whole of the first and second segments. The hairs on the scutellum are usually yellow, or occasionally black. Confusion is most likely with *D. friuliensis* (which is a much larger species with strongly waisted bars on tergites 3 and 4, black antennae and always black scutellar hairs). No other hoverflies fit the description of *venustus* (but see discussion under *hilaris*, which may be no more than a pale-faced form of *venustus*). Wing length 6.25–10 mm.

This species is widespread in England, Wales and Ireland but scarcer in Scotland, although it has been taken as far north as Sutherland. It is a characteristic spring hoverfly, though rarely in numbers, being frequent in May about woodland margins. April to September, peaking in May and early June.

Genus DIDEA

The deep dip in wing vein R_{4+5} is exceptionally well developed for the tribe Syrphini; this character is otherwise only seen in *Lapposyrphus*. The abdomen is broad and rather flat. The deep black ground colour with strongly contrasting yellow, greenish or bluish markings causes *Didea* to look particularly smart compared with similar hoverflies. The markings are generally wedge-shaped, at least on tergite 4 where the central black area is conspicuously triangular in most specimens. The thoracic dorsum has a pair of faint greyish stripes in front, and the pleura are black except for a vertical greyish bar just in front of the wings (the latter feature is found faintly in some other hoverflies such as *Eriozona* s.g. *Megasyrphus*). The leg coloration is also unusual, with the front and mid tarsi jet black (contrasting with yellow or dusky yellow tibiae) and the hind leg black (apart from any paleness about the knee). The stigma is often black.

Identification of species is difficult since so many characters vary. A few new characters are used here, but unfortunately the pattern of wing microtrichia and shape of the alula prove too variable. The true nature of greenish *D. fasciata* needs further assessment; from experience in Finland and Scotland, some specimens have turquoise-blue markings in life, but these fade to greenish in collections.

The larvae of *Didea* are mainly predaceous upon aphids on conifers, but have been recorded from some deciduous trees such as willows and poplars.

Didea alneti (Fallén, 1817)   Pl. 3, fig. 17
                                                        Map: Ball & Morris p. 54

Specimens of this species are rather larger on average than *fasciata* and the markings are usually greenish (possibly turquoise in life, as in Finland). The female is fairly easy to identify since tergite 5 lacks markings and there are long pale hairs on the lateral margins (sometimes some shorter black hairs are present as well) and long pale hairs are dominant on the upper surface of this tergite, even centrally. The male has rather similar hairs on tergite 5 though not quite as obvious since black hairs are present in greater numbers. The male has a rather wide vertex, as in *intermedia*, but the markings on tergite 4 have the front edge almost parallel to the front edge of the tergite, so that there is black in front of the yellow almost throughout. The scutellum has a black rim as in *intermedia*. The dip in vein R_{4+5} is weaker than in other *Didea*. Wing length 9.75–11.5 mm.

During the period from 1894 to 1911, a few specimens were taken in the Forest of Dean, the Wyre Forest and several in the West Midlands including Sutton Park near Birmingham (according to Verrall, 1901). One specimen was found at Colchester in 1893 and another at Fortrose in north Scotland in 1919. There are several records for Kent between 1918 and 1948, and also an Irish record for county Wicklow in 1935. It is possible that a few further reliable records may exist, but seemingly this fine hoverfly is very rare and the only recent records come from Slaley Forest, Northumberland in June and July 1989. May to September, peaking in August.

Didea fasciata Macquart, 1834   Pl. 3, fig. 15
                                                        Map: Ball & Morris p. 54
                                                        Larva: Rotheray Pl. 9f

The markings of *fasciata* are normally orange but eight specimens from the Scottish Highlands (and possibly one specimen from Herefordshire) have a greenish-yellow tinge, and most others from Scotland are yellow rather than orange. A specimen taken alive in Scotland had turquoise markings, fading to greenish-yellow whilst still alive a few hours after capture. The significance of this difference is as yet unclear, but records of greenish or bluish specimens should always be annotated to that effect.

The presence of a yellow club on the halteres will readily distinguish *fasciata* from other *Didea*. Additionally the male has an exceptionally narrow, almost parallel-sided vertex, with the ocellar triangle placed far forwards. In the female the frons has rather broad dust spots reaching forwards near the centre line for much of the middle third of the frons, and generally somewhat diffuse rather than sharp at the edges; the front of the frons has variable yellow and black markings, but if Y-shaped then there is a long stem and the branches of the Y are relatively narrow (compared with *intermedia*). The scutellum has black spots at the front corners at the sides, but the black does not extend as a narrow rim round the hind edge of the scutellum. Wing length 8.25–11 mm.

Though historic records are sparse, recent records show that it is widespread in Britain. It is widely distributed but not common in Ireland. It is listed by Stubbs (1982) as a 'good' primary woodland indicator, but later records suggest that it occurs in woodland of all types, including conifer plantations, secondary woodland and scrub. As mentioned above, most of the specimens from the Scottish Highlands are of a different colour form and there is a possibility that their ecology may be different. A specimen was found flying about small alder bushes on the marshy shore of a loch at Culbin Sands, under identical circumstances to similar turquoise *Didea* in Finland. The habitat for other Scottish records is unknown. Larvae were recently reared through from an aphid colony on a young balsam poplar in a suburban garden in Coventry, following observation of an ovipositing female (Moore, 1999). March to October, although the March record is unusual and the main emergence commences in early May. Peaking twice, in late May to early June, and again in September.

Didea intermedia Loew, 1854   Pl. 3, fig. 16
                                                                               Map: Ball & Morris p. 55

The markings are orange in all British specimens examined and, apart from the fact that the halteres are entirely dark, there is a close resemblance to *fasciata*. *D. intermedia* is rather smaller on average. All available specimens have a black rim to the scutellum (at least extensively so laterally), but this feature is not always distinct. In the male of *intermedia* the vertex steadily broadens posteriorly and the ocellar triangle is not particularly far forwards. In the female the frons has a sharply defined and striking pattern (which seems to be constant); the dust spots only narrowly broaden towards the centre line, leaving a short-stemmed and broad-branched Y-shaped marking which stops well short of the front of the frons. Wing length 7–10 mm.

Compared with *alneti*, all hairs on the margin of tergite 5 are entirely black (in both sexes), but the male vertex is closely similar in both species. The female frons has similar-shaped dust spots in both species, but in *alneti* the black reaches forwards to the front of the frons (there could, however, be confusing variation in both species).

D. intermedia is widespread but with a very patchy distribution in Britain. It has not been recorded from Ireland. Many former records may be misidentifications. In the south of Britain, it has mostly been recorded from coniferised heaths in Dorset, Surrey, the New Forest and Norfolk. In northern Britain, many records come from conifer plantations, especially in South Yorkshire and north-west England. It also seems to be well established in parts of the Scottish Highlands. There seems to be a strong association with Scots pine, and larvae have been found on pine (Evenhuis, 1978). May to September, peaking in July.

Genus DOROS

Doros profuges (Harris, 1780)   Pl. 4, fig. 14
Doros conopseus (Fabricius, 1776), unavailable name   Map: Ball & Morris p. 55

This is an unmistakable hoverfly, being a large narrow species with a dark brown front margin to the wings. This appearance, and the presence of a waisted abdomen, is reminiscent of the conopid fly *Physocephala* except that *Doros* has yellow stripes on the sides of the thoracic disc and narrow yellow bars on the abdomen. Conopids do not have two outer cross-veins parallel with the wing margin. Wing length 11.25–13.25 mm.

Little is known about this rarity, although it is now the subject of a Biodiversity Action Plan. The majority of recent records have been from chalk grassland in the vicinity of woodland edge or scrub edge in Surrey, West Sussex, the Wealden corner of Hampshire, and in Wiltshire. It has also been found on limestone around Morecambe Bay in north-west England and there are old records from Grange, Cumbria. There are more widely scattered old records for the south and the Midlands and a single recent record from Mull in 1991 (Ravenscroft & Barbour, 1992). There is an Irish record from the Burren in 1962 when two males were found but, despite numerous efforts, it has not been found again. It was found for a period of 200 years in the vicinity of Leigh in Essex where, in more recent times, it was reported from the edge of an elm copse, usually seen resting on bramble, but the last report from this area was in 1972. Records are reviewed by Plant (2000). The occurrence of bramble at or near sightings is a common feature of several modern records. Despite its size, this hoverfly is evidently elusive and mimics a large solitary wasp in rather slow flight. A female was observed apparently ovipositing low down on the trunk of an isolated young ash on chalk grassland in Surrey (R. Hawkins, quoted in Stubbs, 1996a), although oviposition was not proven (Morris, 1998b). The larva has been reported abroad from turf and Speight (1988d) describes the puparium, but it remains a mystery how such a large larva of the aphid-feeding type makes a living. However, a 19th century observation suggests that larvae may be associated with ants nesting in wood, most probably *Lasius fuliginosus* according to Speight *et al.* (2001), where they would presumably feed on ant-attended aphids. June to July, peaking in late June to early July.

Genus EPISTROPHE

This is not an easy genus to define. *Parasyrphus nigritarsis* is particularly problematical as it is closer to *Epistrophe* in many respects than to *Parasyrphus*. It is characteristic of *Epistrophe* that the sides of the thorax above the wing are distinctly yellowish, though this coloration is sometimes vague and in any case is far from unusual among the Syrphinae. The legs are extensively yellow, notably the hind femur being entirely yellow in some species, although that is again not a unique character.

The larvae are distinctive, being green and dorso-ventrally flattened with a pale mid-dorsal stripe. They are mostly recorded from trees and shrubs, but are also known to have occurred on tall herbs.

The German fauna has recently been reviewed by Doczkal & Schmid (1994), and Reemer (1999) describes the fauna of the Netherlands. There are a number of additional species which could potentially be found in Britain and these have been included in the key.

Epistrophe diaphana (Zetterstedt, 1843)   Pl. 2, fig. 5
                                                   Map: Ball & Morris p. 56

The distinctive feature is the broad bands on tergites 3 and 4 which narrow abruptly at the side margins. These bands are often distinctly wider than the intervening black areas and are either of uniform width in the centre or are slightly indented on the median line. Bearing in mind that the front edge of the yellow bands is flush with the front edge of the tergites (or virtually so), this type of marking is unique. As a further check, there is a median pair of greyish stripes on the front of the thorax, best seen by looking obliquely from behind, and the antennae are entirely black (both features are shared with *grossulariae*, but the tergite bands are different). The sides of the thorax above the wing base are strongly yellowish. Wing length 7.25–9.75 mm.

This is a rather scarce species, largely confined to the southern counties but also recorded in the past from the Midlands. It is absent from Ireland. It is found along woodland margins and in meadows nearby. There is an observation of oviposition on hogweed, the flowers of which are regularly visited by adults. May to September, peaking in July.

Epistrophe eligans (Harris, 1780)   Pl. 2, fig. 7
                                                   Map: Ball & Morris p. 56
                                                   Larva: Rotheray Pl. 7f

Though very variable, this hoverfly is distinctive through its entire range of patterns. The males are usually rather dark in appearance, markings being confined to triangular spots on tergite 2 (broadly reaching almost the entire margin of the tergite), whilst on tergite 3 there can be a narrow band, often reduced to narrow wedges, or the entire tergite is black. Tergite 4 is normally entirely black although it can have a trace of yellow. The female is a much brighter-looking hoverfly, typically with large spots or bars on tergite 2 (which are only narrowly separated on the mid-line) and a band on tergite 3, whilst tergite 4 may have a narrower band, wedges or be entirely black. Thus the form of the markings on tergite 2 is unusual among the Syrphinae (similar triangular spots are found in *Melangyna cincta*) and it is very unusual to find the markings on tergite 4 much smaller than those on tergite 3 (as in *Dasysyrphus tricinctus*) or tergites 3 and 4 black or virtually so (as in *Melangyna quadrimaculata*). Wing length 6.25–9.5 mm.

As spring begins to warm up, *E. eligans* heralds the hoverfly season really gaining momentum. Blackthorn blossom in late April tends to reveal some freshly emerged specimens and, by the time hawthorn is in flower about a month or so later, this hoverfly is one of the characteristic species throughout much of Britain and Ireland, although much scarcer in Scotland. It will nearly always be found on or near bushes and trees, liking hot sunny wood edges in particular. It is often among the species hovering beside bushes. There is some evidence that *E. eligans* has very flexible emergence times and in recent years it has even been noted in March. As a possible indicator of climate change, it is one species for which all records are useful in order to follow trends in emergence times. March to August, peaking in May.

Epistrophe grossulariae (Meigen, 1822)   Pl. 2, fig. 6
                                                                        Map: Ball & Morris p. 57
                                                                        Larva: Rotheray Pl. 8a

There are few hoverflies with neat parallel bands on tergites 3 and 4 with the yellow uniformly reaching to the front edge, *grossulariae* being distinctive as a moderately large species with the bands broadening at the margins (rather than being pinched by an extension of black). Identification is easily confirmed by looking for the median pair of greyish stripes at the front of the thorax (best seen by looking obliquely from behind). Such thoracic stripes occur in *diaphana* but this species has the yellow bands pinched at the sides. Both *grossulariae* and *diaphana* have black antennae, but the front of the frons is black in *grossulariae* (a complete black stripe in the female) whilst the area above the antennae is yellow in *diaphana*. Wing length 9–12.25 mm.

Umbellifer flowers are a particularly good lure along wood edges or in nearby meadows throughout much of Britain and the species is widely distributed in Ireland. However, it is somewhat local and rarely found in numbers. The larvae are known to go through two or even three years before adults emerge. So far, they have only been found on sycamore. May to October, peak in July.

Epistrophe melanostoma (Zetterstedt, 1843)   Map: Ball & Morris p. 57

Superficially, *melanostoma* resembles *nitidicollis* with orange antennae, but the absence of black hairs on the scutellum clearly separates it from that species. Careful examination is necessary, however, because the number of black scutellar hairs in *nitidicollis* varies from 100% to just a few (Morris, 1998b). It can be separated from *ochrostoma* by examination of the mouth, which is fringed black in *melanostoma* and yellow in *ochrostoma*. It is possible that *Parasyrphus nigritarsis* may run to this species in the key as it has a broad black mouth edge; however, it has dark tarsi and the male hind femur is extensively black at the base, unlike any species of *Epistrophe*. Wing length 9–9.5 mm.

This species is now known to have two very similar allied species: *cryptica* and *obscuripes* (=*similis*) (Doczkal & Schmid, 1994; Schmid, 1999a). These are potential British species and are included in the key. They have been found in the Maastricht district of the Netherlands, which is also the only area of that country from which *diaphana* is known (Reemer, 1999).

This species was first found in Britain in 1989 (Beuk, 1990). Currently, records of *melanostoma* are largely confined to a few southern counties of England, mainly centred on Surrey where it has been found regularly in sunny woodland situations, often on sunlit leaves. May to June, peaking in early May, possibly a little earlier than *nitidicollis*.

Epistrophe nitidicollis (Meigen, 1822)   Pl. 2, fig. 4
                                                                        Map: Ball & Morris p. 58

This species is rather similar to *grossulariae* but may be distinguished at once by the fact that the antennae are orange. Also, the front of the frons is orange. The bands are not as neat, notably with tergites 3 and 4 having a black margin in front of the yellow. The thorax lacks stripes. The femora are entirely orange. The build is less robust, the abdomen being flatter. Confusion is also possible with *melanostoma* and *ochrostoma* (both of which have a yellow-haired scutellum) and

Parasyrphus nigritarsis (which has dark tarsi) and several other *Epistrophe* species which could yet be found in Britain (specimens with entirely yellow hairs on the scutellum would be suspect, for example). Voucher specimens should therefore be retained. Wing length 8–11.25 mm.

Woodland rides and coppice glades in May provide the best conditions and it is usually observed visiting flowering shrubs and umbellifer flowers or resting on sunlit foliage. This species is fairly local in the south and Midlands, but scarce over the rest of Britain as far north as the southern fringes of the Scottish Highlands (D. Robertson, quoted in Stubbs, 1996a). It is also recorded from a single wooded locality in Connemara in Ireland. April to September, peaking in late May and early June.

Epistrophe ochrostoma (Zetterstedt, 1849)   Map: Ball & Morris p. 58

The only species with which *ochrostoma* can be confused are *nitidicollis* and *melanostoma*, both of which also have orange antennae, rather than black. *E. ochrostoma* has yellow scutellar hairs like *melanostoma*, but it has a yellow mouth margin rather than a fringe of black around the mouth.

It is now known that there is another very similar species in Europe, *flava* Doczkal & Schmid (1994), which is well established in inland and coastal parts of the Netherlands (Reemer, 1999); it is included in the key.

At the moment there is just a single record from North Wales (Heaver, 1990). In the Netherlands this species has been recorded visiting the catkins of willows, including creeping willow on dunes (Reemer, 1999). May (April to end of May in Netherlands).

Genus EPISYRPHUS

Episyrphus balteatus (De Geer, 1776)   Pl. 3, fig. 1
Map: Ball & Morris p. 59
Larva: Rotheray Pl. 5f

There can be few more distinctive hoverflies, the occurrence of double black bands on tergites 3 and 4 being unique. However, the strength of these markings is very variable; the anterior black band can be reduced to two black dashes whilst the dark forms tend to have the lateral margins darkened. Thus it would be possible to envisage forms without the anterior dashes or so blackened that the basic markings are obscured. With such extreme examples, reference should be made to the distinctive pattern of faint stripes on the thoracic dorsum, best seen obliquely from behind. There is a narrow median grey stripe anteriorly, flanked by another grey stripe on either side, all these stripes coalescing into an extensive grey area at the back of the thoracic dorsum. Wing length 6–10.25 mm.

This is an abundant hoverfly throughout Britain and Ireland and is recorded in all months in most years. It is also the most frequently recorded species in Britain both in terms of the number of observations and the number of 10 km squares. There is evidence to indicate that some adults succeed in hibernating through the winter, sometimes emerging on mild days even in midwinter. However, the numbers can be boosted enormously by the influx of migrants. Males can often be found hovering in beams of sunlight within the heart of a wood. January to December, peaking in July and August.

Genus ERIOZONA

Megasyrphus, a wasp mimic, has been merged by Vockeroth & Thompson (1987) into the genus *Eriozona*, which historically has accommodated a bee mimic. However, the larvae are very different and it seems best to treat *Megasyrphus* as a subgenus.

Subgenus ERIOZONA

Eriozona syrphoides (Fallén, 1817)   Pl. 4, fig. 15
                                                                 Map: Ball & Morris p. 60
                                                                    Larva: Rotheray Pl. 10a

The thorax and most of the abdomen are black, leaving a contrasting yellow scutellum and strongly reddish tip to the abdomen (the tergite surface is red). The wings have a dark area at the base and another extending from below the stigma to the centre of the wing (although the stigma is only yellow). At first sight *Eriozona* is like an outsized *Cheilosia illustrata* (but the face is yellow in *Eriozona*) or an unusual *Volucella bombylans* (which has the yellow face extended downwards, the sides of the thoracic dorsum yellowish, the arista plumose and the tail lacking a red ground colour). Wing length about 12 mm.

The first British specimens to be reported were taken in 1968 in Snowdonia and made a spectacular addition to our fauna (Crow, 1969) although it emerged that an earlier specimen had been taken at Lancaster in 1957 (see review by Entwistle, 1978). It has subsequently been found throughout western Britain, from the south coast to Sutherland, but remains most frequent in Wales and north-west England. It was added to the Irish list by Speight (1998) who regards it as a recent arrival. It has a preference for mauve flowers such as Devil's-bit scabious, willowherbs and heathers; Haslett & Entwistle (1980) analysed the pollen on adults and queried whether the adults might hibernate. Crow (1983) found adults at hawthorn blossom in the spring and discussed the possibility that the species is double-brooded (rather than hibernating as an adult). Most records are for spruce plantations or deciduous woods where spruce is present, adults being found along rides or at woodland edges. However, in Holland and Belgium most records are for deciduous woods (van der Goot, 1982). Nonetheless, a consensus of opinion in Britain is that *Eriozona syrphoides* is a new colonist which has found a niche in spruce plantations. This view is further supported by the recent description of larvae from 40-year-old spruce monocultures in Czechoslovakia; larvae were feeding on the aphid *Cinara pinea* (Kula, 1983). May to October with a small peak in June and the second larger peak in August.

Subgenus MEGASYRPHUS

Eriozona erratica (Linnaeus, 1758)   Pl. 3, fig. 18
Megasyrphus annulipes (Zetterstedt, 1838)   Map: Ball & Morris p. 59

It would be possible to overlook this hoverfly as a largish specimen of *Syrphus*. There are two very simple field characters in that sternites 1 to 4 each have a complete broad black band and the face has a strong black median stripe. Wing vein R_{4+5} is distinctly dipped and the hairs on the femora and coxae are entirely black. In a pinned series of specimens, *E. erratica* will stand out because the centre of the thoracic dorsum is shining black whereas the thorax of *Syrphus* is a duller greenish-grey hue. The eyes are hairy (rather faintly so) as in *Syrphus torvus*. Wing length 10.75–12 mm.

Records are widespread, with the majority concentrated in northern and western Britain where conifer plantations are most extensive. There are few Irish records, concentrated on the east coast, and it is regarded as a recent arrival. This species should be sought in woodland rides where it is a regular flower visitor, recorded at crosswort and yellow composites. It is possible that this species will be overlooked amongst a profusion of *Syrphus* species, but on occasions it can be quite abundant. Careful attention should be paid to specimens with a somewhat more orange hue to the yellow bands, which may prove to be *E. erratica*. May to November, peaking twice, in May to June and again in August.

Genus EUPEODES

The genus consists of species with a rather oval abdomen, bearing a pattern of spots, lunules or bands. The range of pattern in each species is variable and several of the common species are sexually dimorphic, thus causing great confusion to the beginner. The hairs along the lateral margins of tergites 3 and 4 (and the more posterior tergites) are entirely black, except in subgenus *Lapposyrphus*, but even here all hairs are black as from tergite 4. All other Syrphini with anything resembling the markings of *Eupeodes* will be found to have more extensive pale hairs on the lateral margins of the abdomen, with the exception of *Scaeva* (normally a much larger insect with hairy eyes and inflated frons).

Lunulate spots on tergites 3 and 4 form the basic style of markings, just recognisable even when broad, but sometimes losing this shape and becoming square. The markings are very variable within each species and frequently the spots fuse on the centre line to become partial or complete bands. Such complete bands can superficially look like the *Syrphus*-style moustache band, but in nearly all examples of *Eupeodes* the bands do not reach the lateral margins of the tergites, except in *E. corollae* and *Lapposyrphus*.

There are two subgenera, with *Lapposyrphus* having a distinct dip in wing vein R_{4+5}. The other *Eupeodes* are not particularly easy to identify to species. Most specimens will key out, but atypical specimens may cause problems. Revisionary work on the continent has resulted in the European fauna being increased to over 20 species based on subtle characters. It remains a distinct possibility that more species may yet be found in Britain, even apart from the unnamed taxa in this book. Members of this genus are among the commonest of the Syrphini. *Eupeodes luniger* is a very widespread species and, together with *corollae*, can appear in great numbers during times of migration (or mass emergence). Unless the summer has been dominated by bad weather, these species are usually abundant in late summer and early autumn, often visiting gardens and urban waste ground in great numbers.

With the exception of *corollae* and *luniger*, which are predaceous upon ground-layer aphids, the majority of *Eupeodes* feed on conifer aphids.

Subgenus LAPPOSYRPHUS

Previously only a single species was recognised to occur in Europe, with very few specimens in British collections. P.F. Entwistle obtained a series of specimens from Wales and concluded that there were two species as treated here.

Eupeodes (Lapposyrphus) lapponicus (Zetterstedt, 1838)   Pl. 3, fig. 14
Metasyrphus (*Lapposyrphus*) *lapponicus* (Zetterstedt, 1838)   Map: Ball & Morris p. 69

The abdomen has lunulate spots on tergites 3 and 4 so might be mistaken for *Eupeodes luniger*, but for the distinctive wing venation of *Lapposyrphus*, with R_{4+5} strongly dipped. *E. lapponicus* has the whole of the mouth margin distinctly darkened. The key (p. 92) illustrates the wing microtrichia pattern found in typical specimens. The occiput has the hair fringe grey. Wing length 8.5–10 mm.

Early British records are from the Scottish Highlands, but no specimens have been taken there in recent years. It has not been recorded from Ireland. Recent records are from south-west England; detailed notes are given by Levy & Levy (1998). Larvae have been found feeding at some height in conifers, but have also been found feeding on aphids on spindle and oak. On the continent this is a Scandinavian species. June to July, peaking in late June to early July.

Eupeodes (Lapposyrphus) species A   Map: Ball & Morris p. 72
Metasyrphus (*Lapposyrphus*) species A of
Stubbs & Falk, 1983

The differences between the two species are not obvious. In British specimens the mouth margin is partly yellow (as shown in the key), but the definition of dark and yellow areas is often imprecise so that it may be necessary to examine the inside of the mouth opening to see how opaque the mouth margin may be (some continental specimens have entirely yellow mouth margins). The key (p. 92) indicates wing microtrichia patterns for typical specimens. The post-ocular fringe is golden yellow though the distinction from *lapponicus* is sometimes slight. Wing length about 9 mm.

The distribution of this species in Britain is still poorly known, but the earliest specimens were taken in South Devon in 1947 and the few records are widely scattered over England and Wales. It has not been recorded from Ireland. Recent records have been from pure conifer plantations and from partially coniferised deciduous woodland, the presence of spruce probably being the common factor. Whilst true *lapponicus* is regarded as native, species A is interpreted as a new colonist. A Suffolk site has produced records in both 1997 and 1999, suggesting that a population has become established in the Brecks at least. On the continent this species occurs south of Scandinavia and is, for instance, quite frequent in parts of the Alps. June to September, peaking in August.

Subgenus EUPEODES

There are two fairly distinct groups of species. In one group (*nielseni* and *nitens*) the front femur normally has black hairs near the base on the posterior surface, wing vein R_{4+5} reaches the wing margin at the wing tip or nearly so, and the sternites are black-banded for virtually their full width. In the other group (*bucculatus*, *corollae*, *latifasciatus* and *luniger*) the hairs on the femur are pale near the base on the posterior surface, wing vein R_{4+5} reaches the wing margin well in front of the wing tip, and the sternites have central black patches (rather wide in *bucculatus*). The wing character is very distinctive among Syrphini, but is perhaps rather subtle. It is also worth noting that some species (especially *corollae* and *latifasciatus*) have particularly short, broad, rounded wings. Among medium-sized Syrphini with a broad build, *Eupeodes* includes some of the commonest hoverflies.

It should be borne in mind that there are other European species in this difficult subgenus (Dušek & Láska, 1976; Marcos-García & Láska, 1983; Mazánek *et al.*, 1998, 1999a, 1999b).

Eupeodes (Eupeodes) bucculatus (Rondani, 1857)   Map: Ball & Morris p. 70
Metasyrphus latilunulatus (Collin, 1931)

Superficially, the male of this species closely resembles *luniger* except that the lunulate spots are less wide (almost square) and often fused on the mid-line (rarely so in *luniger*). The female usually has the spots fused into bands on tergites 3 and 4, hence looking rather like *latifasciatus* except that the front edge of the bands is more undulating. Both species have rather long hairs along the lateral margin of the tergites (mainly as long as width of hind tibia). The scutellum has black hairs (as in *luniger*), pale hairs (as in other *Eupeodes*) or a mixture of black and pale. The alula is completely covered with microtrichia in both sexes (partly clear in *luniger*). Wing length 7–8 mm.

As previously defined, '*bucculatus*' appears to be a species complex. An interim approach to identification is offered in the key by separating species B from *bucculatus*, but this is very much a working basis to encourage others to help towards a solution of the taxonomy. However, there still seems to be considerable variation remaining, and at least two forms within the restricted definition of *bucculatus* can be recognised. It is possible that these represent the spring and summer broods, but the differences seem rather extreme to be explained by brood dimorphism, especially the microtrichia of the male.

Form X. Both sexes have a short, rather round third antennal segment. On tergite 5 and sternite 4 the median black bar reaches virtually the full width. In the male, the second basal cell is about 70% covered in microtrichia. Specimens of both sexes were found at Denge Wood, Kent, on 6 & 8 May 1999. They were taken on flowers of wood spurge in a glade at the bottom of a chalk valley.

Form Y. The third antennal segment is distinctly longer than wide. On tergite 5 and sternite 4 the median black bar stops well short of the sides. In the male, the second basal cell is only about 30% covered in microtrichia. The outer side of the hind coxa has some black hairs, best developed in the female (such black hairs are lacking in all other British *Eupeodes*, even in the much darker *bucculatus* form X). Specimens of both sexes were found in Windsor Forest on 27 July 1987.

E. bucculatus in the broad sense has historically been a poorly known and seemingly scarce species in Britain. The recording scheme has accumulated rather more records than had been expected, revealing a widespread distribution in England and Wales, plus a very few records for Scotland extending to the Spey Valley. There are few, scattered records in Ireland. The best areas appear to be in parts of southern England and around Sheffield, where it was reared from amongst aphids on foxglove (Hawkins, 1995). The records in total reveal a very long flight period covering most of the season, with peaks in late May and July to August. Early April to early October.

Eupeodes (Eupeodes) corollae (Fabricius, 1794)   Pl. 2, fig. 12
Metasyrphus corollae (Fabricius, 1794)   Map: Ball & Morris p. 68

The sexes are quite different in appearance. The males have rather square commas on tergites 3 and 4, often partially fused at the mid-line and normally extending into the lateral margins so that at least 50% of the extreme lateral margins are yellow (it is necessary to look closely). The male genitalia are much larger than in other *Eupeodes*, the pre-genital segment being nearly half the width of the posterior margin of tergite 5. The female typically has narrower commas on tergites 3 and 4, which are well separated (in the examples examined), but again close examination will show that much of the extreme lateral margin of these segments is normally yellow. The posterior margins of tergites 2, 3 and 4 also have a well defined grey-shining band (view from behind) which is diagnostic. The black area on the frons in the female extends only a very short distance in front of the ocelli (of the distance between front ocellus and antennae, only about one quarter is black). Wing length 5–8.25 mm.

One of the commonest hoverflies in open habitats, it can be abundant in some years, particularly when numbers are boosted by a migration or mass emergence in midsummer. Patches of flowers in arable fields, meadows, road verges, hedgerows, heaths, gardens and waste ground in urban areas are among the places that *corollae* will be found throughout Britain, although it is not common in Ireland. March to November, peaking in July and August.

Eupeodes (Eupeodes) latifasciatus (Macquart, 1829)   Pl. 2, fig. 13
Metasyrphus latifasciatus (Macquart, 1829)   Map: Ball & Morris p. 69

Though more typically with bands on tergites 3 and 4, the markings can be commas rather similar to those found in *corollae*. The males are variable, but usually have partially fused square spots resembling spectacles, the yellow areas not reaching the lateral margins of the tergites. In the female there is normally a band with the front edge almost parallel with the front edge of the tergite, especially on tergite 3, and this band is pinched at the margins so that only about a quarter of the lateral margin is yellow. Some females have the lateral margins of tergites 3 and 4 black, especially if the band is reduced to pairs of commas (thus resembling *corollae*, although in that species the spots reach the margins). The frons in the female is about half black and half yellow, though some examples are more extensively yellow along the centre line. As a microscope character, it should be noted that the alula is entirely covered in microtrichia (incompletely covered in *corollae*). *E. latifasciatus* usually has the second basal cell completely covered in microtrichia, but note that *bucculatus* form X has about 75% coverage; however, in *latifasciatus* the black marking on tergite 5 does not approach the sides (*bucculatus* form X has the black marking almost reaching the sides). Wing length 6.5–8.5 mm.

Though very widespread throughout Britain, it fluctuates considerably in numbers from year to year, sometimes being very scarce and then becoming fairly common. It is less frequent than *latifasciatus* in Ireland. It has a strong association with open habitats, with a preference for wet meadows with rushes or lush vegetation. March to October, peaking in August.

Eupeodes (Eupeodes) lundbecki (Soot-Ryen, 1946)   Map: Ball & Morris p. 70
Metasyrphus lundbecki (Soot-Ryen, 1946)

This species looks like an extra-large *E. luniger* or a bare-eyed *Scaeva selenitica*. It also resembles *Scaeva* in the presence of an inflated frons (though rather less inflated) and in the extensive absence of microtrichia on the wings (*e.g.* cell r_5 is about a quarter bare as illustrated by Watt & Robertson (1990); see wing venation on p. 53). In many ways it is intermediate between the two genera, but is included in *Eupeodes* because of the bare eyes (eyes always hairy in *Scaeva*).

This species was added to the British list in 1990 on the basis of specimens from Aberdeen in 1976, Fair Isle in 1982 and Dumfries in 1984 (Watt & Robertson, 1990). Two females were found on flowers of angelica on Foula (Shetland) in 1996 (Pennington, 1999). There is also a record from Stiffkey in Norfolk (I. Perry, quoted in Stubbs, 1996a). At the moment it is thought to be a vagrant from Europe where it is regarded as migratory. August.

Eupeodes (Eupeodes) luniger (Meigen, 1822)   Pl. 2, fig. 14
Metasyrphus luniger (Meigen, 1822)   Map: Ball & Morris p. 71
                                                         Larva: Rotheray Pl. 9a, 9b

This is a highly variable species, both in terms of size and colour. The average specimen is rather larger than *corollae*; indeed, it is intermediate in size and appearance between *corollae* and *Scaeva pyrastri*. It has broad lunulate markings on tergites 3 and 4, which are usually very dominant over the intervening black areas in the male; occasionally the spots partially fuse in the mid-line to form a spectacle shape but they do not reach the lateral margins of these tergites. The female frons is black in the posterior third, but there is usually a narrow Y-shaped black extension, flanked by yellowish dust adjacent to the eye margins (specimens with the Y reduced or indistinct are less easy to identify). Occasionally the frons can be darker and approach the state typically shown by *nitens* and *nielseni*, but it does not have the predominantly black posterior hairs on the front femur typical of those species (at most it has scattered black hairs within a mainly yellow pile). The alula is only partially covered in microtrichia (in the rather similar species B, it is completely covered). *Scaeva pyrastri* has hairy eyes and white markings of a different shape. Confusion most often arises from very dark or very pale specimens of *luniger*. Spring females can be particularly dark, with very narrow spots on the tergites and the hind femora black on the basal half or more. These can be very difficult to distinguish from *nielseni* (see that species for a more detailed account of differences). Wing length 6.5–10 mm.

The habitats and distribution are very similar to *corollae* whose migratory behaviour it shares. However, over much of England and Wales it is far more consistent in occurrence and has a substantial resident population. It is widespread but not common in Ireland. Though there is no evidence of hibernation by adults, they can be found exceptionally early and late in the season. March to November, peaking twice with a small peak in May and a much larger peak from July to September.

Eupeodes (Eupeodes) nielseni (Dušek & Láska, 1976)
Metasyrphus nielseni Dušek & Láska, 1976
arcuatus of Coe (1953a), a misidentification.

Pl. 2, fig. 15
Map: Ball & Morris p. 71
Larva: Rotheray Pl. 9c

This species most closely resembles a rather small, dark *luniger* with very narrow, straighter yellow spots on the tergites and a tendency towards more extensive black hairs on the posterior surface of the front femur. The sternites bear broad black markings that almost reach the side margins, although both this character and the black hairs on the front femur are poorly featured in a Suffolk specimen recently obtained (S. Falk). Females have a much more extensively darkened frons than *luniger* and the hind femur is usually dark on its basal two-thirds (rarely more than half in *luniger*). *E. nielseni* shares a number of features with the similar-sized *nitens*, including the tendency to have extensive black hairs behind the front femur, the heavily marked sternites and the extensively darkened female frons. However, the markings on the tergites are very different. Wing length 7.5–9 mm.

With material being so sparse, and substantial difficulties in defining the nature of the species, it was not until 1976 that this species was scientifically described and finally named. The Scottish Highlands are the main home of *nielseni* where it occurs in or at the edges of mature pine forests. The flowers of tormentil and rowan are the best places to search in such situations. In recent years, *E. nielseni* has been found at a number of localities in Dorset, Hampshire, Oxfordshire, Suffolk, Worcestershire (Wyre Forest) and South Wales, suggesting that its range is expanding in response to wider coniferisation. It has not been recorded from Ireland. April to September, peaking in June.

Eupeodes (Eupeodes) nitens (Zetterstedt, 1843)
Metasyrphus nitens (Zetterstedt, 1843)

Pl. 2, fig. 16
Map: Ball & Morris p. 72

This is another very variable species, typically with undulating bands on tergites 3 and 4. Paler males somewhat resemble *latifasciatus* except that the undulation of the bands is more pronounced and the distance from the front margin of the tergite is greater. In darker males, the narrower bands have a very pronounced moustache shape. Occasionally the bands are almost broken to form a pair of lunules, although they are never widely separated in the manner of *nielseni*. The markings on these tergites do not reach the lateral margins or only very narrowly so. Females resemble both *latifasciatus* and *bucculatus*. From the first species, the much darker frons is diagnostic. Compared with all forms of *bucculatus*, the hind margins of the yellow bands on tergites 3 and 4 are less pinched in the middle thus producing V-shaped markings of fairly constant width (these bands are much narrower centrally in *bucculatus*). In both sexes, sternites 3 and 4 have broad black rectangular bands for their full width, a useful character eliminating other *Eupeodes* (except *nielseni* and exceptionally dark *luniger*) and most other similar-looking Syrphini. Wing length 6.75–7.75 mm.

There are scattered records of this uncommon hoverfly for southern and midland England, also for Wales, nearly always from ancient deciduous forest, but most recent records are from the southern part of this range. It has not been recorded from Ireland. There is a continental record of a larva reared from a thistle (*Cirsium*) in alpine grassland, but adults are usually found in broadleaved woodland where they visit white umbellifers and yellow composites. April to October, peaking in May, early July and late August.

Eupeodes (Eupeodes) species B

This species has previously keyed out within *bucculatus*, but is very distinct because it is much more robust and the males have strikingly large markings which may take the form of separated or joined-up spots. Males have a wider frons angle than in *luniger* (which never has joined spots). The females are rather similar to those of *luniger* except than the spots on tergites 3 and 4 are nearly always joined or fully fused as bands. The hind tibia is black in the basal half or more (entirely yellow or hardly any black in luniger). Wing length 9 mm.

Liverpool Museum contains specimens from Wallasey on the coast of the Wirral, Cheshire (including a female with band markings). There is also a specimen from Formby Point on the South Lancashire coast (a female with separated spots). The dunes here have become rather renowned for this large species with exceptionally large markings. Specimens of a similar nature are also known from the Cheshire Plain, extending to near Birmingham. The habitat and appearance are very different from the ancient woodland examples of '*bucculatus*' of either form. Mid May to mid July.

Eupeodes (Eupeodes) species C

This species has only been distinguished in the female, being separated from *luniger* by the broad bilobed black extension on the frons. The hind femur is black in the basal half (as in species B; entirely yellow or hardly any black in *luniger*); nearly all British *Eupeodes* have the hind femur black at the base or more. The second basal cell is entirely covered with microtrichia at the apex (a clear apical patch in *luniger*). The front of the mouth is strongly black, with the dark colour extending up to the base of the knob and, in some cases, higher on the median line of the face, and to a varying extent reaching back to the black area under the eyes (much more heavily marked than in *luniger*). The sternites also have much more extensive black markings, almost reaching the sides of sternites 3 and 4 as rectangular patches. Wing length 8.5 mm.

A number of specimens were found in samples from Malaise traps run in the Sheffield area in 2000. Trap sites were largely in suburban gardens with semi-natural habitat nearby. Insufficient material is at hand to establish the length of the flight period. June.

Genus LEUCOZONA

There are three species in two subgenera. The single species in subgenus *Leucozona* has a dark patch in the centre of the wing whilst this marking is absent in the two species of the subgenus *Ischyrosyrphus*. The genus is reasonably distinctive in that the stigma is a deep brown colour, confusion being unlikely with the few *Dasysyrphus*, *Melangyna* and *Didea* with a similar stigma. Also, most specimens of *Leucozona* have a distinctive pair of very large spots on tergite 2, but these spots are often reduced. The anterior part of the thoracic dorsum has a pair of grey stripes in *Ischyrosyrphus*, but in subgenus *Leucozona* there is a much fainter striped appearance.

Subgenus ISCHYROSYRPHUS

Leucozona (Ischyrosyrphus) glaucia (Linnaeus, 1758)
Pl. 4, fig. 2
Map: Ball & Morris p. 81

The black stigma, yellow scutellum, large quadrate spots on tergite 2 and narrow bars on tergites 3 and 4 serve to readily distinguish this species. The markings on the abdomen are normally yellow but specimens with grey dusted markings are frequent. Occasionally the markings are reduced, the spots on tergite 2 becoming a pair of small faint spots and the bars on tergites 3 and 4 very narrow. Wing length 8–11.25 mm.

This is a rather local species but it occurs in many lowland districts, including Ireland, where there is lush vegetation along woodland rides and wood edges. Umbellifers such as hogweed and angelica are a good lure. One feature of interest in its distribution is its scarcity in East Anglia and apparent absence from the eastern Weald. The larvae are predaceous upon ground-layer aphids. May to October, peaking in July and August.

Leucozona (Ischyrosyrphus) laternaria (Müller, 1776)
Pl. 4, fig. 3
Map: Ball & Morris p. 82
Larva: Rotheray Pl. 8d

In general appearance this species resembles *glaucia* but the scutellum is mainly black, with only the tip yellow, resulting in a very distinctive hoverfly. Though the spots on tergite 2 are normally yellow (rarely absent, apart from grey dusting), the bars on tergites 3 and 4 are usually dusted grey. The bars on tergite 3 are often somewhat reduced at the lateral margins, especially in the male. The front and mid legs are extensively black on the tibiae and tarsi, whereas in *glaucia* these parts are entirely yellow. Wing length 7–10 mm.

L. laternaria is found in similar situations to *glaucia*. The larvae feed on *Cavariella* aphids on umbellifers. It has a similar distribution, but also extends into eastern England. Both species are often found together. May to September, peaking in July.

Subgenus LEUCOZONA

Leucozona (Leucozona) lucorum (Linnaeus, 1758)
Pl. 4, fig. 1
Map: Ball & Morris p. 82
Larva: Rotheray Pl. 8c

A typical specimen is unmistakable in having a conspicuous black cloud in the centre of the wings and large yellow quadrate spots on tergite 2 contrasting with the predominantly black abdomen. The pale markings on tergite 2 often merge and sometimes extend onto the anterior part of tergite 3 and, exceptionally, there are paired yellowish markings on tergite 4. However, the pale markings can be reduced, especially in the male, so that there remains only a trace of yellow at the sides of tergite 2. This latter form can look deceptively like *Cheilosia illustrata* which also has a wing cloud, but *L. lucorum* can be distinguished at once by its yellow scutellum and yellow sides to the face. Wing length 7.75–10 mm.

Recent studies have revealed a very similar species in Europe, at first thought to be *nigripila* Mik, a species from the Caucasus (Doczkal, 1998) and then described as *inopinata* new to science (Doczkal, 2000b). Separation is not easy, especially when the range of variation in Scandinavia is taken into account. Doczkal gave tables of characters, from which a reduced version is offered below (omitting a few characters which do not seem to work well in Britain, such as the front margin of the scutellum which may not always be black in *lucorum*). It would seem that *inopinata* is widespread although with a clustered distribution in parts of temperate Europe. In some sandy districts in the Netherlands it is the predominant species, so districts such as the Breck in East Anglia deserve more careful survey.

Characters for both sexes	*lucorum*	*inopinata*
Hairs on tergite 4:	50-100% white	100% black
Colour of top of thorax:	darker, brown	paler, greenish grey
Hind corner of scutellum:	laterally dark	yellow or tiny spot
Black area on lower face:	virtually no dust	extensive dust
Male characters		
Hind margin of tergite 2:	hairs all/mainly yellow	hairs all/mainly black
Hind corner of tergite 3:	shining	dusted
Female characters		
Coverage of microtrichia on 2nd basal cell:	almost complete	over 50% clear
Hind femur on ventral apical half:	bare	covered in tiny hairs

Lush herbaceous vegetation in damp woodland provides ideal habitat, the hoverfly visiting flowers in dappled sunlight along rides and woodland margins. In such situations this is a characteristic spring hoverfly throughout most of lowland Britain and Ireland, extending more locally to Orkney. May to August, peaking in May and June. Rare fresh specimens in August indicate a partial second brood.

Genus MELANGYNA

There were formerly two subgenera: *Melangyna* was relatively robust and nearly always had rectangular or oval spots on tergites 3 and 4, whilst *Meligramma* was rather narrower-bodied and nearly always had triangular spots on at least one tergite or banded markings. Recent revisions have separated *Melangyna* and *Meligramma* as separate genera. With the exception of *cincta*, the hind legs are black except for any paleness about the knees, a feature in common with some *Parasyrphus* (which are generally more broadly built and either resemble a small *Syrphus* or have semicircular spots). *Didea* also has rather dark hind legs, but these flies are distinctive.

Most species of *Melangyna* are relatively small, narrowly built Syrphini with rectangular or oval spots on tergites 3 and 4 (*cincta* has bands and female *quadrimaculata* is entirely black). The only rather similar hoverfly with paired spots and black hind legs is *Parasyrphus punctulatus*, but this has semicircular spots in the male, while in the female tergites 3 and 4 have slender yellow bars narrowly extended to the lateral margins (compare with female *lasiophthalma*).

The key allows for several European species which could potentially occur in Britain. *M. coei* Nielsen occurs in the lowland part of south-west Norway. Males could be confused with *arctica*, and females with *umbellatarum*. *M. lucifera* Nielsen has been found in the early spring in southern Norway on sallow catkins amongst numbers of *lasiophthalma* (Nielsen, 1980).

The identification of species is not easy. Coe (1953a) provides a fairly useful key ('*Syrphus*', couplet 45 onwards) although there are difficulties, especially with the male face coloration. Speight *et al.* (1975) include a revised key, though certain features, such as the colour of hairs on the hind coxae in the male, are not as useful as one would wish. The latter work comments on the intractable problem of separating *compositarum* and *labiatarum* where, even with comparative material, it is not always clear whether one or two species are involved – a matter still undecided although van der Goot (1981) confidently keys them out.

Melangyna arctica (Zetterstedt, 1838)   Map: Ball & Morris p. 83
                                                              Larva: Rotheray Pl. 6d

The male of this species has black hairs in the middle or posterior half of the thoracic dorsum (view from side), a feature shared only with *ericarum* among the species with spots on tergite 2. The main difficulty is the scarcity of comparative material of the latter species. However, it seems that the dusky brown halteres of *arctica* and the contrast between dark frons and paler dusted face are useful features. Speight *et al.* (1975) draw attention to the face being parallel-sided from the level of the antennae down to the level of the facial knob (widening in *ericarum*), the sides of the thoracic dorsum anterior to the wing base being shining and undusted (dusted in *ericarum*) and the scutellar hairs not exceeding the length of the scutellum (longer in *ericarum*).

The female frons is black with dust spots well developed at the sides, but fading into a diffuse blur centrally. The dust spots reach well forwards on the frons leaving only a narrow undusted crescent anteriorly, but there is a much wider clear zone behind. The hairs on top of the thoracic dorsum can sometimes appear to be entirely pale when seen from the side (usually plenty of black hairs are visible), but black hairs are always dominant towards the sides, especially posteriorly. The hairs on the thorax and scutellum are rather short in comparison with other species. The sternites are densely dusted grey. In a collection this species tends to look small, dark and with dull markings compared with other *Melangyna*. Wing length 5.75–7.5 mm.

M. arctica is widely distributed across northern and western Britain, including Ireland, but is largely absent from central, eastern and south-eastern England. It is commonest in the north, as in the Scottish Highlands, and is scarce in the south. It is reported to prefer conifer woods though it occurs in deciduous woods as well. This species is reputed to often fly high around tree foliage and to exploit flowers of trees, but it is also to be found at low-growing flowers. Larvae are known to be predaceous upon the aphid *Pterocallis alni* on alder. April to September, peaking twice, in May and again in July.

Melangyna barbifrons (Fallén, 1817)   Map: Ball & Morris p. 84

The males lack spots on tergite 2 so only require comparison with *quadrimaculata*. The eyes are bare or virtually bare in *barbifrons* (densely hairy in *quadrimaculata*), but great care is needed in confirming this feature. The hairs on top of the thorax and scutellum are mainly black in the specimens of *barbifrons* examined (pale in *quadrimaculata*), but it is not clear how constant this character may be. The styles of the genitalia are longer and narrower in *barbifrons* (illustrated by Hippa, 1968a). The female is readily distinguished because it has an almost entirely shining frons with at most rudimentary dust spots scarcely projecting from the margins. Wing length 5.75–7.25 mm.

Records are sparse, though widespread in southern and midland England. There is a record for North Wales and a few for northern Scotland. It is absent from Ireland. Old deciduous woodland is preferred where it is among the spring species to be found at sallow blossom. March to June, peaking in April (but reported through to late October elsewhere in Europe).

Melangyna cincta (Fallén, 1817)   Pl. 3, fig. 4
Meligramma cincta (Fallén, 1817)   Map: Ball & Morris p. 84
                                                               Larva: Rotheray Pl. 6e

Identification is very easy since this is the only narrow-bodied hoverfly with parallel yellow bands on tergites 3 and 4 which also has triangular spots on tergite 2. *Meliscaeva cinctella* looks very similar in the field, but is readily distinguished because the spots on tergite 2 are broadly blunt at their inward ends, whereas in *cincta* these spots are acutely pointed towards one another. Wing length 6.25–8.75 mm.

This is a frequent and widespread species in woodland over much of Britain and Ireland though scarcer in northern districts. The larvae have been found in association with the aphid *Phyllaphis fagi* on beech, and also on oak, sycamore and lime. April to November, peaking in May.

Melangyna compositarum (Verrall, 1873)   Map: Ball & Morris p. 85

The separation between *compositarum* and *labiatarum* raises problems. A revision by Speight is in preparation, but in the meantime the treatment given here probably remains unsatisfactory. Collin (1946b) discusses differences in his paper on *ericarum* and Coe (1953a) mentions various characters; the key in Speight *et al.* (1975) acknowledges that reliable differences cannot be found. For males van der Goot (1981) relies on the degree of hairiness of the eyes (followed in our key); *compositarum* is virtually bare (in some specimens the eyes seem to be entirely bare) whereas *labiatarum* has a reasonable covering of pale inconspicuous hairs. The females are more of a problem since the relative density of dusting about the vertex is too unreliable. In the material examined, the face is a whitish grey in *compositarum* and a yellowish grey in *labiatarum* (the face is usually wider in *compositarum*, but this difference is too variable). There is a broader black shining area in front of the frons in *compositarum* (as illustrated in the key, p. 97), but this difference may yet prove unreliable. Wing length 6.25–8.75 mm.

Whatever the validity of the taxonomic distinction between *compositarum* and *labiatarum*, there seems to be a discernible difference in distribution with *compositarum* being predominantly a northern species. It has been stated to be common in Scotland and extends southwards into England. The authenticity of identifications from southern England is open to review. It is included in the Irish list. This species is said to show a preference for coniferous woodland. April to October, peaking in July.

Melangyna ericarum (Collin, 1946)   Map: Ball & Morris p. 85

There is inadequate material to define the variation in features of this species. The males have black hairs dominant on the thoracic dorsum so that comparison is only necessary with *arctica* among species with spots on tergite 2. The pale halteres and pale dusted frons of *ericarum* distinguish this species from *arctica*. Further features for the latter separation are that the face widens to below the level of the facial knob (parallel-sided in *arctica*), the scutellar hairs are longer than the scutellum (as long as scutellum in *arctica*) and the front lateral corners of the thoracic dorsum are heavily grey dusted (sparsely so in *arctica*).

The female frons has a strong dust zone in the central third, leaving shining black areas of equal length in front and behind. The black hairs on the scutellum are easy to see and should be used as an indication to check that the posterior corners of the thoracic dorsum also have black hairs. The definitive feature is the presence of black hairs on the posterior surface of the front and middle femora (this is not used as an initial key character since the legs have to be extended and viewed in good light to be sure whether the hairs are black or pale). The face has a strong black band below, as in *lasiophthalma*, but the sides of the face are dusted so that both yellow and black areas have a grey tinge. The anterior corners of the thoracic dorsum are strongly grey dusted, the same density as the dusting on the pleura immediately below (in *lasiophthalma* the dusting is much sparser, with shining reflections from the anterior corners of the thoracic dorsum). Collin (1946b) discusses this and other *Melangyna* species. The spots on tergites 2, 3 and 4 stop well short of the lateral margins. Wing length 8–10 mm.

This is a little-known species which is native to old forests in the Scottish Highlands. It occurs in native woods of Scots pine, but it is not clear whether it can also live in deciduous woodland in the absence of pine. However, it was found in some numbers at Malham Tarn, West Yorkshire, in a fen at about 300 m altitude and well away from any pines. The record from Oxfordshire reported previously is now considered to be erroneous and should be discounted. There is one old record from Ireland. June to August, peaking in early June.

Melangyna labiatarum (Verrall, 1901)   Map: Ball & Morris p. 86

The features of this hoverfly have been considered under the description of *M. compositarum*. Specimens with even denser eye hairs should be checked for non-British *coei* (see key and generic introduction). Wing length 6.25–8.75 mm.

In the south of England this is a frequent species, but it extends less commonly into the Scottish Highlands. It occurs in association with woodland, including areas where only deciduous trees are present, being most often seen on umbel flowers such as hogweed. Males have been noted hovering in sunlit glades. April to November, peaking twice, in June and again in August.

Melangyna lasiophthalma (Zetterstedt, 1843)   Map: Ball & Morris p. 86
                                                                         Larva: Rotheray Pl. 6f

The males, in having spots on tergite 2 and entirely pale hairs on the thoracic dorsum, only require comparison with *umbellatarum*, *labiatarum* and *compositarum*. The rearward placing of the spots on tergite 2, behind the centre, should be easy to discern. In the female the spots on tergites 3 and 4 do not extend forwards to the front lateral corners (they do extend forwards in

Parasyrphus punctulatus). In most *Melangyna* the sides of the scutellum have a small sharply defined spot at the front corners, but most specimens of *lasiophthalma* have this spot extended into a thin black rim round the lower margin of the scutellum (this feature also occurs in some *arctica* and *ericarum*). The pattern on the face in the male resembles that described in the female below.

The female frons has centrally placed narrow dust spots which do not meet in the centre. The facial pattern of orange and black is distinct and at most only faintly dusted (the basic pattern of a black band at the lower margin of the face hooking up to the lower eye margin is also found in *arctica* and *ericarum*, but dulled by dusting). *M. lasiophthalma* normally has the spots on tergites 3 and 4 extended laterally to the side margins (unusual in the genus), a state closely resembling females of *Parasyrphus punctulatus* except that in the latter species the spots sweep forwards at the margins right up to the front corners of the tergites. Another way of separating these species is that virtually all the apical half of the front tibia is dark in *lasiophthalma* whereas the front tibia is completely or almost completely orange-yellow in *P. punctulatus*. The female can be melanic, but the yellow scutellum has pale hairs on top (unlike melanic *P. punctulatus*). Wing length 7–9.25 mm.

A related European species, *M. lucifera* Nielsen, has the scutellum as in *lasiophthalma*. The males have very small side spots on tergite 2 (see key) and females have more completely yellow front and mid tibiae.

This is a characteristic and relatively frequent spring species at sallow catkins and wild cherry blossom in March and April in deciduous woodland (it shares this season with *arctica*, *barbifrons* and *quadrimaculata*, all of which are very different in character). It is also fond of sunbathing on sunlit tree trunks. However, it is rarely seen after early June. *M. lasiophthalma* occurs widely in Britain. It has not been recorded from Ireland. March to October, peaking in April and early May. The occasional records between August and October may be erroneous.

Melangyna (Melangyna) quadrimaculata (Verrall, 1873)
Pl. 2, fig. 9
Map: Ball & Morris p. 87
Larva: Rotheray Pl. 7a

The males are unusual in having only four spots on the abdomen (hence the scientific name). Comparison is only required with *barbifrons*, but the long pale hairs on the thoracic dorsum and scutellum and the densely hairy eyes of *quadrimaculata* are distinctive (*Platycheirus angustatus* occasionally has this four-spot pattern but its scutellum is black, whereas at least part is dull yellow in *quadrimaculata*). The face is particularly dark (as in *arctica* and *barbifrons*).

The female is entirely black apart from very faint small dust spots on the tergites, occasionally visible from some angles (a black hoverfly in early spring should be checked for this species). There is close resemblance to a *Cheilosia*, but the face has long erect hairs right up to the level of the antennae whereas such hairs in *Cheilosia* are absent or confined to the lower part of the face (the only *Cheilosia* with black legs and a hairy face is *C. variabilis* which is a very much larger species). The only real problem comes in relation to melanic females among other Syrphinae and here it is invaluable to have comparative material (even non-melanic females) to check out likely features. Most melanics retain normal leg coloration, which narrows down the choices very considerably (hind legs black in *Melangyna*). Wing length 7.25–9 mm.

M. quadrimaculata is scarce but widely distributed throughout Britain and Ireland. It is one of the spring hoverflies to be found on sallow and hazel catkins and blackthorn blossom, usually in the vicinity of coniferous woodland. Searching tree trunks close to flowering shrubs can also produce adults, especially when conditions become overcast. The larvae are known to be predaceous upon adelgids on firs. February to June, peaking in April.

Melangyna umbellatarum (Fabricius, 1794)   Pl. 2, fig. 8
                                                                       Map: Ball & Morris p. 87
                                                                       Larva: Rotheray Pl. 7b

This species is very similar to *compositarum* and *labiatarum*. There must have been many past misidentifications based on the colour of the front tibia (yellowish with a narrow black ring), a feature which is far too variable and imprecise. In a comparative series, *umbellatarum* is easily recognised because the thoracic dorsum is shining black (male) or metallic blue-black (female) and the abdominal markings are creamy-white rather than citrus-yellow. The male has bare eyes (but those of *compositarum* can also appear to be similarly bare). In the female the narrower dust band results in a relatively large shining dust-free area above the antennae compared with *compositarum* and *labiatarum*. By far the most reliable character, for those with a microscope, is the extensive absence of microtrichia in the second basal cell. The female of *ericarum* is very similar as regards thorax, frons pattern and second basal cell, but the scutellum is black-haired. Wing length 6.5–8.75 mm.

This is a widespread species as far north as South Lancashire and South Yorkshire that becomes scarcer further north; however, it is rarely abundant. It has a scattered distribution in Ireland where it is scarce and considered to be threatened. The larvae are known to be predaceous upon *Cavariella* aphids on umbellifers. April to November, peaking in August.

Genus MELIGRAMMA

Rotheray & Gilbert (1989) elevated *Meligramma* to generic rank, placing *Epistrophella* in synonymy with it, but retained *M. cincta* (placed in *Fagisyrphus* by some European authors) in *Melangyna*. These changes were accepted by Chandler (1998) and are followed here. However, Thompson & Rotheray (1998) recognise *Epistrophella* as a subgenus of *Melangyna* and treat *Meligramma* as a subgenus of *Melangyna*, as in the first edition. The three species now in this genus present an assortment of colour patterns, either resembling *Melangyna* or being closely similar to the patterns and narrow bodies found in *Meliscaeva*.

Meligramma euchromum (Kowarz, 1885)   Pl. 2, fig. 3
Epistrophe (*Epistrophella*) *euchroma* (Kowarz, 1885)   Map: Ball & Morris p. 91

Though a rather small undistinguished-looking species, it is unique in having oblique spots on tergites 3 and 4 and in the presence of tiny yellow spots on the lateral margins at the junctions between tergites 2 and 3 and between tergites 3 and 4. The oblique spots in the female can be rather elongate, approaching bars in dimensions, and sometimes each pair may meet at the anterior corners. Being a small, rather narrow species, it is most likely to be confused at first glance with *Melangyna* or *Parasyrphus punctulatus* (but *euchromum* has the legs entirely yellow except for the base of the femora in the male, and of course the tergite spots are distinct in shape) or with *Platycheirus* (which has a black scutellum). Wing length 6.75–8 mm.

Records are few for this rare species. It is mainly southern, but records extend north to Morecambe Bay. It has not been recorded from Ireland. Very little is known about its habits. It occurs in woodland, where it can be found basking on sunlit leaves, but specimens are rarely found. Possibly it is overlooked to some extent amid other hoverflies of similar general appearance. April to June, peaking in May.

Meligramma guttatum (Fallén, 1817)   Pl. 3, fig. 6
Melangyna (*Meligramma*) *guttata* (Fallén, 1817)   Map: Ball & Morris p. 91

The appearance of this species is somewhat like a small yellow-spotted *Platycheirus* except that the scutellum is yellow rather than black. It is narrow-bodied (especially in the male) and with paired rounded spots rather as in *Melangyna*. However, there are sharply defined yellow stripes along the sides of the thoracic dorsum (as in *Sphaerophoria*) and often there is a pair of spots, sometimes fused into one, at the back of the thoracic dorsum (nothing else has this feature except the next species). The sides of tergite 1 are yellow (a very exceptional feature shared with *trianguliferum*). The face is yellow or almost completely so, and the frons is also extensively yellow, at least at the sides. The front legs are normally yellow apart from some darkening about the base of the femur. Wing length 5.25–7 mm.

Though records are few, they are widespread in England and there are scattered records from Scotland and eastern Ireland, usually associated with woodland habitat. The larvae have been reared from aphids on sycamore. May to September, peaking in July.

Meligramma trianguliferum (Zetterstedt, 1843)   Pl. 3, fig. 5
Melangyna (*Meligramma*) *triangulifera* (Zetterstedt, 1843)   Map: Ball & Morris p. 92
                                                                    Larva: Rotheray Pl. 8b

As the name would suggest, the markings on the abdomen are rather triangular. Being a narrow-bodied species, the males at least are easily overlooked as yellow-spotted *Platycheirus* (except that the scutellum is yellow) or as small examples of *Meliscaeva auricollis* (but in *trianguliferum* the scutellum has a black spot on either side at the corners, and the female has a strong yellow stripe along the sides of the thoracic dorsum). In female *trianguliferum* the frons is black with only small lateral dust spots (whereas in *auricollis* these spots are large and almost reach the centre line). The back of the thoracic dorsum sometimes has paired yellow spots, and the sides of tergite 1 are often yellow as in *guttatum*.

Some authors have regarded *trianguliferum* as being rather similar to *euchromum*, but the latter species has oblique bars which slope towards the hind corners of tergites 3 and 4. In the available specimens of *euchromum* the scutellum has a black rim (view obliquely from below), a feature not found in other similar-looking species. Wing length 5–8 mm.

M. trianguliferum is another scarce species that is usually taken in woodlands and hedgerows around spring-flowering shrubs such as hawthorn and crab apple, or sunbathing on foliage. It occurs widely in southern England up to Lancashire and West Yorkshire, and there are scattered records as far north as the central highlands of Scotland, but it is seemingly absent from much of Wales. It has not been recorded from Ireland. April to September, peaking in May.

Genus MELISCAEVA

These are narrow-bodied hoverflies with rather elongate wings. The abdomen has bands or triangular spots resembling some *Meligramma* species. A microscopic character is the presence of tiny black flecks along the hind margin of the wings, uniformly interspaced with similar-sized clear spaces (illustrated in fig. 17e of Coe, 1953a) – this feature is otherwise only found in *Episyrphus* among the Syrphini (so examination of the very common *E. balteatus* will indicate what to look for). Some authorities have included our *Meliscaeva* species within the genus *Episyrphus*.

Meliscaeva auricollis (Meigen, 1822)   Pl. 3, fig. 2
                                                                Map: Ball & Morris p. 92

There is a wide range of variation in pattern on the abdomen. Typically tergites 2 to 5 have forwardly projecting median black triangles (a useful initial field character). Tergites 3 and 4 have yellow triangular spots with the hind edge strongly oblique and the upper edge more or less parallel with, but remote from, the front edge of the tergite (in *Meligramma trianguliferum* the male has the front edge of these spots sloping towards the front corners of the tergites whilst in the female the front of these spots is almost flush with the anterior margin of the tergites). The area between the yellow spots may be black or grey. The spotted form has been named var. *maculicornis* Zetterstedt which is typical of the spring generation. In the summer generation this variety is common, but it is more frequent for the spots to be linked up as a continuous yellow band – usually there is a tongue of black almost dividing the band, but there is a range of intermediates towards the uniformly banded condition of *Meliscaeva cinctella*. The key gives three features for separating the intermediates, the colour pattern on the head apparently being reliable but the firmest character is the shape of the alula on the wing. In *auricollis* the alula is distinctly broadened distally, being at least twice as wide at its maximum width compared with the width near the base (in *cinctella* the alula is strap-shaped, being narrow and more parallel-sided). Another feature of *auricollis* is that tergite 2 usually has the yellow area reduced to a narrow oblique bar (typical of the male) or a downward-facing crescent (more usual in the female, an unusual condition in the Syrphini). Wing length 6–9.5 mm.

This is a frequent species in southern and midland England in the neighbourhood of trees, and sparser records extend up to the Central Highlands of Scotland. It is scarce in Ireland where the few records are mostly coastal. The larvae are known to be associated with aphid colonies on a variety of shrubs such as barberries and broom, and on flowers and stems of umbellifers; they have also been found in association with *Psylla alni* on alder. The very early and late dates would suggest that hibernation occurs in the adult to some extent. February to December, peaking in July and August.

Meliscaeva cinctella (Zetterstedt, 1843)   Pl. 3, fig. 3
                                                                Map: Ball & Morris p. 93

The narrow abdomen with parallel yellow bands requires comparison with *Melangyna cincta*. In *cinctella* tergite 2 has spots which are broadly rounded on their inner margins whereas in *cincta* the spots are triangles which are acutely pointed at their inward corners. Sometimes the bands on tergites 3 and 4 have a slight partial median incision and are thus intermediate with *auricollis* –

these intermediates are discussed under the description of the latter species. Wing length 7–9.75 mm.

In the vicinity of trees and bushes this species is present in most districts throughout Britain and is common in the south and in Ireland. The larvae are known to be predators of a range of arboreal aphids. It is not clear whether the species has migratory habits, but it was present in huge numbers about the sallow bushes on Dungeness in 1981 as would be the case if a migratory swarm had arrived; however, a local mass emergence could equally well have been the explanation. April to November, peaking in August and September.

Genus PARASYRPHUS

Members of this genus are relatively small among the Syrphini. In common with *Melangyna*, two *Parasyrphus* (*lineola* and *punctulatus*) have predominantly dark hind legs. Whilst *punctulatus* has spots and thus resembles *Melangyna*, the remaining species have a banded pattern reminiscent of *Syrphus*. It is thus probable that *Parasyrphus* is often overlooked in mistake for diminutive *Syrphus*, but the dark hind legs will immediately sort out the *Parasyrphus*. The main difficulty lies with *P. nigritarsis* which is atypical in having extensively yellow legs as in some *Syrphus* and *Epistrophe*. Checking the squama is necessary to eliminate small *Syrphus*. *Parasyrphus* has rolled margins to the tergites (or weakly beaded in *nigritarsis*) whereas beading is fairly obvious in *Syrphus*. The female of *P. nigritarsis* is so similar to *Epistrophe nitidicollis* and *E. melanostoma* (right down to the bright orange abdominal markings) that it is also keyed out under that genus. *Parasyrphus* has been revised by Speight *et al.* (1975).

These are woodland hoverflies. It is clear that some have become common due to the spread of conifer plantations and it is now difficult to comment as to which species are dependent on deciduous woodland.

Parasyrphus annulatus (Zetterstedt, 1838)   Pl. 2, fig. 10
                                                        Map: Ball & Morris p. 103

This is a particularly small species. The yellow bands on tergites 3 and 4 are often strongly moustache-shaped and are occasionally partially divided into spots on tergite 3. The males are easy to recognise among *Parasyrphus* in having entirely yellow tarsi on the front and mid legs, and yellowish antennae. In the female the pale antennae and the hind femur with both base and apex yellow should serve to identify this species. It may be noted that the dust spots on the frons of the female are very broad, as in *lineola*. Wing length 5.5–8 mm.

The first British record was in Gloucestershire in 1894. *P. annulatus* is very local, but can be common in certain woods in the southern half of England. It seems to be commonest in large ancient deciduous woodlands – almost inevitably there is some coniferisation so the ecological requirements are uncertain. Records are widely spread across mainland Britain, but it would appear to be more abundant in central and southern England. There are only four scattered records from Ireland. April to September, peaking in June.

Parasyrphus lineola (Zetterstedt, 1843)   Map: Ball & Morris p. 103

The black antennae and entirely black hind legs make this species easy to distinguish. Occasionally the knees are slightly yellow, but never with the hind femur as much as one sixth yellow, as in *vittiger*. Wing length 7.25–8.25 mm.

This is a locally common and widespread species throughout Britain that is most frequently noted from conifer woodlands and coniferised heathland. It is uncommon in Ireland where it is considered a recent arrival. Larvae are predators of adelgids and aphids in the crowns of spruce and it been bred from a puparium under the bark of Norway spruce. April to September, peaking in June.

Parasyrphus malinellus (Collin, 1952)   Map: Ball & Morris p. 104

This species was described on the basis of British material (Collin, 1952a). The thoracic dorsum is shining black rather than dull and greenish as in other *Parasyrphus*. In size and appearance within a collection, *malinellus* is most similar to *lineola* and *vittiger*, but the antennae are partly pale (rather than entirely black) and the female frons is only narrowly dusted at the sides anteriorly (broadly dusted in the other two species). For differentiation from related species with pale antennae, the characters given in the key should suffice. Speight *et al.* (1975) refer to the eyes having scattered short hairs in the male of *malinellus* (bare in *nigritarsis*) and in the female the spots on tergite 2 are said to be contracted on the side margins to half their full width whereas in *annulatus* these spots expand at the side margins to reach their full width there – these characters do not function successfully on the material available for the present study. There appears to be greater variation in the extent of yellow on the tibia of female *malinellus* with as much as half yellow (*i.e.* more extensively yellow than illustrated). Wing length 8–9 mm.

The original material was caught between 1932 and 1942 in southern England and the Scottish Highlands. Recent records are widely scattered across mainland Britain, with a strong concentration in Dorset and Somerset. It is considered a recent arrival in Ireland, but is well established and more frequently encountered than *lineola*. This is another species of rides in coniferised woodland and plantations. May to August, peaking rapidly in May. There are also two unusual records for late September and early October.

Parasyrphus nigritarsis (Zetterstedt, 1843)   Map: Ball & Morris p. 104
                                                                   Larva: Rotheray Pl. 7c

This is a singularly difficult species to key out because the markings of tergite 2 are barely golf-club-shaped in the male and not at all in the female. Also, the edges of the tergites have weak beading, unlike other *Parasyrphus*, and approach the state found in *Syrphus*. The males superficially resemble an orange-marked *Syrphus* (but lack the squamal hairs) or an *Epistrophe* with partially pale antennae such as *nitidicollis*. The females resemble these *Epistrophe* species even more closely, since they have the broad orange abdominal markings (all other *Parasyrphus* have yellow markings), partially pale antennae and an orange lunule on the frons (other *Parasyrphus* usually have a black lunule). As both sexes have a broad black mouth rim, there is a particular risk of confusion with the recently added *E. melanostoma*. However, the largely black hind femur of the male, the dark tarsi of both sexes and the rather dull thoracic dorsum contrast with the entirely orange hind femur, extensively orange tarsi and rather shining thorax of these superficially similar species of *Epistrophe*. Females of *nigritarsis* have also been mistaken for *Eupeodes latifasciatus* which can have very similar abdominal markings, although the much paler frons and tarsi of *latifasciatus* will quickly eliminate this species. The face is entirely yellow, in contrast to most other banded *Parasyrphus*, and the hairs of the scutellar dorsum are shorter, as in *Syrphus*. Wing length 8.25–9.25 mm.

Although *nigritarsis* appears to be a rather scarce species, it may be overlooked amongst other yellow-banded syrphids. Records are largely confined to Scotland, northern England and Wales, though it has been discovered in Hampshire, Gloucestershire, Suffolk and Warwickshire in recent years. It was added to the Irish list by Speight (1986b) but is very localised. Most records are from the vicinity of damp woods, including riverside trees. Larvae have been found to feed on the eggs, larvae and pupae of leaf beetles (Chrysomelidae) associated with alder (*Chrysomela aenea*), willows (*Lochmaea capreae*) and docks (*Gastrophysa viridula*) (Rotheray & Hewitt, 1999). Adults visit flowers such as umbellifers and have been found basking on sunlit leaves. May to July, peaking in late May and early June.

Parasyrphus punctulatus (Verrall, 1873)   Pl. 2, fig. 11
                                                              Map: Ball & Morris p. 105
                                                              Larva: Rotheray Pl. 7d

The presence of spots and bars separates this species from other *Parasyrphus* but the rather dark hind legs cause a close resemblance to *Melangyna*. Occasionally *annulatus* has narrowly divided bands, but in that species the antennae are partly pale (black in *punctulatus*) and the front tarsus is orange (dark in *punctulatus*). The male has semicircular spots on tergites 3 and 4 which narrowly reach the front corners of the tergites, quite distinct from any *Melangyna*. The female tergites 3 and 4 have bar-shaped or faintly semicircular markings, but at least on tergite 3 the spots sweep up to the front corners of the tergites. The female frons has narrow dust bars in the central third, closely similar to *Melangyna lasiophthalma* (the latter species has the spots on the tergites reaching the margin well below the anterior corners, and the hairs on top of the scutellum are pale; black in *punctulatus*). Melanic females occur, in which case other characters are needed – females of *punctulatus* have black hairs on top of the scutellum (the scutellum appears to be entirely yellow from above, unlike *M. quadrimaculata*). Wing length 5.5–7.75 mm.

It is important to be aware that other very similar-looking species occur in the European fauna, as allowed for in the key. *P. macularis* (Zetterstedt) is a bit larger and the eyes are distinctly covered in brownish hairs (any hairs in *punctulatus* are pale and inconspicuous); this species occurs widely in Denmark in the spring. *P. tarsatus* (Zetterstedt) and *dryadis* (Holmgren) have an entirely yellow hind tibia (as in *nigritarsis* which has bands on the tergites); both these species occur in Scandinavia so might be found in Scotland. *Syrphus nitidifrons* Becker is said to look like *punctulatus*, but most of the face is yellow and the squamae have the usual dorsal hairs that characterise the genus.

This is a widespread early-spring species in woodland throughout Britain and Ireland. It occurs in both deciduous and coniferous woods, often commonly so. It visits a great range of spring flowers and is often seen at rest on paths. Females have been found laying eggs on the young growth of spruce shoots. March to August, peaking in May.

Parasyrphus vittiger (Zetterstedt, 1843)   Map: Ball & Morris p. 105
                                                            Larva: Rotheray Pl. 7e

The antennae are black, as in *lineola*, but the hind legs are more extensively yellow in *vittiger*, the hind femur being yellow in the apical sixth and the tibia yellowish at both ends (even if obscurely so). Wing length 6.25–8.75 mm.

The majority of records are from northern England and Scotland, but coniferised heathland in southern England is also favoured. It was added to the Irish list by Nash (1975). The larvae have largely been found on conifers (firs, spruce and pines), but are also known from beech and black currant in Switzerland (Goeldlin de Tiefenau, 1974). April to October, peaking in late June and early July.

Genus SCAEVA

Among the Syrphini these are for the most part large species. The frons is inflated (with an exceptionally broad obtuse angle between the eyes where they adjoin the frons in the male), the eyes are densely hairy (unlike *Eupeodes*) and the male head is rather box-shaped in top view, unlike any other syrphid genus. The wings have vein R_{4+5} more dipped than in most Syrphini. Perhaps the most distinctive feature is the extensive absence of microtrichia on the wings (best observed under a microscope), as in *Eupeodes lundbecki* which has bare eyes (like all *Eupeodes*).

Scaeva is a genus very prone to migratory habits. Of the four species, only two occur regularly in Britain. A further species, resembling *selenitica*, has been included in the key since it has been found in some neighbouring European countries and might occur in Britain as a vagrant.

Scaeva albomaculata (Macquart, 1842)   Pl. 3, fig. 13
                                                            Map: Ball & Morris p. 128

The broad oblique bars (as illustrated in the key, p. 103) are quite distinct from those of other members of the genus. The thoracic dorsum has well developed yellow stripes along the lateral margin. Wing length 8.5–9.75 mm.

A single specimen was taken at Jevington, Sussex, on 2 August 1938 (Wainwright, 1942). A second specimen, taken at Freshwater in the Isle of Wight on 16 June 1949 was recently discovered in a museum collection (Palmer, 1996). This is best treated as a vagrant outside its normal range, being predominantly a Mediterranean species.

Scaeva mecogramma (Bigot, 1860)   Pl. R, fig. 19
                                                            Map: Ball & Morris p. 129

The abdominal markings consist of narrow lunulate markings on tergites 3 and 4, usually joining on the mid-line to form a moustache band. The markings on tergite 2 can also be joined on the mid-line. Hence *mecogramma* looks nothing like the other *Scaeva* species and was treated by Coe (1953a) within his large '*Syrphus*' grouping. The wings, however, are extensively bare of microtrichia in the basal half and vein R_{4+5} is moderately dipped. The female frons is typical of *Scaeva* in being yellow apart from a black area around the ocelli, although this yellow area is unusual in being covered by dusting. Wing length 10 mm.

A female was taken on 19 August 1905 at Arniston, a locality believed to be near Dalkeith, Edinburgh. The specimen was probably an accidental import of this Mediterranean species (Collin, 1946a). Larvae have been found in Spain at colonies of the olive-tree psyllid, *Euphyllura olivina* (Rojo *et al.*, 1999), so it is conceivable that mature larvae or puparia could have been imported with olives. August.

Scaeva pyrastri (Linnaeus, 1758)   Pl. 3, fig. 11
                                                    Map: Ball & Morris p. 129
                                                      Larva: Rotheray Pl. 9d

This relatively large conspicuous hoverfly has very characteristically shaped markings. On tergites 3 and 4 there are oblique bars which are narrowed in the middle, but the inner and outer ends are of equal width and the bars do not reach the lateral margins. It is important to check that the bars reach much further forward at their inner ends than at their outer ends. In life these markings are often whitish in appearance (in contrast to other hoverflies with paired markings, including *selenitica*) although the white tends to become yellowish on specimens in collections. Wing length 9.25–12.5 mm.

S. pyrastri occurs on flowers in gardens, waste ground and meadows throughout much of Britain and Ireland though it is rare in Scotland (northern specimens should be checked for *Eupeodes lundbecki* which has bare eyes – see comments under *Eupeodes*). It is believed that *pyrastri* is not a permanent resident but arrives as a migrant and then breeds here; hence, numbers fluctuate wildly between years. Evaluation of records in Ireland shows that this species does not occur before early June and it is therefore concluded that it only occurs as a migrant. Records for early May on mainland Britain suggest that it may occasionally overwinter, but early migration is also a possibility. The larvae have been found in association with various ground-layer aphids. May to November, peaking in August.

Scaeva selenitica (Meigen, 1822)   Pl. 3, fig. 12
                                                    Map: Ball & Morris p. 130

This species resembles *S. pyrastri*, but the markings on tergites 3 and 4 are in fact quite different (a very similar European species, *dignota*, is included in the key). These markings are comma-like bars (tapering towards their outer ends) which extend equally far forwards at both the inner and outer ends, contrasting with the oblique orientation of the markings in *pyrastri*. They are yellow in life, which can result in it being overlooked as a large *Eupeodes luniger*. The hind tibia usually has a black ring, which is absent in *pyrastri*. Wing length 10.5–12 mm.

This is a rather scarce species which is at least a partial migrant. Records are scattered widely throughout Britain north to Orkney though this hoverfly is most often found in southern England where it is most frequently encountered in conifer plantations and on coniferised heathland. In Ireland it occurs in two discrete areas, in the south-west and east coast, where it is not infrequent. The larvae are predaceous upon pine aphids and it was bred from a puparium found under spruce in mid-Wales (Entwistle, *pers. comm.*). March to November, peaking between July and early September.

Genus SPHAEROPHORIA

Among the smaller hoverflies, *Sphaerophoria* is readily recognised. The build is elongate, the abdomen often being parallel-sided in the male or narrowly elliptical in the female. The abdomen bears a yellow and black pattern. The thorax has yellow areas on the pleura and a complete or partial yellow stripe on the lateral margins of the thoracic dorsum.

Whilst the genus may be easy to recognise, the identification of species is not so straightforward. Coe (1953a) included only four species, plus six named varieties. More recent studies have relied on the shape of the male genitalia, with the result that some varieties have been abandoned whilst one has been raised to specific rank. The check list of Kloet & Hincks (1976) included seven species and an eighth was subsequently added (Speight, 1973 & 1976d). These additions resulted from the fact that *menthastri* (now *interrupta*) proved to be a species complex containing five distinct species. During the preparation of the first edition of this book a further species (*batava*), and a form of uncertain taxonomic status, were found during examination of the *interrupta* group, the latter being provisionally referred to as form A. In the following years, two further species were added (*bankowskae* and *potentillae*) and a further specimen (Species B) was recognised as a potentially distinct species. Male genitalia have been illustrated externally by most authors, but Skufjin (1980) has found distinctive features in the palp-like appendages at the base of the aedeagus. The drawings by Stuart Ball (Plates O – Q) of male genitalia have been included to assist in matching the illustrations in the key to the three-dimensional structure seen in a specimen. The pattern on the abdomen is too variable to have confidence in its use in identification at present. Females of the *interrupta* group cannot yet be identified, the first requirement being to obtain females caught *in copula* with identifiable males.

The genus is predominantly associated with dry grassland, but it is apparent that some species prefer woodland rides or marshes. The larvae are predaceous upon ground-layer aphids.

It will be helpful to recognise the following species groups.

rueppellii **Group**. Thoracic disc with yellow side stripe broken. Abdomen short as in *interrupta* group. Includes *loewi* and *rueppellii*.

scripta **Group**. Thoracic disc with yellow side stripe complete. Abdomen in male very long, extending beyond wing tips. Only *scripta*.

interrupta **Group**. Thoracic disc with yellow side stripe complete. Abdomen in male not exceptionally long. A large species complex (remaining species).

Illustrations of genitalia accompany the key and a diagram is included which demonstrates the means of orientation (relax old specimens in order to hinge out genitalia). Considerable care is necessary in identifications based on genitalia and a microscope is essential. It is not particularly easy to match specimens with illustrations. Rather than rush at identifying the first specimens, it is as well to build up a small collection in order to gain experience with recognising the features entailed. It is as well to allow for the fact that several species in the *interrupta* group may be flying together, so a selection of males will need to be caught for study.

Sphaerophoria bankowskae Goeldlin de Tiefenau, 1989   Pl. Q, fig. 1
                                                          Map: Ball & Morris p. 131

Care is needed to separate *bankowskae* from *interrupta*, but the male genitalia of *bankowskae* can be distinguished on the basis of the exceptionally large inner process, the bulging base to the toothed lobe and the strong shoulders of that lobe. Wing length 5.5 mm.

This species was added to the British list by Plant (1990a). At the moment there are just two records, from woodland locations in Essex and Northamptonshire. It is poorly known in Europe despite its widespread distribution. July.

Sphaerophoria batava Goeldlin de Tiefenau, 1974   Pl. P, fig. 3
                                                          Map: Ball & Morris p. 132

The available specimens have spots joined into bands on tergites 2 to 4. The genitalia show features quite distinct from other species, notably the absence of a distinct tooth on the inner curve (as in *interrupta*), but this curve is infilled resulting in a rather straight central section. The apical teeth are unlike those of *interrupta*. A bulge at the base of the toothed lobe on the outer side is also distinct. There is some resemblance to *taeniata*, which has a tooth on the inner curve, but, apart from other differences in the genitalia, the scutellar hairs in *batava* are black rather than yellow as in *taeniata*. Wing length 6 mm.

This species was added to the British list by Stubbs & Falk (1983). Though records are plentiful in some southern districts, there are scattered records throughout Britain north to the Scottish Highlands, and also from Ireland where there are very few records. It is most frequently found on heathland, or along open rides in conifer plantations. Flowers of tormentil and heath bedstraw are good places to search for adults on heathland (this goes for all other *Sphaerophoria* that occur on heaths). May to October, peaking in July and August.

Sphaerophoria fatarum Goeldlin de Tiefenau, 1989   Pl. Q, fig. 4
Sphaerophoria abbreviata authors, misident.   Map: Ball & Morris p. 132

Recent work has shown that *abbreviata* is actually a northern Scandinavian species and British material is now ascribed to *fatarum* following the addition of this species by Speight (1989a). The abdomen generally has spots in pairs or only partially fused. The genitalia are most similar to those of *taeniata* but the position of the projection on the inner curve is different and the shoulder on the toothed lobe is pronounced. Some specimens have the yellow stripe along the sides of the thoracic dorsum broken, as in *loewi* and *rueppellii*, but these species have very different genitalia. Wing length 4.75–6 mm.

This is one of the more frequent species in the Scottish Highlands, open heathy woods and valley bogs being ideal habitat. However, it also occurs in Wales and down to the southern counties of England where it is associated with heaths and woodland rides. It is also frequent in western Ireland. April to September, peaking in late June and July.

Sphaerophoria interrupta (Fabricius, 1805)   Pl. P, fig. 4, Pl. 4, fig. 17
Sphaerophoria menthastri (Linnaeus, 1758)   Map: Ball & Morris p. 133
sensu Vockeroth, 1963   Larva: Rotheray Pl. 5e

The name '*menthastri*' was formerly used in a wider sense, including five of the species that are
now recognised. It was not until the work of Speight (1973) that the genitalia characters were
portrayed in the British literature but, even after that date, some identifications were still based
on the outdated key by Coe (1953a). The markings are very variable and the scutellum can have
dark or pale hairs. The tarsi can be dark as in *philanthus*, but are usually pale. The genitalia are
distinctive in that the toothed lobe has such widely separated teeth; it is possible that form A
below is no more than a variety of *interrupta*. Wing length 4.75–6.5 mm.

S. interrupta is one of the most widespread species throughout Britain and Ireland, but is rarely
as abundant as maps may suggest. It should be noted that many old records of '*menthastri*'
precede the various species splits that have occurred over the last 30 years and, unless based
upon specimens that have been re-examined, should be discarded. Adults are usually recorded
from damp grasslands, but have also been taken on chalk grassland and coastal dunes. The
larvae have been found in association with aphids on red campion and common mouse-ear. April
to October, peaking in July and August.

Sphaerophoria loewi Zetterstedt, 1843   Pl. O, fig. 2, Pl. R, fig. 17 & 18
                                                                 Map: Ball & Morris p. 133

The black antennae serve to separate this species from *rueppellii*, but it should be noted that
some specimens of the latter species can have rather dark antennae. There should be very little
doubt in separating *loewi* from *rueppellii* on the basis of the male genitalia, but the orange legs
and markings of *loewi* are a useful field character compared with *rueppellii*, where these are
yellow. The upper mouth edge is said to be far less projecting than the facial knob in *loewi*
(projects as much as the facial knob in *rueppellii*). Wing length 6–6.75 mm.

Little is known of this very rare hoverfly. It is coastal, with old records for Kent (Gravesend),
Hampshire (Christchurch) and Dorset (Studland Heath). More recently it has been found in
Essex (Stanford-le-Hope), where common reed spread into a brackish creek, in Lancashire
(Leighton Moss) amongst sea club-rush, and in Humberside (Barton-on-Humber), from common
reed in a brackish clay-pit. Further records come from Rye (Sussex), South Wales, the Tay
Reedbeds (Perthshire) and from a site on the Dornoch Firth (Sutherland). There are also recent
records for Ireland, mainly from coastal lagoons, and a surprising inland record for the Scottish
Highlands (near Aviemore), where it was swept from common reed. Coastal brackish marsh is
seemingly the normal habitat, but this hoverfly is very elusive. June to September, peaking in
July.

Sphaerophoria philanthus (Meigen, 1822)   Pl. P, fig. 1, Pl. 4, fig. 19
                                                                 Map: Ball & Morris p. 134

On average this is a somewhat small dark species with the black areas on the abdomen dominant
over the yellow areas. Tergites 3 and 4 often have the spots joined into a band. The mouth rim is
often black and the front four tarsi are usually dark. However, none of these features is constant

or reliable. Identification must be based on the male genitalia, the toothed lobe being very broad (and often black in coloration, but sometimes yellow as in the other species). Wing length about 5.5 mm.

This is a relatively common species on the drier areas of heaths, moorland edges and heathy woods in northern and western districts, including Ireland. It can also be one of the commonest *Sphaerophoria* on western coastal dunes. It is more local in the south-eastern half of England, though often frequent on heathland. May to October, peaking in August.

Sphaerophoria potentillae Claussen, 1984   Pl. P, fig. 2
                                                                  Map: Ball & Morris p. 134

There are few species with which this species can be confused. Unlike most other species, the genital lobes do not exhibit an angular form and are amongst the most distinctive of the genus. Wing length 5 mm.

This species was added to the British list by Stubbs (1989a). To date, *potentillae* is known from just a few wet Culm grassland sites in Devon, and one wet heathland in Cornwall (I. Perry) where it has been found to visit a number of flowers such as buttercups, yarrow and tormentil. It appears to be a rare species in Europe. June and early July.

Sphaerophoria rueppellii (Wiedemann, 1830)   Pl. O, fig. 3, Pl. 4, fig. 20
                                                                  Map: Ball & Morris p. 135

This species is very short-bodied and the abdomen is distinctly broadened towards the apex in both sexes and almost bulbous in the male. It is thus readily distinguished in the field, apart from *loewi* with which it shares the broken yellow stripe on the side of the thoracic dorsum. The legs are typically yellow although a dark-legged form has been named *nitidicollis* Zetterstedt (this is considered to be no more than a colour variety). The antennae of *rueppellii* are usually yellow, but there can be some darkening and occasionally they are entirely dark brownish. There could thus be some scope for confusion with *loewi* which has black antennae. Wing length 4.25–6.5 mm.

Though widely distributed in eastern England, especially in coastal locations, and recorded sparingly in northern England and Scotland, it is a very local and normally uncommon insect. There is a single Irish locality. Perhaps the greatest stronghold is on the dry grassy flood embankments along the Thames Estuary. Other sites are also dry open sunny situations such as coastal cliffs and heathland. Adults have been noted ovipositing on great willowherb. It is not infrequently found in ruderal situations where knotweeds, goosefoots and mayweeds are abundant. It is presumed not to be resident in Ireland (Speight, 1985). May to October, peaking in July.

Sphaerophoria scripta (Linnaeus, 1758)   Pl. O, fig. 4, Pl. 4, fig. 16
                                                                  Map: Ball & Morris p. 135

The males are instantly recognisable in the field since the abdomen is so long, the wing tips reaching only to about halfway along tergite 4, leaving at least the whole of tergite 5 projecting beyond them. The markings are very variable. Females closely resemble those of the *interrupta* group, but the hind femur is broadly bare of hairs near the base since hairs are absent on the posteroventral surface (in the *interrupta* group, as far as is known, all species have only a narrow median ventral line free of hairs). Wing length 5–7 mm.

S. scripta is one of the commonest open grassland hoverflies and is often abundant, even on flowery waste ground in towns. It is found throughout Britain but is much less common in the north. It would seem to be boosted in numbers by migration in some years and it is believed that it may not be permanently resident in the more northern and western parts of its range. In Ireland it is recorded mainly from the east coast and Speight (2000c) suggests it may be an intermittent migrant from Britain which may be entirely absent in some years. April to November, peaking in July and August.

Sphaerophoria taeniata (Meigen, 1822)   Pl. Q, fig. 3, Pl. 4, fig. 18
                                                                              Map: Ball & Morris p. 136

Relatively large specimens with large undivided yellow bands on the abdomen are likely to be this species. The scutellum has yellow hairs (as in some *interrupta*, rarely in other species). Particular care is required in checking the genitalia since *batava*, *fatarum* and form A are very similar (see key, p. 104). Wing length about 6 mm.

There is a very strong concentration of records in the southern counties of England, especially Surrey, West Sussex and Berkshire. There are relatively few records north of the Thames, except for a cluster in the Brecks, but it extends northwards to Cheshire. Scottish records are all old and may be erroneous, coming before recent species splits. Irish records previously published as *taeniata* proved to belong to *batava* (Speight, 1985) and it is now thought to be absent from Ireland. This species prefers wet meadows, often with such plants as rushes and lesser spearwort. It is not unusual to find it in numbers on ruderal ground in the presence of mayweeds. It has been reared from a puparium found on common reed. May to October, peaking in late August to early September.

Sphaerophoria virgata Goeldlin de Tiefenau, 1974   Pl. P, fig. 5
                                                                              Map: Ball & Morris p. 136

Being a small dark species with dark tarsi, there is a close resemblance to *philanthus*. The toothed lobe on the genitalia is also large, but more rectangular and with a pronounced shoulder and only one strong tooth. The hairy lobe is small and narrow. The genitalia seen from below have characteristic shoulders. Some specimens have the yellow stripe along the sides of the thoracic dorsum broken, as in *loewi* and *rueppellii*, but these species have very different genitalia. Wing length about 6 mm.

This species was added to the British list by Speight (1976d). It is most frequently encountered on heathland and along heathy rides in conifer plantations. It is known mainly from the central Scottish Highlands and on the heaths of Dorset, Hampshire and Surrey. Otherwise there are a few scattered records for Wales, the West Midlands and northern England. It has not been recorded from Ireland. June to September, peaking in July.

Sphaerophoria form A

Pl. Q, fig. 5
Map: Ball & Morris p. 137

A specimen closely resembles *S. interrupta* except that there is a small projection on the inner curve of the genitalia lobes and the teeth on the toothed lobe are of very unequal length, but not to the extent found in *interrupta*. The scutellar hairs are mostly yellow, as in many *interrupta*. The chances are that it is no more than a variety of this species, but it seems helpful to indicate the existence of such a form. If more material can be found, the taxonomic status of this form can be more thoroughly considered. Wing length 6 mm.

The single specimen was taken in Hampshire in July (S. Falk).

Sphaerophoria species B

Pl. Q, fig. 2
Map: Ball & Morris p. 137

The male genitalia have a number of distinctive features, including short lobes bearing short hairs. It is possible that it is an aberrant specimen of a more generally known species, but such affinities are not clear.

A single male was taken in Blean Woods, East Kent, in 1976 (A. Stubbs), but no additional specimens have been found despite further searches. May.

Genus SYRPHUS

Though one of the commonest and most familiar of hoverfly genera, errors in identification have been very frequent in the past. The genus is confirmed by reference to the long hairs on the dorsal surface of the squama. These hairs can be seen even with a magnifying glass providing the wing is outstretched so that the squama is fully extended. All too often the hairs have been overlooked because of haste or poor lighting. Also, if the wings are not outstretched, the long hairs on the fringe of the squama are mistaken for dorsal hairs, or alternatively the dorsal hairs are not clearly visible so are regarded as being absent. Thus specimens of *Syrphus* are incorrectly forced through a key into another genus, or superficially similar specimens belonging to other genera are casually regarded as *Syrphus* because this is thought the most plausible common genus. Many people have found the squamal character difficult and have run into trouble because Coe (1953a) placed this character so early in his key. There is, however, no avoiding the discipline of using the squamal character but some advice can be given.

Syrphus species have moustache bands on tergites 3 and 4, meaning that the bands are undulating and that they extend to the lateral margins, at which point they sweep forwards and are usually narrowing (occasionally the band on tergite 3, or more rarely also that on tergite 4, may be divided into spots). It is not infrequent for the bands to lack obvious undulations, thus being rather straight, but the bands always sweep forwards at the lateral margins (in *Epistrophe diaphana* the front edge remains straight). The only genera with such bands are as follows:

— *Eupeodes nitens*. Slightly smaller than the average *Syrphus*. Sternites with broad black bands across full width.

— *Eriozona erratica*. A large broad species with strong black bands across the full width of the sternites, and wing vein R_{4+5} strongly dipped. Face with a strong black stripe.

— *Parasyrphus*. Much smaller than the average *Syrphus*. The hind legs are more extensively black, except in *vittiger* (which has a dark central stripe on the face) and in *nigritarsis* (which has a broad black mouth rim and brighter orange abdominal markings in life). Tergites with sides rolled (or weakly beaded in *nigritarsis*).

— *Syrphus*. Normally larger than *Eupeodes* or *Parasyrphus*, but exceptionally small specimens can occur. Sternites with black central spots obviously not reaching side margins, or spots absent. Hind legs with at least the basal half of the tibia clear yellow. Sides of the tergites beaded in part. The only real scope for confusion is between very small female *ribesii* and female *Parasyrphus nigritarsis* (both have an entirely yellow hind femur and tibia), or male *vitripennis* and male *P. nigritarsis* (both have an extensively black hind femur).

Identification of the species can give problems, especially in the males. In recent years there has been much revision of *Syrphus*, raising the European list to ten species. To our long-standing and familiar three species must be added *rectus*, although its credentials as a separate species in Europe are somewhat suspect. The following notes provide an aid to awareness of the alternative species, since one or two more may yet be recognised as occurring in Britain, at least as vagrants.

The four known British species have the following characters:-

— Top of thorax entirely dusted greyish-green, somewhat dull.

— Tergites with extreme lateral margins entirely black.

— Tergite 2 with golf-club-shaped spots.

— Tergite 3 and 4 with moustache bands (rarely separated into spots).

— Eyes bare or hairy (hairy in *torvus* only).

The additional European species include some different features:-

— Top of thorax with shining stripes. (*admirandus* Goeldlin de Tiefenau and *auberti* Goeldlin de Tiefenau)

— Tergites with extreme lateral margins entirely yellow. (*attenuatus* Hine, *sexmaculatus* (Zetterstedt) and female *stackelbergi* Kuznetzov; latter in Lapland)

— Tergites 2 and 3 with spots (*nitidifrons* Becker, *sexmaculatus*, female *stackelbergi*), or spots or narrowly divided bands. (*auberti*, *attenuatus*, *admirandus*)

— Eyes always bare (never hairy).

— Frons entirely shining black. (*nitidifrons*)

— Face extensively black. (*stackelbergi*; Lapland)

Of the potential extra species, *nitidifrons* is perhaps the most likely. The squamal hairs may be poorly developed or absent and, as a species with spots rather than bands, it could easily be overlooked for *Melangyna lasiophthalma* since both occur in the early spring and both have a wide dark mouth margin (especially when seen in side view). The essential feature is that the extreme lateral margins of the tergites are continuously yellow (as also in *attenuatus*). In the

Netherlands *nitidifrons* occurs in sandy districts with forests of pine and Douglas fir where adults have been found on flowering shrubs such as willows, blackthorn and rowan (Barendregt, 1983). The East Anglian Breck could provide similar areas in Britain.

There remains uncertainty over the status of British specimens in which the bands on tergites 3 and 4 are divided into lunulate spots, so such specimens ought to be retained and records annotated accordingly, especially in *vitripennis*.

The larvae are predaceous upon a wide variety of ground-layer and arboreal aphids. They can be found overwintering in leaf litter beneath aphid-infested sycamores.

Syrphus rectus Osten Sacken, 1875

Specimens have been found in Ireland and elsewhere in Europe that appear to correspond to North American *Syrphus rectus*. These are ascribed to a new subspecies, *bretolensis* Goeldlin de Tiefenau, 1996 (Speight, 1999b). The snag is that males of *rectus* are indistinguishable from *vitripennis* (the usual sex for reliably distinguishing species). The female of *rectus* has a mainly yellow hind femur, thus resembling *ribesii*, but the incomplete covering of microtrichia on the wings equates with *vitripennis*.

Therefore, in essence it is like *vitripennis*, but the female has the hind femur mainly yellow (black except for a yellow apex in *vitripennis*); in *rectus* darkening is restricted to the extreme base and often there is a dark smudge near the middle on the anterior side. If the hind femur of a female were entirely yellow, it would be necessary to check the microtrichia of the second basal cell (entirely covered in *ribesii*, partly clear of microtrichia in *rectus*). See Speight (1999b) for further discussion and an alternative key.

For the present it is as well to follow the opinion of those specialists who believe in the above interpretation, but there remains the possibility that at least some of these specimens might be a yellow-legged form of *vitripennis*. We shall have to await someone doing genetic profiling or other detailed investigations to be sure. The few published records of *rectus* so far, in Britain and the rest of Europe, give no indication of any specific habitat association and it is probably a very mobile species that could turn up practically anywhere.

The first specimen from the British Isles ascribed to *rectus* was found in Ireland when a female was caught in a Malaise trap running from 12 August to 2 September 1999 at Glenveagh National Park, Donegal (Speight, 1999b). A single female reared by Colin Plant from Bishops Stortford, Hertfordshire, in June 1987 proved to belong to this species (Plant, 1991) and subsequently four more specimens have been recognised in Britain. August to September (but will probably be found to occur in the spring).

Syrphus ribesii (Linnaeus, 1758)   Pl. 2, fig. 2
                                                           Map: Ball & Morris p. 140
                                                           Larva: Rotheray Pl. 6a – 6c

The female used to be instantly recognisable within the genus because the hind femur is entirely yellow (rarely intersexes occur in which the hind femur is black-ringed, but at least the base remains yellow), but it is now necessary to check for *rectus*. Both sexes have the basal cells of the wing completely covered in microtrichia (as in *torvus*). The latter character is the best means of separating males of *ribesii* from those of *vitripennis*, and females from those of *rectus* (which have bare areas free of microtrichia). In the male, the presence of black hairs on the anterior surface of the yellow portion of the hind femur is a feature used by Coe (1953a) and is apparently reliable although not always easy to see (similar black hairs are found in *torvus* but not *vitripennis*). Specimens with divided bands on tergites 3 and 4 are referable to var. *interruptus* Ringdahl. Wing length 7.25–11.5 mm.

This is one of the most familiar hoverflies throughout Britain and Ireland, often being abundant in gardens, hedgerows, waste ground and many other habitats. It is multiple-brooded with a long season. The noticeable hum that often emanates from tree canopies in woodland during summer seems mostly attributable to the males of this species as they rest on foliage with their wings vibrating at high frequency. March to November, peaking twice, in late May and early June, and again from July to September.

Syrphus torvus Osten Sacken, 1875   Map: Ball & Morris p. 141

The presence of hairs on the eyes distinguishes *torvus* from its allies. These hairs can be seen with a hand lens, but it is necessary to get the lighting right; they are inconspicuous in the female. In other respects it superficially resembles the other species of *Syrphus*. In both sexes, microtrichia entirely cover the basal cells of the wing. In spring specimens, the bands on the tergites are typically rather narrower than *ribesii* and *vitripennis*, giving a darker appearance in the field, although this is less evident in the summer brood. Wing length 8.5–11.75 mm.

Amongst a profusion of *Syrphus* this species is easily overlooked; it should be found in most districts throughout Britain and Ireland, especially about woodland. Though *torvus* has a long season, it seems more prone to short peaks than the other species. It tends to have three peaks and is often one of the common species at sallow catkins before other species of *Syrphus* have emerged. It can also be one of the commoner hoverflies in late autumn, but the July peak is less noticeable due to the abundance of many other hoverflies at the same time. March to November, peaking three times, in late April, July and October.

Syrphus vitripennis Meigen, 1822   Pl. 2, fig. 1
                                                               Map: Ball & Morris p. 141

Being a bare-eyed *Syrphus*, comparison is necessary with *ribesii* and *rectus*. The female hind femur is always black for much of its length, including the base (completely or mainly yellow in *ribesii* and *rectus*). In both sexes the basal cells of the wing are partly free of microtrichia (as in *rectus*, but completely covered in *ribesii*). For males see the comments under *ribesii*, but this sex is apparently indistinguishable from *rectus*. Specimens in which the bands on tergites 3 and 4 are divided into lunulate spots have been referred to var. *strandi* Duda (it is just possible that this could prove to be a separate species). Wing length 7.25–10.25 mm, but typically somewhat smaller than *torvus* and *ribesii*.

This is another common and widespread species throughout Britain and Ireland in a wide range of habitats. *S. vitripennis* is a noted migrant. March to November, peaking slightly in May, but most abundant in July and August.

Genus XANTHOGRAMMA

These hoverflies readily attract attention because of their very smart appearance in life, the yellow markings on the frons, thorax and abdomen, and extensively yellow or orange legs, standing out boldly against the deep black ground colour.

Recent unpublished studies by C. Kassebeer indicate that *X. pedissequum* will need to be split into three species. Vouchers for all occurrences of the *pedissequum* group should be retained for checking, pending his publication.

The use of the name *citrofasciatum* of the British list has been confirmed as priority historic usage, thus overruling the confusing recent usage of the name *festivum* (2001, *Bulletin of Zoological Nomenclature* **58** (3): 241. Opinion 1982 (Case 3090)).

Xanthogramma citrofasciatum (De Geer, 1776)   Pl. 4, fig. 5
Xanthogramma festivum (Linnaeus, 1758) of some recent   Map: Ball & Morris p. 146
authors, overruled

The markings on tergite 2 are narrow wedge-like triangles, the horizontal length being about twice as great as the length of the triangle along the lateral margin of the tergite. The legs (femora, tibiae and tarsi) are entirely orange or orange-yellow. The wings have a medium-brown coloured stigma and surrounding patch, but this grades into the general brown tinge of the front margin of the wing (the wing patch in *X. pedissequum* is far more clear-cut). Wing length 6.5–10.25 mm.

This is largely a southern English species that occurs as far north as southern Cumbria and North Yorkshire. It is much less abundant than *X. pedissequum*. It occurs in Ireland in a band stretching across the centre of the country. Adults are most frequently encountered on well-drained grasslands with extensive nests of the mound-building ant *Lasius flavus*. They have also been noted on grazing marshes with extensive anthills. Larvae have been found in the nests of the ants *Lasius alienus* and *L. niger* (Hölldobler, 1929) where they feed on ant-attended root aphids (Rotheray *et al.*, 1996). April to September, peaking in late May and early June.

Xanthogramma pedissequum (Harris, 1776)   Pl. 4, fig. 4
                                                                  Map: Ball & Morris p. 147

Until recently *pedissequum* was considered a readily recognised species in the field and hence easily recorded without the need for voucher specimens. Some subtle variation seemed no more different from that of many other hoverflies. The greatest variation is on the thoracic pleura, generally out of sight in collections where specimens have been pinned dorsally, with a gradation from one to four yellow spots, intermediates having some of the spots dull and weak. An extreme spotted form was described as *flavipleura* by Coe (1957), but the type specimen from Yugoslavia has gone missing. Study of a long series on the continent is tending towards a revision which splits *pedissequum* into three species, but unfortunately the details have not been published in time for inclusion here. True *pedissequum*, as now interpreted, has a single vertical yellow stripe on the sides of the thorax, situated in front of the wing, sometimes with weak additional spots. The new species have additional clear yellow markings, but there is considerable variation and these markings alone do not appear to provide a reliable character to distinguish between members of the species group.

The easiest distinction from *citrofasciatum* is on tergite 2, the much dumpier yellow triangles contrasting with the elongate slender ones in *citrofasciatum*. Whilst the front two pairs of legs are yellow, the hind femur has a black pre-apical ring and the apex is orange, and the hind tibia and tarsus are also dusky orange, usually with the trace of a dark ring halfway along the tibia (all yellow in *citrofasciatum*). The wings have a brown stigma, the dark area extending somewhat behind, thus forming a broad dark strip (less uniform and clear-cut in *citrofasciatum*). Wing length 7.25–9.75 mm.

X. pedissequum is widespread in grassland and in open woodland rides, especially where the turf is short and some bare ground is exposed, as along paths. The flight is very low and sometimes males will be seen hovering only a few centimetres above the ground. The flowers utilised are also very close to the ground, but more usually the fly will be seen sitting on foliage or on bare ground. Larvae have been found regularly in nests of *L. niger* and *L. flavus* (Pontin, 1960; Foster, 1987). The species is largely found south of a line between Aberystwyth and the Wash being scarce in northern England and rare in Scotland north to the southern fringes of the Highlands. It has not been recorded from Ireland. Current records suggest that it is associated with less well drained sites than *X. citrofasciatum*. May to September, peaking in late June and early   July.

CHAPTER 9

SUBFAMILY MILESIINAE

This large subfamily contains about two thirds of our hoverfly fauna. The constituent genera are very varied, with many suggested means of classification into tribes. Coe (1953a) recognised several subfamilies, but this is not a satisfactory course. With only minor adjustments the 1976 check list has been followed here. *Microdon* has been placed in its own subfamily in recognition of its treatment in a number of modern reference works.

In the British literature, the paper by Goffe (1952) is still relevant for the recognition of the major division between the Syrphinae and the Milesiinae (though many of his other ideas on tribal classification are now outdated). This division is definable as regards structure of larvae, pupae and adults, as well as larval habits, with relatively few intermediates. The following table gives a simplified summary of the main points of difference, after Goffe (1952).

	Milesiinae	Syrphinae
Adults	Humeri hairy and head not fitting closely to the thorax.	Humeri bare and head fits closely over front of thorax, largely covering humeri.
	Abdomen of male with 4 visible segments (before pre-genital segment).	Abdomen of male with 5 visible segments (before pre-genital segment).
	Spiracle of third abdominal segment located at or near anterior corner of side.	Spiracle of third abdominal segment located in middle of side.
Larvae	Normally not much flattened beneath; normally with 7 pairs of prolegs, in most cases with tiny recurved hooklets.	Flattened beneath; without prolegs though flattened pad-like swellings may be present.
	Tend to be broadest in middle, narrowing a little towards both ends.	Broadest posteriorly, tapering anteriorly to a small pointed head.
	Posterior end tapers to a terminal posterior spiracular process, which may be of rat-tailed maggot type.	Posterior spiracular process placed somewhat dorsally, always short, never telescopic.
Puparium	Dumpy oval, swollen throughout.	Swollen anteriorly, but thin and flatter posteriorly.
	Anterior spiracles often form conspicuous horns.	Anterior spiracles usually not developed at all or very inconspicuous.
Larval Habitat	Plant material, decaying organic matter (only on aphids in Pipizini, mainly specialising on adelgids and other wax-secreting aphids).	Aphid-feeders (avoiding wax-secreting species); rarely also on caterpillars.

Reference to the plates will show that in practice most adults can readily be allocated to subfamily, and often to tribe, even from superficial appearance. Use of the keys will, however, be found essential in some cases.

Chapter 4 gives a summary of the larval habitats and there are further remarks under each tribe and genus.

Tribe CALLICERINI

The conspicuously long antennae with a long terminal arista make the single genus in this tribe distinct from other British hoverflies. In the living insect, the white tip to the arista is very striking. However, it is far less apparent in dead specimens, especially older ones in collections.

Genus CALLICERA

In general appearance the three species are bee-like. With the long antennae, there is a resemblance to the soldierfly *Stratiomys longicornis*, but the wing venation is very different. There are three species known in Britain. A revision of the European fauna (Speight, 1991b) recognised six species. It was revealed that British specimens previously ascribed to *aenea* should correctly be identified as a very similar species, *aurata* (in Europe *aenea* has a peak in May/June, earlier than *aurata*, although records extend to September). *C. fagesii* Guérin-Méneville has a flight period extending from April to mid July, and has been found in the Netherlands and Belgium. The sixth species, *macquartii* Rondani, is an autumnal species of southern Europe.

Larvae of all three British species have been discovered in water-filled cavities in tree trunks.

Callicera aurata (Rossi, 1790)   Pl. 9, fig. 2
Callicera aenea authors, misident.   Map: Ball & Morris p. 22

The long white arista and brassy abdomen are rather similar to *spinolae*. However, the femora are mainly black, distinctly so in most specimens. The front tarsus is at least half dark since segments 3, 4 and 5 are black. The abdomen is often glossy brass coloured, but the males can have a rather conspicuous central black area which is not found in *spinolae*. British material previously attributed to *aenea* has proved to belong to *aurata* (Speight, 1991b). *C. aurata* differs from *aenea* in that the last three tarsal segments are black (rather than yellow or greyish) and the top of thorax is mainly shining apart from anterior median dust stripes (entirely covered in thin greyish dust in *aenea*, plus or minus denser stripes). Wing length 10–12.5 mm.

Though individuals have been noted as far north as Cumbria, this rare fly is mainly found in southern England. There would appear to be no distinct habitat pattern for these records, a garden in south-east London and a shop window in Worthing being just as typical as the countryside. A specimen was found about birch logs on a common in North Hampshire. Records are nearly always of solitary specimens. There are relatively few records of flower visits, but they include hawthorn, white umbellifers and ivy. Because of its unpredictable nature, this is perhaps one of the most difficult species to find. Larvae occur in water-filled cavities in trees, with proven occurrence up to 18 m above ground in beech (Rotheray, 1991), but also from a variety of other trees including birch (Perry, 1997). June to September, peaking in July and August.

Callicera rufa Schummel, 1841   Pl. 9, fig. 3
                                                    Map: Ball & Morris p. 23
                                                    Larva: Rotheray Pl. 13e

The abdomen is black with steely reflections, with a fringe of sparse reddish-orange hairs on the flanks as seen from above, and the thorax also has reddish-orange hairs. It is thus very different in general colour from the other two species. The legs are orange except for tarsal segments 4 and 5 which are blackish. The arista is short and of a dirty white colour. Wing length 9.75–11.25 mm.

Ancient pine woods in Scotland provide the main habitat for *rufa*, but adults are very rarely encountered. They have been seen sitting on pine trunks, or more rarely on stumps. Following the discovery of the larval habitat, surveys of water-filled rot-holes for the easily recognised larvae and puparia have shown that *C. rufa* is widely distributed across northern Scotland (Rotheray & MacGowan, 1990). Larvae are found in water-filled cavities in trees and stumps, mostly of Scots pine, but also in larch and spruce. The puparia occur in fissures and between plates of bark on their host tree (Coe, 1938, 1939c, 1941b and 1953a). June to August, mainly in August according to Rotheray & MacGowan (1990).

Callicera spinolae Rondani, 1844   Pl. 9, fig. 1
                                                    Map: Ball & Morris p. 23

Superficially *spinolae* looks very similar to *aurata* and one really needs comparative material. The abdomen is brassy, but at the hind margins of tergites 2 and 3 there are conspicuous dull bands together with fairly obvious fringes of golden hairs. These features are only very slightly developed in *aurata*. The femora of the female are entirely orange (base dark in *aurata*), whilst in the male the femora are mainly dark, as in *aurata*. The date of capture is a further clue to identification since this is an autumn species, but late examples of *C. aurata* are not unknown and the date alone should not be used to confirm an identification. Wing length 12–15 mm.

This species is unusual among British hoverflies in being largely found in East Anglia. It was first discovered in 1928, near the Suffolk coast (Morley, 1942). It would seem that the main centre of distribution is around East Suffolk, central Cambridgeshire and the adjacent margin of south Norfolk, but there have been recent records from Hertfordshire and Essex. Concern about its status led to its inclusion as a Priority Species in the UK Biodiversity Action Plan, and work has been ongoing to investigate its biology in more detail. Larvae have been found in water-filled rot-holes in a number of tree species, including beech, horse-chestnut and field maple. Breeding trees are not necessarily large or ancient. The adult is very elusive, but is generally found on the flowers of ivy growing on walls and large trees about the edge of small partly wooded estates or large gardens. September to October, peaking in September.

Tribe CHEILOSIINI

The tribe takes its name from *Cheilosia*, the dominant genus. The other three genera in the British fauna only contain a few species (*Ferdinandea*, *Portevinia* and *Rhingia*). The face is fairly normal (with a knob) in *Cheilosia* and *Ferdinandea*, but it is extended in the lower half in *Portevinia* and markedly so in *Rhingia*.

The wide eye rim (zygoma) is not found in other Milesiinae, the rim consisting of a narrow strip bounded by the eye on one side and a groove on the other. Sometimes the rim is of a different texture or is very strongly defined in other ways. In the tribe Cheilosiini the rim is usually distinct to a level above the knob, but it then pinches in somewhat towards the eye margin and promptly expands again and reaches out to just below the antennae. In very hairy species such as *Cheilosia illustrata* the rim may be a little difficult to see (this species is distinctive enough anyway). Though the tribe is an assemblage of rather dissimilar genera, at least the number of genera is small and they are all very distinct.

Whilst *Cheilosia* and *Portevinia* share a phytophagous larval habit (feeding on live plants) which is unusual in the British Syrphidae (see also Merodontini), the genera *Rhingia* and *Ferdinandea* have other larval habitats. Studies of the larvae and male genitalia of *Cheilosia* suggest that it may be a false grouping that will require splitting into several genera in the future. The bare-eyed, black-legged species with fused antennal pits (*Nigrocheilosia* group) are particularly distinctive, exhibiting a genitalia configuration that is far closer to the other genera of the tribe than other *Cheilosia*. The three fungus-feeding species are also distinct in having fused antennal pits (seemingly a 'ground plan' feature of the tribe); these are separated in all other 'higher' *Cheilosia* species.

Genus CHEILOSIA

With at least 37 species this is our largest hoverfly genus. As so often happens in a large genus, many of the species are superficially similar and, moreover, the majority of the species lack distinctive markings. Most species are of moderate size but the size range is considerable, from small species such as *C. mutabilis* with a body length of 6 mm to *C. variabilis* which can be 12 mm long. The general drab dark appearance is misleading since on closer inspection there is a wide range of distinctive characters that can be used in identification, and there are some very attractive species.

The key by Coe (1953a) enabled a fair number of species to be identified with moderate ease. However, there were points where it was possible to go seriously wrong because the definitions were misleading or erroneous, or did not allow for variation in colour or shape. The shape of the face profile is subject to greater variation than allowed for in most keys so less reliance on this character is called for. Most collections contain misidentified material. In the course of the 1983 study, several species additional to the British fauna were recognised, explaining some of the tangles in earlier keys, and this edition covers yet more species. At a critical level this is a difficult genus with a shortage of reliable characters in some species groups. The male genitalia had widely been thought to be poor in characters, but more recent work has revealed their vital importance for critical separation between otherwise similar species. The drawings by Steven Falk (Plates B – N) of dissected male genitalia have been included to assist with the identification of problem specimens and to increase the chance of additional species being detected here. For the purposes of this book, macroscopic features enable most specimens to be placed with reasonable confidence. However, there remain specimens which do not fit the key and some of these may represent additional species – more material is needed to resolve such questions.

For someone unfamiliar with *Cheilosia*, the prospect of a long key may be somewhat daunting. Hence the key to groups of *Cheilosia*, with accompanying notes, will hopefully break up the genus into manageable units, albeit artificial ones. The species descriptions concentrate on comparison of species within these groups. Always bear in mind that further species could occur in Britain and that, when more material is at hand, it may be possible to recognise that what is currently treated as one species may in fact comprise two or more species. Vouchers should be kept, especially where rare species are concerned or where the specimens do not agree with the description.

There are many more species in Europe so it is likely that further additions to the British fauna will be made. Thus a critical eye is called for in recognising specimens that could be something new, and the value of retaining material of the various species from a variety of habitats and seasons cannot be stressed strongly enough. In some cases brood dimorphism leads adults of the spring and summer generation to have a different appearance; an extreme case concerns *proxima*, in which the spring and summer broods were treated as separate species (species E and D) in the first edition of this book.

Cheilosia larvae feed on higher plants or, in the case of a few species, in fungi. Abroad, there are even species associated with conifer resin and cambium. A list of known plant associations is given in Chapter 4. The point to emphasise here is the importance of recording the association between adult *Cheilosia* and possible foodplants. In some cases flowers frequented by the adult have proved to be the larval foodplant. In other cases it is a question of recognising that the common factor between different sites is the presence of certain suitable plant species. One should always be looking for clues to solve such questions, and oviposition behaviour is an especially good lead. Another point of equal relevance is the recognition that populations of a species seem to exhibit differences in ecology or seasonality, suggesting that more than one species may be involved.

It should be noted that umbellifer flowers can be a very productive source of *Cheilosia* adults in late spring and summer, and up to ten species can be encountered on a good patch of flowers on some chalk and limestone sites. Sallow and blackthorn flowers are also good lures for a suite of species in spring. Males of many species hover in loose swarms at varying heights above the ground and in some species (such as *variabilis*, *semifasciata* and members of the *antiqua* group) they appear to defend small territories from a perch on sunlit foliage.

NOTES ON GROUPS OF *Cheilosia*

The groups adopted here are ones of convenience, providing a means of dividing this large genus into manageable units. In some cases there is a resemblance between species which may suggest an evolutionary relationship, but in other cases the groupings are very artificial.

The species are described in alphabetical order for the genus as a whole.

(A) ILLUSTRATA Group [*illustrata*]

There is only one species, a furry bee mimic with a conspicuous dark cloud on the wing.

(B) VARIABILIS Group [*barbata, griseiventris, lasiopa, latifrons, variabilis, vulpina*]

This is a distinctive group, the sides of the face having hairs which project stiffly at right angles from the surface. The hairs are usually obvious even if sparse but can be pale and feeble, especially in *latifrons*. To see the hairs to best advantage the face should be viewed obliquely from in front so that any erect hairs stand out in silhouette. It is essential to avoid confusion with a pile of downcurved hairs which clothe the face in some other *Cheilosia* species. It should also be noted that various other hoverflies have erect hairs on the face, including black female *Melangyna quadrimaculata*, *Chrysogaster* and *Melanogaster* (the males of the latter have a facial knob and the tergites can be somewhat shining), but they lack the well developed eye rims (zygomas) of *Cheilosia*. The legs are partly pale except that some specimens of *variabilis* have entirely black legs. The antennae are black except in *barbata*, *latifrons* and some *griseiventris*. The eyes are hairy except in female *griseiventris* and *latifrons*.

(C) ALBITARSIS Group [*albitarsis, mutabilis, ranunculi*]

The front tarsus has segments 2, 3 and 4 orange whilst segments 1 and 5 are dark; the legs are otherwise entirely black or with only a slight paleness at the bases of the front and mid tibiae. However, in some specimens of *albitarsis* the pale segments can be murky orange or the tarsus is entirely black. To avoid confusion where dark-legged specimens are concerned, the keys to the *antiqua* and *impressa* groups include *albitarsis*. The eyes are hairy in the male and bare in the female. The antennae are dark. The *pagana* group also has a partly yellow front tibia, but with the first tarsal segment yellow, or if this segment is dark, the rest of the tarsus is dark; both sexes have bare eyes and most females have a yellow-tipped scutellum or orange antennae.

(D) ANTIQUA Group [*antiqua, ahenea, nigripes, pubera, sahlbergi, vicina*]

Most keys to *Cheilosia* recognise a group having entirely black legs. Unfortunately, collections tend to be littered with misidentifications as a result of insufficient care when examining the legs or because some species vary in this character. It is essential to examine all pairs of legs with good lighting to see whether the knees, the tips of the tibiae or the tarsi are partly pale. The construction of the key in Coe (1953a) is beset with pitfalls when the leg coloration does not agree with typical specimens. For instance, *carbonaria, pubera, semifasciata* and *variabilis* can have the knees and the base of the tibiae dark or pale, so this key avoids these points of confusion.

The eyes are bare in all true members of the *antiqua* group as defined here, thus putting uncertain black-legged species into other groups. *C. impressa* is included in the key since, although it has hairy eyes, these are so pale and faint in some specimens that they may not be detected with a hand lens. The females of *C. albitarsis* often have entirely black legs.

In Coe's key, emphasis is placed on the distinctive knob in *vicina*, this being very protruding and horizontal on its upper margin (view from side). However, it should be noted that some specimens of *vicina* are less extreme and that several other members of the *antiqua* group can be confusingly similar.

(E) PAGANA Group [*longula, pagana, scutellata, soror*]

Eyes are bare (as in the *antiqua* group and in females of the *albitarsis* group; also in some *latifrons* and *griseiventris*). The bases of the front and mid tibiae are black-ringed or at least broadly yellow, and the mid tarsus normally has the basal segments clear yellow, except in some *longula* (a yellow mid tarsus is also a feature of the *grossa*, *bergenstammi*, *illustrata* and *proxima* groups). The sternites are glossy, except for dusting on sternite 1 in some species, or lightly so throughout in *soror*. The antennae are orange or dark, the arista bare or pubescent. The scutellum is yellow-tipped in the females, except *pagana*, while *scutellata* and *longula* can also have pale spots on either side of the lower face (never so in other groups).

(F) IMPRESSA Group [*impressa*]

In Britain there is only one species which always has the combination of black legs and hairy eyes, *impressa*. However, some other species can produce specimens which approach this description, a point allowed for in the key (*carbonaria* group and male *albitarsis*). It should be noted that there are several other species in Europe with black legs and hairy eyes.

The eye hairs are pale. Usually they can be seen easily (if viewed against a dark background), but sometimes they are very weak and sparse. Thus *impressa* is repeated in the key to the *antiqua* group.

(G) GROSSA Group [*albipila*, *chrysocoma*, *grossa*, *nebulosa*; also *fraterna*, *uviformis*]

This group comprises four densely furry species, the erect fur being entirely pale on the thorax and the scutellum. The thorax has a brownish tinge to the ground colour, contrasting with the black face (less obvious in *nebulosa*). The scutellum lacks bristles along the hind margin. The hind tibia is completely pale or may have a smudge-like indistinct darkening on the anterior and posterior faces (in common with some members of the *bergenstammi* group). All members except *nebulosa* are fairly large robust species. The key explains the inclusion of the two species unrelated to *grossa*.

(H) PROXIMA Group [*proxima*, *velutina*, species B]

These are medium-sized, robustly built flies with hairy eyes. The sternites are entirely dusted (as in *ahenea* and *pubera* in the *antiqua* group), but care needs to be taken since from some angles the sternites may appear to be shining (viewing obliquely from the side usually reveals dusting). The antennae are normally dark and the tibiae are usually extensively pale on at least the front legs. There is a superficial resemblance to the larger specimens of *vernalis*, but that species has highly glossy sternites.

(I) CARBONARIA Group [*carbonaria*, *cynocephala*, *semifasciata*, *vernalis*]

Most species are very black-bodied, the legs usually with partially yellow tibiae, and the sternites are mainly or completely glossy (as in the *pagana* and *bergenstammi* groups). The antennae are black or dusky orange, rarely clear orange. *C. semifasciata*, with its partly dusted sternites and grey dust spots on the male abdomen, does not really fit with the rest of the group.

(J) BERGENSTAMMI Group [*bergenstammi*, *psilophthalma*, *urbana*]

Though a very artificial assemblage of species, they share some features in common with the *grossa* group. The tibiae are normally narrowly black-ringed, but in most specimens the ring is incomplete so that the dorsal surface remains narrowly yellow (sometimes not easy to discern). The mid tarsus is clear yellow on the basal segments (as in some species in the *grossa*, *illustrata*, *pagana* and *proxima* groups). The sternites are entirely glossy or only partly and faintly dusted in *urbana*. The third antennal segment is orange, except in most *vernalis* which is placed in the *carbonaria* group but repeated in this key because of its similarity to the present group. The eyes are usually hairy, but some *bergenstammi* lack hairs.

Cheilosia ahenea (von Roser, 1840)   Pl. B, fig. 1
Cheilosia laskai Speight, 1978

The legs are black or with just a trace of paleness about the knees. The only other species with legs of this type and with strongly dusted sternites is *pubera* (in *ahenea* the dusting can be weak in the centre of the sternites). *C. ahenea* is a blacker looking insect (rather more brassy coloured in *pubera*). The face is extensively free of dusting, with a sharp boundary to a well defined band of white dust immediately below the antennae (in *pubera* the face is extensively dusted with the general dusting merging into the denser band below the antennae). It may be noted that the face profile in some females can resemble that of *vicina*. Wing length 5.5–9 mm.

It was discovered in the British Isles from permanent, unimproved limestone grassland and the landward side of machair dune-systems in western Ireland (Speight, 1978b) with 16 records between 1979 and 1985 from counties Clare, Donegal, Fermanagh, Sligo and Mayo (Speight & Claussen, 1987; Nelson, 1988) and subsequently from machair grassland on Islay in the Inner Hebrides in 2000 (Parker, 2001). It has been found by sweeping low-growing vegetation where it occasionally visits flowers such as mountain everlasting, hawkweeds, buttercups and dandelions. Further searches of machair in the Hebrides may reveal this species to be more widespread. Although it has so far been found in Britain and Ireland either on calcareous grassland or calcium-rich machair, no such link with calcareous sites is apparent in central Europe where this species can be widespread and common (Speight, 2000c). Peak late May, extending into June.

Cheilosia albipila Meigen, 1838   Pl. G, fig. 1, Pl. 6, fig. 2
                                                          Map: Ball & Morris p. 26

This is a fairly large attractive species. The thoracic dorsum has a brownish hue enhanced by the long pile and the abdomen is a steely black, especially in the female which has sparser pale brown hairs. The antennae are clear orange. The female is instantly recognisable since this is the only *Cheilosia* with all the femora entirely orange. The male is less easy to distinguish but the extensively shining frons and very long hairs on the anterior surface of the hind femur serve to distinguish it from the smaller *nebulosa* and *uviformis*. Wing length 8.75–10.75 mm.

C. albipila is an early-spring species which is widespread in Britain and Ireland, including Ireland. It occurs locally in fens, marshes and wet meadows where its larval foodplant, marsh thistle, grows. On the continent it is reported from a much wider range of thistle species (see table in Chapter 4). Being an early species, it visits such flowers as sallow catkins and as likely as not will be found 'sunbathing' on pale-coloured dry herbage in sheltered spots where the warmth of the sun is most favourable. Eggs are laid on leaves and newly growing flower spikes of thistles in open sunny situations. By midsummer larvae are easy to locate in a burrow which extends from a few centimetres above the ground into the base of the stem below ground. Outward sign of attack is usually lacking, but the most robust plants are best investigated. Infestation rates can be fairly high, enabling rapid confirmation of occurrence by inserting a knife blade vertically through a stem, twisting to see if a brownish-stained burrow is present, and then opening up the burrow downwards (sometimes other insect burrows are predominant, often that of a moth caterpillar extending far up a stem). Normally there is a single larva, readily identified by a tiny dagger-point projection from between the hind spiracles. Beyond August the larvae have usually left the burrows to pupate close by in the soil (Rotheray, 1988a). March to June, peaking in April.

Cheilosia albitarsis (Meigen, 1822)   Pl. G, fig. 2, Pl. 6, fig. 13
                                                                            Map: Ball & Morris p. 26
                                                                            Larva: Rotheray Pl. 1e

This is a robust species, especially in the female which has a short broad abdomen. In sunlight the thorax is often a bluish black, contrasting with a dull bronze abdomen. It normally has the characteristic orange front tarsal segments 2, 3 and 4 (the specific name refers to the pale front tarsus). However, these segments are often murky orange or even entirely dark, especially in the female. In side view, the male has the thoracic hairs black and those of the abdomen pale and erect whilst in the female the thoracic dorsum has a mixture of very short inclined black hairs intermixed with golden ones and the abdomen has sparse adpressed golden hairs. The female has a short broad oval abdomen, usually broader than the thorax (as in *fraterna*) and the short-haired scutellum has only a few rather short marginal bristles. There is a very similar species, *ranunculi*, which has recently been split from *albitarsis* (see *ranunculi* for details of recognition). The only other species with a similar pattern of orange tarsal segments is *mutabilis*, a small narrow species which has a different combination of coloured hairs on the thorax and abdomen. Wing length 7–9.5 mm.

C. albitarsis is a spring species which is widespread and abundant in Britain and Ireland, including Ireland. The host plant is creeping buttercup. Occasionally females may be seen landing in the middle of the upper side of a leaf, walking up to the tip, then walking down the underside and following the stalk to ground level in order to lay an egg on the lower part of the stem. Larvae have been found at the rootstock (in the shade, though open situations may suffice) (Rotheray, 1991). Damp meadows, marshes and woodland clearings are typical situations where adults may be found at buttercup flowers or sunning on foliage. April to August, peaking in late May and June (note that this paragraph is based on data for '*albitarsis*' before the separation of *ranunculi*).

Cheilosia antiqua (Meigen, 1822)   Pl. B, fig. 2
                                                                            Map: Ball & Morris p. 27
                                                                            Larva: Rotheray Pl. 1f

It is a feature of the *antiqua* group that the upper surface of the facial knob often projects horizontally. Coe (1953a) referred to this feature in *vicina* but omitted to say that many specimens of *antiqua* are similar, even if less extreme – hence misidentifications have been frequent. The two can be instantly separated in the male since *antiqua* has a shining frons (even by the eye margins) whereas *vicina* has a heavily dusted dull frons. In both sexes *antiqua* is on average larger and less deeply black. The male usually has a lateral tuft of black hairs at the base of tergite 2 (all lateral hairs black on tergite 2 in one specimen) and there are dense hairs of uniform length on the thoracic dorsum, whereas in *vicina* longer hairs clearly project above a shorter general pile. Care should also be taken to eliminate *nigripes*, which is closer to *antiqua* in size and has an extensively shining frons. It shares with *vicina* the longer hairs on the thoracic dorsum and has noticeably darkened wings and a rather coarsely punctate thorax (finely punctate and strongly shining in *antiqua*). The thoracic hairs of *antiqua* are usually black. The separation of females is less easy, but the hairs are longer (about twice the width of an ocellus) and semi-erect as opposed to only the length of an ocellus and strongly adpressed in *vicina* and *nigripes*. It is not uncommon for novice recorders to confuse this species with males of *Melanogaster hirtella* which are considerably smaller. Wing length 5.75–8.25 mm.

The western side of England is the most favourable area for *antiqua* and it occurs in Wales and Ireland. It is rather more localised and scarce on the eastern side of England and in Scotland, extending northwards to Sutherland. Larvae have been found singly in primrose (also oxlip and cultivated primulas) growing in the shade; they tunnel down the rootstock and leave evidence of the infestation through pale brown plant fragments at the openings to their tunnels (Rotheray, 1991). *C. antiqua* is a woodland hoverfly, being local but not infrequent in the spring. The species is occasionally recorded as late as September but the majority of records are before the end of July. Specimens taken after June should be treated with particular caution and vouchers retained. April to August, peaking in May in England but June in Scotland.

Cheilosia barbata Loew, 1857   Pl. G, Fig. 4
                                                                   Map: Ball & Morris p. 27

This species is rather smaller than most members of the *variabilis* group and should be readily recognised by the reddish basal area on the third antennal segment (pale areas on the antennae are otherwise confined to the *latifrons* sub-group, among the hairy faced species, but these lack the strong scutellar marginals of *barbata*). In the male the hairs along the axis of the tergites are very short, mainly less than half the width of the hind tibia and inclined at about 60°. The lateral hairs in the male are of more or less even length except for a few black hairs at the tip of tergite 4. The hind femur has very short hairs beneath in the female (in common with *variabilis* and *lasiopa*) and the males have short hairs apart from long anteroventral hairs (as in *variabilis* and *lasiopa*). The arista of both sexes has more conspicuous pubescence than in other species in its group. Wing length 7–8 mm.

C. barbata is a scarce species of calcareous woodland, scrub and grassland which has been mainly found chalk downs in Surrey and the Chilterns, and on limestone in Warwickshire. There are also some records from East Anglia and it has been found in abundance on flowers of wild parsnip at one Suffolk Breckland site, suggesting a possible foodplant. It has not been recorded from Ireland. June to September, peaking from mid July to mid August.

Cheilosia bergenstammi Becker, 1894   Pl. H, fig. 1, Pl. 6, fig. 8
                                                                   Map: Ball & Morris p. 28

Moderately large *Cheilosia* with orange antennae and black-ringed orange tibiae are very likely to prove to be this species. It is possible to find specimens with the hind tibia completely orange, as in *fraterna*, so the separation of such examples is considered under that species. It may be noted that the male has long erect rich brown hairs on the thorax and abdomen, often with some black hairs on the thoracic dorsum and fine black bristles on the hind margin of the scutellum;

rarely there are some black hairs on top of the abdomen. In the female the hairs on the thorax and scutellum are very short, partly dark, and erect. The scutellar bristles are normally distinct. Wing length 7.25–9.25 mm.

C. bergenstammi is variable and it is possible that further species will be separated. For instance, variation occurs in the face profile, the density of eye hairs and the distribution of black hairs on the thorax and tergites. Vouchers should be retained. The very similar *lenis* Becker has dense long eye hairs, even on the lower part of the eyes, and tergite 4 has erect hairs in the female. It occurs in the Netherlands, but its only known larval foodplant (the ragwort *Senecio fuchsii*) does not grow wild in Britain.

This is a very widespread species throughout Britain and Ireland; it is, however, very local. A clue to finding the species is its use of ragwort as a larval foodplant. The adult will often be found on the flowers of ragwort or in the vicinity of this plant. Larvae live in the stem base and cause the plant to wilt. The usual larval foodplant is common ragwort (Smith, 1979), although it is likely that other species of ragwort are utilised, and it has been recorded laying eggs on hoary ragwort on the continent. Waste ground in urban areas, neglected fields, rough grassland and similar open areas provide likely habitat. Males occasionally form large hovering swarms at heights of about 1.5–3 m. This is typically a double-brooded species. May to September, peaking twice, in late May to early June, and again from mid July to August, the second brood tending to be more abundant.

Cheilosia carbonaria Egger, 1860   Pl. H, fig. 2
Map: Ball & Morris p. 28

A black (cf. carbon) medium-sized species, it has proportionately very long wings and a rather long narrow abdomen that tends to be widest at the posterior corner of tergite 3 (typically widest at the posterior corner of tergite 2 in other *Cheilosia*). The wings are rather strongly darkened, almost as much so as in *cynocephala*. The eye hairs are blackish (as in *cynocephala* and *vernalis*), but the facial knob is placed much lower on the face than in these species, almost approaching the state found in *semifasciata*. The legs can appear entirely black, although usually there is some dull orange at the base of the tibiae, or they can be distinctly pale on parts of the tibiae and on the base of the mid tarsus. In the male the hairs on the axis of tergites 3 and 4 are black and those on 4 strongly adpressed. The lateral hairs are pale apart from any black hairs at the posterior corners of tergite 4. The female abdomen is pale haired on the lateral margins. Wing length 8–9 mm.

C. carbonaria is a scarce species found in southern England and largely occurring south of the Thames, but with a few records as far north as Derbyshire. Previously it was thought to be confined to ancient woodland, but recent evidence suggests that this is not so, although it is most frequently encountered in woodland rides. It has not been recorded from Ireland. April to September, peaking twice, in late May and early June, and again in late August and early September.

Cheilosia chrysocoma (Meigen, 1822)   Pl. E, fig. 1, Pl. 6, fig. 5
                                                                           Map: Ball & Morris p. 29

The body is covered in a beautiful foxy red fur making this a particularly attractive hoverfly. The ground colour of the abdomen and thorax is of a uniform brownish hue and the orange third antennal segment has the slight trace of a point near the tip of the upper edge. Wing length 8–10.25 mm.

Unfortunately this is rather an uncommon species. Records are widely scattered in England, south Scotland, Wales and Ireland, with a strong bias towards western districts. There is a concentration of localities in Gloucestershire, Herefordshire, Worcestershire and Oxfordshire. Typical situations are woodland rides or glades at the edges of woods, nearly always in or close to marshy conditions, especially where calcareous soils are present as on the borders of fens or in limestone woods. Females have been observed to oviposit on angelica. The adult in flight resembles the solitary bee *Andrena fulva* whose females are tawny orange, so it is as well to net any bee-like insect of the right colour when in suitable habitat. Adults have a liking for sitting on sunny paths and occasionally may be found at flowers. March to June, peaking in May.

Cheilosia cynocephala Loew, 1840   Pl. H, fig. 3
                                                                           Map: Ball & Morris p. 29

This closely resembles the highly variable *vernalis*, and can be quite difficult to separate from darker-haired examples of the latter. In the field, the deep bluish-black appearance of *cynocephala*, with wings that are distinctly darkened in the middle, can be very obvious, although this can be less so in artificial light. The abdomen is much more extensively black-haired in both sexes, especially along the lateral margins. Tergites 3 and 4 are almost entirely black-haired laterally, except at the extreme front corners. In *vernalis* such black hairs rarely occupy more than the posterior half of the margins. The female also has long decumbent pale hairs along the posterior margin of tergite 4 (all short and adpressed in *vernalis*). The thoracic dorsum is always entirely black-haired (usually some pale hairs are present in *vernalis*) and the punctures rather coarse. The legs are more extensively dark with all tarsi blackish (in *vernalis* the basal segment of the middle tarsus is yellowish). The female frons has a broad lateral zone of rather coarse pitting, contrasting with sparse pits in the centre (in *vernalis* the lateral zones are usually narrower with sparser pits). Wing length 6.25–7.25 mm.

Records are widely scattered, including a number from Scotland, but the majority lie in counties south of a line between the Severn and the Wash. It has not been recorded from Ireland. Most records are from chalk or limestone districts, with a significant concentration of reports from Dorset. Larvae have been reported from musk thistle, a plant most typically associated with calcareous soils. In Warwickshire an association with welted thistle is apparent and it has been recorded from a wider range of thistles on the continent. There would appear to be a small spring generation, but the bulk of the records are from the middle of June onwards peaking in early September. May to October.

Cheilosia fraterna (Meigen, 1830)   Pl. I, fig. 1, Pl. 6, fig. 10
includes *Cheilosia* species C of first edition.   Map: Ball & Morris p. 30

The moderately large build and entirely orange hind tibia are features otherwise only shared with the *grossa* group, *soror* and by exceptionally pale-legged specimens of *bergenstammi*. The female abdomen is particularly short and broad (as in *albitarsis*). The antennae are orange, as in most other similar species (although not normally as bright orange as *bergenstammi*). The male has relatively short thoracic hairs which are mostly pale, but with a black band of hairs between the wing bases. The bristles on the scutellum are often indistinguishable from the hairs. The female has short, almost adpressed hairs on top of the thorax, and the hairs on the scutellum are very short so that the fine, often pale scutellar bristles are obvious. A difficulty arises with exceptional specimens of *fraterna* in which there is some darkening of the hind tibia, or of *bergenstammi* in which the hind tibia is completely yellow. In the male of *fraterna* the black band of hairs across the thoracic disc is dense and composed of obviously inclined hairs, whilst the hairs on the scutellum are short, those on the hind margin being scarcely more than half as long as the scutellum (in *bergenstammi* males, even if black hairs occur between the wing bases, they otherwise look little different from the hairs in front and behind, whilst the hairs on the scutellum are long, the longest marginal hairs or bristles being almost as long as the scutellum). In the female the hairs in the centre of the thoracic dorsum are adpressed, and semi-adpressed on the top of the scutellum (in *bergenstammi* the hairs on the thorax and scutellum are inclined at 45° or are more upright). Dwarf specimens (including 'species C' of the first edition) can closely resemble *vernalis*, but the latter species tends to have a very distinct dark ring on the hind tibia, and an extensively darkened third antennal segment. Wing length 6.5–10.25 mm.

C. fraterna is a frequent species found throughout Great Britain. Its status as an Irish insect is uncertain. It was added to the Irish list by Speight *et al.* (1975) on the basis of a single specimen which cannot now be traced and the Irish specimen subsequently recorded in Nash & Speight (1976) has proved to be misidentified (Speight, 2000c). It occurs in damp meadows and marshes where the adults show a particular affinity for buttercup flowers (in size and shape they resemble *albitarsis*, but the leg coloration is different). The host is marsh thistle, but a wider range of thistles is reported on the continent. In a study in Scotland, eggs were laid from late June onwards, near the tip of the upper surface of leaves on stems and in rosettes where there was a core of leaves about 10 cm in diameter. There was a single egg per leaf; on hatching the larvae tunnelled into the protruding mid-vein about 3 cm from its base. The tunnel extended towards the roots, sometimes breaching the hollow centre of the stem and burrowing down to the base of the plant. In rosettes, the larvae tunnelled in a spiral around the core down towards the roots, where they may make an internal cavity (the larval spiracles lack the special features of *albipila* and *grossa*; larvae of *proxima* feed externally below ground on the stem base and roots). By late July larvae were leaving the plants to pupate in the soil, some soon producing adults, but others not emerging until the following year. Thus there was a partial second generation laying eggs in early September, with larvae completing development and leaving the plants by mid October. Clearly the exact timing will vary according to the season and climatic zone. A parasitic wasp (*Bracon* sp.) was bred from larvae of the hoverfly (Rotheray, 1988a). March to September, peaking twice, in late May to early June, and again with a smaller peak in late August.

Cheilosia griseiventris Loew, 1857   Pl. I, fig. 2
                                                            Map: Ball & Morris p. 30

Examination of the series of *latifrons* in museum collections revealed a form with distinctive characters which, when separated out from the rest of the series, corresponded with the largest and most elongate specimens. These equate with *griseiventris* of Sack (1932), a name which Collin had applied to a series in the Verrall-Collin Collection (Hope Department, Oxford). Van der Goot (1981; also *pers. comm.*) does not include this species or know of it, but it seems reasonable to refer to the species as *griseiventris* pending further resolution of the matter, noting that there are relatively few hairy-faced species to choose from. We have not been able to see the type.

In the male the frons and face are about equally dusted. The ratio of head width to head height is about 5:4 (10:9 in *latifrons*), the frons being particularly broad. The eyes meet for a distance which is equal to or less than the length of the ocellar triangle. Tergites 2 and 3 are less than twice as wide as long and, viewed obliquely from behind, have the faint lateral greyish areas triangular. The third antennal segment is usually completely dark. Average body length 10.5 mm; wing length 9 mm.

The female is best distinguished on the basis of the long hairs on the disc of the scutellum, many of them as long as the median width of the hind tibia. The ratio of head width to height is about 4:3 (7:6 in *latifrons*); the frons and face are relatively broad and more heavily dusted (especially the front corners of the frons). Though not a fully reliable character, the base of the hind femur is usually orange for one-tenth to one quarter of its length (base usually black or very narrowly orange in *latifrons*). Average body length 10 mm; wing length 8.5 mm.

Assertions that *griseiventris* is conspecific with *latifrons* have been made on several occasions, but are countered by the facts that the males of both species remain easily separable in all of their broods, dwarf male specimens of *griseiventris* still retain their diagnostic features, and one does not find intermediate males at sites where the two species occur together. However, females are often difficult to identify, especially small specimens of *griseiventris* with the hairs above the scutellum damaged. What is more, *griseiventris* appears to have only two generations per year, in contrast to three in *latifrons*. Even if this species proves not to be the true *griseiventris*, it is clearly a good species.

Most records lie south of a line between the Severn and the Vale of Pickering, but there are outliers on the North Wales borders. Speight (2000c) does not accept that this is a valid species, but notes under *latifrons* that the "two segregates into which this taxon is subdivided by British authors could both be recognised among Irish material", from which we may conclude that *griseiventris* also occurs in Ireland. In southern Britain it occurs in fens, calcareous or neutral grasslands, coastal dunes and broad woodland rides. In contrast to *latifrons*, it seems to avoid acidic soils. The larvae are unknown but are thought to be associated with yellow composites such as hawkbits (as suspected in *latifrons*), hawk's-beards or cat's-ear. April to September, peaking twice, in May and again from mid August to early September.

Cheilosia grossa (Fallén, 1817)   Pl. I, fig. 3, Pl. 6, fig. 1
                                                                        Map: Ball & Morris p. 31
                                                                        Larva: Rotheray Pl. 2a, 2b

Superficially this species resembles *albipila* but on average it is somewhat larger (vying with *illustrata* and *variabilis* as the most robust in the genus). The black antennae immediately separate *grossa* from other members of its group. Wing length 8.5–11.75 mm.

This is a widespread, but easily overlooked, early-spring species throughout Britain and Ireland. It occurs in a variety of habitats ranging from damp meadows and woodland rides to grass heath and shingle, provided that thistles are abundant. The hosts include marsh thistle, spear thistle, slender thistle and musk thistle. Eggs are laid in early spring on the tips of newly growing flower spikes when they are only a few centimetres tall. By July larvae are becoming mature in burrows in the lower part of stems. The best method of searching is to look for large plants with splayed stems, the central shoot having aborted only a few centimetres above ground as a result of multiple larval attack (single larvae may not outwardly affect the growth of the plant). Larvae will be found in the central stem (or may move out into the bases of side shoots), but mature larvae are often just below ground level beneath a chewed-up mass of frass inside the base of the stem; the hind spiracles have a distinctive flange on either side. Note that cattle trampling or mechanical damage can also cause stems to splay out. By late summer, larvae have left the plant to pupate in the soil. The parasitic wasp *Phygadeuon grossae* was reared from an overwintered puparium (Rotheray, 1988a). Adults can be found at sallow catkins from as soon as they flower, and sometimes at other early spring flowers such as blackthorn, colt's-foot and dandelion. Males hover beside bushes in flower and sometimes form loose swarms at a height of 2–6 m. March to May, peaking in late March and early April in the south.

Cheilosia illustrata (Harris, 1780)   Pl. E, fig. 2, Pl. 6, fig. 3
                                                                        Map: Ball & Morris p. 31

This is an attractive furry bee mimic with a dark wing cloud. The body is mainly pale-haired, but usually has a well developed black band of hairs across the centre of the thorax and another across tergite 3. The black ground colour of the face, the front of the thorax and the front of the abdomen are obscured by pale dust. The black hair bands can be much weaker, especially in the male, so that entirely pale-haired forms are less recognisable, apart from the wing cloud. The tip of the abdomen often has faintly reddish or orange hairs. There is little chance of confusing this species, though dark male *Leucozona lucorum* look somewhat similar because of the dark wing cloud. Wing length 8.5–10.25 mm.

C. illustrata is a widespread and abundant midsummer species on umbellifer flowers in hedgerows and at woodland edge throughout Britain and Ireland, wherever hogweed or angelica is present. Rotheray (1999b) found larvae tunnelling in the roots of large plants of hogweed in the autumn, and notes that it has been reared from wild parsnip on the continent. April to September, peaking in July.

Cheilosia impressa Loew, 1840   Pl. J, fig. 1
                                                                    Map: Ball & Morris p. 32

This compact, smallish species is often distinctive in the field because of its steely blue-black thorax (as in *albitarsis*, which is much larger) and obviously yellowish wing-bases. The eyes also tend to be distinctly reddish in life. These features may be less obvious indoors and in pinned material. This species is almost unique in the known British fauna in having the combination of completely black legs and hairy eyes (*variabilis* shares this combination whilst *albitarsis* and *carbonaria* can occasionally approach this state). Unfortunately some females have feebly hairy eyes so it has been necessary to construct the keys so as to cover the situation when this character is not discernible with a hand lens. Wing length 5.75–8 mm.

Alder carr and other wet woods, or damp riverside situations with trees, provide suitable habitat. Adults are usually found on umbellifer flowers, especially water-dropworts and angelica. In Germany females were observed laying eggs in May on plants of greater burdock: subsequently larvae were found on the surface of the roots; 75% of larvae produced a second generation of adults, the remainder going into diapause to complete development the next year (Schmid, 1999b). Puparia are formed under the soil surface near the host. This species is widespread in England and Wales, but is rare in Ireland and has been recorded near Stirling in Scotland (D. Robertson, quoted in Stubbs, 1996a). May to September, peaking from mid July to August.

Cheilosia lasiopa Kowarz, 1885   Pl. F, fig. 2
Cheilosia honesta; Verrall, 1901, misident.   Map: Ball & Morris p. 32

The females are readily recognised within the *variabilis* group by means of the very short but strong bristles along the hind margin of the scutellum, much shorter than half the length of the scutellum. The zone of decumbent pale hairs on tergite 3 is limited to the posterior half in the sub-lateral area. The hind femur is very short haired. The hairs on the thoracic dorsum are short and semi-decumbent and the males have relatively short pale hairs on the lateral margin of tergites 3 and 4 (about as long as the width of the hind tibia); the hairs on the axis are even shorter and inclined at 60° (*vulpina* is more hairy). The antennae are black (unlike *barbata*). Wing length 7.25–9 mm.

C. lasiopa is locally common in southern England as far north as Merseyside and southern Yorkshire, but is distributed as far as the Central Highlands of Scotland. It has not been recorded from Ireland. A variety of habitats are used, including woodland rides, coastal dunes (in the west of its range), waste ground and sheltered heathland edge. Females have been observed laying eggs at the base of the leaves of greater plantain and ribwort plantain; larvae eat cavities into the main root of the latter (Stuke & Carstensen, 2000). Adults are most frequently found visiting the flowers of cow parsley or sunbathing on foliage near to the foodplants. Males hover low over the ground or short vegetation. April to August, peaking in late May and early June.

Cheilosia latifrons (Zetterstedt, 1843)   Pl. J, fig. 2
Cheilosia intonsa Loew, 1857   Map: Ball & Morris p. 33

Specimens are very variable in size, the largest being of medium size for a *Cheilosia*, though it never matches the size of a typical *griseiventris*. The entirely pale hairs and orange antennae are shared with a number of other *Cheilosia*, but only with *barbata* and *griseiventris* among the hairy-faced species. In the male the frons is distinctly shining, although not brilliantly. The head viewed from in front is more rounded than in *griseiventris*, the ratio of width to height being about 10:9 (5:4 in *griseiventris*). The eyes meet for a distance greater than the length of the ocellar triangle. Tergites 2 and 3 are about twice as wide as long (producing a proportionately shorter abdomen than *griseiventris*) and the vague silvery lateral spots (viewed obliquely from behind) are rectangular and sometimes fused. Females have the hairs on the scutellum short, often strongly inclined and about half as long as the median width of the hind tibia. The head is almost round in front view, the ratio of width to height being 7:6 (4:3 in *griseiventris*); the face is also relatively narrower. The base of the hind femur is dark, in common with most of the rest of its length, or occasionally narrowly orange. The third antennal segment is more inclined to be reddish at its base. The above features should enable separation from *griseiventris*. Wing length 5.5–7.5 mm.

C. latifrons is a very variable species in many characters, even where a series is taken on one occasion. It is possible that extra species may eventually be separated. It may be noted that in *barbata* the scutellum of the male has black hairs and bristles, that of the female having adpressed pale hairs and conspicuous black marginal bristles.

The species is widespread, including Scotland and Ireland, although the position is confused by the separation of *griseiventris*. A wide variety of habitats are exploited, ranging from dry grassy heathland to marshy grassland. Abroad, females have been observed ovipositing on autumn hawkbit (Schmid & Grossman, 1996); an association with yellow composites such as hawkbits and hawk's-beard has long been suspected in Britain. April to October, with three apparent peaks, in May, July and September.

Cheilosia longula (Zetterstedt, 1838)
Pl. D, fig. 1
Map: Ball & Morris p. 33
Larva: Rotheray Pl. 2c, 2d

This is a relatively small, narrowly-built species that resembles *scutellata* by virtue of dark antennae and, in females, the possession of a yellow-tipped scutellum and pale facial markings. However, the facial knob seen from above is clearly triangular with the swelling starting well clear of the eye margins (see illustration in key). In the male the thoracic dorsum has a light covering of dust when viewed from the front (undusted and strongly shining in *scutellata*), and tergite 3 lacks obvious shining areas at the front corners. In both sexes the legs are darker, especially the tarsi and the hind tibia (only basal quarter pale). Females have a tendency to have the hind metatarsus strongly swollen. Wing length 6–7.5 mm.

It is widely distributed across mainland Britain, with three concentrations of records: on southern heathlands and other sandy locations; in Yorkshire and Lancashire; and in central and northern Scotland. Records are few and scattered in Ireland. Adults are normally found in acidic woodland composed of birch or conifers, or on adjacent heathland and moorland. It breeds in the *Boletus*-type of fungi, including species of *Leccinum* and *Suillus*; reports from truffles on the continent perhaps need confirming. In a Scottish pine wood, up to 80 larvae were found in a single fungus, and the infestation rate was about 50%. In August and September infested fungi collapsed to the ground as larvae developed, third-instar larvae being found submerged in semiliquid fungal material. By September or October the larvae had pupated in the leaf litter and soil beneath the fungal remnant (Rotheray, 1990c). May to November, peaking in July and August.

Cheilosia mutabilis (Fallén, 1817)   Pl. J, fig. 3, Pl. 6, fig. 14
                                                                          Map: Ball & Morris p. 34

Small, slender *Cheilosia* with extensively darkened legs should be carefully checked to see whether the characteristic front tarsus of *mutabilis* is present. The only other species with such a front tarsus are *albitarsis* and *ranunculi* which are very much bigger and have orange halteres. The female of *mutabilis* is slender. The male thoracic dorsum also bears a thin brown dusting (view from the front), a feature only otherwise shared with *longula*. The female has inclined pale hairs on the thorax and semi-adpressed black hairs along the centre line of the tergites. In most males the bases of the front and mid tibiae are dusky rather than strictly black. In the female they are rather clearly orange on their basal quarter. Females have bare eyes in contrast to the males, although in some males these hairs can be rather sparse. Care should be taken when naming this species, as it is not uncommon for inexperienced recorders to ascribe specimens of *albitarsis* with partially darkened halteres to *mutabilis*, but *mutabilis* is much smaller and narrower. Wing length 4.75–6.75 mm.

Although there are a few Scottish records, there is a marked concentration of records in south Lancashire and south Yorkshire with a wider scatter to the south. It has not been recorded from Ireland. It occurs in a range of habitats, including heaths, open spaces in conifer plantations and in some deciduous woodlands (possibly on drier heathy rides). The larvae have been found in the roots of welted thistle (not really a heathland plant). April to August, peaking in July.

Cheilosia nebulosa Verrall, 1871   Pl. L, fig. 1, Pl. 6, fig. 4
                                                                          Map: Ball & Morris p. 34

The name *nebulosa* refers to the nebulous smudge-like brown shadings on the wing, one in the centre and another towards the wing tip. However, such markings are often indistinct, which can invite confusion with species such as *albipila* and *uviformis*. It is therefore best to use other characters to support a determination. It is usually considerably smaller than *albipila*, and the male has a very broad, heavily dusted frons that is extensively or completely yellow-haired. The eyes meet for a distance equal to the length of the vertex (this distance is distinctly longer than the vertex in *albipila*). *C. uviformis* shares the heavily dusted frons but it is narrower and bears black hairs, and the scutellum has black hairs around the rim (sometimes with differentiated bristles). The female of *nebulosa* has the hind femur largely darkened (orange in *albipila*), a very broad frons (over one-third the head width at the front) and body hairs shorter than *albipila* and with those on tergites 2 and 3 adpressed. Females of *uviformis* usually have marginal bristles on the scutellum and a much narrower frons. Wing length 6–8.5 mm.

This species is very scarce, occurring in southern England, East Anglia, north-west England and east-central Wales, as well as Ireland and Scotland. Woodland rides and wood edges by marshy ground probably provide the most favourable habitat, sallow catkins being one of the best lures. April to June, peaking in May.

Cheilosia nigripes (Meigen, 1822)   Pl. B, fig. 3, Pl. 6, fig. 15
                                                          Map: Ball & Morris p. 35

The nature of this species has been poorly interpreted in the past. In particular Coe (1953a) simply indicated that the male of *vicina* has pale short hairs on the thorax when in fact it can also have entirely black hairs as in *nigripes*. Moreover the face profile can be rather reminiscent of *vicina* in some specimens.

The shining frons in the male gives a clear distinction from *vicina*. Females are very difficult to separate, especially if the face profile is like that of *vicina*, although some specimens do have a sloping upper side to the knob which makes confusion less likely. All the female specimens available have tergite 5 about twice as wide as long (typically one and a half times as wide as long in *vicina*). *C. nigripes* has rather brownish-tinged wings with a white area at the base of cell r_1 (much weaker contrast in *vicina*). The wing bases (inwards of the basal cells) have blackened veins (female *vicina* usually have brown veins here). Wing length 6.5–7.5 mm.

Many past records of this rare species must be discounted. Authentic specimens are mainly from the Chalk of southern England and it seems plausible that the Gloucester record in Coe (1953a) from a Cotswolds limestone locality is correct. However it has recently been confirmed from a site in Yorkshire, well within the range of *vicina* (R. Crossley). Searching is most profitable at buttercup flowers at the foot of chalk downs, especially in damp meadows, in glades or at woodland edges. Males sun themselves on leaves in sheltered situations. May to July, peaking in June.

Cheilosia pagana (Meigen, 1822)   Pl. K, fig. 1
                                                          Map: Ball & Morris p. 35

There is a considerable range in size, some specimens being among the smallest *Cheilosia*. The female is conspicuous in the field because it has a huge orange third antennal segment, clearly wider than the front femur, but the males are less obvious with their small antennae. The males, when live and seen in sunlight, often have strong reflective grey triangles on the sides of the abdomen. *C. pagana* has very obvious features separating it from the other three members of the group (*longula*, *scutellata* and *soror*). In *pagana* the lateral margins of tergite 4 in the male have hairs of uniform length (instead of longer black hairs at the posterior corners) and in the female all the hairs are angled obliquely backwards (in female *longula* and *soror* at least the front half has lateral hairs projecting straight out and in *scutellata* there are a few such hairs at the front corners). The arista is bare, or almost so. The female has an entirely black scutellum (rarely so in related species) and the male face is entirely glossy black (other species have some dusting visible towards the side of the knob at some angles). Small *bergenstammi* females resemble *pagana* in the field but the third segment is never so large and the eyes will soon be seen to bear sparse but obvious hairs once examined with a strong hand lens or microscope. Wing length 4.75–8.5 mm.

The variation in certain characters requires further study. There are considerable differences in the shape of the third antennal segment and in the nature of pits on the inner surface which vary in position or are absent (cf. *Brachyopa*), but differences can occur within a series collected together at the same spot. There is also a degree of brood dimorphism that follows the general pattern seen in *proxima* and *vulpina*. Thus, the spring generation tends to produce larger specimens with more extensive pale hairs which tend to be longer, and the arista tends to have shorter pubescence. Summer specimens tend to bear extensive black hairs on the thoracic dorsum and tergites and have the arista more obviously pubescent. However, intermediates are frequent.

C. pagana is a common species throughout Britain and Ireland. A wide range of habitats are used, both wooded and open. It occurs frequently on spring-flowering shrubs such as sallow and blackthorn, also umbellifer flowers including cow parsley, and is very partial to lesser celandine in spring. Males can often be found sunbathing on tree trunks (particularly the spring brood), and can occasionally be found hovering in loose swarms at heights of 2–5 m, especially in the vicinity of dead tree trunks or electricity poles. It has been reared from larvae found in the rotting roots of cow parsley in the autumn, although it is almost certain that various other umbellifers are also used (including angelica and hogweed, according to continental records). It is possible that this may be a species complex with sibling-species in different host plants. March to October, peaking twice, in May and early June, and again in August.

Cheilosia proxima (Zetterstedt, 1843)   Pl. K, fig. 2
Cheilosia species D and species E of first   Map: Ball & Morris p. 36
edition.

This is another highly variable hoverfly that may prove to contain additional species. The overall appearance is much like *vernalis*, but the sternites are dull and the eye hairs are whitish. In the male, the legs are mainly black apart from the front and mid tibiae, which are broadly black-ringed, and the extreme base of the hind femur. The female legs are more extensively pale with the basal tarsal segments of the front and mid leg varying from brown to yellow, and narrower rings on all tibiae. The face in side view shows a well developed knob with strong indentations above and below, and a protruding upper mouth edge (*velutina* has a much flatter face and a receding mouth edge). The hairs on top of the thorax are often extensively black and, with careful orientation, longer hairs will be seen to protrude above a shorter pile (in *velutina* these hairs are all pale and of equal length). Wing length 6.25–8.5 mm.

Since the publication of the original account in 1983, the taxonomic status of species D and E has been clarified: they roughly represent the two generations of *proxima*, species E typically being the spring brood and species D the summer generation. As in *pagana* and *vulpina*, spring specimens tend to be larger, with more extensive pale hairs and a less pubescent arista. As pale abdominal hairs in all *Cheilosia* tend not to be adpressed, the overall effect is to produce a rather more hirsute-looking spring form, but intermediates are common and occasionally very pale-haired specimens can be encountered in summer.

C. proxima is frequent and widespread, but rare in Scotland. It has not been recorded from Ireland. It is particularly fond of yellow and white umbellifers, such as hogweed and wild parsnip, where these grow along woodland margins and in rides. Larvae were found from late June (in Scotland) in rosettes of marsh thistle about 10 cm in diameter. Larvae make a spiral furrow down towards the roots, remaining external, the last instar being spent among the lateral roots. A second generation of young larvae was found in late August to September, but the subsequent mature larvae had left to pupate by mid October. A single parasitic wasp

(*Phygadeuon* sp.) was reared (Rotheray, 1988a). May to August, peaking twice, in May, and again in July and August.

Cheilosia psilophthalma Becker, 1894   Pl. L, fig. 2

Though this species is difficult to recognise in the field, it is easy to define with a microscope since it is the only *Cheilosia* with both partly yellow legs and completely black tarsal claws (other partly yellow-legged *Cheilosia* have the basal half or more of the tarsal claws yellow). It is most likely to be confused with *urbana* (which has bicoloured claws). Male *psilophthalma* have silvery reflecting sides to tergite 3 (view obliquely from behind, moving the specimen around until the spots catch the light). These spots reach inwards, but leave the median third black (in *urbana* they reach further inwards and can sometimes be fused). Wing length 6-7mm.

This species has only recently been adequately distinguished from the closely similar *urbana* by Claussen & Kassebeer (1993). Speight re-examined Irish material which had previously been attributed to *praecox* (now *urbana*) and found that all the Irish specimens he examined were *psilophthalma*; however, this was not true of the specimens from Great Britain to which he had access (Speight, 1996a). He gives a key to separate *mutabilis*, *urbana* (as *praecox*) and *psilophthalma*. Claussen & Kassebeer (1993) illustrate the male genitalia of these species and also *latigenis*, a new species which is part of the same species complex but has so far only been found in the Pyrenees.

C. psilophthalma was initially recorded only from Ireland (Speight, 1996), but it can now be confirmed from mainland Britain with recent records from Berkshire, Suffolk and Warwickshire (S. Falk). It is typically found on and around spring-flowering shrubs such as sallow, blackthorn and apple (often alongside *urbana*) in the vicinity of unimproved grassland bearing the larval foodplant. It has been reported from hawkweeds on the continent and its host in Britain is probably mouse-ear hawkweed (females have been found sitting on the rosettes in spring at several sites in Warwickshire – S. Falk), a host it would share with *urbana*. However, whilst *urbana* larvae feed in the roots, *psilophthalma* attacks the above-ground parts. April to June.

Cheilosia pubera (Zetterstedt, 1838)   Pl. C, fig. 1, Pl. 6, fig. 16
                                                                                   Map: Ball & Morris p. 37

The legs are typically black, but occasionally specimens with broadly pale knees are found. Thus Coe (1953a) was incorrect to ascribe this species solely to his black-legged part of the key. The heavily dusted sternites and bare eyes require comparison only with *ahenea*, the characters for separating these two being given in the key. In the field *pubera* will be recognised among other small robust *Cheilosia* by its bronze colour. The female has tergites 6 and 7 nearly square, rather than rectangular as in *antiqua* (M. Drake, quoted in Stubbs, 1996a). Wing length 7–8 mm.

This is largely a northern English species with records extending into southern and western Scotland, including Mull, but there is a strong concentration of records in Norfolk and two records from Hampshire. There are also records from Ireland where it is scarce. This is very much a species of fens where it is usually found at flowers of marsh-marigold, or sunning on vegetation, along scrub edge or within open structured sallow scrub, although on Mull it was found beside a large open pond. Water avens has been reported to be a larval foodplant on the continent. April to July, peaking in May.

Cheilosia ranunculi Doczkal, 2000   Pl. G, fig. 3

In the field this species looks identical to *albitarsis* from which it has only recently been split (Doczkal, 2000a); unfortunately the females still cannot be separated. The males are most easily distinguished by the shape of the last segment of the front tarsus, which is much wider at its base than tip (parallel-sided in *albitarsis*). Tergite 2 has all the lateral hairs pale (some black ones are usually present in *albitarsis*). Among various subtle features, tergite 4 has only reclining hairs on its posterior margin (some erect black ones in *albitarsis*). The front margin of the top of the thorax has a narrow band of brownish hairs (all hairs black or few pale ones in *albitarsis*), but this is a difficult character in practice. The third antennal segment is a bit larger, broader and browner (round and blackish in *albitarsis*). If the genitalia are hinged out, the apical lobes (surstyli) are seen to be parallel-sided (a distinct basal bulge in *albitarsis*). Wing length 8.5–9.5 mm.

A flurry of re-examination of collections and new field work has led to the provisional conclusion that this species is widespread, at least in the southern and central England (*e.g.* re-examination of 50 male '*albitarsis*' from Warwickshire produced 19 *ranunculi*) and that it prefers rather drier better drained soils, although both species can occur in the same locality. The host plant is almost certainly a buttercup, but it seems questionable whether two such closely related hoverflies feed on creeping buttercup; bulbous buttercup would seem to be a potential candidate on dryish sites, having a corm-like swelling underground. Late April to May.

Cheilosia sahlbergi Becker, 1894   Pl. C, Fig. 2
                                                                  Map: Ball & Morris p. 37

In the field, both sexes are of a slightly bronzy hue. The sternites are dusted, as in *pubera* and *ahenea* among the black-legged species. The fur on the thoracic disc is pale brown, as in the other two species, but there are longer fine black hairs projecting through it. The face profile can resemble that of *vicina*. Wing length 6.5 mm.

Since *sahlbergi* is our only mountain *Cheilosia*, the habitat alone should give a strong indication of its identity. It is a poorly recorded species of the Scottish Highlands where it has been found at altitudes of 750–1,000 m on mountains with locally base-rich soils, but also on high ground on some more acid mountains. On Beinn a' Chuallaich a specimen was found on the flowers of tormentil in a somewhat boggy area near a stream on open montane heathland, and at Ben Lawers on saxifrage flowers by boggy flushes. In the Alps, buttercups are a particularly good lure. The larvae have been found in association with alpine bistort, where they seemed to be grazing externally on the roots (G. Rotheray). Speight (1974b) reports it occurring from May to early June (for Europe as a whole), while in Scotland it has been found in June and July.

Cheilosia scutellata (Fallén, 1817)   Pl. D, fig. 2, Pl. 6, fig. 12
                                                                  Map: Ball & Morris p. 38

In general appearance this species is rather like *longula*, including the female having a yellow-tipped scutellum and pale patches on the face, but most specimens are larger and the front and mid tarsi have the basal segments clear yellow (there can be some darkening above the front metatarsus). The third antennal segment tends to have the tip slightly paler, rather than being uniformly dark as in *longula*. The male face, seen from above, has the facial knob strongly swollen into a hemispherical shape with the face extending almost at right angles from the eye margins (see illustration in key). This is less extreme in the female, although the face remains much more swollen than *longula* and does not produce the neat triangular shape found in that species. There are many other differences from *longula*. Male *scutellata* have the thoracic dorsum more strongly shining without any dusting on the disc (view from front), and the shining lateral patches on tergite 3 are large and obvious. The genitalia of the two species are very different. The face of the female often has more obvious yellow patches. Problems can arise if the antennae are missing, because, aside from the orange third antennal segment of *soror*, there are fewer obvious features separating *scutellata* from that species than from *longula*. However, *scutellata* has much shorter hairs on the eye margins, a larger and more swollen facial knob (in both top and side view) and stronger scutellar marginal bristles. The head is larger in proportion to the body in both sexes, the facial spots of female *scutellata* are rarely apparent in *soror*, and the male genitalia are very different. Wing length 6–9 mm.

C. scutellata is a frequent species in lowland districts of Britain and Ireland, with a thin scattering of records in Scotland. Woodland is especially favoured but it can occur on heathland, calcareous grassland and coastal dunes. It has been reared from *Boletus* and allied fungi, as well as from truffles, and there are reports from *Agaricus*. Adults are usually encountered on umbellifer flowers, and have been observed hovering in small swarms at about head height in sunlit parts of woods. May to October, peaking in July and August.

Cheilosia semifasciata Becker, 1894   Pl. F, Fig. 1
Cheilosia fasciata Schiner & Egger of Coe (1953a)   Map: Ball & Morris p. 38
(a misidentification).   Larva: Rotheray Pl. 2e, 2f

There is little relationship between this small narrow species and other members of the group. The sternites are partially dusted, the face profile is exceptionally low and the male has dull grey dust spots on tergites 2, 3 and 4. These rectangular spots are not particularly obvious and are best seen by looking obliquely along the abdomen from in front. The legs are black or have the knees and base of the tibiae dark dusky orange.

Females are confusing to identify, although their small elongate build, time of year and location should give a lead. The abdomen lacks grey spots and the legs are either black or with some dull orange as in the male. The scutellar bristles are usually indistinguishable and the face has well developed downy hairs (but not projecting at right angles as in the *variabilis* group). The eye hairs are dark (as in *vernalis*, a more dumpy species with some clear yellow on the legs). Wing length 6–7 mm.

Old records exist for a few woods in Cambridgeshire, Kent and Hampshire, and there are recent records for north Hampshire, North Wales and Ireland. The larvae are leaf-miners recorded from orpine (now scarce in British woods) and navelwort (common in western Britain and Ireland). Each larva hollows out five or six leaves, producing a small round exit hole on the underside of each leaf, moving on as the food supply is exhausted. Similar observations have been made in Hampshire on orpine and North Wales on navelwort, mainly on plants in shaded damp situations (see Rotheray, 1988b). In North Wales, patches of navelwort growing on rocks and walls are easy to locate and infected plants are fairly conspicuous, so systematic survey is possible, but most apparently suitable locations fail to reveal mined leaves. Plants growing in exposed situations lose their leaves early, so a micro-climate which allows the plants to provide larval food for a sufficiently extended period will probably prove to be the critical factor. The males have been observed sunning on the ground close to woodland margins. March to July, peaking in early May.

Cheilosia soror (Zetterstedt, 1843)   Pl. D, fig. 3
                                                        Map: Ball & Morris p. 39

Though variable in size, many specimens are among our larger *Cheilosia*. The female has a yellow-tipped scutellum, as in *longula* and *scutellata*, but does not seem to develop the pale facial markings often seen in those species. Unlike them, *soror* has an orange third antennal segment, sometimes dark near the tip, and thus resembles *pagana* or *bergenstammi* (the latter usually has distinct eye hairs). The arista is distinctly pubescent (*pagana* and *bergenstammi* have a bare or almost bare arista). The presence of long hairs on the antero-ventral surface of the hind femur, some of which are quite as long as the width of the femur, is a pointer but has not proved to be completely reliable in separating *soror* from *pagana*. However *soror* never has the numerous black spines along the full length of the ventral surface as shown by *bergenstammi*. Misidentifications have been common in the past. Wing length 7.5–9 mm.

This is a largely southern English species with the majority of records occurring south of a line between the Severn and the Wash, with outlying records from the Morecambe Bay area and North Wales. It is mainly known from chalk and limestone habitats but has also occurred in some clay woodlands in Surrey and even been recorded from a cemetery in south London where it is possible that there are artificial calcareous influences. It is found on umbellifer flowers in grassy glades in woodland rides and on open calcareous grassland. The larvae are reported to have been bred from truffles. June to October, peaking from August to early September.

Cheilosia urbana (Meigen, 1822)   Pl. L, fig. 3
Cheilosia praecox (Zetterstedt, 1843)   Map: Ball & Morris p. 36
Cheilosia globulipes Becker, 1894

This is a rather small slender species with extensively orange legs, including most or all of the front and mid tibiae and tarsi. The hind tibia usually has a narrow black ring in the male but tends to be entirely orange in the female. The antennae may be black or dull orange, occasionally brighter. The difficulty has been with small specimens of *bergenstammi*. However, compared with this species *urbana* has the third antennal segment distinctly longer than broad (usually roundish in *bergenstammi*), the hind femur lacks the numerous black spines along the entire ventral surface, the male eye hairs are white rather than brown, and the female never has a dark ring (complete or otherwise) on the hind tibia. Greater difficulty arises with two species recently added to the British list, *psilophthalma* and female *uviformis*. The smaller, darker third antennal segment will usually separate it from these, and the pale bases to the tarsal claws are in contrast to the entirely black claws in *psilophthalma*. Male *urbana* typically has obvious though weak scutellar marginal bristles (undifferentiated in male *psilophthalma*), but these can occasionally be absent. Fortunately the genitalia of the two species are somewhat different. In the female frons, the median groove is usually only present in the front section behind the lunule and is either absent or very weak in front of the ocellar triangle (in *psilophthalma* and *uviformis* it is obvious as far back as the ocellar triangle). *C. uviformis* is also typically larger and the sides of sternites 2 to 4 are dusted (scarcely dusted and shining throughout in *urbana*). Wing length 5.75–6.5 mm.

Occasionally, female specimens occur with the front and hind metatarsi swollen to about twice their normal size (Plate 6, fig. 7). There was considerable uncertainty about the true taxonomic status of these specimens, which were assigned the name *C. globulipes* Becker, 1894. However, since the first edition of this book was published, *globulipes* has been synonomised with *C. urbana*.

There are records from England, Scotland and Wales where it is local but widespread. It was believed to occur in Ireland until the discovery of *psilophthalma* (Speight, 1996a). Irish specimens of '*praecox*' proved to be *psilophthalma* and this species has been withdrawn from the Irish list. It occurs on grassland, heathland, open areas in woodland, and disturbed sites such as quarries, especially where the foodplant and spring-flowering shrubs occur in combination. Adults are particularly fond of sallow and blackthorn flowers, and males often hover in loose swarms at heights of 2–3 m. Males also defend small territories from sunlit perches. The larvae have been reported to mine the basal rosettes and roots of mouse-ear hawkweed on the continent (Claussen, 1980). March to October, peaking in May. Records later than June should be treated with caution.

Cheilosia uviformis Becker, 1894   Pl. M, fig. 1
Cheilosia argentifrons Hellén, 1914   Map: Ball & Morris p. 39
? Species A of the first edition

This species was added to the British list from Irish material as *argentifrons* by Speight (1986c). It looks rather like a clear-winged *nebulosa* or a large *urbana* or even, in the male, a narrowly-built *velutina*. However, the completely dusted frons, hairy eyes and extensively pale legs of the male present a combination unique to this species and *nebulosa*. Some males can have the scutellar marginal bristles indistinguishable from the long marginal hairs; this brings them out in the *grossa* group, but the scutellar margins have some black hairs here in contrast to *nebulosa* and *albipila* (which share the reddish antennae of *uviformis*). Where scutellar marginal bristles are present, the dusted sternites, entirely pale hairs on the thoracic dorsum and rather poorly produced facial knob and upper mouth edge bring it close to *velutina* (see that species for differences). *C. velutina* was one of the original determinations of species A of the first edition, which is now believed to be *uviformis*. Females resemble a large *urbana* but have a larger, rounder, mainly red third antennal segment, longer body hairs everywhere and a median groove on the frons extending back to the ocellar triangle. The eye margins, face, lower occiput and sternites are more heavily dusted (the latter are usually obviously dusted at their sides but more shining in the middle). Difficulty may also be experienced with female *psilophthalma* which has a similar third antennal segment, but it has distinct black spots on the tibiae, a broader and less dusted frons and (like *urbana*) shorter body hairs throughout. The male genitalia are rather different from *urbana*, more closely resembling *psilophthalma* (though still varying from that species in detail). Wing length 8–9 mm.

Historically, *uviformis* has been a poorly understood species on the continent. When redefined (Speight & Claussen, 1987, as *argentifrons*), it was possible to note a male from Smeekley

Wood, Derbyshire, taken on 20 May 1977, and females taken in 1985 by lakeside willow and alder carr in Leitrim and Westmeath, Ireland (plus only four other European records, from France and Germany) (see Speight, 1986c, for details of Irish records). Further British records are now available, extending the distribution further north to Scotland. Woodland that is seasonally flooded seems to be the preferred habitat. Males are thought to be elusive since they hover at a great height (7–10 m) and females are very inconspicuous when resting on clumps of dead grass. In Ireland females were found at the flowers of hawthorn and sallow, and searching such flowers is apparently the best way of locating the species. Early to late May.

Cheilosia variabilis (Panzer, 1798)   Pl. F, fig. 3, Pl. 6, fig. 6
                                                                 Map: Ball & Morris p. 40

This is a large robust insect with a rather elongate, somewhat parallel-sided abdomen and long dark wings. As such it is usually distinctive in the field and in collections, especially the males, but smaller or less narrow specimens are not so readily recognised. Many specimens have entirely black legs and, among those which also have hairy eyes, *variabilis* is distinctive in having a hairy face. However, *variabilis* can have dark orange on the basal part of the tibiae which then makes it a less distinctive fly and can result in confusion with species such as *lasiopa*.

The males may be separated on the characters given in the key, but some additional comment on the females may be useful. The frons, in the anterior half, bears a fairly dense cover of short pale hairs which are inclined forwards. Among these hairs there are sparse erect black ones which project well above the pale ones, a distinctive character once the angle of view and light are right. In addition, the female shows other unique features among the hairy-faced group. The zones of sub-lateral flattened pale hairs on the abdomen are only slightly developed and are more posteriorly placed than in other species, on tergite 3 being confined to the posterior one third in the area just inside the lateral margin of the segment. The hind femur has a well developed series of short spines ventrally along much of the apical half and the pale ventral hairs are short, mostly less than half the width of the femur. Wing length 7.75–10.25 mm.

C. variabilis is a common species over much of Britain and Ireland, especially along lush wood edges and similar situations. Males patrol territories from sunlit perches, but do not hover with any regularity. In Britain the larvae eat the root nodules of common figwort and have been found burrowing in the stem bases of water figwort (Stubbs, 1996a). The adults visit flowers of the larval foodplants. April to September, peaking in late May and early June.

Cheilosia velutina Loew, 1840   Pl. M, fig. 2
                                                                 Map: Ball & Morris p. 40

This is a robust, medium-sized *Cheilosia* with a rather flat face (especially in the male) and a perpendicular or receding mouth margin. However the mouth margin varies in its degree of protrusion and some specimens of related species can look very similar, especially *proxima* with which it is most frequently confused because of its similar build and dusted sternites. The third antennal segment of *velutina* is at least partly clear orange (entirely dark or only obscurely orange in *proxima*). The male of *velutina* lacks a well defined lip below the facial knob (sharply defined in *proxima*) and the thoracic dorsum has entirely yellow hair of very even length (usually partly black and of varied length in *proxima*). Compared with *proxima*, the female has the edge of the frons adjacent to the eye margins dusted, and the thoracic dorsum bearing a shorter pile of more even length. The patches of pale hairs across the tergites are very conspicuous in the field, as in *proxima* and *vulpina*, and it can resemble a small female *vulpina*. Male *uviformis* with differentiated scutellar marginal bristles can key out close to *velutina*, but that species has an entirely dusted frons, lacks broad black rings on the tibiae and has a narrower build. Wing length 7.25–8.25 mm.

Most records are from eastern England south of Yorkshire, though there are isolated records for Wales, Scotland and Ireland. Recorded habitats include chalk grassland and waste ground, and it is usually found visiting umbellifer flowers alongside *proxima*. The fact that it is found on waste ground may suggest that its larval foodplant is a ruderal species. It is a difficult species to identify with certainty and voucher specimens should be retained for confirmation. June to September, peaking in late July and early August.

Cheilosia vernalis (Fallén, 1817)   Pl. M, fig. 3, Pl. 6, fig. 9
                                                               Map: Ball & Morris p. 41

In many respects this species is easy to recognise. It is a small yet robust black species, with the tibiae having strong orange bases and tips. Sternites 2 to 4, and often 1, are brightly shining and entirely undusted. The eye hairs are very dark. Confusion is only likely with smaller specimens of *cynocephala*. Wing length 4.5–6.75 mm.

This is a highly variable species with larvae that appear to exploit a variety of plant species, so there is a possibility that additional species will be recognised within what we currently call *vernalis*. One of the most variable characters is the extent of yellow versus black hairs. The palest-haired male specimens can have black hairs restricted to a central patch in the hind part of the thoracic dorsum, and either restricted to the axis of tergites 2 and 3 or missing altogether. Such forms predominate in spring. Summer specimens can have the thoracic dorsum almost entirely black-haired (although some yellow hairs usually remain obvious at the front) and have the black hairs on tergites 2 to 4 spreading to the hind lateral corners of these tergites (though never occupying as much of the lateral margins as *cynocephala*). Females vary in similar fashion, but usually retain some adpressed black hairs on the axis of the tergites, even in the palest spring specimens. Further variation affecting both sexes includes the shape of the facial knob in profile, with some specimens showing a rather abruptly produced upper edge, whilst it is distinctly sloping in others. The third antennal segment can vary between all black and substantially reddish. The length of the scutellar marginal bristles can vary from equal to the length of the scutellum to only half of its length. In the female, the basal tarsal segments of the mid leg can vary between brown and clear yellow.

This is a very widespread and locally frequent species throughout Britain and Ireland, including Ireland. It is found on open ground including waste ground, road verges, dry meadows, heath margins, open woodland rides and other such situations. Adults are usually found on low-growing flowers, especially composites. Larvae have been reared from yarrow (from the root gall of the tephritid *Dithryca guttularis*) and more questionably from scented mayweed. Certainly yarrow and scented mayweed are among the flowers on which adults may be found. There are continental rearing records from smooth sow-thistle (Bańkowska, 1980) and goatsbeard (Sønderup, 1941). There is also a continental record of a puparium being found under the decaying leaves of hoary mullein, but the correct identification of the fly is open to doubt (Stuke, 2002). March to October, with peaks in May and again in July and August.

Cheilosia vicina (Zetterstedt, 1849)   Pl. C, fig. 3
Cheilosia nasutula Becker, 1894   Map: Ball & Morris p. 41

This is a rather smaller and deeper black species than *antiqua* (the most frequent of the species with which it could be confused) and rather slender in the male. The upper surface of the facial knob is horizontal and thus even more strongly developed than in *antiqua*. The male has both long and short hairs on the thoracic dorsum, and tergites 3 and 4 have areas of short decumbent black hairs along the axis. The female has short adpressed black hairs on the thoracic dorsum, the length of which is about equal to the width of an ocellus. In *antiqua* such hairs are usually extensively yellow, fairly upright and about twice as long as the width of an ocellus. *C. nigripes* is even more similar (see comments under that species) and, now that it is known to occur within the range of *vicina* in Yorkshire, careful screening of any *vicina* from limestone woods is recommended. Wing length 5.25–7.75 mm.

C. vicina is primarily a northern and western species, including Ireland where there is just one known locality; very nearly all records lie north of a line between the Severn and the Humber. In the Scottish Highlands it is one of the most frequent *Cheilosia*. It may be found at low-growing flowers (and has even been recorded hidden under the canopy of petals of globeflower in dull weather) along woodland margins and in a variety of other situations, including well above the tree line on mountains. Males seem to patrol territories from low sunlit perches. Since there have been so many misidentifications in the past, its status in the south is uncertain. For present purposes all records for south-east England are treated as erroneous. On the continent, lady's mantle has been shown to be a larval foodplant. In Britain common lady's mantle is very widespread in much of the north and Midlands and even occurs very locally in the south-east. May to August, peak from mid June to mid July.

Cheilosia vulpina (Meigen, 1822)   Pl. N, fig. 1, Pl. 6, fig. 11
                                          Map: Ball & Morris p. 42

Brood dimorphism, known in some bivoltine *Cheilosia*, is most strongly developed in this species, and the summer brood was regarded as a separate species, *C. conops* (Becker, 1894), until relatively recently. The largest, hairiest specimens occur in the first generation. They have a virtually bare arista and even the facial profile varies slightly from the summer brood. Some of these individuals are as large as *variabilis*, but the abdomen is not so elongate, the tibiae of the front and mid legs are clear orange or yellow at their bases and the hind femur is more distinctly hairy beneath.

Males are decidedly hairier than *variabilis*, with the hairs on the disc of tergite 4 upright and about three times as long as the apical width of the hind femur (adpressed and less than the apical width of the tibia in *variabilis*). Females have very conspicuous patches of pale hairs across tergites 2 to 4, as in the smaller *proxima* and *velutina* (but scarcely evident in *variabilis*), and obvious dusting on the upper part of the occiput (shining in *variabilis*). Specimens of the second brood are *lasiopa*-sized and not quite so obvious in the field. They can easily be distinguished from *lasiopa* by their longer scutellar marginal bristles; also male *vulpina* has much longer hairs on the lateral margins of tergite 4. *C. barbata* shares the long scutellar marginal bristles and a hairy face but should be instantly recognised by its partially red third antennal segment and smaller, narrower build. Attention is also drawn to the possible presence of *gigantea* in Britain (the suspected identity of species B). Females are likely to closely resemble bare-faced *vulpina*, although males are more narrowly built. Wing length 7–10 mm.

This species has a southern distribution, but a few records extend to North Yorkshire and there is a single record by the Firth of Forth. Though Coe (1953a) includes Ireland, Speight *et al.* (1975) and Speight (2000c) omit *vulpina* from the Irish list. It is most frequently encountered on umbellifer flowers and occurs in a range of grasslands, woodland clearings, heathland and coastal dunes. Males have been seen hovering a few centimetres above a woodland ride and visiting flowers of daisy. The larvae have been reported from decaying tissue in the roots of cultivated globe artichoke in France, but nothing is known of its host plants in Britain. April to September, peaking twice, in June and again in August.

Cheilosia species B of Stubbs & Falk, 1983   Pl. N, fig. 2
? *Cheilosia gigantea* Zetterstedt, 1838 or   Map: Ball & Morris p. 43
ingerae Nielsen & Claussen, 2001

The single male is quite distinct from named British species. It is believed to be either *gigantea* Zetterstedt or the very similar *ingerae* Nielsen & Claussen, recently described from Scandinavia. It is a rather large, elongate hoverfly (similar in size to *bergenstammi* or *griseiventris*), extensively black-haired, and keys to the *proxima* group in having entirely dusted sternites. The specimen looks very different from *proxima* but the definable differences are few. The hairs on top of the thoracic dorsum and on top of tergites 3 and 4 are all black (rarely so in *proxima*) except for a narrow fringe in front and of fairly even length (long hairs project above a shorter pile in *proxima*). The wing is more pointed, with the costal cell and base of cell r_1 colourless, contrasting with a yellower tinge to the cells behind (in *proxima* the wing is more generally brownish).

In a key to Fennoscandian species of the *proxima* group (Nielsen & Claussen, 2001), the British specimen runs to *gigantea/ingerae* but the genitalia of the British specimen have minor differences making its identification uncertain. It has dark hairs fringing the upper part of the squama (at the base of the wing) as in *ingerae*, which is regarded as a key character of this new species. *C. ingerae* is a scarce species of northern and mountain districts, whilst *gigantea* is a widespread species in mountains and lowlands which is moderately common in Denmark. In most regards *gigantea* seems the more likely to occur in Britain. Since the single British specimen does not entirely agree with either of these two described species, it seems best at present to continue to treat it as 'species B' until more material is available.

The antennae are small and black. The face is black and with a moderate-sized knob. The eyes have pale hairs. The thoracic dorsum has long hairs of uniform length; except for a narrow pale fringe in front, these hairs are entirely black across the full width of the thoracic dorsum (as seen from the side, although viewed from in front the hairs reflect light and appear to be mostly pale). The scutellum has very fine marginal bristles which are almost indistinguishable from the hairs. The legs are black except that the tibiae are dull orange in the basal third and apical eighth. The hind femur has the ventral hairs short, but the anteroventral and posteroventral hairs are as long as the width of the femur; there are black hairs anteriorly on the apical half and more extensively about the apex. The wings have a yellow stigma and are blackish at the extreme base. The abdomen has pale hairs along the sides except for black hairs on the posterior quarter of tergites 2 and 3 and the posterior third of tergite 4; much of the pregenital segment is black-haired. The axis of tergite 1 is pale-haired, as is all but the hind margin of tergite 2, and there are longish black hairs on the axis of tergites 3 and 4. The hairs on the sternites are pale. Wing length 8 mm.

The specimen was found on flowers of sweet cicely on the banks of the River Dee at Ballater, a locality within the Central Highlands of Scotland, on 30 May 1981 by I. MacGowan, but several specific searches since then (*e.g.* by I. MacGowan and S. Falk in 1985 and 1986) have failed to produce further specimens. If, as suspected, this is *gigantea*, then it may well be confined to north-east Scotland since its foodplants are northern dock (largely confined to this area, plus a limited area in northern England) and Scottish dock (very rare – near Loch Lomond). It so happens that *gigantea* is widespread in Denmark, but does not occur further south in countries bordering the North Sea; the distribution of northern dock is similar. May and presumably June.

Genus FERDINANDEA

These medium-sized hoverflies are unmistakable. The black thoracic dorsum has greyish longitudinal stripes, rather like *Helophilus*, but there are stout bristles along the lateral edges. The abdomen is brassy coloured or bluish black. The wings have clouded inner cross-veins.

Ferdinandea cuprea (Scopoli, 1763)   Pl. 5, fig. 1
                                                                   Map: Ball & Morris p. 73
                                                                   Larva: Rotheray Pl. 3b

There are distinct small but thick spines on all the tibiae, these being black or sometimes yellow. Though the abdomen is spoken of as being brassy coloured, viewed closely the colour can seem black, especially in artificial light. The thoracic dorsum has predominantly black hairs. Wing length 7.5–11.25 mm.

F. cuprea is widespread, although rarely abundant, in woodland throughout much of Britain and Ireland. Whilst occasional specimens will be found at flowers this hoverfly is easily overlooked because of its fondness for sitting on tree trunks, wooden posts or on dead leaves in dappled light. Larvae have been recorded from the sap of wounds on trunks of oak and ash. Trees infested with goat moth (*Cossus cossus*) are suitable and puparia have been found around the roots of such trees. March to November, peaking in June, after which numbers of records remain fairly constant with a slight rise in late August and early September.

Ferdinandea ruficornis (Fabricius, 1775)   Pl. 5, fig. 2
                                                                   Map: Ball & Morris p. 73

Considerable care is necessary when recording this species since the shining blue-black abdomen can be confused with that of *F. cuprea*. The tibiae lack bristles or occasionally there are a few small ones on the hind tibia. The thoracic dorsum has abundant fine yellow hairs plus sparse stronger black hairs; the grey stripes can be very poorly developed in some specimens. Wing length 6.25–9 mm.

The very few records come mainly from southern England and the Midlands, with a few records extending northwards to North Wales and Yorkshire. It has not been recorded from Ireland. There would seem to be a very strong association with trees infested by goat moth (*Cossus cossus*) where an abundant supply of sap is available; unfortunately the moth itself is something of a rarity nowadays. April to August, with indications of peaks in late April to early May, and again in July and August.

Genus PORTEVINIA

Formerly the single species was placed in *Cheilosia* but the face lacks a knob, the lower part of the face being somewhat extended instead. Like *Cheilosia*, the larvae are plant feeders and the genitalia are very similar to species in the *antiqua* group of that genus (excluding *impressa*).

Portevinia maculata (Fallén, 1817)

Pl. 5, fig. 6
Map: Ball & Morris p. 126
Larva: Rotheray Pl. 1c, 1d

Even apart from the characteristic shape of the face, the species is very distinctive. The build is robust with paired greyish dust spots on tergites 1 to 4. The legs are black and the antennae bright orange. No other British hoverfly meets this description, although *Cheilosia fasciata* Schiner & Egger, a species of the near continent that exploits the same foodplant, shows a remarkable resemblance (but has a different face profile). Wing length 6–8.25 mm.

Though rather local, the distribution is widespread including western Scotland and Ireland. Males can be found sunning, with their wings held in delta fashion, on the leaves of ramsons in the dappled light of woodland. Females are elusive and may best be sought flitting low down amongst the plants rather than sunning themselves on leaves. The time to search is when the flowers are at their best, usually from mid May to early June according to the season and district. The larvae live in the bulbs and are best sought in the winter between January and March, when they are growing most actively. In January the larvae are fairly mature, although at this time of year there is no evidence of the presence of the plant on the woodland floor. Extensive damage has been found in the preferred larger bulbs, attack being by loose spiral tunnelling into the flesh of the bulb and infection is betrayed by discoloration. The growing shoot is often attacked and killed, but secondary growing shoots can result (Speight, 1986a; also Rotheray, 1991). The host plant has a liking for calcareous soils. April to July, peaking in late May to early June.

Genus RHINGIA

The long snout, in combination with a dark thorax and largely orange abdomen, makes the genus very easy to recognise. There is a further European species which may have gone undetected in mountainous areas in Britain, *Rhingia borealis* Ringdahl. It is best distinguished by the slightly longer hairs on the arista; on its apical two-thirds the hairs are almost as long as the arista is thick at the base (in the other two species the arista is almost bare since the hairs are no longer than half the basal thickness) (Speight, 2000b). This difference is not easy to see and not an encouraging start to a key; hence the onus to check for this species in Britain is left to those able to handle this character in the field!

Rhingia campestris Meigen, 1822   Pl. 5, fig. 4
                                                                   Map: Ball & Morris p. 127
                                                                      Larva: Rotheray Pl. 3a

In many specimens the abdomen has a black stripe along the axis, thus giving instant
identification. However, the black stripe is often reduced or absent thus giving the appearance of
having an almost completely orange abdomen as in *rostrata*. It is thus essential to check for the
presence of a black line along the lateral margins of the tergites. Wing length 6–9.5 mm.

This is a very common fly throughout Britain and Ireland in districts where cows are present, but
it strays widely and can even occur in urban areas. The adult hoverfly will normally be found in
open woodland or along woodland edges or hedgerows where it uses its long snout to advantage
in deep flowers such as red campion and bugle. The larvae breed in cow dung where they are
exceedingly well camouflaged in the surface layer (the wide occurrence of adults suggests other
types of dung may also be used). Populations of *campestris* are known to undergo substantial
crashes that have recently been shown to follow periods of severe drought. April to October,
peaking twice, in late May to early June, and again in late August to September.

Rhingia rostrata (Linnaeus, 1758)   Pl. 5, fig. 5
                                                                   Map: Ball & Morris p. 127

The abdomen is extensively orange, sometimes with a slight axial stripe on tergites 1 and 2, but
notably having the margins of the tergites without any black. The tergites have black hairs near
the sides and at least on the posterior half of tergite 4 (rather than almost completely pale) and the
tibiae are entirely orange (black ring on at least hind legs in *campestris*). In the female the
thoracic dorsum (view from side) has hairs which are much shorter than the width of the third
antennal segment. The snout is shorter than in *campestris*. Wing length 7.5–9.5 mm.

The occurrence of *rostrata* is very erratic since it may suddenly appear abundantly in various
woods and then will not be seen for many years. Whilst this is a scarce species, quite a number
of records have been reported in some recent years with the south Chilterns, Wealden counties,
and parts of South Wales and the Welsh borders being especially favoured. Nothing is known
about the larval habitat requirements, but badger latrines have been suggested as a possibility.
May to June, and August to October, probably as two broods but with the later brood being more
abundant and peaking in September.

Tribe CHRYSOGASTRINI

The presence of a concave face, smoothly leading to a projecting mouth margin, is characteristic
of the tribe. The only exceptions are males of the genus *Chrysogaster*, these having a knob like
Cheilosia, although no distinct eye rim is present at the side of the face beside the eye (*i.e.* no
zygoma). The top of the abdomen is particularly flat in *Chrysogaster*, *Lejogaster*, *Melanogaster*,
Orthonevra and *Myolepta*. The hind femur has small spines on the ventral surface, but these are
very difficult to detect in some species. Many Xylotini have a concave face but members of this
tribe are mostly of very different appearance, as reference to the plates will show.

The tribe name Chrysogastrini is retained here. More recently, there has been major revision of
the genera allied to *Chrysogaster*; that genus has been split with the recognition of *Melanogaster*,

whilst *Riponnensia* has been separated from *Orthonevra* (Maibach *et al.*, 1994a). *Hammerschmidtia* is treated as a subgenus of *Brachyopa* in Thompson & Rotheray (1998).

Larvae live in dead wood, in sap runs, in aquatic or sub-aquatic situations or in decaying vegetable matter.

Genus BRACHYOPA

The orange-brown coloration of the abdomen is rather unusual among hoverflies and the face, antennae and legs are yellow or orange-brown. The wings have the upper outer cross-vein joining vein R_{4+5} very close to the wing-tip, cell r_5 having a long triangular apex reminiscent of *Heringia*.

The presence of a grey thorax and orange-brown abdomen would give good excuse for overlooking these hoverflies in mistake for anthomyiids and muscids of similar appearance. However, the thorax of *Brachyopa* does not bear the long bristles found in such calypterates (at most there are a few bristles near the lateral margins of the thoracic dorsum). The abdomen is often darkened posteriorly, especially in dried specimens, but there is no distinct pattern of markings.

The European fauna includes four additional species that occur in neighbouring countries, and these are included in the key. It is useful to note that some specialise on conifers such as spruce; *testacea*, for example, has been observed at recently-cut stumps and could colonise British conifer plantations. Some European species are large and deceptively like *Hammerschmidtia* except for the wing-venation character.

Larvae of *Brachyopa* live in sap runs or in decaying sap under bark of fallen trees and branches. Adults will often be found hovering within a few centimetres of their breeding sites, even where these are shaded, or at rest on dead trunks or sap runs. They also occur at flowers, especially those of hawthorn and apple.

Brachyopa bicolor (Fallén, 1817)   Map: Ball & Morris p. 19
Larva: Rotheray Pl. 10b

The scutellum is grey dusted in the front half and there is usually a distinct transverse depression crossing it. The third antennal segment is rather broad and bears on its inner surface a small circular pit. A similar pit is also present in *B. pilosa*. Wing length 6.5–9.25 mm.

It used to be taken in some numbers in the New Forest and there are records for East Anglia, Essex, Hertfordshire, Middlesex, Surrey, Sussex and the Wyre Forest. Recent records also exist for the New Forest, where it has been taken at a goat moth seepage on oak (I. Perry quoted in Stubbs, 1996a), also from the Windsor area and from Glapthorne Cow Pasture Reserve, Northants (G. Boyd). It has not been recorded from Ireland. This has proved to be the rarest member of the genus and many old records are suspect since all *Brachyopa* were called '*bicolor*' until it was realised that four species were involved (Collin, 1939). The early stages have been found at sap runs on oak and beech (Rotheray, 1991); adults are typically found around beech trees, but have also been noted at sap runs of horse-chestnut and birch (I. Perry). May to July, peaking in June.

Brachyopa insensilis Collin, 1939   Map: Ball & Morris p. 19
                                                                             Larva: Rotheray Pl. 10c

The front edge of the scutellum is only narrowly grey dusted, so close inspection is necessary. The third antennal segment is relatively narrow and lacks a pit (sometimes there is the trace of a slight depression, but not a deeply sunken pit). The wings are proportionately much longer than in other *Brachyopa*. Wing length 6.5–7.25 mm.

The main area of distribution is southern England, but it extends sporadically to northern Scotland and there are two widely separated Irish records. The special habitat is oozing sap runs on trees such as elm, horse-chestnut, ash, lime and beech, such conditions being obvious because of the brown discoloration of the bark. *B. insensilis* has been found on or seen hovering adjacent to such sap runs at a height extending to 6 m above ground, and probably also occurs higher up the trees. After the demise of elms from Dutch elm disease (mid-1970s – 1980s), there was concern for the status of *insensilis*, but it was subsequently found that sap runs on horse-chestnut were suitable and that larvae of *insensilis* were easy to find on this tree. Though previously regarded as a rarity, current experience suggests that this species should occur wherever there are horse-chestnuts with sap runs, including suburban parks and roadsides where this tree is frequently planted. April to July, peaking in June.

Brachyopa pilosa Collin, 1939   Map: Ball & Morris p. 20
                                                                             Larva: Rotheray Pl. 10d

Of the two species with an entirely yellow scutellum, *B. pilosa* has the humeri grey dusted above (and less strongly so at the sides). There is a small circular antennal pit, usually removed from the lower margin of the third antennal segment by its own width. Wing length 7.5–8.5 mm.

For some years after its discovery this hoverfly was only known from males, but females have now been found. It is of interest that *B. pilosa* is seemingly scarce in the New Forest, yet is one of the frequent species in Windsor Forest (the reverse of the situation in *B. bicolor*). There are other scattered records in southern England north to Peterborough, and in South Wales, but notably it appears to have a liking for beech woods on the North Downs in Surrey. In recent years it has also been found at a number of sites in northern Scotland from around Inverness to Sutherland. It has not been recorded from Ireland. *B. pilosa* has a strong association with large beech trees, adults hovering by stumps or unhealthy trunks; they have also been found to be numerous in association with white or grey poplar. At Windsor, the males sometimes swarm around flowering wild cherry and it has been found at flowers of bird cherry in Sutherland (P. Entwistle, quoted in Stubbs, 1996a). Larvae have been found under the bark of recently felled or recently dead aspen and oak, and a puparium under a bark flake of beech (Rotheray, 1991). April to July, peaking in June.

Brachyopa scutellaris Robineau-Desvoidy, 1844   Pl. 7, fig. 11
                                                                             Map: Ball & Morris p. 20

The combination of an entirely yellow scutellum and yellow humeri will help serve to identify this species. The antennal pit is large and kidney-shaped, but be warned that with only a lens it may be difficult to discern the shape, and confusion with a round pit is possible. If in doubt, then the specimen will require vetting. Wing length 6.5–7.75 mm.

With a distribution extending to Morayshire in Scotland and including Ireland, this is the most widespread member of the genus. Larvae have usually been found in sap runs occurring close to the ground on a wide variety of deciduous trees including ash and elm, and even on yew. Adults can be difficult to spot, perhaps because they favours sap runs which are low down and often hidden in the vegetation, and sweeping foliage near to suitable trees can be the best way of finding them. On occasions they are very abundant, and on some days the species can be found at many localities, flying around suitable trees and basking on sunlit leaves, but it seems to have a rather short emergence period in any given area. April to August, peaking in May.

Genus CHRYSOGASTER

Coe (1953a) treated the genus in the broad sense with three subgenera, but *Lejogaster* and *Orthonevra* were regarded as separate genera in the 1976 check list (some spelling changes had also been introduced). It is clear that these taxa are related and it is a matter of opinion how they should be treated. Speight (1980) commented on the distinctions between these genera. More recently, *Chrysogaster* was further split into two genera, with the former *C. hirtella* and *C. macquarti* allocated to *Melanogaster*, and *Riponnensia* was separated from *Orthonevra* (Maibach *et al.*, 1994a).

With regard to these five genera, the abdomen has a flattened dorsal surface and lacks clearly defined coloured markings. The females have transverse furrows across the frons (usually incompletely so, and somewhat indistinct in a few species). The males of *Lejogaster* have the eyes separated on top of the head (as in only a few other genera).

The males of *Chrysogaster* and *Melanogaster* have eyes which meet on top of the head and there is a facial knob (less obvious in some species). The flattened area on top of the abdomen is normally dull although a problem can arise with some female specimens where the black abdomen is somewhat shining, but the furrows on the frons may help avoid the assumption that such specimens belong to *Cheilosia*. The *Cheilosia* key makes allowance for initial error with *Chrysogaster* and *Melanogaster*.

Speight (1980) provided a revised key to the genus (then including *Melanogaster*). He included *viduata* (Linnaeus), a non-British species with black antennae and smoky wings which could yet be found here. The male has a matt-black stripe on the front of the thoracic dorsum and the female has tergites 3 and 4 shining, even on the top. The pleura have a dusted area above the front coxae (as in *cemiteriorum*).

The larvae are aquatic or semi-aquatic. Those of *Melanogaster* have the posterior spiracles adapted for piercing air spaces in aquatic plants whilst those of *Chrysogaster* do not (Hartley, 1961; Maibach *et al.*, 1994a, c).

Chrysogaster cemiteriorum (Linnaeus, 1758)   Pl. 7, fig. 4
Chrysogaster chalybeata Meigen, 1822   Map: Ball & Morris p. 43

The unique character within the genus is the presence of grey dusting on the pleura just above the front coxae (discounting the area in front of the coxae and front spiracle). Whilst dusting is obvious in some specimens, this is not always so and care is necessary lest the legs mask the area concerned. Hence the use of other characters is of value.

In the key it will be seen that the males are separated from *virescens* on the basis of a rather flat face, a normally unambiguous character. The females have rather clear wings apart from strongly yellow wing bases. Wing length 5.25–6.5 mm.

This is a species of lush meadows and fens, usually near scrub or wood margins. It is widely distributed across England, Wales and Ireland, extending to southern Scotland with an isolated record from near Inverness, but rather scarce in south-east England. It has a fondness for umbellifer flowers. May to September, peaking in July and early August.

Chrysogaster solstitialis (Fallén, 1817)

Pl. 7, fig. 5
Map: Ball & Morris p. 44
Larva: Rotheray Pl. 10f

The wings are particularly dark (but note that some specimens of *C. cemiteriorum* are also quite dark). The face is relatively narrow and, in life, the eyes are bright red (in the field it is particularly distinctive, being a dark-winged hoverfly with red eyes). The male thoracic dorsum is strongly matt black but, as a further check, the hairs on the top of the scutellum are exceedingly short (view from side), such hairs also being present on the thoracic dorsum where they are overtopped by hairs of far greater length (the other four species in the genus have long hairs on both scutellum and thoracic dorsum). The female has purple reflections on the thoracic disc, either over most of the surface or towards the sides. This species is prone to show faint pale spots on tergites 3 and 4, especially in the female, a circumstance most prevalent in teneral (newly emerged) individuals. Wing length 6–7.25 mm.

C. solstitialis is widespread over much of Britain and Ireland, though scarce in the Scottish Highlands. It is usually found where umbellifers occur in damp places beside bushes or trees; hogweed, angelica and water-dropworts are very attractive. Larvae live in organically rich mud at the edge of ponds and streams in woods. Late May to October, peaking in July and August.

Chrysogaster virescens Loew, 1854

Map: Ball & Morris p. 44

The thorax and scutellum have a greenish reflection which is strongly developed in some females but less obvious in many specimens. The antennae are usually orange but it is not uncommon to find specimens with very dark antennae, so care needs to be taken to check other key features. The face profile in the male is strongly developed. With comparative material it will be found that the hairs near the lateral margin of tergite 3 are longer and entirely pale compared with *Melanogaster hirtella*. Wing length 5.75–6.75 mm.

A very similar species, *rondanii* Maibach & Goeldlin de Tiefenau, has recently been described from the Netherlands and some other European countries. The male has a broader face with the knob almost absent, and the top of thorax has long erect black hairs. The female thorax and scutellum are covered in short pale hairs, with pale hairs at the margin, whereas *virescens* is almost bald with black hairs at the margin. Habitat details are lacking at present (Maibach & Goeldlin de Tiefenau, 1995).

C. virescens is to be found on bogs and in wet acid pastures, although adults sometimes congregate at flowers some distance away. It is seemingly widespread throughout Britain and

Ireland, but very local. This is one of the characteristic species of the valley bogs of Surrey, the New Forest and Dorset. It is of interest that another closely related bog species, *Melanogaster aerosa*, has its peak much later in the season. May to October, peaking from mid May to early June (the source and reliability of records after early August are questionable).

Genus HAMMERSCHMIDTIA

Hammerschmidtia is usually treated as a separate genus, but there is clearly a strong relationship to *Brachyopa* and it is reduced to subgeneric status by Thompson & Rotheray (1998). There are some strong bristles at the sides of the thoracic dorsum.

Hammerschmidtia ferruginea (Fallén, 1817)
Pl. 7, fig. 12
Map: Ball & Morris p. 74
Larva: Rotheray Pl. 10e

There is little chance of confusion with known British *Brachyopa* since the fly is larger and the thorax has an orange ground colour. Also the arista is short-plumose, and the face more extended (see illustration in the key, p. 128). The abdomen can be entirely or partly orange, although some specimens have a rather darker brown abdomen with a vague pattern of paired pale brown spots on tergites 3 and 4. Wing length 8.25–9.75 mm.

This rarity is only positively known from a few sites in the Scottish Highlands. Adults are associated with aspen, occurring on stumps, logs and sound trunks. Larvae have been found under bark of recently fallen aspen (Rotheray, 1991). The adult has also been taken at flowers of rose and observed on herbage by pignut flowers at a wood edge. There are very few suitable stands of aspen and this species is therefore considered to be very vulnerable and is listed as a Priority Species under the UK Biodiversity Action Plans. Late May to July, peaking in June.

Genus LEJOGASTER

These are entirely metallic green, bronze or blue hoverflies, with a concave face in both sexes. They lack dull areas on top of the abdomen and the entire margins of the tergites are shining. The males have the eyes separated on top of the head.

Larvac have been reported from decaying vegetation of a floating mat of bulrush and other plants in an old pond (Hartley, 1961); identification is attributed to *L. tarsata*, but this requires confirmation.

Lejogaster metallina (Fabricius, 1777)
Pl. 7, fig. 6
Map: Ball & Morris p. 80

Whilst the male has a somewhat slender oval abdomen, the female abdomen is very broad. The male is instantly identifiable because of the large black third antennal segment which is wider than long – there are no other green hoverflies like this. Females are less obvious, having normal-sized antennae with the third segment about as long as broad, either black or with some orange coloration beneath. The female thoracic dorsum has erect pale hairs as in *Melanogaster hirtella* (the latter species has dark halteres and dull lateral margins to tergite 1). Wing length 4.75–6.5 mm.

This is a widespread species throughout most of Britain and Ireland, but is apparently more plentiful in wetter regions such as west Wales and in coastal districts with good-quality ditches on grazing levels. It is mainly associated with wet meadows (often with rushes), marshes, fens, mildly acid boggy flushes and similar situations. In common with several *Chrysogaster* species, *metallina* has a strong liking for buttercup flowers. May to October, peaking in June and early July.

Lejogaster tarsata (Megerle in Meigen, 1822)   Pl. 7, fig. 7
Lejogaster splendida (Meigen, 1822)   Map: Ball & Morris p. 80
                                                                 Larva: Rotheray Pl. 11a

Though a rather small hoverfly, it is particularly attractive because of its metallic colours. The males tend to have a green thorax and a bronze or reddish-copper coloured abdomen. The antennae are not expanded as in *metallina*. The females also usually have a greenish tint on the thorax, but the centre of the abdomen usually has strong blue reflections from some angles. The third antennal segment in this sex is much longer than broad and there is a conspicuous orange area ventrally. Note that the much larger *Riponnensia splendens* can meet the general description of *tarsata* in the females. Wing length 4.5–6 mm.

There has been some confusion resulting from misidentifications in the past. This seems to be a rather scarce and local species, though occasionally abundant where it occurs. Most confirmed records are from the fringes of coasts and estuaries, or at most from a few miles inland, although in the Midlands, it has recently been found in association with boggy flushes in and around ancient wet woodland. It has been found beside mildly brackish ditches on coastal levels, in brackish coastal marsh (at the transition to freshwater marsh) and at fen flushes and lakeside marsh close to the coast. In some of the sea lochs of the west coast of Scotland it occurs in iris beds along the edge of freshwater seepages on the shore-line. Inland records are more unusual and, though some relate to brackish conditions, it is less easy to explain the rare occurrence of this species in the absence of saline influence. Though mainly southern, it has been found in Wales, south-east Ireland and in Scotland. May to September, peaking in late June and early July.

Genus MELANOGASTER

Formerly this genus was part of *Chrysogaster*; two species have been separated into the new genus *Melanogaster* (Maibach *et al.*, 1994b). They are somewhat smaller and darker with less evidence of iridescence than the species remaining in *Chrysogaster*. The larvae have the posterior spiracles adapted for piercing air spaces in aquatic plants.

Melanogaster aerosa (Loew, 1843)
Chrysogaster macquarti Loew, 1843   Map: Ball & Morris p. 88

The general appearance is very similar to *hirtella* though usually somewhat larger in size. There has been much confusion between these species in the past. The males of *aerosa* have a dense pile of completely black hairs on the thoracic dorsum, the longest hairs at the sides being shorter than the maximum width of the tibiae (view from in front) (in *hirtella* these hairs are partly pale brownish, at least towards the sides, and the longest hairs towards the sides are longer than the maximum width of the tibiae). The female has short, pale yellow hairs on the thoracic dorsum (view from side), these hairs being semi-adpressed (usually inclined by very much less than 45°) and their length about that of an ocellus (in *M. hirtella* these hairs are also pale, but they are nearly erect and their length is about twice that of an ocellus). It is invaluable to have comparative material before identifying *aerosa*. Wing length 5.5–7 mm.

A very similar species, *parumplicata* (Loew, 1840), may occur in Britain. The male has a weak facial knob (very pronounced in *aerosa*) and the female facial profile (side view) is gently curved (very angular in *aerosa*) between the antennae and the lip.

The sparse records extend from southern England to Scotland and Ireland. The species occurs on bogs and boggy flushes, sometimes being found at heather and other flowers on drier ground nearby. However, in some places it occurs in non-acid marshes, as on grazing marshes with high-quality ditches as at Pevensey Levels in Sussex, a typical habitat for *hirtella* (this emphasises the need for great care in identification). It has also been found in wet ancient woodland of rather calcareous character in Warwickshire. The emergence peak is much later than in *hirtella*. Mid June to early September, peaking in July and August.

Melanogaster hirtella (Loew, 1843)   Pl. 7, fig. 3
Chrysogaster hirtella Loew, 1843   Map: Ball & Morris p. 88

Smallish very black specimens with black antennae, and the wings clear or only slightly brownish, will usually prove to be this species. The females often have a shining abdomen (non-British *viduata* has dusted pleura above the front coxae). Further comments are made under *aerosa*. Wing length 5–6 mm.

M. hirtella is a common and widespread species throughout Britain and Ireland. It prefers the richer types of marshes or water margins with emergent vegetation. The larvae are aquatic, with modified hind spiracles for penetrating the air spaces within aquatic plants. There is an association with various aquatic and semi-aquatic plants, such as bulrush and sweet-grass, the larvae living in the adjacent mud at the base. May to mid August, peaking in late May and early June.

Genus MYOLEPTA

The genus is easy to recognise. The abdomen has broad orange margins to tergites 1 and 2, often also on tergite 3, leaving a black stripe down the centre of these tergites; the end of the abdomen is entirely black. Such a pattern is otherwise confined to *Tropidia* which has a large triangular process near the apex of the hind femur, whereas in *Myolepta* the hind femur is merely somewhat swollen and bears a few small spines beneath. The female of *Myolepta* has a concave face but in the male there is a knob which, however, is placed exceptionally low on the face. The face has a white dust band below the antennae. The third antennal segment is orange.

The genus is known to breed in rot-holes in trees. The separation of the two species is discussed by Collin (1950).

Myolepta dubia (Fabricius, 1805)   Pl. 7, fig. 1
Myolepta luteola (Gmelin, 1788), preoccupied   Map: Ball & Morris p. 96
                                                                        Larva: Rotheray Pl. 13f

The key characters should enable identification of most specimens. Additionally, sternite 3 is noticeably shining at the sides in both sexes whereas in *potens* this sternite is entirely dulled by dust. However, the separation from *potens* can be difficult so, if there is any doubt, the specimen should be referred for critical examination. It has been noted in the field that this species can be overlooked as *Cheilosia impressa* owing to the yellow coloration showing through the wings and giving the impression of yellow wing-bases. Wing length 6–8.75 mm.

The distribution is confined to England, south-east of a line from Somerset to The Wash. Whilst some localities are major ancient forests, others, such as Wicken Fen, would not meet that description. Larvae were found in a small rot-hole of an old beech from which was dripping a black watery liquid at about 3 m up (Hartley, 1961) and more recently larvae have been found in similar situations. Prolonged winter drought may limit survival. There is some evidence to suggest that emergence of *M. dubia* is confined to a very short period in any one locality, and on some days it has been found at several locations. May to September, peaking in July.

Myolepta potens (Harris, 1780)   Pl. 7, fig. 2
                                                                     Map: Ball & Morris p. 96

As indicated under *dubia*, identification may require specialist advice. Wing length 6.25–7.25 mm.

This extremely rare species was discovered by John Cowley, a Somerset naturalist, in 1945 at Loxley Wood, a site near Shapwick at the edge of the Somerset Levels. Collin established its identity and located three older specimens in collections (Collin, 1950). Between 1946 and 1949, Cowley and Fonseca found several more specimens in this area, and also 25 miles further north at Combe Dingle near Bristol. It was not seen again until 1961 when six larvae were found by J.C. Hartley in a rot-hole at Ashton Court not far from Combe Dingle (Rotheray, 1991). More detailed notes are given by Levy & Levy (1998). Recent searches for adults in its former haunts have failed to relocate the species, but it remains possible that searching for larvae could be a better strategy and larvae were discovered in rot-holes in a horse-chestnut at Moccas Park NNR, Herefordshire, from which adults emerged in 2002 (A. Godfrey). A revision of the European species of this genus is awaited, but the Herefordshire specimens appear to be the same as those from Somerset. It is listed as a Priority Species on the UK Biodiversity Action Plan. It would be fascinating to clarify the true status, distribution and ecology of the two *Myolepta* species. Mid May to early July.

Genus NEOASCIA

Many specimens are among the more minute hoverflies. The abdomen is strongly waisted in the females, the basal tergites being narrow and the end of the abdomen bulbous. The males are overall more slender, lacking pronounced expansion of the end of the abdomen, but the waist is usually clearly discernible – the swollen hind femur and concave face should leave no room for doubt as to the genus. As illustrated in the key (p. 134), the outer cross-veins are bent at a sharp angle compared with the related genus *Sphegina*. The names for species were revised by

Thompson (1981). *N. aenea* and *dispar* of Coe (1953a) became *meticulosa* and *tenur* respectively; *interrupta* was added to the British list in 1981 (Falk *et al.*, 1981).

Stackelberg (1970) separates the genus into two subgenera: those with a continuous bridge of chitin above the hind coxae (see illustration in key p. 134) he refers to as subgenus *Neoascia* and those without a complete bridge are referred to as subgenus *Neoasciella*. This distinction is not recognised by Thompson and *geniculata* is typically intermediate between the two states.

There is a chance of further species being found in Britain. A clear-winged species with a blunt-ended facial projection and the front femur and mid tibia yellow (careful of discoloured specimens) equates with *N. floralis* Meigen of some authors, now called *annexa* (Müller, 1776) (Thompson, 1981). This species is widespread in Europe. *N. unifasciata* (Strobl), which has tergite 2 entirely black, is found in similar situations to *obliqua* (both may fly together), particularly in upland situations. Illustrations of the genitalia of five British species plus *annexa* may be found in Coe (1953a), supplemented by Falk *et al.* (1981) for *interrupta*.

There are few breeding records, but larvae have been found in decaying vegetation around ponds, and in farmyard manure. The tiny adults fly low and slowly like small inconspicuous solitary wasps and are easy to overlook even when visiting small low-growing flowers such as forget-me-nots and fool's water-cress.

Neoascia geniculata (Meigen, 1822)   Map: Ball & Morris p. 97

Identification is not easy since the features are subtle. It is best to rely on males where the third antennal segment is short and broad as illustrated in the key. However, the shape of the antennae in female *tenur* sometimes approaches the condition in this species, though *tenur* has a wide chitin bridge above the hind coxae, this bridge characteristically being very narrowly fused or very narrowly separated in *geniculata* (a rare situation in other *Neoascia* species). For females, the more strongly curved sides to tergite 2 would seem a useful character. If there is any doubt on identification, withhold placing a name. The markings are very similar to those of *tenur*, typically in the male with a large central spot on tergite 3, while in the female the abdomen is often entirely black. The apex of the hind femur is often an indeterminate dusky orange. Wing length 3.75–5 mm.

N. geniculata has a wide distribution, extending to Ireland and Scotland, where suitable habitat is available. It occurs by ditches, ponds and lakes where there is lush emergent vegetation such as sweet-grass and sweet-flag. For reasons not yet apparent it is much more localised than other species in such habitat, although on occasion it can be abundant. May to October, peaking in July.

Neoascia interrupta (Meigen, 1822)   Pl. 7, fig. 15
                                                                   Map: Ball & Morris p. 97

The most distinctive feature is the presence of spots on the sides of tergite 4 which are not found in other *Neoascia*. Occasionally these spots can be rather obscure, especially in the male. Both sexes also have spots or bars on tergite 3 and the female normally also has spots on tergite 2. In the female the sides of tergite 2 are straight. Among species with infuscated cross-veins, this is the only one with a short third antennal segment. The chitin bridge is widely broken, as in *obliqua* but in strong contrast to *podagrica*. Wing length 3.25–4.75 mm.

N. interrupta was added to the British list by Falk *et al.* (1981), although a specimen from Kent dated 1951 had stood unrecognised in a collection under *podagrica*. It has proved to be widespread in eastern England up to South Yorkshire and there is a single record from North Wales. Semi-brackish ditches on the coastal levels of Kent and Essex support the species but only very locally, especially in the richer ditches with fool's water-cress. It has also been found inland in Essex, Surrey, Sussex and Warwickshire in lush emergent vegetation of ponds, marshes, ditches and canals. The most frequent feature in common between sites is the presence of bulrush. April to September, peaking in June.

Neoascia meticulosa (Scopoli, 1763)   Map: Ball & Morris p. 98
Neoascia aenea Meigen, 1822 of Coe (1953a)

Among the clear-winged species, the most obvious feature is the extensively yellow legs; the front tibia is mostly yellow, the front and mid femora are half yellow, the hind femur is strongly yellow at the apex, and the hind tibia is only narrowly black-ringed. The third antennal segment is elongate, most markedly so in the female. The male commonly has a yellow band on tergite 3 and the female abdomen is black with a deeply constricted waist on tergite 2. Wing length 4–5.5 mm.

Lush marshes and water edges with such plants as sweet-grass provide the habitat for this local but widespread species. Larvae have been found between submerged leaf sheaths of bulrush, and puparia have been found on bulrush growing through a floating mat of vegetation (Hartley, 1961). Southern districts are the most suitable, extending to York and Preston; further north it is much more sporadic and largely confined to valleys. In Wales it is mainly found near the coast and it occurs in Ireland. April to October, peaking in late May and June.

Neoascia obliqua Coe, 1940   Pl. 7, fig. 16
                                                                  Map: Ball & Morris p. 98

The main feature in both sexes is the presence of oblique bars on tergite 2. Both sexes also have spots or bands on tergite 3. The chitin bridge above the hind coxae is widely separated, as in *interrupta*. The abdomen is rather short and apically bulbous (more elongate and slender in *podagrica*). Care is necessary when recording this species, keeping a watch for specimens without markings on tergite 2 (may be *unifasciata* which on the continent flies with *obliqua*). Wing length 3.5–5.5 mm.

One of the best places to search is at beds of butterbur, where adults sit on leaves or fly gently among the leaves; it is quite likely that the larvae feed on decaying leaves or petioles. This discovery has led to a much better understanding of its distribution. Further surveys may prove it to be still more widespread as it has probably been overlooked as *podagrica*. The strongest concentrations of records are in Lancashire, Derbyshire and parts of Yorkshire, but it occurs sparsely across much of southern England and Wales, and into northern and western Scotland. It has been recorded from Ireland (Anderson, 1987b) although there are very few records. April to October, peaking in June.

Neoascia podagrica (Fabricius, 1775)   Pl. 7, fig. 14
                                                                    Map: Ball & Morris p. 99
                                                                       Larva: Rotheray Pl. 11c

The infuscated outer cross-veins are normally apparent but could be overlooked in pale specimens. Thus it should be noted that the third antennal segment is elongate (at least twice as long as wide) and the male normally has bands on both tergites 2 and 3 (as only in *obliqua*), whilst the female also has spots or bars on tergites 2 and 3 (as in *obliqua* and some *tenur*). The chitin bridge above the hind coxae is usually well developed (as in *tenur*). The female has tergite 2 deeply constricted (unlike *tenur*). Wing length 3.5–5 mm.

Whilst this ubiquitous species can occur in marshes and at waterside habitats, compared with other *Neoascia* it is perhaps more typical of hedgerows, wood edges and even gardens, in fact wherever there is lush or rich herbage. However, it maintains the generic habit of flying low. Larvae have been reported from wet decaying manure (Hartley, 1961). April to November, peaking twice, in late May and early June, and again in August.

Neoascia tenur (Harris, 1780)   Pl. 7, fig. 13
Neoascia dispar (Meigen, 1822) of Coe (1953a)   Map: Ball & Morris p. 99

Confusion is most likely with *geniculata* as previously discussed. The males will normally cause little problem since the third antennal segment is relatively narrow and about one and a half times as long as broad. The females are very similar to *geniculata*, but the lateral margins of tergite 2 are less waisted. The hind femur has black tips or occasionally there is a very faint trace of orange coloration. The male abdomen often has a yellow band on tergite 3, whilst that of the female may be entirely black with varying strength of spots or bars on tergites 2 and 3. The chitin bridge above the hind coxae is always well developed, a feature only otherwise shown by *podagrica*. Wing length 3–5.25 mm.

The distribution extends throughout Britain and Ireland, this species being one of the most constant members of the genus in marshes and fens, especially by edges of standing water. It is particularly abundant beside eutrophic lakes on southern heaths and at the richer types of boggy ground in all parts of Britain. It is frequently associated with beds of bulrush and common reed. April to November, peaking in July.

Genus ORTHONEVRA

The males have eyes meeting on top of the head (as in *Chrysogaster*) but lack a facial knob (as in *Lejogaster*). In both sexes the abdomen is usually distinctly dull on top and with the entire lateral margins (even on tergite 1) shining. However, many females are less obviously dull on top of the abdomen. Here one may note that the thoracic dorsum of *Orthonevra* tends to have a somewhat pitted surface, sometimes with stripes, the third antennal segment is longer than broad (except in *O. brevicornis*) and the legs of *O. geniculata* are partly yellow (black in other *Orthonevra* and all *Chrysogaster* and *Lejogaster*). By checking against the descriptions it should be possible to avoid any confusion. In this genus there are extra European species which could yet be found in Britain. The length and shape of the third antennal segment, the width of the face and the nature of the upper outer cross-vein are among the characters to compare. In a recent revision *Orthonevra* has been split, with *splendens* placed under *Riponnensia*.

Larvae are said to occur in organically rich mud by ponds and streams in woods, Hartley (1961) citing *brevicornis* and *Riponnensia splendens*. See also Maibach *et al.* (1994a, c).

Orthonevra brevicornis (Loew, 1843)   Map: Ball & Morris p. 100
                                                           Larva: Rotheray Pl. 11b

As a relatively small species with a short extensively orange third antennal segment, it may look superficially similar to a *Chrysogaster*. The stigma has a tiny dark spot at the base. The male resembles *Chrysogaster* except that the face is concave (in fact there is a faint trace of a knob, but the mouth margin projects so much that confusion is unlikely). Also, in male *Chrysogaster* the frons has long black hairs whereas in *brevicornis* there are very pale hairs. The third antennal segment is usually dark above and orange below (in *Lejogaster tarsata* the eyes do not meet in the male). The female has erect pale hairs on the thoracic dorsum, a feature otherwise only found in combination with black antennae in *Melanogaster* (among related genera). The face at the level of the antennae is much wider than the width of an eye (view face from in front) whereas in *Lejogaster metallina* these widths are about equal. The female frons is very deeply furrowed. The upper outer cross-vein is somewhat re-entrant. Wing length 5–6.25 mm.

O. brevicornis is an uncommon species of marshes, fens and woodland, especially where groundwater seepages are present, but it may easily be overlooked among other '*Chrysogaster*'. It has been found in scattered localities, largely in England and Wales, but it is also known from a few localities in Scotland. It was deleted from the Irish list by Speight (1985). May to September, peaking in June.

Orthonevra geniculata (Meigen, 1830)   Pl. 7, fig. 9
                                                           Map: Ball & Morris p. 100

As the only member of the *Chrysogaster* group with partly yellow legs, this species is instantly recognisable. It is a small species (like *nobilis*), often with wings slightly smoky in the male, and with distinctive dark marks at the inner end of the stigma and on cross-vein r-m. The bases of the tibiae are clear orange and often the hind tarsus is extensively pale. The third antennal segment is three times as long as wide. Wing length 4.5–5.5 mm.

Some other European species have partly yellow legs. If the dark wing markings mentioned above are missing (*i.e.* stigma uniformly brownish and r-m not darkened), then specimens should be checked further. *O. elegans* Meigen has a narrow black band across the eye (normally still visible even in pinned specimens) and all its antennal segments are more elongate: the third antennal segment is four times as long as wide. *O. intermedia* Lundbeck lacks the dark eye-band and the antennae are not so elongate (third segment as in *geniculata*).

O. geniculata is to be found about boggy areas in the Scottish Highlands and occurs in scattered suitable localities down to southern England, for example the valley bogs of the New Forest. It is very scarce in Ireland with a total of only eight records. More rarely it occurs in fens, as in parts of East Anglia and Oxfordshire. It is usually to be found singly. April to July, peaking in May.

Orthonevra nobilis (Fallén, 1817)   Pl. 7, fig. 8
Orthonevra species A *sensu* Stubbs (1996)   Map: Ball & Morris p. 101

A small species, like *geniculata*, it is distinguished by having black legs and the third antennal segment about twice as long as wide. The stigma is dark and there is often slight darkening of the centre of the wing, in combination giving a clue to identification in the field. The third antennal segment is rather pointed at the apex. Females have a small tubercle at the apex of tergite 4. Wing length 4–5.75 mm.

Some females with antennae like *nobilis* lack the tubercle on tergite 4 and have other marked differences in the hind part of the abdomen. Such examples have been found in Dorset and South Wales, but males seem to be typical *nobilis*. The Dorset example was referred to as "species A" in Stubbs (1996a) and mapped as *O. paranobilis* (*nomen nudum*) in Levy *et al.*, 1992, but these peculiar specimens are now interpreted as intersexes.

Though rarely seen in any numbers, this species is very widespread in marshes, fens and damp woodland clearings, but often strays into drier habitats. It also occurs in Ireland where it is infrequent in the south and east. It is a regular flower-visitor that can be found at a wide range of umbellifers, including burnet-saxifrage and wild carrot that are usually associated with drier ground. May to September, peaking between late June and early August.

Genus RIPONNENSIA

This genus has been separated from *Orthonevra* (Maibach *et al.*, 1994a). The broad, very flat face is a feature, but more relevant is the occurrence of bristles on the stem vein of the wing (these are difficult to see without a microscope). The male genitalia also have special features. Apart from our single British species, there are two other European species with elongate antennae that are unlikely to occur in Britain.

Riponnensia splendens (Meigen, 1822)   Pl. 7, fig. 10
Orthonevra splendens (Meigen, 1822)   Map: Ball & Morris p. 128

Being much larger in size than the species of *Orthonevra*, this species is easy to recognise. The broad belt of whitish dusting across the face (more obvious in some specimens than others) is the definitive feature (note that some *Melanogaster*, such as *M. hirtella*, also have a broad belt of dusting, but this is not so uniform in width).

The males are rather elongate for the genus. The thorax and margins of the abdomen are green or copper coloured, contrasting with the matt-black top of the abdomen. The female thorax is often greenish and the short oval abdomen often has blue reflections on top. The female colour combination is not unlike that of *Lejogaster tarsata*, a much smaller species, but *R. splendens* has a strong pair of grey stripes on the front of the thoracic dorsum in both sexes. Wing length 5.5–7 mm.

As a species of lush marshes, fens and wet woodland rides and clearings, it is most frequent in southern districts, although it is widespread in the Midlands and Wales. Records are sparse in Scotland, but it is widespread and frequent in Ireland. It particularly likes umbellifers and meadowsweet in sheltered places by bushes and trees. May to October, peaking in July.

Genus SPHEGINA

These hoverflies are on the whole larger than *Neoascia*, with a conspicuously longer narrow waist in both sexes. The outer cross-veins have rounded angles (as illustrated in the key) and lack infuscation. The front and mid femora are always pale with at most a slight incomplete dusky ring (a condition in *Neoascia* mainly confined to species with infuscate outer cross-veins). The males have a yellow patch on tergite 3 and sometimes also on tergite 4. The females have varying amounts of yellow on these tergites, or the abdomen can be entirely black. *Sphegina* species are found in woodland and, unusually for a hoverfly, prefer to keep within fairly dense shade. They are most often taken by sweeping although occasionally they can be found at flowers. The larvae occur in accumulations of decaying sap under bark in damp woodlands.

There is a chance of further European species being found in Britain. The male genitalia of the three British species in subgenus *Sphegina* are illustrated by Coe (1953a).

Subgenus ASIOSPHEGINA

Sphegina (Asiosphegina) sibirica Stackelberg, 1953   Map: Ball & Morris p. 139

This species was added to the British list by Stubbs (1994). It is a little larger than the other British *Sphegina* and is readily separated because the chitinous plate behind the hind coxae is incomplete. The lower part of the side of the thorax (sternopleuron) is shining rather than dusted. In both sexes tergite 2 is long and narrow (as in male *clunipes* and *elegans*). The face is yellowish (unlike *verecunda*). Newly emerged specimens of this species are yellow in colour and some gradually darken, but the body colour is highly variable, some specimens being black and some quite strikingly black and yellow patterned (note some other *Sphegina*, in particular *S. elegans*, can be yellow). The humeri are normally dark, but in teneral individuals, or those with more extensive yellow markings, they can be yellow.

This species should be sought in damp deciduous woodland, especially birch in the Central Highlands of Scotland, and in conifer woodlands where it has been found to be numerous on occasions. Adults visit flowers of pignut and perhaps other umbellifers, not infrequently at some distance from the woodland edge. Though first found on the mainland opposite Skye in 1992, the earliest British specimen located so far is from Ardachy, Inverness, on 13 June 1976. Currently, there are records for a few places in the Central Highlands of Scotland, South Wales and the Welsh borders, but it is likely to prove more widespread. It has not been recorded from Ireland. June and July.

Subgenus SPHEGINA

Sphegina (Sphegina) clunipes (Fallén, 1816)   Pl. 7, fig. 20
Map: Ball & Morris p. 138
Larva: Rotheray Pl. 11d

The female abdomen has the apex of tergite 2 particularly wide. The yellowish-tinged lower part of the face is a feature shared with *elegans*, but the humeri are dark. Wing length 4.75–7 mm.

This is overall the most frequent member of the genus and is well represented in Ireland and Scotland, even extending to north Sutherland. It occurs in a wide range of deciduous woodland, but nearly always with a fairly lush herb layer, rather than very dry woods. In addition to occurring under bark of fallen timber, larvae have been found in sap runs. It should be found in most districts with old woods, especially in damper areas, once one is attuned to the methods of finding these hoverflies (searching and sweeping flowers in shade and dappled light in damp woodland). April to September, peaking in June and July.

Sphegina (Sphegina) elegans Schummel, 1843
Sphegina kimakowiczi Strobl, 1897   Map: Ball & Morris p. 138

The female abdomen has tergite 2 particularly long and narrow. The face is partly yellowish, as in *clunipes*, but the humeri are conspicuously yellow. Wing length 5–6.75 mm.

This species is not quite as frequent as *clunipes*, but is by no means rare and sometimes the commonest *Sphegina* in a wood and often found together with *clunipes*. It extends well up into Scotland, but has few Irish records. May to September, peaking in June and July.

Sphegina (Sphegina) verecunda Collin, 1937   Map: Ball & Morris p. 139

The abdomen is not as long as in the other two species, tergite 2 being particularly short. The face is entirely dark grey (lower part pale in *clunipes* and *elegans*). Wing length 5.75–6.25 mm.

This species is much less frequent that the previous two species, but occurs in similar situations. It is widely distributed as far north as the southern Lake District and Durham, but there are very few records for Scotland. It has not been recorded from Ireland. It seems to be scarce or absent from much of East Anglia and Lincolnshire. May to October, peaking in June.

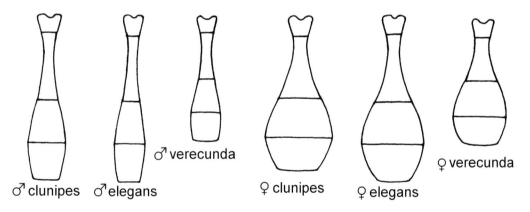

Text fig. 7. Abdomens of *Sphegina* (*sensu stricto*).
Male abdomens (which are slender) are on the left, female abdomens (which are bulbous) are on the right. *S. elegans* is the most slender species and *verecunda* the shortest – note in particular the width and length of tergite 2. Both sexes of *sibirica* have tergite 2 slender as in male *elegans*. Be sure your specimen is a *Sphegina* since *Neoascia* look very similar.

Tribe ERISTALINI

This group of hoverflies is one of the easiest to recognise. The strong downwards loop in vein R_{4+5} is only otherwise found in *Merodon* (whose outer cross-vein is re-entrant); a loop (weak or strong) is also found in a few of the *Syrphus* group (*Didea* and *Eupeodes* (*Lapposyrphus*), which have bold Syrphini-pattern markings on a rather flattened abdomen).

There are two styles of body pattern. Wasp-like species are characterised by *Helophilus* and the closely allied genera *Parhelophilus*, *Anasimyia* and *Lejops*. All have a sharply defined pattern of pale stripes on top of the thorax (except some individuals of *Anasimyia*). In this group of genera the eyes do not meet on top of the head in the males. The remaining genera are bee-like. *Eristalis* includes the well-known drone-fly, *E. tenax*, as well as less perfect bee mimics; *Mallota* looks convincingly like a bee, *Eristalinus* and *Myathropa* less so.

A significant factor in grouping these genera as a tribe is the remarkable rat-tailed maggot larva, whose telescopic breathing tube enable the larva to live submerged in water, wet mud or between the sheaths of partly submerged water plants such as bulrush. Only *Sericomyia* larvae could be confused with eristaline larvae, but they have a much broader thoracic region at the front. The adults are often found around ponds and ditches which provide breeding sites, but the commoner species may be abundant a long way from water, often in search of flowers or sometimes hibernating sites. *Myathropa* and *Mallota* are associated with rot-holes, the former genus being common away from its breeding sites.

Genus ANASIMYIA

The members of the genus used to be placed in *Helophilus* with which they share the thoracic stripes and the rather swollen hind femur. However, in *Anasimyia* the build is narrow and the appearance is dark, the thoracic stripes being narrow (occasionally absent) and the grey or yellowish markings on the abdomen being restricted.

Anasimyia may be treated as a subgenus of *Lejops* in the future, but there are opposing opinions. Certainly the two genera are close in a number of characteristics such as the narrow build, the double-banded hind tibia and the heavily dusted sternites. Whilst three of Coe's *Helophilus* species are allocated to *Anasimyia*, there are now five species as a result of splitting his '*lunulatus*' and '*transfugus*'. The genus has been revised by Claussen & Torp (1980) and the position in Ireland and Great Britain reviewed by Speight (1981b) and Stubbs (1981a) respectively.

Adults will be found at their aquatic breeding sites, often in association with tall emergent vegetation.

Anasimyia contracta Claussen & Torp, 1980   Pl. 12, fig. 9
                                                    Map: Ball & Morris p. 15

This is a dark species which is especially slender in the male. It was previously confused with *transfuga*. The specific name is derived from the contracted margins on tergite 2 which are quite distinct, but close examination is required since, when viewed from above, the hind femur can assist the optical illusion that the margins are straight. The markings are narrow and strongly

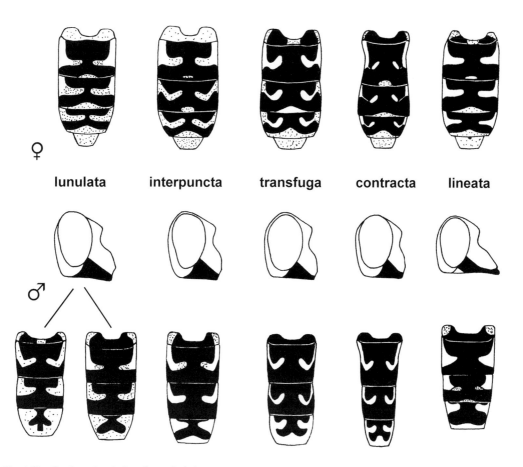

Text fig. 8. *Anasimyia* heads and abdomens.
Female abdomens above, male below. Pale markings have a yellowish or grey ground colour, sometimes obscured by grey dusted areas which are shown stippled. Two male abdomens are shown for *lunulata*, that on the right being typical, that on the left being an unusual specimen from Studland (Dorset) which requires further investigation.

angled hooks, but the outer limb can be reduced leaving the inner portions as small coloured spots. Wing length 5–7.25 mm.

There is a very close association with bulrush at the margin of ditches, ponds and lakes, the adults sitting on the leaves or found in close proximity. In such situations this hoverfly is widespread and locally frequent in southern England, extending to Wales and Ireland and reaching Nairn in Scotland. May to September, peaking in June and July.

Anasimyia interpuncta (Harris, 1776)   Pl. 12, fig. 8
                                                                Map: Ball & Morris p. 15

Until recently, *interpuncta* was not recognised as a separate species because of confusion with *lunulata*. In fact *interpuncta* is a larger darker hoverfly with a more compact face. The key illustrates the difference in markings on tergite 3, where the lateral margins of the markings are truncated so that the pale areas are angled forwards, and also tergite 4 where black areas are extensive on the front edge and in the hind half of the tergite. So little material is currently available that the extent of variation is unknown and it is possible that specimens will be found which are not readily separated. Wing length 7 mm.

A. interpuncta is largely found in East Anglia (*e.g.* Woodwalton and Wicken Fens) and in Essex, but has also been found on coastal grazing marsh in north Kent and at Pevensey Levels, East Sussex: similar habitats elsewhere would be worthy of further investigation. It has not been recorded from Ireland. On most sites there is a strong association with reed sweet-grass. Adults have been found at flowers of marsh-marigold in a water meadow in Norfolk (Withers, 1983). It is possible that *interpuncta* has been overlooked because of its early emergence. April to August, peaking in May.

Anasimyia lineata (Fabricius, 1787)   Pl. 12, fig. 7
                                                                Map: Ball & Morris p. 16
                                                                Larva: Rotheray Pl. 14c

Superficially this species resembles *lunulata*, but it is instantly distinguished from all other Eristalini by its long snout which tapers to a point. Both sexes are rather dark, but the male tends to have triangular orange markings on the tergites, especially so on tergite 2, whilst the female markings can be orange or grey. In the latter colour phase such females might be assumed to belong to a separate species. In the material examined this is the only member of the genus in which the hind femur has a black patch extending from the anterior to posterior surface without a break above. Wing length 6.25–8.25 mm.

A. lineata is characteristic of lushly vegetated pools of mesotrophic or eutrophic character where plants such as iris, bulrush, bur-reeds, sweet-grass and willowherbs are present. This includes the less acid areas of wet heath in southern England, valley marshes in northern and western districts, and flooded quarries and gravel pits. Sometimes it will be found in numbers at low-growing flowers, such as those of lesser spearwort, and can be swept from such vegetation even in dull weather. Larvae are recorded as feeding on decaying bulrush (Hartley, 1961), but the species often occurs in localities without this plant. This local but widespread hoverfly extends its distribution to Ireland and Scotland. May to September, peaking in June and July.

Anasimyia lunulata (Meigen, 1822)   Map: Ball & Morris p. 16

This is a relatively small compact species in which the rather small yellow markings are often dusted grey. The markings somewhat resemble those of *lineata* but the face is not pointed and the hind femur is entirely yellow along the dorsal line. The key illustrates the differences from *interpuncta*, tergite 3 having markings with a straight hind edge without deviating forwards at the lateral margins of the tergite while tergite 4 has the black area greatly reduced. Text figure 8 illustrates an unusual male form which requires further study. Wing length 5–6 mm.

There is a strong association with bogs, perhaps avoiding extremely acid conditions but occurring in true bogs to a greater extent than other species. However, little is known of this very scarce species. Records are few but widespread, extending from southern England to Wales, Scotland and Ireland. May to September, peaking in July.

Anasimyia transfuga (Linnaeus, 1758)   Pl. 12, fig. 10
                                                                   Map: Ball & Morris p. 17

This dark hoverfly has steeply inclined hooked markings, like a tick, with the inner limb strongly oblique (unlike *interpuncta*). Similar markings are found in *contracta*, but *transfuga* has the lateral margins of tergite 2 straight (look carefully in case the hind legs create an optical illusion). Until recently the distinction between the latter two species had not been recognised. Wing length 6.5–7 mm.

Though a very localised species, records are widespread over much of England and Wales. It is scarce in north-east England and Scotland, and occurs in Ireland. Accumulated data now show it to be less frequent than *contracta* and, though it can occur alongside that species, it shows no obvious association with bulrush, preferring other tall emergent pond-side vegetation such as bur-reed and sweet-grass. May to September, peaking in July.

Genus ERISTALINUS

There are only two species in the genus and superficially they look similar. The body is black, like so many hoverflies in other groups, but even in flight one should be able to learn to recognise *Eristalinus* by the low fast darting flight and stout build. Once caught, the spotted eyes are usually distinctive (may fade in preserved specimens) and quite unlike those of any other hoverflies, and the abdomen is at least partly glossy. It is worth noting that poorly developed stripes are sometimes present on the thorax which may result in confusion with *Helophilus* and allied genera (which always have some grey or yellow markings on the abdomen); even the blackest *Eristalis* of similar size has at least a narrow pale hind margin to the tergites.

Eristalinus aeneus (Scopoli, 1763)   Pl. 11, fig. 9
                                                                   Map: Ball & Morris p. 60

With its entirely glossy black or greenish bronze abdomen, this is a magnificent hoverfly and a pleasure to see when it is in numbers. The thorax is entirely black (in the specimens examined). In the field, *aeneus* may often be recognised as having a more elongate, less wrinkled body than that of *sepulchralis* and it is usually significantly larger. To be sure of identification it is necessary to check that the eyes are hairy on the upper part only, the lower half being bare. Wing length 6.25–9.5 mm.

E. aeneus is essentially a coastal species, occurring on both rocky and saltmarsh shores where larvae have been found in rotting seaweed. Most records are for the south coast of England, but it has been found further north, into northern Scotland, and is frequent around the Irish coast. Occasionally specimens are found well inland, but these are likely to be wind-blown strays or artificially transported, and no permanent inland populations have been found. March to November, peaking in July and hibernating as an adult.

Eristalinus sepulchralis (Linnaeus, 1758)   Pl. 11, fig. 10
                                                                          Map: Ball & Morris p. 61

Though superficially black and featureless, close examination will reveal grey thoracic stripes (on most specimens) and the abdomen is glossy black or bronze at the sides. The males have a dull black broad hourglass-shaped patch in the centre of tergites 3 and 4, but in the females such dull areas are reduced to a central spot which is often only vaguely discernible. Thus in doubtful specimens it is necessary to look at the eyes in order to check that the entire surface is covered in pale hairs and (if a male) the eyes are narrowly separated (they touch in *aeneus*); the hairs on the lower part of the face are often weak, but with good lighting they can be seen to extend well below halfway down. Wing length 6.5–8 mm.

This species is generally seen around ponds and in marshes where there is a large amount of decaying vegetation or where cattle trampling and dung has resulted in enrichment. The larvae are known to occur in decaying vegetation in ponds, and in wet manure. The adults are often very lively and thus easy to overlook so it is necessary to catch darting black flies of the right size or to cautiously approach flowers or sunbathing spots. There is a wide distribution throughout Britain and Ireland, but conditions are most suitable in lowland and coastal districts. April to October, peaking in July but consistently abundant from June to August.

Genus ERISTALIS

The drone-fly, *Eristalis tenax*, is a good hive bee mimic and *E. intricarius* is passable as a bumblebee mimic. Other species vary in their degree of mimicry as far as human perceptions are concerned. Real bees have long antennae.

All species are very variable in the degree of development of the pale markings. The abdomen may be entirely dark, or with markings on tergite 2 only, or with markings also on tergite 3, exceptionally on tergite 4 as well. Heal (1979a, 1979b) gives a classification for such markings on *tenax* and *intricarius*; the same system could be used for other *Eristalis*.

Members of this genus are among the most abundant of hoverflies. Though they breed in organically rich ponds and ditches, the adults may fly some distance to spots where a profusion of flowers attract them. Several extra species occur in neighbouring countries in Europe. The larvae of some common species were described by Hartley (1961) and that of *rupium* by Maibach & Goeldlin de Tiefenau (1991).

There are two subgenera, all species except *tenax* being placed in subgenus *Eoseristalis*.

Subgenus EOSERISTALIS

All members of the subgenus are pale on the basal half of the hind tibia, or it is completely pale. They lack the conspicuous hair fringes found on the hind tibia in the subgenus *Eristalis*.

Eristalis (Eoseristalis) abusivus Collin, 1931   Map: Ball & Morris p. 61

In general appearance, including size and the presence of clear wings, *abusivus* is closely similar to *arbustorum* (particularly in the males) and *interruptus* (more so in the female), sharing the range of coloration of the abdomen from black to brightly marked. The arista of *abusivus* is almost bare, the hairs being very short (much longer in other *Eoseristalis*), but this can be awkward as a field character. An easier feature is that the mid tibia is entirely pale, or only vaguely dusky at the tip, whereas in other similar species the mid tibia is strongly darkened at the tip. The thoracic dorsum has faint but distinct stripes, far more obviously so than in other species, especially in the female. Wing length 8–9.5 mm.

It is widespread in England, Wales and Ireland, and occurs in Scotland north to Inverness. Though a local species, it must often be overlooked in the field. It can be the commonest *Eristalis* in some coastal districts, especially where marshland habitat is available. There are also inland records but its occurrence here is less predictable. Larvae have been reported from mud at the edge of a pond. March to October, peaking in July and August with a further large peak in October.

Eristalis (Eoseristalis) arbustorum (Linnaeus, 1758)   Pl. 11, fig. 6
                                          Map: Ball & Morris p. 62

The presence of a completely pale-dusted face distinguishes this species very easily. However, difficulty is created when the face becomes rubbed and a central black stripe starts to develop, since the very similar *abusivus* typically has a narrow stripe. The key has made allowance for such confusing specimens. The markings on the abdomen are very variable. The darkest males have orange markings confined to the lateral one-sixth of tergite 2. The palest ones have these spots occupying all but the middle one-fifth, and extensive yellow markings on tergite 3. Females have any orange markings restricted to the sides of tergite 2 but, whilst these can be large and bright in some individuals, they can be reduced or absent in others, resulting in some females being black with only thin white apical rims on each tergite. Superficially there is a close resemblance to *abusivus* and *interruptus*. Wing length 7–10 mm.

This is a common species, occurring throughout Britain and Ireland. It is familiar in gardens, urban waste ground and other open habitats and will visit a wide variety of flowers. Larvae have been reported from farmyard drains and temporary pools with cow droppings, so presumably other polluted situations also suffice. April to November, peaking in July and August.

Eristalis (Eoseristalis) cryptarum (Fabricius, 1794)   Pl. 11, fig. 8
                                          Map: Ball & Morris p. 62

Recognition is easy since the legs are almost completely bright orange and the antennae are orange. Tergite 2 has large orange markings shaped as in *interruptus*, but usually the rest of the abdomen is black apart from a thin white or orange rim at the hind margin of each tergite. The wings have a diffuse orange coloration in front, this being very variable in its strength of development. Wing length 6.5–10 mm.

This species has declined considerably over the last 100 years and is currently regarded as Endangered and facing potential extinction in the United Kingdom (hence it is Priority Species in the UK Biodiversity Action Plan). The status based on early records was reviewed by Morley (1940). Though always regarded as a south-western rarity, old records show that it was present on the Dorset heaths up to 1938, and widespread in the New Forest where it was last recorded in 1951. Records extend further west through Somerset, Devon and Cornwall, and there is a curious unconfirmed record for Gloucestershire. It was recorded in southern Ireland, but there have been no records in over 50 years and it is now considered extinct (Speight, 1985). When it became apparent that a 1978 record from Dartmoor might have been the last British sighting, exploration of this area by S. Ball and R. Morris in 1993 was successful in rediscovering the species (Levy & Levy, 1994), but only in a very restricted area. Between 1998 and 2000 it was found at ten sites, distributed as four populations, but numbers of individuals were very small and the areas suitable for larvae apparently tiny.

Studies on Dartmoor, commissioned by English Nature, have begun to clarify the ecology of the hoverfly. Here the required situation is mildly acid small boggy runnels, *Sphagnum* moss often being a component, but the hoverfly chooses only very discrete areas of the apparently available habitat. The adults have a long flight season, the main observational peaks being at the flowers of bogbean in the spring, bog asphodel in summer and Devil's-bit scabious in late summer to early autumn, although visits to other flowers such as bramble have also been reported. There would seem good reason to suggest that spring and autumn generations are the strongest, but that there may be a confused pattern of emergence including a minor summer peak. *Eristalis* larvae typically like nutrient-rich conditions, yet acid bogs are generally nutrient-poor. Females have been observed to lay eggs on or close to very fresh cow dung, which may be a key factor in obtaining a more enriched situation for the larvae.

Thus it is beginning to look as if the rarity of this hoverfly can be explained: It appears to be exceedingly finicky in selecting only tiny parts of larger areas, those with small boggy runnels (a feature much reduced by drainage); it needs a succession of flowers through the season (over-grazing and fire may be problems); and it needs the right type of dung, seemingly fresh cow dung being preferable. Many heaths have gone through phases without grazing, and the recent problems experienced by the cattle industry create uncertainty over the future management of cattle-grazed heaths. It is a mystery why the species has apparently been lost from the New Forest, despite its extensive bogs with traditional grazing, but the quality of this habitat has been in decline. March to late September.

Eristalis (Eoseristalis) horticola (De Geer, 1776)   Pl. 11, fig. 3
                                                             Map: Ball & Morris p. 63

Attention is easily drawn to this species since most specimens are particularly bright. The bigger examples are distinct from *tenax* and *pertinax* because of the shorter broader abdomen whilst the smaller specimens are unlike *arbustorum* or *interruptus* because of the diffusely darkened area across the wing below the stigma. A very similar wing shade is also present in *rupium* (less pronounced in the male of *rupium*, but still better developed than most *horticola*) and *intricarius*, and occasionally *pertinax* (usually much more diffuse in this species). However, the occasional *horticola* without such a wing shade will still run out in the key. Wing length 8.25–11.5 mm.

Hippa *et al.* (2001) have used the name *lineatus* (Harris, 1778) (as *lineata*) for this species for the reasons given in Note 13 in the check list (Chandler, 1998).

Most districts throughout Britain and Ireland are likely to harbour this species, but it is rarely plentiful and is much more local in the north. It usually occurs within the vicinity of bushes or trees. April to October, peaking in July.

Eristalis (Eoseristalis) interruptus (Poda, 1761)   Pl. 11, fig. 7
Eristalis nemorum (Linnaeus, 1758)   Map: Ball & Morris p. 63

Superficially this species resembles *arbustorum* and *abusivus* in size and general appearance although the markings of the male are not so prone to variation and the black hind margin of tergite 2 extends more fully towards the hind corners (usually stopping well short in *abusivus* and *arbustorum*). Females can have conspicuous orange spots on tergite 2 or none at all (as in *abusivus* and *arbustorum*), but where present they remain well separated from the hind margin, unlike *arbustorum*. The characteristic quadrate stigma on the wings is very small and dark brown (note that it has sharp boundaries and is placed shortly before the end of vein Sc; there is absolutely no extension of coloration, however slight, to a position below the tip of Sc). The black face stripe is well developed, far more so than most rubbed *arbustorum* and much more than typical *abusivus*. A specimen with a yellow face stripe has been found, but the stripe is distinct in being dust-free compared with the sides of the face. Wing length 8.25–10.5 mm.

By carefully checking the smaller *Eristalis* in the field, it will often be found that this is one of the commonest species. It occurs throughout Britain and Ireland and frequents a wide range of situations, especially open habitats such as meadows and wasteland. Larvae have been found in farmyard drains and other similarly enriched situations. April to October, peaking in July and August.

Eristalis (Eoseristalis) intricarius (Linnaeus, 1758)   Pl. 11, fig. 4
                                                                          Map: Ball & Morris p. 64

The body is much more furry than in other *Eristalis*; indeed with a looped vein R_{4+5} it looks more like *Merodon* except that the tibia is pale in the basal half (all black in *Merodon*). The face has a dark ground colour. The scutellum is yellow but the ground colour of the body is otherwise variable, ranging from black to forms with tergites 2 and 3 extensively orange at the sides. The latter forms may seem less obviously like *intricarius* so it is helpful to know that all forms (available for this study) retain a covering of black hairs on the sides of the thorax. In both sexes, the hairs of the thoracic dorsum can vary from all red to all black, although the scutellum always remains orange-haired. The male abdomen can be entirely yellow- or orange-haired (sometimes with a whitish tail) or have extensive black hairs on tergite 2. The female abdomen is more typically black-haired on tergite 2 and the base of tergite 3, with the tip conspicuously white-haired. A dark form was named var. *furvus* by Verrall (1901). Wing length 8.25–12 mm.

It is so easy to get lulled into expecting all hairy *Eristalis* to be *intricarius*. There is a very similar species, *anthophorinus*, which occurs commonly in nearby parts of Europe. The hairs on the sides of the thorax are usually pale brown (black in *intricarius*), the squamae are pale (dark in *intricarius*) and on close inspection the arista is almost bare or very short-haired (as in *abusivus*) rather than long-haired (as in *intricarius*). Two additional hairy species occur in Europe, but are obviously different and for the most part uncommon.

Though generally occurring in low numbers, this is a widespread species throughout Britain and Ireland. As well as occurring at flowers, males are often to be seen hovering at some height above the ground. Marshy and woodland localities are preferred, especially where sallow shrubs and lush tall herbs are present. Adults are partial to sallow and blackthorn blossom in spring, and the flowers of umbellifers, meadowsweet and thistles in summer. Larvae have been found in farmyard drains and in ponds with decaying vegetation. March to November, peaking in July.

Eristalis (Eoseristalis) pertinax (Scopoli, 1763)   Pl. 11, fig. 2
                                                                        Map: Ball & Morris p. 64

Being a large species, comparison with *tenax* and *similis* is required. *E. pertinax* has an entirely orange front tarsus (unlike both those species) and the hind tibia is pale in the basal half (unlike *tenax*). In the male the abdomen is long and gently tapering, the female abdomen also being rather more tapering than the robust and more cylindrical abdomen of *tenax*. However, the differences in build can be deceptive in the field so it is necessary to check the leg characters. Tergite 2 has triangular orange markings of varying size and brightness at the sides (usually larger and brighter in summer specimens) and a conspicuous pale hind margin in some summer specimens. Indeed, brood dimorphism is particularly strong in this species, with the spring generation almost without exception having longer paler body hairs than subsequent generations and usually (although not invariably) less conspicuous orange markings. This is thought to relate to the rate of development and is not dissimilar to the brood dimorphism that occurs in some *Cheilosia* or *Meliscaeva auricollis*. Wing length 8.25–12.75 mm.

This is a common and widely distributed species throughout Britain and Ireland; in fact it is often one of the most abundant hoverflies wherever there are suitable flowers. Larvae have been found in farmyard drains and other organically rich situations. It starts to emerge very early and must have several broods. Males are often seen hovering in woodland rides, with each male hovering at a height of 1–5 m and seemingly holding a small territory of a few metres square (which is defended vigorously). March to November, with peaks in May and August.

Eristalis (Eoseristalis) rupium Fabricius, 1805   Pl. 11, fig. 5
                                                                        Map: Ball & Morris p. 65

Typically the females are rather dark-bodied (at most with rather dull triangular markings on the sides of tergite 2) and with a distinct dark area on the wing below the stigma. The males tend to be brighter coloured (abdominal markings like *interruptus*) and with fainter wing markings closely resembling those of *horticola*. However, the species can be immediately separated from other British *Eristalis* except *cryptarum* (which has bright orange legs) because the hind metatarsus (basal tarsal segment) is pale. Some British specimens lack the dark area on the wings, these usually being newly emerged (it may take several days for the dark areas to develop their deep colour). Wing length 7.75–11.25 mm.

There are two rather similar European species, *piceus* and *pseudorupium*, that occur in Denmark and Belgium (one of which also occurs in the Netherlands). Until recently their separation was difficult; revisionary work is best exemplified by Hippa *et al.* (2001). Whilst *rupium* is said to have the stigma three to three and a half times as long as wide, some British male *rupium* more resemble the other two species which have a shorter stigma. An initial indication is the dullness of the hind margins of the tergites compared with the entirely shining condition in *rupium*. The top of the thorax is rather weakly shining in *rupium*; it is dulled by light yellowish-grey dust in *piceus* (shining in *pseudorupium*). Wing markings are very weak in *pseudorupium* (virtually absent in the male; a former name for this species was *vitripennis*) and strongest in *rupium*. It is essential to check the genitalia in the males. The female tergite 3 in *pseudorupium* has adpressed hairs on the hind third and there is a dull band on the hind margin (erect hairs, but for a tiny hind fringe, and entirely shining in *rupium* and *piceus*). In female *piceus* the wing marking extends to the upper cross-vein (r-m) whilst in *rupium* the markings extend down the lower cross-vein (m-cu). Any supposed British specimens of these extra species should be checked by a specialist.

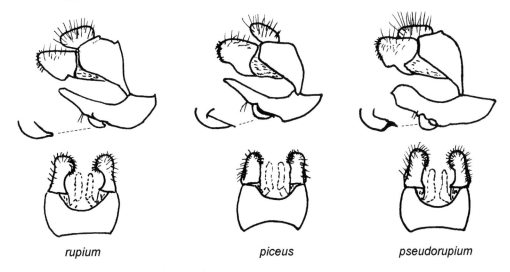

rupium   *piceus*   *pseudorupium*

Text fig. 9. Male genitalia of *Eristalis rupium* group.
Male genitalia in side (top) and dorsal view (below). The enlargement in the side view shows detail of the aedeagus. (Based on Hippa *et al.*, 2001)

Wales, northern England and Scotland are favoured by *rupium*, but it has not been recorded from Ireland. It occurs in lush marshy spots with plenty of flowers, either in sheltered valley bottoms and forest glades or more rarely in more exposed situations up to 300 m where the required marshy habitat is available. Even in suitable country, the species can be very local. In Switzerland, larvae were found in an alpine situation where a stream entered a lake, in calcareous wet pasture which was trampled and mildly eutrophic, and having a flora including marsh-marigold (Maibach & Goeldlin de Tiefenau, 1991). May to October, peaking in July.

Eristalis (Eoseristalis) similis (Fallén, 1817)   Map: Ball & Morris p. 65
Eristalis pratorum Meigen, 1822

This is a large species with an appearance somewhat intermediate between *pertinax* and *tenax*. However, the front tarsus is black (entirely yellow in *pertinax*), the face is extensively dusted (*tenax* has a wide black facial stripe) and the hind tibia is broadly pale at the base (like *pertinax*, but unlike *tenax*). Aside from some *pertinax*, *similis* is also distinct from the remaining *Eristalis* in having dense greyish dusting on the sides of the thorax and on the femora. The markings of the male abdomen closely resemble the pattern shown by male *interruptus* with a similar range of variation. The female has markings resembling those of summer-brood female *pertinax*, and would probably not stand out as different in the field. Wing length 10–11 mm.

In March 1990 a specimen was discovered on disturbed ground at the edge of an ancient wood in Warwickshire (Falk, 1990). A second specimen was found in a ride in a conifer plantation in Derbyshire during July 1997 (Brackenbury, 1998) and it is likely that more records will be made if people check *pertinax* and *tenax* a bit more carefully. There would seem to be two generations on the nearby continent, the first seen in early spring and the second in midsummer. Males have been observed hovering 2–4 m above woodland tracks, and both sexes can be found sitting on sunny tracks and at flowers (Speight, 1988c). It is easy to check all large *Eristalis* in the spring at flowering shrubs and other situations when hoverflies are rarely abundant, but in midsummer there are so many distractions that noticing *similis* will require extra diligence. This species is often plentiful in southern Europe in wooded districts and it has been spreading north in recent decades, although it varies greatly in abundance from year to year in the Netherlands – suggesting that it is still at least partially a migrant. British examples thus far might have been migrants, but it is likely that it is, or will become, fully established. March and July (probably most months through to the autumn).

Subgenus ERISTALIS

Eristalis (Eristalis) tenax (Linnaeus, 1758)   Pl. 11, fig. 1
Map: Ball & Morris p. 66
Larva: Rotheray Pl. 14e

This is a particularly good hive bee mimic, particularly when hovering between flowers with its hind legs held low to resemble pollen sacs. The name 'drone-fly' refers to its close resemblance to drones (male hive bees). It is a large robust species, differing from *pertinax* in the presence of a dark front tarsus, and from both *pertinax* and *similis* by the stripes of dark hairs down the eyes, the almost completely dark hind tibia with long hairs on the dorsal and ventral surfaces, and the very broad black face stripe. The abdomen varies in colour from black to forms with conspicuous orange markings. Wing length 9.75–13 mm.

It is widespread and abundant throughout Britain and Ireland. Newspaper reports of hive bees still being abundant in late autumn on Michaelmas daisy and other garden flowers, sometimes with accompanying pictures, will often prove to be this species. Females hibernate in houses and any suitable outdoor crevices they can find, and emerge on warm days in late winter and early spring. Consequently, this is one of the few hoverflies which is reported in every month of the year, but there are relatively few records in midsummer in many districts. Larvae live in organically rich and polluted ditches and drains, the run-off from dung and silage heaps in farmyards, etc. January to December, peaking in August and September.

Genus HELOPHILUS

The body has a bold pattern, the thorax with yellow and black stripes and the yellow abdomen with distinctive black markings.

The genus is here considered in its restricted sense (*i.e.* excluding *Anasimyia* and *Parhelophilus*) with five species. In many districts *Helophilus pendulus* is the commonest species of hoverfly with a distinctly striped thorax, but care must be taken not to confuse it with two more local species, *trivittatus* and *hybridus*. *H. groenlandicus* is only so far known from north-west Scotland and is much darker in appearance than the other four. *H. affinis* has been recorded only once so far, as a vagrant to Fair Isle, but care is needed since it could easily be overlooked. There are several more European species of *Helophilus* in the northern tundra.

A similar species that could potentially be found in Britain as a vagrant is *Mesembrius peregrinus*. It resembles *H. pendulus* in shape and size, but it has a yellow face and the front tarsus is yellow (*H. trivittatus* is larger and more elongate, sometimes with a yellow front tarsus; *affinis* has a yellow front tarsus, but a black face stripe). In the males the eyes narrowly meet and the front tarsus is flattened and broad (eyes well separated and tarsus normal in *Helophilus*). In the females, tergite 3 has a narrow grey dust band all the way across just before the hind margin (no *Helophilus* are like this). *M. peregrinus* is a southern European species that occurs from southern Germany south to the Mediterranean.

Helophilus affinis Wahlberg, 1844.   Map: Ball & Morris p. 74

It is not surprising that this has only recently been recognised in Britain since it resembles the commonest species, *pendulus* and *hybridus*, in having a black-striped face. The crucial, but far from obvious difference, is that the hind margins of tergites 2 and 3 in *affinis* are dark (behind the main posterior black band), whereas in *pendulus* and *hybridus* the posterior black band does not quite reach the hind margin, leaving a narrow yellow stripe. However, this *affinis* character is shared by *groenlandicus*. Notably the front tarsus is entirely yellow-brown in *affinis* (black in *groenlandicus*). Wing length 8.5–10.5 mm.

A specimen of *affinis* was found in The National Museums of Scotland standing under *hybridus*; it had been taken by Sir Arthur Duncan on 11 August 1982 on Fair Isle (Stuke, 1996). It seems reasonable to suppose that the fly had successfully made a very long crossing over the North Sea. This northern European species used to be regarded as an extreme rarity further south, but in recent years it has been seen more frequently as a migrant, as in Denmark where there are now widespread records, especially from those parts closest to Sweden (Torp, 1994). Since 1980 it has been recorded for the first time in north-west Germany, the Netherlands and Switzerland (Speight, 1988c). Nielsen (1997) states that this species is widespread in the southern lowland parts of Norway and notes its occurrence in open forest and flowery meadows (visiting meadow buttercup, yarrow, oxeye daisy, common ragwort, valerians and raspberry). In Denmark, where its habitats are forests and plantations on heaths and moors, it has been seen at flowers such as creeping thistle, marsh thistle and rosebay willowherb; oviposition was observed at a water-filled wheel track (Torp, 1994). The distribution extends to the northern tundra so even the most exposed parts of Scotland may provide potential habitat. August (mid May to early September in Denmark).

Helophilus groenlandicus (Fabricius, 1780)   Pl. 12, fig. 2
                                                                            Map: Ball & Morris p. 75

This species is most similar to *affinis* in having a black-striped face and black hind margins to tergites 3 and 4. However, *groenlandicus* has the front tarsus black (yellowish in *affinis*). Speight (1988c) draws attention to differences in the shape of the frons (see illustration in key, p. 143). In the field it should be recognisable by its dark appearance. The legs are extensively black; the thorax is blacker than usual for the genus because the pale stripes are somewhat narrower, and the abdomen has a greater area of black. The lateral yellow markings on tergite 2 tend to be pointed towards the centre line whereas in *affinis*, *pendulus* and *hybridus* these markings are very blunt at the inner ends. Wing length 8.75 mm.

This species is known in Britain from just a few specimens from the coast of north-west Scotland and the Inner Hebrides. It is really an arctic species and may only be a vagrant to Britain, but the poorly worked islands off the Scottish coast or the adjacent mainland may yield further records. July.

Helophilus hybridus Loew, 1846   Pl. 12, fig. 3
                                                                            Map: Ball & Morris p. 75

In size and general appearance this species is very similar to *pendulus*. The male is usually distinctive in having continuously broad yellow sides to tergites 2 and 3, whereas there is a dividing black bar near the posterior edge of tergite 2 in the female and in both sexes of *pendulus*. The hind tibia of *hybridus* normally has the distal two thirds black, but just occasionally only half is black (as in exceptional examples of *pendulus*). The female of *hybridus* has black hairs on the hind part of tergite 5, differing from the female of *pendulus* which has yellow hairs. Less obvious, but easy to see with a microscope or hand-lens, are the yellow hairs on the yellow apical part of the hind femur (black hairs on all or most of the yellow part in *pendulus*). Wing length 8.5–11.25 mm.

It is a local species throughout Britain and Ireland, typically occurring around pond or ditch margins where the water is very shallow and submerged grass grows on blackish mud. Larvae have been recorded feeding in the decaying rhizomes of bulrush. Adults can be abundant at breeding sites, but they seem less prone to stray than the other species. In some localities it is common only in early spring before *pendulus* appears in conspicuous numbers. April to October, peaking in July and August.

Helophilus pendulus (Linnaeus, 1758)   Pl. 12, fig. 1
                                                                            Map: Ball & Morris p. 76
                                                                            Larva: Rotheray Pl. 14d

Most specimens of *pendulus* are easily separated by the black on the hind tibia being restricted to the distal third. Just occasionally, however, the black is a little more extensive and the comments under *hybridus* should then be consulted. The body pattern is very similar in both sexes. Wing length 8.5–11.25 mm.

This common and very widespread hoverfly occurs throughout Ireland and as far north as Shetland in Britain. Larvae have been found in farmyard drains, very wet manure and very wet old sawdust. Adults may occur in numbers around muddy puddles, ditches and the shallow margins of ponds, but as a notable wanderer it is perhaps more readily found away from water in any sunny situation which may attract hoverflies. Though frequently found at flowers, this species is commonly seen sitting on leaves and often emits a buzzing sound whilst resting in this fashion. April to November, peaking in July, but abundant from June to August.

Helophilus trivittatus (Fabricius, 1805)   Pl. 12, fig. 4
Helophilus parallelus (Harris, 1776) of 1976 check list   Map: Ball & Morris p. 76

This very handsome hoverfly is rather larger and longer in build than the other species and the yellow side-patches on the abdomen are very pronounced in both sexes. There should be little difficulty in recognising this species in the field because the face is entirely yellow including the central stripe (rarely the stripe is reddish-brown in which case the pattern on the abdomen should be checked) and the abdominal markings are lemon-yellow rather than buff as in *pendulus* and *hybridus*. However, if you find a dumpy '*Helophilus*' similar in build to *pendulus* but with a yellow face, then check the key and notes in the introduction to the genus for the possibility of *Mesembrius peregrinus* (the male of this species has eyes that meet on top of the head). In *trivittatus* the black areas look neater than in *pendulus* and *hybridus* since the black extends to the hind margin, or nearly so, on most tergites (there is usually an obvious yellow rim in the other two species) and the grey markings on tergite 4 are very conspicuous, tending to be paler than other species (very pale grey) and inclined to form a single band pinched in the middle (usually represented by yellow or darker grey paired spots in other species). The mid tarsus is normally yellow whereas the other species have at least the distal segments black. Wing length 10.25–12.25 mm.

H. trivittatus is widely distributed, but never common, and only single specimens are usually found, leaving doubt as to whether a stray or a breeding site has been located. Its presence in Ireland was confirmed by Speight & Nash (1993) and records appear to be increasing in frequency over recent years (Speight, 2000c). It is frequently found visiting thistles and will visit a variety of other flowers such as umbellifers and mayweed. There is a tendency for it to occur in coastal areas and it also regularly occurs in drier situations than is typical of the genus. These observations suggest that it is highly mobile. It is regarded as a migrant on the continent and the resident population may be augmented by migrants. May to October, peaking in August.

Genus LEJOPS

The genus is closely related to *Anasimyia* but the black antennae and longitudinal markings on the tergites make this a very easy hoverfly to recognise.

Lejops vittatus (Meigen, 1822)   Pl. 12, fig. 5
                                                                                  Map: Ball & Morris p. 81

In size it equals the larger *Anasimyia* or is significantly bigger. The males tend to be very dark with the markings on the thorax and abdomen relatively inconspicuous, but the females have much bolder grey markings. The paired longitudinal bars on tergites 3 to 5 are unlike the markings of any other Eristalini. Wing length 8–10 mm.

This is a scarce coastal species with most records from the marshes of the Thames Estuary. There are also recent records from Norfolk (Halvergate Marshes), Kent (Romney Marsh), Sussex (Pevensey and Lewes Levels), Somerset (Somerset Levels and Bridgewater Bay) and Gwent (Gwent Levels). Old records to the west of London appear genuine (there is also an undated specimen in the collection of the Natural History Museum from Felden, Herts), but are interpreted as strays. There is a close association with sea club-rush growing along ditches or in adjacent marsh, indicative of brackish conditions, where females can be found feeding on pollen. Imhof (1979) also records it feeding on the pollen of bulrush. The hoverfly may be swept from sea club-rush or, on gentle disturbance of the vegetation, seen in brief sluggish flight. In hot weather, however, the flight can be more lively, but keeping low. May to September, peaking in early July.

Genus MALLOTA

In western Europe there are some furry bumblebee mimics that might not immediately be recognised as belonging to this genus, but they should key through without difficulty because of the wing venation. *M. fuciformis* (Fabricius) is the easiest to recognise since it has very hairy eyes; *M. megilliformis* (Fallén) and *M. tricolor* Loew have bare eyes (the latter with the top of the thorax having a band of black hairs between the wing bases). These species are described in detail by Maibach & Goeldlin de Tiefenau (1989).

Mallota cimbiciformis (Fallén, 1817)   Pl. 11, fig. 12
                                                                            Map: Ball & Morris p. 83
                                                                            Larva: Rotheray Pl. 14b

This is a particularly fine mimic of the hive bee and, even if recognised as a hoverfly, it is easily passed over as a dark form of *Eristalis tenax* since the size and robust build are comparable. However, *Eristalis* lacks the swollen hind femur of *Mallota*, and bee mimics with a swollen hind femur in the tribe Xylotini lack the loop in vein R_{4+5}. The thoracic dorsum is covered in dense pale brown hairs and the scutellum is yellow. The abdomen is black and rather cylindrical, with variably developed orange side markings near the base (as in many examples of the hive bee and *Eristalis tenax*). Wing length 11.25–12.5 mm.

Unfortunately this hoverfly is something of a rarity though records are widespread as far north as Lancashire and Yorkshire. It is also known from southern Scotland, but has not been recorded from Ireland. There seems to be no special association with ancient forest – it was even bred from trees in Hyde Park in central London. Adults have been noted flying at great speed over patches of bramble and a male noted feeding at the flowers (Hanson, 1985). Larvae have been found in water-filled rot-holes, both small and large, and the puparia occur just above in drier detritus, often at some height above the ground. Overall, this is an elusive species, requiring a discerning eye at flowers and investigation of solitary 'hive bees' showing an interest in rot-holes. June to September, peaking in June and July.

Genus MYATHROPA

This distinctive yellow and black species can be regarded as a wasp mimic, so superficially it has little in common with *Mallota* which is a bee mimic. However, both specialise in wet rot-holes in tree trunks as breeding sites.

Myathropa florea (Linnaeus, 1758)
Pl. 11, fig. 11
Map: Ball & Morris p. 95
Larva: Rotheray Pl. 14f

The general appearance is closely similar to brightly marked *Eristalis*. However, it can be immediately recognised by the distinctive pattern of grey spots and bars on the thoracic dorsum. *M. florea* is very variable in size and strength of markings, giving the deceptive appearance that several species may be involved. Spring specimens tend to have the yellow abdominal markings smaller and duller than summer specimens, some of which are very handsome. Wing cell r_1 is usually open, in contrast to *Eristalis*. Wing length 7–12 mm.

This is a widespread and often common species in wooded districts throughout Britain and Ireland. Larvae occur in rot-holes or in water-filled cavities full of decaying leaves as may occur between the root bases of trees (they have even been reported from wooden water butts containing accumulations of decaying leaves). Puparia are found just above the surface of the wet wood detritus or the water, either buried in decaying wood or exposed. Adults are particularly fond of large umbel flowers and males can sometimes be found hovering in beams of sunlight in woodland at about head height. May to October, peaking in July and August.

Genus PARHELOPHILUS

To some degree the three species in this genus resemble *Helophilus pendulus* since the pale thoracic stripes are broad, but one can soon learn to distinguish them even in flight because *Parhelophilus* species are somewhat smaller and more hairy, with a more dumpy build and a brighter orange appearance. It is always worth catching several specimens since frequently two species are flying together, and to examine males if possible since the characters of the females are less precise. Identification of females in Coe (1953a) was not entirely satisfactory, but Barendregt (1980) considered a number of alternative characters. The recent addition of *P. crococoronatus* to the European fauna by Reemer (2000) needs to be noted. The rat-tailed larva of *frutetorum* has been found between the leaf sheaths of bulrush. It is probable that all members of the genus have similar habits in association with this or other plants of similar growth form.

Parhelophilus consimilis (Malm, 1863)
Map: Ball & Morris p. 106

In general appearance this species looks rather darker, but in scanning through a collection (and in the field) the feature which gives a clue that a specimen is worth checking is that the tip of the front tibia has a black spot dorsally, whereas in the two commoner species black markings are absent or not so clear in this plane of view. Also the central pair of stripes on the thorax tend to be grey rather than yellowish-grey. The face profile has the mouth edge produced well forward and the male hind femur lacks either a projection or a brush of hairs at its base (but remember that male eyes are separated and do not confuse with females, which lack the swollen genitalia at the tip of the abdomen). Wing length 7.5–8.5 mm.

P. consimilis is the rarest of the three species in the genus. It occurs by pools in habitats which are transitional between bog and fen, often in association with bulrush but not necessarily so. Records exist for the southern half of England (notably the south-west), and the Norfolk Broads, as well as South Wales. It has also been found in Ireland and the Galloway coastal belt of south-west Scotland. May to August, peaking in July.

Parhelophilus frutetorum (Fabricius, 1775)   Pl. 12, fig. 6
                                                                          Map: Ball & Morris p. 106

The male is very easy to distinguish once the location of the projection on the hind femur is appreciated; this feature is easily seen in the field with a hand lens. Separation of the females from *versicolor* requires much more care, but in side view tergite 5 has all hairs yellow (black posteriorly in *versicolor*) and tergite 4 has erect black hairs in the posterior quarter (semi-erect in *versicolor*). The long black hairs behind the upper corner of the eyes in the female may be difficult to use as a field character, but provide a valuable check at home. Wing length 7–9 mm.

A recently described European species, *P. crococoronatus* Reemer, is very similar and is included in the key. The projection on the male hind femur is shorter and bears some longer hairs, giving a spur-like appearance. The species is known from Portugal and southern France suggesting a Lusitanian distribution. It is therefore possible that it could be found in south-west England or southern Ireland.

In southern England *frutetorum* is a widespread species that is often encountered along open pond sides and ditches with bulrush. However, it regularly turns up some distance from suitable breeding sites, *e.g.* around scrubby woodland edge and patches of tall herbs, and is much less faithful to wetlands and water bodies than *versicolor*. It becomes scarcer further north but reaches Lancashire and there is a thin scatter of records in southern Scotland. It has not been recorded from Ireland. April to September, peaking in June.

Parhelophilus versicolor (Fabricius, 1794)   Map: Ball & Morris p. 107

It is wise to be cautious in recording this species, confidence being greatly increased if examples of *frutetorum* are available for comparison. In the male the brush of hairs on the hind femur is not conspicuous, so the first decision is whether the *frutetorum* projection is present. If not, look carefully to check the presence of the brush as opposed to its absence in *consimilis* (the latter species has a black tip to the front tibia). It is necessary to be alive to the fact that the eyes of male *Parhelophilus* are widely separated, so as to avoid confusion with a female (whose abdomen is tapered). The female has the face short but distinctly bulbous when seen in profile; the occiput (back of head behind the eyes) can have some very short black hairs in the lower half, but it lacks the long black hairs behind the top corner of the eyes as found in *frutetorum*. The body hairs are shorter than in *frutetorum* in both sexes, and in the male the pale markings of the abdomen are usually more extensive, with the black posterior margin of tergite 2 usually stopping well short of the side margins. Wing length 7–9 mm.

This species is strongly associated with lushly vegetated water margins and large wetlands, especially where dense tall herbs and carr are present. It is often found in the company of *frutetorum*, but rarely strays far from obvious breeding sites. However, *versicolor* has a somewhat wider range, extending northwards to Scotland and westwards to Ireland where it is widely distributed, although uncommon. April to August, peaking from May to July.

Tribe MERODONTINI

The three British genera are very dissimilar in general appearance. The face lacks a knob, being flat or with only the mouth edge jutting forwards or, in the case of *Merodon*, with the face concave and strongly jutting out. The face has long hairs across the entire width or, in *Psilota*, is rather more bare in the centre line. The hind femur is somewhat swollen with small black spines beneath near the apex, in *Merodon* the swelling being strongly developed and with the spines placed on the posterior edge of a ventral triangular projection (as in *Tropidia*). In *Eumerus* and *Merodon* the upper outer cross-vein is weakly or strongly re-entrant, and *Merodon* has vein R_{4+5} deeply looped as in the Eristalini. The wing venation of *Psilota* is more like *Brachyopa*; indeed the general appearance is much closer to a member of the Chrysogastrini. A feature of importance in linking these genera is the presence of a flat bare central strip at the hind margin of tergite 1, though this is barely discernible in *Psilota*.

The larval biology of *Eumerus* and *Merodon* is distinct among British hoverflies in that both genera are recorded as feeding on bulbs of various plants. The placing of *Merodon* by Coe (1953a) in his Eristalinae was clearly inappropriate because the larva is not a rat-tailed maggot. The larvae of *Psilota* are now known to occur in sap runs, which is not too dissimilar from a diet of decaying bulb tissue.

Genus EUMERUS

The genus is very distinctive in having the combination of a flat hairy face and a re-entrant upper outer cross-vein in the wings. These small but robust flies are further typified (in the British fauna) by oblique greyish bars on the abdomen which are inset into slight depressions, and also by the swollen hind femur.

Though only four species are involved, difficulty has commonly been met in identifying most of them, partly because undue emphasis was placed upon stigma colour, which is very unreliable. Some of the awkward species may be keyed out on the characters of the hind legs, but unset specimens may cause difficulty because the underside features of the hind femur cannot be easily seen if the legs are folded up (the legs will not unfold unless the dead specimen has relaxed for several hours). Many more species are known in Europe, especially in the Mediterranean region.

Eumerus funeralis and *E. strigatus* are called the Lesser Bulb Flies by horticulturists (*Merodon* is the Large Bulb Fly) on account of the larvae causing damage to bulbs in gardens. *E. sabulonum* is associated with sheep's-bit. The larval habitat of *ornatus* is still unknown; however it is almost certain that bulbs or roots of wild plants are used. In the Netherlands, *E. sogdianus* Stackelberg is said to occur in districts with fields of potatoes and onions and could be found in similar situations in eastern England. There is plenty of scope for clarifying the ecological separation of *Eumerus* species.

Eumerus funeralis Meigen, 1822   Map: Ball & Morris p. 68
Eumerus tuberculatus Rondani, 1857   Larva: Rotheray Pl. 1a

The build of *funeralis* is particularly short and compact. The male has a rather elongate rectangular third antennal segment with the arista arising midway along the straight upper edge (as in some *strigatus*). The third antennal segment in the female tends to be rounded (rather than somewhat rhomboid as in *strigatus*), but some specimens are not easily distinguished on this character.

The hind femur is strongly swollen and somewhat arched, the synonym *tuberculatus* being derived from a rounded tubercle near the base beneath, this being best developed in the male. Since it is not always easy to see the tubercle, it is worth noting that there is a glistening black area free of hairs ventrally near the base of the hind femur, being continuous with the apical area free of hairs between the central black spines; in general appearance in side view the hairs seem overall sparser and shorter basally than in *strigatus*.

Sternite 4 in the male is deeply incised. The shape is clearly seen in a fresh specimen, but the halves tend to overlap in a dried specimen. The parameres have a rounded club at the ends. Wing length 3.5–6 mm.

This is a widely distributed species that is frequently found in gardens, but is perhaps less common in the wider countryside. The distribution extends into the Scottish Highlands. In Ireland, it is confined to urban gardens and areas of horticulture. The flight is low and relatively fast for a small insect; in general behaviour it may easily be overlooked for a small blackish bee or wasp. It is often noticed in gardens because of its habit of sunning itself on stones or leaves. In addition to attacking the bulbs of garden daffodil, the larvae must also have other hosts in the wild, bluebell being a logical possibility. Speight (1985) states that it is not established in Ireland and points out that it was not found in Great Britain until early in the 20th century. He concludes that this mainly central and southern European species was probably introduced to Britain via the international trade in bulbs. April to October, peaking in June and August.

Eumerus ornatus Meigen, 1822   Pl. 7, fig. 19
                                                                                 Map: Ball & Morris p. 66

On average, specimens are larger and more elongate than normally found with the other species and the head of the male is noticeably large and globular. The abdomen is relatively long and narrow though broader near the base. The ocellar triangle is placed well forward from the back of the head in both sexes, the distance from the back margin of the compound eyes being equal to the length of the ocellar triangle. The eyes of both sexes may seem bare on casual inspection, but with a microscope and good lighting it is possible to discern sparse small hairs. The hind femur is moderately swollen and (in side view) there are long whitish hairs stretching for almost the full length beneath (anteroventral, ventral and posteroventral).

The male genitalia are distinct from the other species since there is a pair of conspicuous orange spheres (seen by viewing the abdomen from beneath). The hind margin of sternite 6 is straight, but at each hind corner there is a process bearing a black apical spine (this feature may be obscured in a dried specimen and normally requires a microscope to be seen). Wing length 4.5–6.75 mm.

Woodland rides and edges are the preferred habitat, especially at ancient woodland sites. It flies low over paths or just above herbage and will sometimes settle on bare banks and dead branches in dappled light. Though rarely found in numbers, this species will probably be found to be locally frequent in many well wooded districts in the south. Its distribution extends to southern Cumbria. It has not been recorded from Ireland. May to September, peaking in late June and early July.

Eumerus sabulonum (Fallén, 1817)   Pl. 7, fig. 18
                                                          Map: Ball & Morris p. 67

Apart from its distinctive reddish-coloured abdomen, *sabulonum* has various characters not found in the other three species. The moderately swollen hind femur is devoid of long hairs beneath, the stout black spines being almost as long as any of the hairs. The scutellum is bare of discernible hairs. The eyes of both sexes are bare and in the female the frons is markedly rugulose (rough warty ridged surface). In the male, sternite 4 has an extremely shallow V-shaped hind edge. Wing length 3.25–5.25 mm.

Sand dunes and earthy coastal cliffs on the south coast of England, and extending northwards to North Wales and Ayrshire, provide the habitat of this species. There is also an old inland record for the southern margin of Dartmoor, possibly referable to a sandy area on the floor of a river valley. It has not been recorded from Ireland. In the field this is an easily overlooked species, somewhat resembling a small reddish bee in flight and often blending into its background when settled on the ground. In Britain adults have been observed at the flowers of sheep's-bit, and females have been seen apparently laying eggs at the base of this plant (Stubbs, 1997); in Denmark oviposition has been confirmed and larvae were found feeding singly in small cavities surrounded by brownish plant tissue at the bases of the leaves (Munk, 2000). May to September, peaking in June and July.

Eumerus strigatus (Fallén, 1817)   Pl. 7, fig. 17
                                                          Map: Ball & Morris p. 67

In common with *funeralis* the hind femur is strongly swollen, but there is no trace of a tubercle near the base. The hind femur displays long whitish hairs beneath, which are especially dense in the basal half – the only shining black area free of hairs beneath is in the apical part between the minute stout black spines. The male of *strigatus* is normally distinct from that of *funeralis* in having a squarish third antennal segment with the arista arising quite near the upper corner, but there is too much variation to allow this to be a reliable character.

Sternite 4 in the male has a V-shaped hind margin, with a short notch at the bottom of the V (*E. sogdianus*, which occurs in the Netherlands, would key to *strigatus* but sternite 4 only has a wide shallow notch). Care must be taken with dried specimens since *funeralis* can look superficially similar. The parameres in profile have toadstool-like caps on the ends (these stick-like processes on the male genitalia can only be seen clearly with a microscope). Wing length 4–6.25 mm.

This species should occur in most lowland areas. Its distribution extends northwards to the edge of the Scottish Highlands and it has also been found in southern Ireland where it is confined to coastal grassland. *E. strigatus* tends to be commoner in midsummer after the spring peak of *funeralis*. It attacks garden daffodils and larvae have been recorded from the rhizomes of iris and also parsnips, potatoes, onions and the bulbs of other *Allium* species. As a consequence, it is more frequent in the wider countryside than *funeralis* and has been found in abundance in some wetlands (where iris is the most likely larval foodplant). March to October. The few records from March and April seem to be unusual and the main emergence commences in late May. Two peaks, in June and again in August.

Genus MERODON

There is only a single, though very variable species which appears to have been introduced to Britain from the continent in the second half of the 19th century. There are many more species in Europe, especially in the eastern Mediterranean where it becomes the dominant hoverfly genus. It is possible that more species could turn up in imported bulbs.

Merodon equestris (Fabricius, 1794)   Pl. 12, fig. 11
                                                                        Map: Ball & Morris p. 93
                                                                        Larva: Rotheray Pl. 1b

This is a densely hairy bumblebee mimic with a great range of colour forms. In general size and build, as well as in the presence of a loop in vein R_{4+5}, it resembles *Eristalis intricarius*. The latter species has the basal half of the tibiae pale whereas the legs in *Merodon* are entirely black and rather more robust. Other bumblebee mimics include *Volucella bombylans* and *Arctophila superbiens* (also with black legs) and *Eriozona* (legs partly pale), but these have a black patch on the wing below the stigma (wing clear in *Merodon*). The triangular projection beneath the distal parts of the hind femur is not found in other bumblebee mimics. Wing length 8.5–10.25 mm.

Merodon equestris is notable for its range of colour forms. It is thus able to mimic a variety of bumblebee patterns such as black with a red tail (*e.g. Bombus lapidarius*), black and yellow with a white tail (*e.g. B. lucorum*) and tawny (*e.g. B. pascuorum*). On the whole *Merodon* tends to look a bit long in the abdomen for a bumblebee, but it is easy to be fooled at first sight. An interesting study can be designed to record the relative frequency of the colour forms at different localities, especially if the relative frequency of the colour forms of bumblebees is also noted. For this reason it is worth listing the colour forms which have been named, since about 80% usually fit and the rest can often be allocated to intermediate forms.

Thorax black-haired	Tail grey, yellow or orange	*validus* Meigen
Thorax tawny-haired anteriorly, black-haired posteriorly	Tail whitish, buff or red	*equestris* Fabricius
Thorax tawny-haired	Abdomen also tawny-haired	*narcissi* Fabricius
	Abdomen tawny with a transverse black band on tergite 3	*transversalis* Meigen
Intermediates		♀ *equestris* × ♂ *transversalis* ♂ *equestris* × ♀ *validus*

Some forms are sex-specific, *e.g. validus* only in the female and *transversalis* only in the male. Some authorities have recognised a further form called *bulborum* (Rondani). There seems some inconsistency over the use of this name since it has been used to describe red-tailed specimens of form *equestris* (Brown, 1951) or specimens of form *equestris* with a black-haired scutellum instead of tawny (Hodson, 1932b).

The distribution includes much of Britain and Ireland. In favourable localities it can be found commonly especially in late spring and early summer. It particularly likes warm sunny sheltered spots and is fond of flowers such as dandelions. Males patrol territories from low perches or the ground which they defend actively, and the darting and hovering flight is reminiscent of the bee *Anthophora acervorum* (males of which could be mistaken for *Merodon* as they also frequent gardens and sheltered flowery spots). Because this hoverfly can be a horticultural pest, attacking daffodil and other bulbs, it has been given the common name Large Narcissus Fly or Large Bulb Fly (the Lesser Bulb Fly is *Eumerus*). Normally, however, this species is to be found quite harmlessly in the countryside where woods with bluebells provide an ideal situation. The eggs are laid on a leaf at ground level where the leaves have begun to splay into a rosette. The larva burrows into the bulb where it lives for about 300 days before pupating in the soil. The flies emerge in the morning, 90% of them between 8 and 10.30 am. In captivity the life span of adult flies has been recorded as 5 to 24 days in the female (average 17) and 6 to 18 days in the male (average 11) (Hodson, 1932b). In another study the estimated length of life was between 3 and 11 days (Conn, 1976a). April to September, peaking in late May and June.

Genus PSILOTA

Psilota anthracina Meigen, 1822   Pl. 5, fig. 3
                                                               Map: Ball & Morris p. 126

Being of a compact build and of a bluish-black colour, this species could readily be overlooked as a muscid fly such as *Hydrotaea*. The males can also look deceptively like *Cheilosia impressa* in the field. In life the eyes are bright red (muscids can have similar eyes), but the colour soon dulls in dead specimens. The flat hairy face, slightly jutting forwards at the mouth margin, and the black appearance has made it logical to key *Psilota* with the Pipizini, although it has the flat bare central strip at the hind margin of tergite 1 characteristic of Merodontini (even if poorly developed). The strongly yellowish front portion of the wing with a conspicuously yellow stigma should serve to distinguish *Psilota*. Wing length 6–7.5 mm.

Records are few and the species is considered to be a rarity in southern England and the Midlands. Large ancient woodlands and parklands such as the New Forest, Windsor Forest and Richmond Park are amongst its localities, but it is not entirely confined to such special sites. Adults visit hawthorn, and more rarely other flowers, and it is possible that alert observation of black flies in this situation in the spring and early summer may lead to the realisation that this hoverfly is not quite so rare after all. In Germany larvae were found in accumulations of decaying sap under the bark of a recently fallen spruce (together with *Brachypalpoides*, *Sphegina clunipes* and *Brachyopa pilosa*). In a farmhouse garden in Switzerland a storm-damaged pine about 25 years old had split at a fork 3 m above ground, revealing an internal pocket of decay containing rotten wood, sap and water; larvae of *Psilota anthracina* were found at a depth of about 70 cm, but no other insects were present (Kassebeer *et al.*, 1998). A female has also been observed in Europe ovipositing in the exit hole of the wood-boring beetle *Cerambyx cerdo* in an ancient oak (Speight *et al.*, 2001, quoting Doczkal, *pers. comm.*). April to July, peaking in early June.

Tribe PELECOCERINI

These are tiny hoverflies with yellow or grey spots or bands, as well as a black scutellum, thus superficially resembling small *Platycheirus*. However, the face is very different, the whole of the lower half extending forwards. The partially orange antennae seem particularly large for such small flies and the arista is thickened and exceptionally short (shorter than the length of the third antennal segment).

There are two genera, *Chamaesyrphus* and *Pelecocera*. Coe (1953a) placed them together in his subfamily Pelecocerinae, but the 1976 check list moved *Chamaesyrphus* into the Cheilosiini. In our view the genera are related, so they are together again here; Thompson & Rotheray (1998) go a step further and treat *Chamaesyrphus* as a subgenus of *Pelecocera*. We have retained tribal rank for the Pelecocerini as in the 1976 check list.

Genus CHAMAESYRPHUS

The tergites have orange or grey spots, the coloration sometimes being obscure. The arista is placed about halfway along the dorsal edge of the third antennal segment or nearer the apex. The wings are unusual in that the wing tip is displaced further back than in other genera, R_{4+5} curving rearwards and the costal vein consequently reaching round the end of the wing.

These are hoverflies of the Caledonian pine woods. Attention is drawn to the occurrence in Europe of *lusitanicus* Mik which has long white hairs on portions of the upper part of the pleura in front of the wing bases (heaths or coastal sandy ground in Scotland could yield this species). The taxonomy of British material needs a thorough review. For the present we have followed Coe (1953a), but have regarded the position of the arista on the third antennal segment as an unreliable character.

Chamaesyrphus caledonicus Collin, 1940   Pl. 5, fig. 20
                                                                   Map: Ball & Morris p. 25

As currently interpreted, this species is distinguished by the lack of a bristle on the pleura just below and in front of the wing base. The sides of the thorax are strongly dusted. The certain female specimen in the Natural History Museum is small and feeble, with poorly defined greyish spots on the abdomen. Some of the material placed under this species by Coe is now not regarded as being this species (Speight, *pers. comm.*). Wing length 4–5 mm.

This little known and extremely rare hoverfly was discovered in Britain by Dr D. Sharp at "Boat-o'-Garten" in July 1903, but was identified as *C. lusitanicus*, a species known otherwise only from Spain and Portugal. In August 1935, C.J. Wainwright and J.E. Collin caught "a few specimens at Culbin Sandhills" and Collin was able to compare them with types of *lusitanicus*, concluding that they belonged to a new species (Collin, 1940). More recently, it has been taken by I. Perry in Rothiemurchus in July 1988 and again at Culbin Sands (under pines planted on the dunes) by A. Wass in July 1991. The only other record available is a specimen in the Natural History Museum collection taken in July 1917 by J.J.F.X. King from "Rannoch". July to August, peaking in July.

Chamaesyrphus scaevoides (Fallén, 1817)   Pl. 5, fig. 19
                                                                    Map: Ball & Morris p. 25

This species is variable; in particular, the position of the arista can be in the middle of the dorsal edge of the third antennal segment, or nearer the apex. The abdomen normally has distinct yellow spots. The pleura have a yellowish bristle in front of the wing base (on the upper hind corner of the mesopleuron), but it should be borne in mind that the bristle may get knocked off so it is as well to look on both sides to increase the chances of finding one intact. Wing length 4–6.25 mm.

C. scaevoides is widely distributed across northern Scotland, usually in Caledonian pine forests, but occasionally in conifer plantations. Adults are frequently found visiting tormentil flowers among heathy vegetation and along ride margins. June to August, peaking in late June.

Genus PELECOCERA

The antennae are unlike those of any other British hoverfly. The third antennal segment is deeply semicircular with a straight upper edge, and the thickened arista is at the apex.

Pelecocera tricincta Meigen, 1822   Pl. 5, fig. 18
                                                                    Map: Ball & Morris p. 107

This tiny hoverfly is named *tricincta* after the three bands of yellow across the abdomen. Actually, on close inspection the bands are often found to be narrowly divided into spots. The antennae are so distinctive that further description is unnecessary. Wing length 3.5–5.25 mm.

The strongholds of this very local hoverfly are the heathlands of east Dorset and the New Forest, but it has been reported more widely in recent years, from Devon, the Isle of Wight and heathland in Surrey and Sussex, indicating that search on other southern heaths is needed. It prefers wet heathland (*e.g.* areas with cross-leaved heath) as at the margins of bogs. Another recently discovered population is associated with boggy pool margins within coniferised parts of the Longleat Forest complex in Wiltshire – a very different habitat to its other known sites. There are reports of it being plentiful, but for the most part it is likely to be taken singly or in small numbers by sweeping, or found visiting flowers such as tormentil along the edges of paths. May to September, peaking in July.

Tribe PIPIZINI

Of all hoverfly groups, there are none to compete with the Pipizini for the scale of past confusion. Not only have the species caused problems enough, but the recognition of the genera has been a headache to grapple with. Whilst there remain some difficulties, in particular within the genus *Pipiza*, it is hoped the treatment here will show that the Pipizini are not as difficult as their reputation suggests.

The first step, that of recognising the tribe, is mercifully straightforward. These are small to moderate-sized hoverflies with a black ground colour, sometimes with a pair of spots on tergite 2 (*Platycheirus rosarum* has a pair of spots on tergite 3) or more rarely with spots on both tergites 2 and 3. The face lacks a knob, so is flat, and is covered in long downward-directed hairs. There are no other hoverflies of this description (*Eumerus* has a similar face, but the abdomen has grey oblique bars) apart from *Psilota* which for convenience appears in the generic key to Pipizini although it belongs to the tribe Merodontini.

Separation of the genera has appeared unnecessarily complicated because Coe (1953a) followed Collin (1952b) in the use of characters which many people found difficult to discern (the presence or absence of hairs on certain parts of the pleura, and the relative shape of the projection of the frons). However, there are much simpler ways of recognising the genera – reference to wing venation, antennae and a few other easily seen features being sufficient.

The Pipizini are believed to occupy a basal position within the aphid-predator lineage of the Syrphidae (Rotheray & Gilbert, 1999). Structurally they have the basic features of the Milesiinae, yet biologically they have more in common with the Syrphinae. The Pipizini show a preference for wax-secreting aphids (families Thelaxidae, Pemphigidae, Adelgidae etc.), such hosts occurring on tree branches, in galls, and underground around roots. The adults tend to have relatively inconspicuous habits, and their small size and frequent lack of coloured markings result in these species being all too easy to overlook in the field.

Data submitted to the Hoverfly Recording Scheme suggest that, even after taking into account that some of the species are small and elusive, the Pipizini are under-recorded. This would seem to reflect an unwillingness to attempt what is in part a difficult group. However, there are some readily identifiable species and, even if recorders cannot identify material themselves, specimens should be retained and submitted to the Recording Scheme for identification.

Genus HERINGIA

These are narrowly-built, entirely black pipizines with a long sloping upper outer cross-vein (as in *Pipiza*), but with the frons more sloping and less produced so that the antennae are placed low on the head. The male genitalia are particularly long and slender. *Heringia* is divided into two subgenera that have been treated as separate genera until recently. In subgenus *Neocnemodon*, the male hind and mid trochanters have a ventral projection at the base, this being absent in the subgenus *Heringia*. *Heringia* females have distinct narrow dust bars on the frons, these being small and rounded or absent in *Neocnemodon* females.

The larvae are associated with a variety of aphids, especially gall-forming aphids on elm and poplar, but there are also records of associations with conifer-feeding aphids.

Subgenus HERINGIA

There are now two species known in Britain, which differ from *Neocnemodon* in having the third antennal segment longer than wide (often with some orange at base beneath). The male mid and hind trochanters lack long spurs.

Heringia (Heringia) heringi (Zetterstedt, 1843)   Pl. 5, fig. 10
                                                                  Map: Ball & Morris p. 77

Though very variable in size, the females are often much smaller than the males. The male genitalia have a characteristic three-toothed median plate at the tip of the larger process (the aedeagus). The males usually have predominantly dark brown or black hairs on the head, thorax, abdomen and the anterior side of the hind tibia (most such areas have white hairs in male *senilis*). However, some can have predominantly pale hairs on the thoracic dorsum and tergite 2, so the genitalia should always be checked to be certain of the identification. Unlike the male, the female always has whitish hairs on top of the thorax and on the legs, resulting in a rather nondescript appearance. However, the combination of a strongly sloping upper outer cross-vein and an elongate third antennal segment enables ready identification. Wing length 5.5–6.25 mm.

The following comments are based upon information which was published or reported before the recognition of *senilis* and could relate to either species.

In southern England this is a local species to be found along woodland margins. It is much scarcer in the north, though records extend to Skye and it has been recorded only three times in Ireland. It has been bred from large blister galls on the leaves of elm (especially English elm) formed by the aphid *Schizoneura lanuginosa*, and it has also been bred from an aphid gall on willow (Chandler, 1969), although the specimen is female so its identity cannot be confirmed (P. Chandler, *pers. com.*). May to August, peaking in late May and early June.

Heringia senilis Sack, 1938

The entirely white hairs on the abdomen, thorax, eyes, face and anterior (outer) face of the hind tibia of the male easily distinguish this species from *heringi*, though the females of both species share a white-haired appearance. This has long remained a poorly defined species, but new studies have demonstrated a subtle but important difference in the male genitalia; as illustrated in the key, there is a median plate lying between the pair of apical lobes which is almost truncate at the apex rather than having the three-toothed character of *heringi*. The third antennal segment of the male is about twice as long as wide (much shorter in male *heringi*), though note that antennae of female *heringi* are similarly proportioned. The female of *senilis*, according to some literature, lacks dust bars on the frons, but other studies, including the British series reared in association with males, reveal that dust bars are present as in *heringi*, and so the separation of the two species in this sex seems impractical. Wing length 6 mm.

Attention was drawn to this very widespread European species in the first edition. In late summer 1999, a collection was made of spiral galls of the aphid *Pemphigus spirothecae* on the leaf-stalks of Lombardy poplar from two sites on the outer fringe of south-east London (Jones, 2001). The galls contained *Heringia* larvae, which were kept overwinter in a dormant state in glass tubes, these larvae pupated in April 2000 and adults emerged in May. More larvae were found the next summer, producing adults in 2001. These hoverflies proved to be *senilis*. The larvae are apparently adapted to escape attack from specialised aphid guard 'soldiers'. An adult was caught on wasteland at Peterborough on 27 July 2001; aspen was close by, but the nearest Lombardy poplars were distant. Since it is unlikely that galls are in a suitable state until midsummer, there may be only a single brood of *senilis*, early emergence of adults occurring under artificial conditions. July.

Subgenus NEOCNEMODON

The former genus *Neocnemodon* is now considered as a subgenus of *Heringia*. Coe (1953a) used the name *Cnemodon*. The distinctive features of *Neocnemodon* include a rotund third antennal segment (note some yellow beneath: all black in *Pipiza*), while the males have strongly developed spurs on the mid and hind trochanters. These spurs are conspicuous in side view and some species also have well developed spurs on the mid coxae. The females are somewhat nondescript apart from lacking distinct dust spots on the frons, but the *Heringia*-type wing venation and the presence of a round third antennal segment with an orange patch below should serve to distinguish most specimens quite easily. However, some females have a rather rhomboid third antennal segment, as in *Pipiza*, and the orange patch at the base (also present in *Heringia*) can be obscure or rarely absent.

A useful way of separating the females is by reference to the wing venation. In *Neocnemodon* the distance along vein M_{1+2} between the two outer cross-veins is equal to at least half the length of the lower outer cross-vein, whereas in *Pipiza* this distance is a quarter to one third.

Coe (1953a) included three species in his genus *Cnemodon* (*latitarsis*, *verrucula* and *vitripennis*). Following a revision of the genus in Europe (Delucchi & Pschorn-Walcher, 1955 & 1957), Collin (1960) added *pubescens* to the British list. Stubbs (1980b) added *brevidens*, bringing the total to five species in Britain and Ireland. The review by Speight & Smith (1975) helps clarify the confusion in past application of names and illustrates the claspers of the male genitalia; their key includes *fulvimanus* (Zetterstedt) which has yet to be found in Britain. Female identification was unsatisfactory prior to the publication of a comprehensive key in Stubbs (1996a) which covered all five British species. Although *fulvimanus* is included in the key to males in this edition, it has not yet proved possible to include it in the female key.

In the field the males appear to be particularly slender and the females are most similar to *Pipizella* (but the antennae are short in *Heringia*). Adults can be found at flowers, especially in mid May. However, they are more often found resting on sunlit foliage in hedgerows or along the margins of sunny rides. Females fly very close to the ground at the edges of woodland rides, being difficult to observe amidst grass shoots. Delucchi and Pschorn-Walcher report that the larvae feed on adelgids on trees, although Coe (1953a) cites a reference to the prey being coccids on Lombardy poplar. Whilst *Neocnemodon* occur in purely deciduous forest on the continent, *latitarsis* and *vitripennis* have been found attacking the woolly aphid *Dreyfusia piceae* on European silver-fir, so fir plantations may prove worth searching for adults. The difficulty of finding *Heringia* may be due to their spending much of the time out of reach in trees.

Heringia (Neocnemodon) brevidens (Egger, 1865)   Map: Ball & Morris p. 77
Neocnemodon brevidens (Egger, 1865)

The flap-like projection on the posterior surface of the basal segment of the male front tarsus is distinct from all other species (there is a small projection of a similar type on the mid tarsus). The face is mostly white-haired (black in other species). Wing length about 6 mm.

The first known British specimen was taken in 1949 on flowers of marsh-marigold in south-west London. A second specimen was taken in a park with a pond in north London. There are around a dozen widely scattered records as far north as the Lancashire coast. Although the larvae are unknown, there is a possible association with poplars and willows. For example, adults have been found in numbers beneath a 'black poplar' at Woodwalton Fen. May to August, peaking in July and August.

Heringia (Neocnemodon) latitarsis (Egger, 1865)   Map: Ball & Morris p. 78
Neocnemodon latitarsis (Egger, 1865)

The male front metatarsus is strongly swollen, being about twice the width of the second tarsal segment. In side view, it will be found that sternite 3 has a keel-like projection. The second sternite has a clump of dense long black hairs near the base. It is worth looking out for *fulvimanus* (yet to be found in Britain) which has a similar keel, but the front metatarsus is not swollen and sternite 2 only has sparse short hairs. Wing length about 6 mm.

There are scattered records for southern England and one for Midlothian in Scotland. It was added to the Irish list by Speight *et al.* (1975), but on the basis of female specimens only. The only male specimen of subgenus *Neocnemodon* that has been found in Ireland proved to be *vitripennis*, so the status of this species as an Irish insect is uncertain. It has been taken on cow parsley flowers beside sallow scrub and trees such as black poplar (Stubbs, *pers. obs.*). The larvae have been found attacking the woolly aphid *Dreyfusia piceae* on firs, and other aphids on apple, poplar and elm. May to October, with two peaks, in May, and July and August.

Heringia (Neocnemodon) pubescens (Delucchi & Pschorn-   Map: Ball & Morris p. 78
Walcher, 1955)
Neocnemodon pubescens (Delucchi & Pschorn-Walcher, 1955)

The male front metatarsus is not swollen but there is a hollow beneath, as in *vitripennis*. The predominance of black hairs on the thoracic dorsum is not met with in other species, although *latitarsis* can have some black hairs in front. Wing length about 6 mm.

The majority of records are from southern England as far north as Yorkshire, but there are also scattered records from Scotland. It is usually encountered in woodland rides, especially where coniferisation has occurred. On occasions large numbers have been found at the male flowers of dog's mercury where it fringes a ride beside a conifer plantation (subsequently clear-felled) at Castor Hanglands NNR, Cambridgeshire. This plant is wind-pollinated, the pollen being the attraction for the hoverfly. April to September, peaking in May.

Heringia (Neocnemodon) verrucula (Collin, 1931)   Map: Ball & Morris p. 79
Neocnemodon verrucula (Collin, 1931)

This is the only British species with an entirely unmodified male front metatarsus (also non-British *fulvimanus*, see under *latitarsis*). There is a tubercle on sternite 4 (absent in other species) but this is not easy to discern. For doubtful specimens, see the discussion under *vitripennis*. Wing length about 5 mm.

Records are few and widely scattered as far as north-east Scotland. It was found in a woodland ride in Herefordshire in company with *pubescens*. May to June, peaking in late May.

Heringia (Neocnemodon) vitripennis (Meigen, 1822)   Pl. 5, fig. 11
Neocnemodon vitripennis (Meigen, 1822)   Map: Ball & Morris p. 79

The male front metatarsus superficially appears to be unmodified (as in *verrucula*) but closer examination reveals the presence of a hollow beneath as in *pubescens*. This feature may not be easy to see with a hand lens, but the coloration of hairs as given in the key should be easy to discern. Wing length 4.5–5.5 mm.

To say that *vitripennis* is the commonest species is misleading since it is only infrequently found. Nonetheless it has a wide distribution, at least within England, and has been recorded in northern Scotland. It was added to the Irish list by Speight (1986b) from a single male specimen. The larvae are mainly predaceous on adelgids and have been found attacking the woolly aphid *Dreyfusia piceae* on firs, and also coccids on Lombardy poplar. Woodland rides and margins provide typical habitat. May to October, peaking in June and July.

Genus PIPIZA

The genus provides one of the most infuriating and intractable taxonomic problems one could find anywhere among the British Diptera. The key in Coe (1953a) is highly unsatisfactory. There is a confusing wealth of names in the literature and only some of the types have been re-examined – there is a morass of chaos here. There seem to be few firm characters to use in species identification, with great variation in these characters, and the genitalia do not greatly help though more detailed work may meet with more success in future. Earlier hope over the use of microtrichia has been somewhat dashed. Despite considerable efforts it is possible to do no more than offer a partial solution.

There is still uncertainty as to how many British species there are, and over the means of identification of the various taxa. Nonetheless, it is to be hoped that a reasonable percentage of *Pipiza* can be firmly allocated to a species name as defined here, even if ideas have to be adjusted in due course. It is clearly essential that vouchers be kept for all records.

The genus is fairly easy to recognise. The wing venation is rather similar to that found in *Heringia* (upper outer cross-vein steeply inclined). The abdomen is entirely black (as in *Heringia*) or commonly with a pair of orange spots on tergite 2 (as in *Trichopsomyia* but in no other hoverflies) or more rarely with a pair of spots on tergites 2 and 3 (unlike any other Pipizini). The male frons is not inflated (inflated in *Heringia* with the upper part of the frons high above the base of the antennae). In both sexes the frons extends rather far forwards so that the antennae are almost on a conical projection; in side view the face profile (in most specimens) shows a shallow but distinctly concave curve. The third antennal segment is always black and the shape usually rather angular, often rhomboid (unlike females of subgenus *Neocnemodon*) (*P. dubia* Lundbeck of Europe clearly belongs to this subgenus).

Members of the genus are commonly found along woodland margins, often sitting on foliage of bushes, brambles or herbage with the wings held flat but half open in a V or delta shape. Sometimes specimens will also be seen at flowers. The larvae have been found on herbage or bushes (those of the continental species *festiva* Meigen have been reared from the leaf-stalk galls of *Pemphigus spirothecae* on poplar (often common on Lombardy poplar) so this is a species worth looking out for).

There is a possibility of further species being found in Britain in addition to *festiva* mentioned above (discussed under *luteitarsis*). *P. quadrimaculata* (Panzer, [1804]) has four spots on the abdomen, as in some male *fenestrata*; it is a readily recognised species because the abdomen is so broad relative to its length. Extra species could well lie within the *noctiluca* complex.

Pipiza austriaca Meigen, 1822

Pl. 5, fig. 17
Map: Ball & Morris p. 108
Larva: Rotheray Pl. 5a

This is a relatively robust and long-bodied species, though small specimens do occur. The abdomen in both sexes is normally entirely black with faint bands or bars of whitish hairs, only rarely with spots on tergite 2 (females of all other species except some *lugubris* have spots on tergite 2, although one has to check closely with discoloured specimens, and any bars of white hairs are even more faint). The wings usually have a dark patch, this being very strongly coloured deep brown in some specimens and almost as well defined as *lugubris*. In typical specimens the hind femur is considerably thickened by the development of a pair of ridges beneath near the apex, the apex becoming abruptly narrow, but specimens with thinner legs occur (but the femora are never as narrow as in *lugubris*). In the male the lateral hairs on tergite 1 are pale whilst those on the pregenital segment are black (this combination is not found in other species except *lugubris*). In the female the hairs along the axis are black on tergites 1 to 5 except for a narrow band of pale hairs on each of tergites 2, 3 and 4 (rather similar to some *noctiluca*, but the hairs on the lateral margins are almost entirely pale, entirely so on tergite 1). Wing length 6–8 mm.

P. austriaca is local but widespread in England and also occurs in Wales, Scotland south of the Highlands, and Ireland. It has been bred from larvae found feeding on *Cavariella* aphids on hogweed. It is normally found along woodland margins and in lush meadows, and adults can sometimes be found visiting flowers such as buttercups and hogweed. May to September, peaking in June.

Pipiza bimaculata Meigen, 1822

Map: Ball & Morris p. 108

The description of Coe (1953a) is imprecise, the separation from *noctiluca* being especially awkward in practice. The simplest expedient was to call small specimens *bimaculata* and larger ones *noctiluca*, a procedure fraught with frequent misidentifications.

The main problem lies with the tremendous variation within what we currently regard as *noctiluca*, with many specimens approaching *bimaculata* in size and coloration. However, there is a consistency in rigorously-screened *bimaculata* that suggests that it is probably distinct from *noctiluca*. It is a tiny pipizine (smaller than most *Heringia*) with the tarsi very dark in both sexes (dwarf *noctiluca* seem always to have the basal segments of the four front tarsi pale). In the female the hairs on top of the scutellum are short compared with those in *noctiluca* (see key). In the male, the long series in the Natural History Museum shows that in the majority of cases *bimaculata* has spots on tergite 2 whilst the typical form of *noctiluca* does not. *P. bimaculata* has entirely clear wings in the male, and at most a hardly discernible darkening in the middle in the female. This leaves very few specimens which cannot be allocated with any degree of reasonable confidence. Wing length 4.5–6.5 mm.

P. bimaculata is widely distributed across the British mainland, but the majority of records are from southern England. It is also reported from Ireland (Speight *et al.*, 1975). May to September, peaking in late May and early June.

Pipiza fenestrata Meigen, 1822   Pl. 5, fig. 15
                                                      Map: Ball & Morris p. 109

This is another rather unsatisfactory species and sinking it as a form within *noctiluca* would be the simplest expedient. However, there seems good reason to believe that *fenestrata* exists as a separate entity (though it may need another name), the complication arising because one of the forms of *noctiluca* acts as an intermediate.

Typical *fenestrata* comprises relatively large specimens. The male has pale greyish-brown hairs on the face (dark in *noctiluca*, except form B); the face distinctly widens below the antennae; the ocellar triangle is narrow (hind ocelli separated by one and a half times the width of an ocellus) and the wing microtrichia can be nearly complete in the basal cells. Moreover, the males can have spots on tergite 3 in addition to those on tergite 2 (this combination does not occur in other British species, though *quadrimaculata* of Europe has 4 spots and partly dark tarsi; it is a shorter oval species with complete microtrichia on the wings in both sexes); sometimes the abdomen of male *fenestrata is* entirely black. The females have an elongate oval abdomen with particularly large spots on tergite 2 (sometimes occupying half the length of the segment) and sometimes a smaller pair on tergite 3. In side view tergite 4 is pale-haired with only a narrow anterior fringe with black hairs, whilst tergite 5 is entirely black-haired; cell cu_1 has a small bald patch among the microtrichia within the cell at its base (*i.e.* as opposed to a bare margin at the edge of the cell); the frons has a slight depression (pit) in the centre; and the legs tend to have the bases of the tibiae and tarsi paler than most *noctiluca*. Specimens which seem intermediate to *noctiluca* should be allocated to *noctiluca* form F. Wing length 7–9.25 mm.

P. noctiluca form F is transitional to *P. fenestrata*. The only real distinctions of form F are that the male has dark hairs on the face, the face widens slightly below and the ocellar triangle is wider. The main distinction of form F from typical *noctiluca* is the presence of spots on tergite 2.

P. fenestrata occurs as far north as the Scottish borders, and literature records suggest that it may occur in Scotland but it is difficult to know how many of these records are reliable. There is a preponderance of old records, but this may simply reflect an unwillingness amongst recorders to tackle this genus. April to September, peaking in late May and early June.

Pipiza lugubris (Fabricius, 1775)   Pl. 5, fig. 16
                                                      Map: Ball & Morris p. 109

This species is distinguished by the presence of a dark wing patch with sharp boundaries (other species have the outer edge fading out). Within such a variable genus this character is slender evidence of a distinct species and it has been suggested that *lugubris* should be regarded as falling within *noctiluca*. However, in both sexes the pattern of black hairs (as given in the key) differs from that found in *noctiluca*, and the males have whitish hairs on the face. It is felt that the separation of *lugubris* should be retained. *P. austriaca* can have wing markings approaching the state found in *lugubris*, and some *lugubris* records have proven to be this species, but comparative material of the two species reveals just how much less swollen the hind legs of *lugubris* are. What is more, *austriaca* males have black hairs on the face and the females have tergite 4 extensively black-haired (mainly pale-haired in *lugubris*). Wing length 6–7.5 mm.

Occurring as far north as southern Cumbria (old records), with a strong concentration in south Lancashire, this is largely a southern species. Adults are usually found in woodland situations, but have been found sufficiently frequently in wetter locations with meadowsweet to suggest that there might be an association with wetland habitats. May to October, peaking in late August.

Pipiza luteitarsis Zetterstedt, 1843   Pl. 5, fig. 14
                                                                   Map: Ball & Morris p. 110
                                                                   Larva: Rotheray Pl. 5b

One of the few certainties in *Pipiza* is the fact that this is a distinct species. The name derives from the yellow front and mid tarsi, only the apical segment sometimes being dark. There are often orange spots on tergite 2 in both sexes, but the males, in particular, can have the spots only vaguely represented by grey dusting. The jowls are extremely wide (about as wide as the third antennal segment) and the thoracic dorsum lacks the striations found in all other similar species towards the posterior corners. The tergites are entirely pale-haired in the female whilst in the male the lateral hairs on tergites 1 to 4 are entirely pale. Wing length 6.5–8 mm.

There are two continental species worth looking out for which also have pale front and mid tarsi and hence would key to *luteitarsis*. *P. fasciata* Meigen has spots on both tergites 2 and 3. *P. festiva* Meigen has spots on tergite 2 (joined into a bar in a female in the Natural History Museum) and with striations near the posterior corners of the thoracic dorsum.

This species is uncommon but widespread, including Ireland. It is one of the hoverflies to watch out for along woodland rides containing elm, where the larvae feed on *Schizoneura* aphids which curl the leaves of the elm. Males are often noted hovering at about 2–3 m and defending sunny spots around elm scrub. April to August, peaking in late May and through June.

Pipiza noctiluca (Linnaeus, 1758)   Pl. 5, fig. 13
                                                                   Map: Ball & Morris p. 110
                                                                   Larva: Rotheray Pl. 5c

Last, but not least, it is tempting to regard this very variable species as a species complex. Forms such as *bimaculata*, *fenestrata* and *lugubris* can be raised to species rank by tradition, but there seem to be other forms that are equally distinctive. Unfortunately, intermediates muddy the waters to no small extent. The least satisfactory course seems to be to use *noctiluca* as a dustbin of convenience – instead it seems more likely to foster closer study if an attempt is made to separate out forms which may repay further study. *Pipiza* is complicated enough without describing more species of doubtful status so here reference is made to forms by giving each of them a code letter so that there is a descriptive label for future work.

Typical *noctiluca*, if one can even speak in such terms, varies considerably in size, towards *bimaculata* (small) on the one hand and *fenestrata* (large) on the other. The male has entirely black hairs on the face (except in form B) and in this respect is distinct from all other species except *bimaculata* and *austriaca*. The face is normally parallel-sided and fairly narrow, but in some specimens broadens below towards the condition found in *fenestrata*, whereas *bimaculata* has a broader face. The abdomen is unspotted in the male and has a pair of spots on tergite 2 in the female (only very rarely absent). A wing shade is usually present, even if faint, and tends to be stronger in females but always with the outer edge fading gradually. In the male the hairs on the tergites are black on the lateral margins, except for the basal half of tergite 4, and are often at least narrowly pale at the base of tergites 2 and 3; in side view all the hairs along the axis are black. In the female the hairs along the axis of tergites 2 and 3 are black, but the extent of pale hairs on tergite 4 is highly variable, with varying amounts of black hairs at the base along the axis. The extent of black hairs on the female face and thoracic dorsum is highly variable. The tarsi are usually partly orange, at least on the basal two segments of the mid tarsus, though occasionally this is reduced to a dull brown (although rarely blackish as in *bimaculata*). Wing microtrichia are extensively absent at the base of the first basal cell in the male, and they are absent from about two thirds of the second basal cell in the female. If the female has any bare areas at the base of cell cu_1, such bare areas are adjacent to the veins rather than truly within the cell. Wing length 6.5–8 mm.

The typical form is widespread in England and Ireland. Its status in Scotland is uncertain. This species has been reared from *Cavariella* aphids on hogweed and from a variety of other ground-layer aphids. Adults are frequently found along wood edges and hedgerows, usually to be seen sunbathing on foliage but also visiting flowers. April to September, peaking in late May and early June.

The following forms, among many subtle variations, are considered worthy of comment.

Form A. In both sexes the wing microtrichia are extensively absent from the alula, and in cell 2a are extensively absent at the base, including a gap along the hind margin (*i.e.* along the wing margin) in the basal half. There are three specimens of this sort in the Natural History Museum, including a male (with an entirely black abdomen) and two females with spots on tergite 2. This could be a variety of *noctiluca*, but intermediates fall well short of the condition described, so this could be a separate species. The specimens are from Devon, Herefordshire and the New Forest (a damaged specimen, probably of this form, is from Worcestershire). July.

Form B. There is a male specimen with the facial hairs mainly pale brown (rather than black); the flat frons patch is broadly elliptical (rather than broadly truncate in front) and the second basal cell is three fifths clear of microtrichia (instead of almost completely covered in microtrichia). The specimen was taken in Cornwall in July (collected by I. Perry, in the collection of A.E. Stubbs). In the key in van der Goot (1981) this would run to *signata* Meigen *sensu* Lundbeck on the basis of the male face hairs being pale (supposed to be white).

Form C. A male specimen with spots on tergite 2 has the head far broader than in typical *noctiluca*; the flat area on the frons is very rounded and does not reach as far forwards as is normal. The specimen was taken in Herefordshire in May (in the collection of A.E. Stubbs).

Form D. Males with black abdomens have the hairs along the lateral margins of the tergites entirely black (instead of some pale hairs at the margins of tergites 3 and 4). This may seem a rather small difference, but five such specimens have been taken, all in mid August on the Chalk in the Chilterns, two of them from one spot (Stubbs, *pers. obs.*). There are intermediates, however, so the distinction may be irrelevant.

Form E. Female forms with the hairs on the axis of tergites 3, 4 and 5 entirely black are relatively few. These could equate with the male segregate form D and may be equally irrelevant as a separate form. Specimens have been found between May and August in Middlesex, Berkshire and Anglesey (Stubbs, *pers. obs.*).

Form F. This is reserved for specimens which are distinct in the male by the presence of a pair of spots on tergite 2 (apart from form C). The presence of black hairs on the face indicates an affinity with *P. noctiluca*. This form is intermediate to *P. fenestrata* and the distinction of this form in both sexes is discussed under that species.

Key to forms of noctiluca.

Males

1.	Wing margin clear of microtrichia along at least half of the hind margin of cell 2a.	Form A
—	Microtrichia in cell 2a complete at least along hind margin.	2
2.	Second basal cell at least half clear of microtrichia. Face hairs sometimes pale.	Form B
—	Second basal cell more completely covered in microtrichia.	3
3.	Tergite 2 with yellow spots.	4
—	Tergites entirely black (slight grey dust spots can be present).	5
4.	Head not wide, rather round as seen from above.	Form C
—	Normal transverse head (broader than high).	Form F
5.	Tergites 3 and 4 with some pale hairs on lateral margins.	Typical *noctiluca*
—	Tergites 3 and 4 with entirely black hairs on lateral margins.	Form D

Females

1.	Wing margin clear of microtrichia along at least half of hind margin of cell 2a.	Form A
—	Microtrichia in cell 2a complete along at least hind margin.	2
2.	Hairs along axis of tergites entirely black.	Form E
—	Hairs along axis partly pale.	3

3.   Typical *noctiluca* (as per main key).   Typical *noctiluca*

—   Intermediates to *fenestrata*, including specimens   Form F
     doubtfully so placed (as per main key or as
     regards microtrichia in cell cu₁).

Genus PIPIZELLA

These are small compact hoverflies with rather elongate antennae. They never have spots on the abdomen. The upper outer cross-vein is not strongly oblique, but usually bent halfway along and often meeting vein R_{4+5} almost at right angles. Some specimens have the upper outer cross-vein a little more oblique or (rarely) bent in the basal third, but the condition is nowhere nearly as extreme as in *Pipiza* or *Heringia*. Many misidentifications have been made in the past and there is a chance of more species being discovered, so voucher specimens should be retained. Other species occur in Europe, including *annulata* (Macquart) in which the basal segment of both the front and mid tarsus is pale, contrasting with the black colour of the remaining four segments. A female from Surrey with yellow metatarsi on the front and middle legs could be *annulata*, but with no other material this identification cannot be confirmed (Morris, 1998b).

All three British species have been recorded as utilising subterranean root aphids as larval prey, so this would seem to be the particular niche of this genus. The habits of the adult are discussed under *viduata*.

Pipizella maculipennis (Meigen, 1822)   Map: Ball & Morris p. 111

The name derives from a dark wing patch, but this is often faint, resembling the indistinct coloration that can occur in other species. Identification requires great care! Both sexes were thought to be distinctive in having black hairs along the entire axis of tergite 3 (also tergite 4 in the male), but it now appears that some male *virens* are similar; in the female it is necessary to have the lighting just right to be sure of the presence of black hairs on the axis. In both sexes, the eye hairs are dark in the upper half and, in the female, the top of the head has iridescent reflections. The pale hairs on the thorax of the male are whitish (yellow in *virens*). The antennae are more elongate even than *virens*, markedly so in the female. The front tarsus is entirely dark, even the basal segment, and the mid tibia is extensively dark. Wing length 5.25–6 mm.

On available information this is a very rare species. It was found near Colchester in the 19th century and a female was collected by Sir C.H. Andrewes at Shalfleet in the Isle of Wight in 1954 (specimen in Natural History Museum). Another female was taken at Wisley, Surrey in 1965 and a male near Mutehill in Dumfries in 1979 both by A.E. Stubbs. The Dumfries specimen was taken on the edge of an estuary so it is interesting that the Essex and Isle of Wight localities could apply to similar situations. Zwölfer (1958) mentions that this species (if correctly identified) was reared together with *Syrphus* sp. from populations of the aphids *Anoecia corni*, *A. major*, *A. nemoralis* and *Tetraneura ulmi* (it is not clear whether *Pipizella* was using all these aphid species as prey). Since the original text was written, a few additional records have been reported, but this remains an elusive and rare species. June to August, peaking in July.

Pipizella viduata (Linnaeus, 1758)   Pl. 5, fig. 7
Pipizella varipes (Meigen, 1822)   Map: Ball & Morris p. 111

The build is more compact than in the other two species, especially so in the female. The antennae are shorter, the third antennal segment being about 1.5 times as long as wide in the male and about twice as long as wide in the female. The hind tibia has a fringe of hairs on the anterior surface which is only about as long as the width of the tibia, but some specimens have longer hairs (resulting in confusion with other species). The male is most readily recognised by the genitalia which are best hinged out to reveal a particularly elongate shape. The surstyli in side view are elongate and tear-drop-shaped. Wing length 3.75–5.25 mm.

This is a relatively common species found widely throughout Britain and Ireland, though perhaps prone to under-recording through its small size. It is characteristic of dry grassland as on chalk and limestone, heathland verges, cliff tops and landslips, coastal shingles, sand dunes, woodland rides and clearings, and disturbed ground, even that in urban areas. It has a particular liking for bedstraw flowers, but can also be found at other low-growing flowers. However, on other occasions, it will be found flying very low among short grass or about bare patches of earth, as along paths, its erratic searching flight mimicking that of a small black wasp. It has been found associated with the root aphid *Anuraphis subterranea* attended by ants (*Lasius niger*) on wild parsnip, ovipositing on the stems just above ground level in two peak periods, late May and early August (Dixon, 1959). A further association with root aphids on rosebay willowherb suggests a wide host range. May to September, peaking in late June and early July.

Pipizella virens (Fabricius, 1805)   Pl. 5, fig. 8
     Map: Ball & Morris p. 112

This is typically slightly larger and longer-winged than *P. viduata*, with particularly long hairs on the anterior surface of the hind tibia. The third antennal segment is about twice as long as broad in the male and about 2.5 times as long as broad in the female. The male has a bronzy tinge to the black body and most of the pale hairs are yellow, enhancing the bronze-coloured appearance. The genitalia are compact, as in *maculipennis*, and have distinctively shaped surstyli (in side view) with a slender apical 'finger'. The male eyes touch each other for a distance about two thirds of the length of the ocellar triangle (about half the length in *viduata*). The abdomen is more elongate than *viduata*, with tergite 2 somewhat less than twice as wide as long (usually at least twice as wide as long in *viduata*) though there is some variation between specimens. The female can be awkward to identify with certainty, but most closely resembles *maculipennis*. The eye hairs in *virens* can be entirely pale, or can have some dark hairs, but these are confined to the very top. Wing length 5–6.25 mm.

P. virens is generally a scarce and local species but is far from rare in central England, northwards to north Lincolnshire. It has not been recorded from Ireland. A variety of habitats are utilised, especially coarse grassland, grassy rides and clearings in woodland, and disturbed ground. It has been reported on the continent in association with aphids on the roots of umbellifers; if this is correct, then the localities in which we have found it would suggest a possible association with species such as cow parsley, hogweed and wild parsnip. May to September, peaking in late June and early July.

Genus TRICHOPSOMYIA

The generic name used by Coe (1953a) was *Parapenium*. There is a single species recorded in Britain, but three species are known in Europe, including *lucida* (Meigen, 1822) which occurs as close as the Netherlands. If *lucida* does occur in Britain, it might be mistaken for a curious *Heringia*. Reference to the colour plates shows the rather broad blunt wing of *flavitarsis* (Pl. 5, fig. 9a), but *lucida* has longer wings and an apical cross-vein very like *Heringia heringi* (Pl. 5, fig. 10a). The male has the spots on tergite 2 rectangular rather than round and the female body is very shining (see under genus for key characters).

Trichopsomyia flavitarsis (Meigen, 1822)   Pl. 5, fig. 9
                                                            Map: Ball & Morris p. 142

The wing venation and the elongate third antennal segment suggest *Pipizella*, but *T. flavitarsis* can be readily separated because the hairs on the anterior surface of the hind tibia are black. Also, the female has a pair of round spots on tergite 2 (more reminiscent of *Pipiza*) though these spots can become obscure in dried specimens. Wing length 4–6 mm.

Whereas the Pipizini are predominantly a southern group, *T. flavitarsis* is more of a northern species. It is fairly common in the Scottish Highlands on moorland and wet heath, from woodland margins to well above the tree line. It occurs southwards more locally and appears to exploit a greater variety of habitats here, including rich fen (*e.g.* Woodwalton and Wicken), damp areas of calcareous grassland (*e.g.* Castor Hanglands and limestone quarries) and a fly-ash tip (Herald Way Marsh, Coventry). It is relatively common in Ireland, especially in the west. Adults can be found on low-growing flowers and the males have been found hovering in numbers in the sheltered lee of a building on the lower slopes of a mountain. The larvae are associated with the gall-forming psyllid *Livia juncorum* on jointed rush, but almost certainly use psyllid colonies on other rushes at some of its southern sites. May to September, peaking in June and July.

Genus TRIGLYPHUS

Triglyphus primus Loew, 1840   Pl. 5, fig. 12
                                                            Map: Ball & Morris p. 142

Being a very small black pipizine, it is easily overlooked. *T. primus* can at once be told apart from all other British hoverflies by the fact that the abdomen has only two large tergites, 2 and 3. Tergite 4 is minute and often not visible at all from above; rarely the female tergite 4 is as much as half the length of tergite 3. Wing length 4.25–5 mm.

Coe (1953a) cites the then known British records and refers to its occurrence on commons and in gardens. Jefferies (1976) updated the records with a review of the period 1968 – 1973. It is now known to be fairly widespread in eastern England as far north as South Yorkshire, with a concentration of records in south Lancashire and the Sheffield area. It can be encountered in a variety of habitats, including heathland edge and rank grasslands of various sorts, but in areas such as east London, Warwickshire and Sheffield there is a clear association with brown-field sites and other disturbed sites with plentiful mugwort. It was found on Salisbury Plain, Wiltshire where mugwort was abundant on ground churned up by tanks. Persistent sweeping in summer months can reveal it to be present at many suitable-looking sites, but rarely in any numbers. The larvae appear to be specific to galls induced by the aphid *Cryptosiphum artemisiae* on mugwort. May to October, peaking in late August.

Tribe SERICOMYIINI

The members of this tribe are large hoverflies belonging to two genera, with *Arctophila* being a bumblebee mimic and *Sericomyia* having two wasp mimics. They have a plumose arista, as in the Volucellini, but the upper outer cross-vein is not re-entrant. *Arctophila* is treated as a subgenus of *Sericomyia* by Thompson & Rotheray (1998).

The members of this tribe have rat-tailed maggot larvae similar to the Eristalini, but with a broader thoracic region.

Genus ARCTOPHILA

Arctophila superbiens (Müller, 1776)   Pl. 8, fig. 8
Arctophila fulva (Harris, 1780)   Map: Ball & Morris p. 17

There is a close resemblance to an entirely orange-haired bumblebee though with a dark patch on the wing below the stigma. Sometimes the hairs are grey rather than orange-brown. The thorax always has a yellowish ground colour, but the abdomen may either have a similar ground colour or be vaguely blackish. It closely resembles a large *Criorhina berberina* var. *oxyacanthae* in the field (and *C. floccosa* to a lesser extent), but has a dark wing patch. The rare yellow-haired form of *Volucella bombylans* is a similar size but has a re-entrant upper outer cross-vein. Wing length 10–13.5 mm.

This is largely a northern and western species that is relatively frequent in west Wales and parts of south-west and north-west England. It is also widespread in Scotland, but rather localised. It is mainly found in northern and western Ireland. It is largely absent from south-east England, but old records are known from woodland in the Cotswolds and Berkshire. There are also records from parts of Norfolk (which support a number of largely northern species). The very late peak has probably led to some under-recording. Adults favour the margins and clearings of wet acidic woodlands and are particularly attracted by the flowers of Devil's-bit scabious at the end of the summer. A female was seen ovipositing in deep, water-filled hoofprints of horses along a shaded muddy path by a stream. May to November, peaking in September.

Genus SERICOMYIA

Sericomyia lappona (Linnaeus, 1758)   Pl. 8, fig. 6
                                                                    Map: Ball & Morris p. 130
                                                                    Larva: Rotheray Pl. 14a

A little smaller than *silentis*, it is nonetheless a handsome species. The abdomen has narrow bars, almost or quite meeting in the centre, which are whitish in life though often becoming dull yellow in a pinned specimen. The scutellum is dull orange and the legs are entirely orange or the bases of the femora can be black. A melanic female has been reported. Wing length 9.25–11.25 mm.

Widely distributed across northern and western Britain and in Ireland, but also occurring on the boggy heathlands of southern England. It often occurs with *silentis*, but is generally the scarcer of the two. May to September, peaking in June.

Sericomyia silentis (Harris, 1776) Pl. 8, fig. 7
Map: Ball & Morris p. 131

The majority of specimens are large. The abdomen has conspicuous wedge-shaped yellow bars which at the margins of the tergites are wider than the intervening black areas. The scutellum is typically blackish or dark brown, but can be dull orange with black front corners in extreme specimens. The legs are reddish-orange (darker than *lappona*), usually with the base of the femora darkened. Wing length 9.5–14 mm.

This is by far the commonest member of the tribe and is widespread in Britain and Ireland, though more local in the south-east and very scarce in central England. It is principally found in upland and western sites, favouring boggy heaths, acid wet meadows or woodland clearings and margins with similar vegetation on a peaty or sandy soil. Adults can be found about potential breeding sites such as peat cuttings, ditches and tiny pools among purple moor-grass, but are also found far from obvious breeding sites suggesting it is a very mobile species. For example, it has established itself at Wicken Fen and other sites in the area over the course of the last decade or so. The flowers of Devil's-bit scabious are especially attractive to this hoverfly. May to November, peaking in July.

Tribe VOLUCELLINI

These are large broadly-built hoverflies which mimic bumblebees or have the warning colours (yellow, orange or white) used by hornets and other wasps. The antennae are strongly plumose and the face is conically elongate downwards as in the Sericomyiini, but Volucellini have the upper outer cross-vein re-entrant. The tribe is represented by a single genus containing five species. The larvae are short-tailed (unlike Sericomyiini).

Genus VOLUCELLA

Adults occur in midsummer and are most easily found at flowers, especially umbellifers and brambles along woodland margins and in urban wasteland. They will even turn up in gardens and like buddleia flowers. British *Volucella*, except *inflata*, are associated with bee and wasp nests either as scavengers in the bottom of the nest or as ectoparasites of wasp larvae (*inanis*). Adults of *pellucens* apparently walk straight into the wasps' nest without hindrance in order to lay their eggs (Nixon, 1934). Larvae are most active late in the season when the host nest is in decline and, in *Vespula rufa* nests, *Volucella* larvae will feed on abandoned wasp larvae, although if adult wasps are still active they may remove the fly larvae (Edwards, 1980; who does not clarify the ecology of individual species). *Volucella* larvae are most readily obtained in the late autumn after the nests have been vacated by their owners. It is useful to note the position of nests while they are still active so that they are easily located once abandoned. Adults are said to be commonest in the year following an abundance of wasps.

Volucella bombylans (Linnaeus, 1758)   Pl. 8, fig. 1
                                                                       Map: Ball & Morris p. 143

Unlike other *Volucella*, this is a bumblebee mimic. The plumose antennae, elongate face and dark mark midway along the wing are a distinctive combination, only otherwise found in *Arctophila superbiens*. *V. bombylans* has two main colour forms. One of these is black-haired on the thorax and base of the abdomen with an orange-red tail and obscure reddish side-patches on tergites 2 and 3. This mimics bumblebees such as *Bombus lapidarius* and *ruderarius*, but occasionally this form has a white tail. It could be mistaken for *Criorhina ranunculi*, though that species flies much earlier in the year, lacks a plumose arista and has a very swollen hind femur. The second common form, often found flying alongside the previous one, has a white tail and bright yellow hairs on the sides of the thoracic dorsum, scutellum and front corners of tergite 2. Tergite 2 can have quite distinct yellowish side-patches beneath the hairs. This latter form is sometimes referred to as var. *plumata* De Geer and is a particularly good mimic of bumblebees such as *Bombus hortorum* and *jonellus*. It can occasionally have an orange tail. There is also a rare entirely brown-haired form known from Ireland; in the example available the surface of tergite 2 has orange side-patches visible beneath the hairs like some *plumata* and could be mistaken for *Arctophila*, but has a re-entrant cross-vein. *Eriozona* looks rather like a red-tailed var. *bombylans* when sitting on a flower, but it has a short, entirely bright yellow face and the arista is not plumose. *Cheilosia illustrata* is much smaller and should not cause confusion. Wing length 8–14 mm.

It occurs widely throughout Britain and Ireland, especially in wooded districts and scrubby grasslands, with a rather earlier peak than other *Volucella* species. Larvae have been recorded from the nests of the German wasp (*Vespula germanica*), but almost certainly use nests of the common wasp (*V. vulgaris*) too. However, the review by Alford (1975) suggests that bumblebees are a major host, the larvae occurring as scavengers amongst nest debris under the comb and sometimes attacking the brood itself. The female *bombylans* enters the bumblebee nest for oviposition and, if stung, has a reflex causing it to deposit eggs immediately. May to September, peaking in June.

Volucella inanis (Linnaeus, 1758)   Pl. 8, fig. 4
                                                                       Map: Ball & Morris p. 144
                                                                           Larva: Rotheray Pl. 4a

There are only two species with a yellow- and black-banded abdomen. *V. inanis* differs from *zonaria* in that tergite 2, the scutellum and the pale areas on the thoracic dorsum are yellow rather than chestnut coloured. The most certain difference is that sternite 2 is yellow in *inanis*. The top of the thorax usually has black stripes which are often fused. *V. inanis* is a smaller species. Wing length 12.25–14.25 mm.

The outer suburbs of London and the adjacent countryside have been the main focus of distribution, this being a relatively frequent species in some years, even in gardens, though distinctly local. Since 1999 there have been reports of *inanis* from Norfolk, Cambridgeshire, Leicestershire, Warwickshire, Staffordshire, Northamptonshire and Nottinghamshire that clearly indicate that it is expanding its range to the north. However, it also appears to have contracted eastwards with very few recent records from central-southern and south-western counties although there are older records west to South Wales and Cornwall. The recording scheme would welcome all records of this species to follow the changes it is currently undergoing. It has been found in association with the nests of the German wasp, *Vespula germanica*, and the hornet, *Vespa crabro*. June to September, peaking in early August.

Volucella inflata (Fabricius, 1794)   Pl. 8, fig. 3
Map: Ball & Morris p. 144

There is a strong resemblance to the common species *pellucens* except that the markings on tergite 2 are deep orange. The scutellum is orange, as are the sides of the thoracic dorsum. Wing length 11–12.75 mm.

Records are largely confined south of a line between the Severn and The Wash. Heavily wooded districts are ideal and it can be locally common in the most favourable areas such as the Weald, South Hampshire, the Isle of Wight and South Devon. Unusually for a *Volucella*, this species is associated with sap runs rather than with the nests of social Hymenoptera. Adults have been observed ovipositing in sap runs on a tree trunk; larvae, thought to be of this species, were found at the same location (S. Miles, *pers. comm.*) and larvae have been found in sap runs caused by the wood-boring caterpillars of the goat moth, *Cossus cossus* (Rotheray, 1999a). May to September, peaking in late June and July.

Volucella pellucens (Linnaeus, 1758)   Pl. 8, fig. 2
Map: Ball & Morris p. 145
Larva: Rotheray Pl. 3f

A very large black hoverfly with most of tergite 2 white can only be this species. Wing length 10–15.5 mm.

Most districts throughout Britain and Ireland are likely to harbour this species, especially about woods and copses. It is one of the characteristic species to be found on flowers of bramble, although it occurs on other flowers such as umbellifers as well. Males are often to be seen hovering several metres above ground in woodland glades or beside trees, the white tergite 2 being sufficiently translucent to be seen from below. Larvae live in the nests of social wasps. May to October, peaking in mid June to July.

Volucella zonaria (Poda, 1761)   Pl. 8, fig. 5
Map: Ball & Morris p. 145

As one of our largest and most spectacular hoverflies, it will easily be recognised by its yellow- and black-banded abdomen once the possibility of it actually being a hornet is discounted. However, it is as well to check that the specimen is not the closely related *inanis* which lacks chestnut areas and which has sternite 2 yellow rather than black. *V. zonaria* is chestnut on tergite 2 and also on the scutellum and much of the thoracic dorsum, which are shining rather than matt as in *inanis*. *V. zonaria* exhibits some sexual dimorphism which occasionally makes separation of males from *inanis* more difficult. In these cases, the centre of the thoracic dorsum can have darker stripes and much reduced chestnut markings, but the stripes are rarely deep black as in *inanis*. The wings are extensively orange-yellow in the basal two-thirds and there is a small dark patch near the wing tip (*inanis* is somewhat similar). Wing length 15.5–19.5 mm.

Verrall (1901) only knew of two specimens which were reputed to be British. Subsequently a few definite British specimens were captured, mainly in the southern coastal counties, and these were regarded as vagrants. Such a large species would not have easily been overlooked. Thus there was great excitement when this spectacular hoverfly became established in Britain in the 1940s. The journals carry numerous notes recording its presence, non-dipterists frequently contributing to the sightings (no doubt some of these records actually apply to *inanis*). Though *zonaria* fluctuates in abundance from year to year, currently it is often quite frequent in the outer London suburbs and surrounding countryside and even occurs in central London. There is also a long-standing urban population in Bristol where it is quite frequent within the city, but rarely seen in the surrounding area (Gibbs, 2002). Otherwise it occurs along the south coast of England from Kent to Cornwall. It has a greater tendency to come indoors than other *Volucella*, often causing alarm among people who do not realise that it is a harmless hoverfly. Larvae have been found in wasps' nests, especially those of the common wasp, *Vespula vulgaris*, and German wasp, *V. germanica*.

Current evidence shows this species to be expanding its range into Suffolk and Norfolk, and north and west from London into Hertfordshire and along the Thames valley. Detailed recording is needed to follow this change in range and the recording scheme is keen to receive as many records as possible. May to November, peaking in August.

Tribe XYLOTINI

This tribe (subfamily in Coe, 1953a) is treated here as in the 1976 check list. Such a simple course links together a group of hoverflies whose predominant larval habitat is dead wood. The discussion of the treatment of tribes, genera and subgenera in the Xylotini given in the first edition is omitted as outdated. Suffice it to say that the generic and subgeneric groupings are now firmly established and this revision follows the most recent British check list (Chandler, 1998).

Genus BLERA

Blera fallax (Linnaeus, 1758)   Pl. 10, fig. 5
Cynorrhina fallax of Coe (1953a)   Map: Ball & Morris p. 18

As a black hoverfly with red-tipped abdomen and yellow face, there is no scope for confusion among medium-sized hoverflies. There is sexual dimorphism in that the male is more extensively red – only the first two tergites are black in the male whereas the first three are black in the female. Wing length 8–9.5 mm.

The Scottish Highlands are the haunt of this handsome hoverfly. Though present in reasonable numbers in old collections, there are very few recent records. Its distribution roughly equates with the major pine forests of the eastern Highlands. It has been found in the Spey Valley sunning on pine trunks and flying about the base of large live native pines, especially those with a thick mass of flaky bark exposed edge-on at ground level. Larvae have been found in rot-holes in pine stumps (Rotheray & MacGowan, 2000). The current status of this Endangered species gives serious cause for concern and it is listed as a Priority Species under the UK Biodiversity Action Plan. Late May to mid August, with two peaks in June and August.

Genus BRACHYPALPOIDES

The genus was proposed by Hippa (1978) to accommodate *lentus*, a species placed in *Xylota* by Coe (1953a) and in *Xylotomima* in the 1976 check list. Thompson & Rotheray (1998) treat it as a subgenus of *Xylota*. It lacks a spur on the male hind trochanter and lacks long hairs on the metasternum between the mid and hind coxae, as in our *Chalcosyrphus*, differing mainly on genitalia characters. The spines beneath the hind femur occupy most of the width near the apex, having only a slight median gap.

Brachypalpoides lentus (Meigen, 1822)   Pl. 9, fig. 14
Xylota lenta of Coe (1953a), *Xylotomima lenta* of   Map: Ball & Morris p. 21
1976 check list.

The black body bears a blood-red belt across the abdomen (fades to a duller colour in collections) and the legs are entirely black. Thus this relatively large xylotine hoverfly is very distinctive and very handsome. Wing length 10–12 mm.

It is a local and rather uncommon species of southern forests, with sparse records extending to the Central Highlands of Scotland and to Ireland. It particularly favours beech trees and has been observed to fly into hollows at the base of live trees, though it is likely to use other species such as oak and birch because it can occur at sites which lack beech. Adults occasionally visit hawthorn flowers, but are perhaps most often seen flying through undergrowth or around herbage near to old trees, the unusually rich red colour of the abdomen providing a good clue that it is about (even before you get a proper look). The larvae are found in decaying heartwood of beech and probably oak, especially in live trees that have decay exposed at ground level. April to August, peaking in June.

Genus BRACHYPALPUS

This genus of mining bee mimics is typified by *laphriformis*, a species with a swollen hind femur (which is strongly arched in the male). The hind femur has two rows of short black spines beneath with a broad intervening belt free of spines. In side view, the metasternum (underside of the thorax between the mid and hind coxae) is bare. A second species, *eunotus*, has now been placed in *Chalcosyrphus* by Hippa. Further species occur in Europe.

Brachypalpus laphriformis (Fallén, 1816)   Pl. 10, fig. 6
Brachypalpus bimaculatus (Macquart, 1829) of   Map: Ball & Morris p. 21
Coe (1953a)   Larva: Rotheray Pl. 12d

The male has a rather parallel-sided abdomen (reminiscent of *Xylota*) though this is broader in the female. The thorax is hairy, the abdomen only sparsely so. The abdomen is black, but sometimes with orange at the sides of tergites 1 and 2, and a similar-coloured narrow band may occupy the extreme hind margin of the tergites. Wing length 8.5–10.75 mm.

Ancient forests provide the habitat for this species. It is widespread in southern England and Wales and extends sporadically into northern England as far north as Cumbria. It was taken in eastern Ireland between 1928 and 1934 and, although feared extinct (Speight, 1981a), it was confirmed to be still present by Speight (1985) at a single locality in Wicklow. It is rather elusive and regarded as a rarity, though in some parts of the New Forest it can be locally frequent in some years. Adults are often seen around dead beech, especially standing hollow trunks broken off 2–4 m above ground. It has been seen at similarly structured ash trees. Usually it is seen hovering close to such trees or settled on the surface. Occasionally it is found at rest on horizontal large trunks or even at wood-yards within forests. In flight it resembles an *Andrena* or *Osmia* bee. Larvae have been found in rot-hole exudate in yew, and in a water-and-sap-filled cavity behind fractured bark about 2 m up a live oak, but recent work suggests that they are mainly associated with wet, sloppy decay in oaks (Rotheray, 1991). May to August, peaking in June.

Genus CALIPROBOLA

Caliprobola speciosa (Rossi, 1790)
Pl. 10, fig. 9
Map: Ball & Morris p. 22
Larva: Rotheray Pl. 13b

Few hoverflies are as magnificent as *speciosa*. It is a large species of rather slender build, having a dark metallic green abdomen displaying a band of golden hairs across the base of tergites 2, 3 and 4. The long legs are bright orange on the tarsi, tibiae and tips of the femora. The face, frons and antennae are orange. The wings are suffused with orange in the front half, turning to a dark brown near the wing tip. Wing length 11–12.5 mm.

Unfortunately this fly is a great rarity, being currently only known from Windsor Forest and the New Forest though there are tantalising old records for Derbyshire and Yorkshire. It is associated with ancient beech trees and more rarely oak. It has been bred from a hollow beech stump and it is in such sun-trap situations, or a hollow on the ground caused by fresh wind-blow of a tree, that the adult can be seen warily sunbathing. Occasionally it sits on foliage in the sun or on the ground in dappled light beside a tree-trunk; more exasperatingly it will perhaps be seen flying fast through woodland. Larvae occur in rotting heartwood, particularly beech, and can occur deep down into decaying roots. May to July, peaking in June.

Genus CHALCOSYRPHUS

There are two subgenera in Britain, *Xylotodes* (resembling *Brachypalpus*) and *Xylotina* (resembling *Xylota*). The underside of the thorax bears long hairs between the mid and hind coxae (view from side) whereas superficially similar genera are bare in this region. The hind femur has short spines across the entire width ventrally near the apex. In the British species the abdomen is much shorter than in related genera.

Subgenus XYLOTINA

Superficially there is a close resemblance to *Xylota*. The differences are numerous but rather subtle (Hippa, 1978), but include the absence of a spur on the hind coxa in the male.

Chalcosyrphus (Xylotina) nemorum (Fabricius, 1805)   Pl. 9, fig. 13
Xylota nemorum of Coe (1953a), *Xylotomima nemorum* of   Map: Ball & Morris p. 24
1976 check list.

In having two pairs of pale spots on the abdomen, there is a resemblance to *Xylota abiens*, *X. jakutorum* and *X. florum*. However, *C. nemorum* has the hind tibia black or only dull orange at the base (as in *X. abiens* – see description of that species for differences). Both sexes are very short-bodied, the abdomen being little longer than the thorax (including the scutellum). Thus, the tergites are strongly transverse (wider than long). In the males, the orange spots are square, separated by a thick black cross whose limbs are of equal length. The female markings are generally less sharp and normally greyish-orange or grey. The hind femur in side view is much wider towards the apex (compare width at one third from the base with the width two thirds from the base). The hind tibia on its ventral face has a fringe of small erect hairs throughout almost its entire length (absent in *abiens*). The female of *Tropidia* has a short abdomen with an orange pattern as in *nemorum*, but the hind femur of *Tropidia* has a triangular projection beneath the apex. Wing length 6.5–8.25 mm.

The distribution extends to south-east Sutherland in Scotland, and to Ireland. Very dark specimens were found near Ullapool, Wester Ross. However, southern districts are the most favourable, but even here this hoverfly is distinctly local and rarely common. It is to be seen sunbathing on large fallen tree-trunks and cut stumps, especially beech trees in ancient forests. However, it is occasionally common on the sunny margins of alder woods, sitting on foliage in the sun. Larvae have been found overwintering under bark of logs and branches lying in wet situations, choosing logs in which decay has hardly begun (Hartley, 1961). May to October, peaking in June.

Subgenus XYLOTODES

Having decided that *eunotus* belonged to *Chalcosyrphus* rather than *Brachypalpus*, Hippa (1978) erected the subgenus *Xylotodes* to accommodate this species. *Xylotodes* is a mimic of mining bees or hive bees with the hind femur straight, but swollen.

Chalcosyrphus (Xylotodes) eunotus (Loew, 1873)   Pl. 10, fig. 7
Brachypalpus eunotus of Coe (1953a)   Map: Ball & Morris p. 24

Though superficially similar to *Brachypalpus laphriformis*, the abdomen is much shorter in the male and there is a pair of faint large greyish semi-rectangular bars on tergite 2. The thoracic dorsum is faintly striped and dull (less obviously striped and shining in *laphriformis*). The hind femur is not arched (arched in male *laphriformis*). The wings are similarly marked to *laphriformis* except that cross-vein r-m carries a much darker cloud. The male abdomen bears a pair of square grey spots on tergite 2. The female resembles the male, but is much more broadly built and has conspicuous pairs of rectangular spots on both tergites 2 and 3. This sex could easily be overlooked as a *Criorhina asilica*, though that species has a conspicuous brown pile on the thoracic dorsum and lacks such a dark cloud over r-m. Wing length 9.5–10.5 mm.

There are very few older British specimens, but recent efforts have shown that it occurs more widely in the Welsh borders up to North Wales, and in the Midlands. It is also known from

Somerset and Dorset, but is not recorded from Scotland or Ireland. It was first taken in woodland near Ledbury, Herefordshire, in 1899. In 1953 C.O. Hammond took a specimen at Cothill Fen, Oxfordshire, which was flying back and forth over a shaded pool. In 1977 a specimen was found sitting on a log in a shaded stream in the Wyre Forest, Worcestershire (Stubbs, *pers. obs.*), an observation which has led to the discovery of many more adults in similar situations. The best technique for finding the species is, therefore, to search for adults sitting on or flying around semi-submerged logs in dappled shade along wooded streams, or to search sunlit foliage, *e.g.* nettle beds, in the vicinity of such logs. Males patrol small territories from sunlit perches on wood or foliage. It has also been taken several times in a Malaise trap at one of its sites on the Welsh borders. Semi-submerged wood is the habitat of the larvae, a niche apparently not occupied by other British hoverflies with the possible exception of *Xylota florum*. At two of its three Warwickshire sites, fallen trunks of old grey poplars appear to be the breeding site, though old willows and alders were more probable at the third. April to July, peaking in May and early June.

Genus CRIORHINA

These are large species with an elongate face bearing a slight but distinct knob. The thorax is densely furry, but the abdomen varies in furriness so that some species are bumblebee mimics whilst one species (*asilica*) is more like a hive bee or large mining bee. The wing tips are faintly darkened and most specimens have darkening around the inner cross-veins. Larvae can be found in decaying heartwood of a variety of trees, including stumps, and are mainly associated with underground wet-rot in decaying roots (Rotheray, 1991). Adults visit flowers, and are frequently seen at hawthorn blossom in particular (although the early-flying *ranunculi* is more typically seen at shrubs which flower earlier in the season). They can also be found resting on sunlit leaves in sheltered situations such as sunny rides and clearings in woods.

Criorhina asilica (Fallén, 1816)   Pl. 10, fig. 4
                                                                    Map: Ball & Morris p. 49

C. asilica is a hive bee or mining bee mimic and more narrowly built than the other three species. The thorax has dense short pale brown hairs, but the abdomen is sparsely hairy revealing a black somewhat glossy surface with paired bars of orange or greyish dusting on tergites 2, 3 and often 4. Tergite 1 is densely grey-dusted throughout. The female abdomen is more robust than that of the male. When close to wooded rivers and streams, care should be taken not to confuse this species with the female of *Chalcosyrphus eunotus* (see that species for differences). Wing length 9.5–11.25 mm.

Though records extend northwards to the Scottish border, this is predominantly a southern species, always scarce and local. It has not been recorded from Ireland. Ancient broad-leaved woodland is the typical habitat, although it can form strong populations at certain ancient fenland sites with old willows and alders (*e.g.* Woodwalton Fen). Hawthorn flowers are one of the best places to search. April to July, peaking from mid May to mid June.

Criorhina berberina (Fabricius, 1805)   Pl. 10, fig. 3
                                                          Map: Ball & Morris p. 49

There are two colour forms to this hairy bumblebee mimic. The 'typical' form is brown-haired on most of the thorax and on the hind part of the abdomen, the intervening part of the body being black-haired. Variety *oxyacanthae* Meigen is entirely brown-haired, the thorax being of a brighter hue. The latter form was once regarded as a separate species; it is as frequent as the typical form in some districts. The surfaces of tergites 2, 3 and 4 are about equally shining (only obscurely so) and the lateral tuft of hairs on tergite 2 grades gently back into the hairs placed more posteriorly. Var. *oxyacanthae* is rather similar to *floccosa* (see text to that species), but the abdomen lacks areas of conspicuous dusting (very faint bands of dusting are present but are obscured by the hairs) and carries a long pile of even-length hairs. *Arctophila* is even more similar in the field and also has an extended face, but there is a dark patch on the wing below the stigma and it has a plumose arista. Because of the long flight period of *berberina*, there is the real possibility of the two species flying alongside one another at some sites. Wing length 8–12 mm, with some females very large and broadly built (matching the size of *Arctophila*).

All *Criorhina* are scarce, but this is the most frequent species overall and has the longest flight period. It is found mainly in southern forests, but has been reported as far north as Perthshire and Mull. It is widespread and not uncommon in Ireland. Ancient broad-leaved woodland is the typical habitat, although it can occur in association with old trees in old hedgerows and wetlands. April to September, peaking in June.

Criorhina floccosa (Meigen, 1822)   Pl. 10, fig. 2
                                                          Map: Ball & Morris p. 50
                                                          Larva: Rotheray Pl. 12e, 12f

Being a brown bumblebee mimic, comparison is necessary with *berberina* var. *oxyacanthae*. Aside from the long tufts of whitish hairs at the front corners of the sides of tergite 2, *floccosa* has only short inconspicuous hairs on the tergites so that the ground surface is clearly visible. The surfaces of the tergites are heavily dusted and dull (except narrowly at the sides). The colour of the dusting varies between black, grey and orange according to point of view and the specimen. Many males have the tergites predominantly black-dusted with grey-dusted patches on each side of tergite 2 and a weak suffusion of orange dust that increases towards the tip of the abdomen (thus creating the effect of a broad black band across the base of the abdomen). The females tend to lack the grey patches on tergite 2 and to have more orange dusting, especially on tergites 3 and 4, creating the impression of a largely orange insect. It is helpful to have comparative material of *floccosa* and *oxyacanthae* (other features such as the more extended frons of *floccosa* will then be apparent). The wings lack the sharply defined dark patch found in *Arctophila*. Wing length 10–13 mm.

There are a few scattered records for Ireland and for Scotland, but this is mainly a southern species. Adults show an interest in cavities about the base of live trees (*e.g.* ash, beech and elm), perhaps more so than other *Criorhina*. It is also more often found outside woodland, about hedgerow and parkland trees. April to August, peaking in late May and early June.

Criorhina ranunculi (Panzer, 1804)   Pl. 10, fig. 1
                                                                    Map: Ball & Morris p. 50

This is the largest *Criorhina*, with a swollen, strongly arched hind femur that contrasts strongly with the relatively slender straight hind femur of other *Criorhina*. It is a good furry bumblebee mimic, mostly black-haired but with red-tailed and white-tailed forms. The hairs on the scutellum can vary from yellow to black. The hind legs are a good clue to identity, but there is a superficial resemblance to *Volucella bombylans* and *Eriozona* (both have a dark wing patch and yellow on the face) or to *Pocota* (dark wing patch and orange-haired front to thorax) or *Eristalis intricarius* (pale bases to tibiae and often more extensively pale-haired). Wing length 11.25–14 mm.

As with the other species of the genus, it is mainly a southern hoverfly but a few records extend to north Scotland and there are four Irish records. It is an early spring species, occurring at sallow catkins and blossom of blackthorn, wild cherry and cherry laurel. Occasionally it is found at hawthorn and sycamore flowers, but by June it seems to prefer to fly in the evening. Adults tend to favour the tops of flowering shrubs, but with practice can be distinguished using binoculars from queen bumblebees and *Eristalis intricarius*. Male *ranunculi* do not hover in the sustained manner of male *intricarius*, but female *intricarius* are more easily confused when high up. The males have a fast flight as they search blossom for females and are very aggressive, head-butting queen bumblebees and other hoverflies such as *Eristalis pertinax*. A male has also been observed hovering in the shade close to the base of a tree, in territorial fashion, presumably awaiting the arrival of a female. March to July, peaking in late April.

Genus POCOTA

The genus is of a robust build, but with a very small head. The hind femur is slender and with only the minutest spines beneath near the apex.

Pocota personata (Harris, 1780)   Pl. 10, fig. 11
                                                                    Map: Ball & Morris p. 125
                                                                    Larva: Rotheray Pl. 12c

This is a broadly built hairy bumblebee mimic. It has a particularly small head, about half the width of the thorax including the hairs. The thoracic dorsum has the hairs yellow-orange in the front half and black behind; such a clear-cut pattern is only otherwise found in some varieties of *Merodon*. The abdomen is largely covered in black hairs, but there is a conspicuous patch of yellow-orange hairs dominating the sides of tergite 3, and white or pale yellow hairs on tergite 4 forming the 'tail'. The yellow-orange hairs of the thorax and tergite 3 are actually a bright sulphurous yellow in live specimens, but fade to a duller orange following death. *Pocota* has a conspicuous dark mark on the wing below the stigma (much weaker in *Criorhina* and absent in *Merodon*) and thus has some resemblance to *Volucella bombylans* and *Eriozona* which do not have the clear-cut banding on the thorax. Wing length 11–13 mm.

This seems to be a rare species, but may prove to be easier to find by searching for larvae. Most records are for southern England, across to Devon, but it has been found as far north as Duncombe Park, North Yorkshire, and south of the Wirral, Merseyside. It breeds in rot-holes above ground level, especially liking beech, and on a few occasions it has been bred in numbers from such situations (*e.g.* Shillito, 1947). Fortunately the adult sometimes flies nearer the ground – a white-tailed bumblebee that looks too good to be true and hovering around tree trunks is worth netting to check out. It is rarely observed visiting flowers but has been found at umbellifers, hawthorn and apple, especially in late afternoon and early evening. Males have been observed hovering around flowers on rare occasions and do this in a particularly laboured manner with the abdomen angled downwards and emitting a very distinctive loud buzz. April to July, peaking in late May.

Genus SYRITTA

Syritta pipiens (Linnaeus, 1758)   Pl. 10, fig. 8
Map: Ball & Morris p. 140
Larva: Rotheray Pl. 11e

The build is narrow with paired orange or grey spots on tergites 2 and 3, those on 2 reaching forwards to merge with pale lateral margins on tergite 1. The hind femur is very strongly swollen, bearing a ventral ridge with tiny spines near the apex, and typically has an orange bar which partially bisects the black area halfway along the femur (the black can be more extensive so that the orange bar is absent). The sides of the thorax are densely covered in grey, almost silvery, dusting. There is another European species, but this is Mediterranean (*flaviventris* Meigen, a paler species with a long spine at the base of the hind femur on the inner surface). Wing length 4.25–7 mm.

S. pipiens often occurs in abundance, especially at flowers in urban areas, rough meadows, along hedgerows and in marshy situations. It is widely distributed throughout Britain and Ireland though scarcer in the more remote parts of Scotland. In flight it mimics a solitary wasp, but its precision flying with moments of hovering between jerking darts forward will give the game away. This distinctive behaviour correlates with the exceptional male eyes with enlarged facets at the front, and slightly inwardly converging; this adaptation is assumed to enhance its forward binocular vision. Larvae live in compost, manure, silage and other rotting organic matter, sometimes occurring in large numbers. Sometimes there is an explosion in numbers that may be due either to mass emergence of locally bred flies or to mass movement; under such circumstances long-distance migration might be involved, so it is worth checking for *S. flaviventris* (see above). April to November, often especially abundant in July and August.

Genus TROPIDIA

Tropidia scita (Harris, 1780)   Pl. 10, fig. 10
Map: Ball & Morris p. 143

The abdomen bears a black and reddish-orange pattern. The hind femur is swollen and very strongly arched with a large ventral triangular process near the apex, its posterior surface bearing small black spines. The males have the entire lateral margins of tergites 2 and 3 broadly reddish, leaving a narrow black stripe down the centre of the abdomen. This pattern is also found in *Myolepta* (which has a cylindrical hind femur). The female usually has the reddish areas reduced to paired spots, thus being reminiscent of the *Xylota* pattern (*e.g. Chalcosyrphus nemorum*), but the spots on tergite 2 reach up onto the lateral margins of tergite 1 and the hind femur remains absolutely diagnostic. On the continent there is a more hairy species with orange antennae, *Tropidia fasciata* (Meigen). Wing length 5.5–8.25 mm.

Open fens and lush marshes provide the ideal habitat, and it is most frequently encountered in the vicinity of reedbeds. In such situations it is local but fairly widespread in southern and eastern England. Further north it is much more restricted and often confined to the coastal belt, extending to southern Scotland. It is widespread and frequent in Ireland. In Belgium a larva was found beneath the leaf-sheaths of bulrush, but attempts to repeat this observation in Belgium and the UK were unsuccessful; an emergence trap over litter of common reed yielded an adult. The assumption is that larvae occur typically in wet debris and litter at the margins of water (Decleer & Rotheray, 1990). May to October, peaking in June and July.

Genus XYLOTA

These robust, rather parallel-sided hoverflies have one of three different patterns on the abdomen. The hind trochanter in the male bears an apical spine, developed to varying degrees. The hind femur is swollen, but is straight and characterised by two rows of spines beneath, usually with a wide gap between rows throughout. The hind tibia is entirely pale in the basal third or half (except in *abiens*).

The species-groups based on body pattern are as follows.

segnis Group. Abdomen with an orange or reddish belt occupying tergites 2 and 3, tergite 4 black (*segnis*, *tarda*).

sylvarum Group. Tergite 4 with conspicuous adpressed golden hairs, at least at sides (*sylvarum*, *xanthocnema*).

florum Group. Tergites 2 and 3 each with a pair of spots, tergite 4 black. (*abiens*, *jakutorum*, *florum*).

Larvae are reported from dead wood, but some species are known to also use other decaying plant material. Adults get nourishment from the surface of leaves and normally do not visit flowers (see *jakutorum* and *segnis* for exceptions).

Xylota abiens Meigen, 1822   Pl. 9, fig. 10
                                                                 Map: Ball & Morris p. 147

This is a relatively short-bodied species with pairs of spots on tergites 2 and 3; the hind tibia is only obscurely pale at the base. There is thus a rather close resemblance to *Chalcosyrphus nemorum*, but with the following differences: The ventral surface between the mid and hind coxae does not have long hairs, the hind femur is almost straight and of fairly uniform width in side view (equal width at one third from base and at two thirds from base), the male hind trochanter has a small posterior projection and the hind tibia on its ventral surface does not have a fringe of erect black hairs throughout its length. However, it is somewhat more narrowly built than *nemorum* and could be confused with small *jakutorum* specimens although the hind tibia is only narrowly pale at the base (broadly pale in *jakutorum*). Wing length 6–8.25 mm.

There are widely scattered records in Britain as far north as Cumbria, and from Ireland, but this is an uncommon species. It is usually restricted to woodland close to streams and ponds. Larvae have been found in the decaying roots of pines, although other trees are probably also used. May to September, peaking in June and July.

Xylota florum (Fabricius, 1805)   Pl. 9, fig. 8
Map: Ball & Morris p. 148

In the first edition, '*coeruleiventris*' was segregated from *florum* and has now been renamed *jakutorum*. *X. florum* can be readily distinguished from the *coeruleiventris*/*jakutorum* pair: in male *florum* tergite 2 is longer than wide and has elongate orange spots. In the female the spots on tergites 2 and 3 are orange, and the grey dust spots on the frons are pointed towards the middle and do not meet.

Another narrow-bodied European species, *meigeniana* Stackelberg 1964, could easily be confused with *florum*. In male *meigeniana*, the genital bulge at the end of the abdomen has whitish hairs (black or brown in *florum*, but can appear pale at some angles because they reflect the light). In the female, the hind femur has only short erect white semi-dorsal hairs which are confined to a small area near the base (in *florum* there are additional longer erect hairs extending along the basal quarter or more). Differences in dust-free areas on the upper front parts of the sides of the thorax (Andersson, 1988) can be difficult to see and interpret. Wing length 9–10 mm.

X. florum is thinly but widely distributed in England and Wales and is known from two widely separated localities in Ireland. Its woodland sites are by water or in moist valleys, adults sitting on fallen trees such as beech or sunbathing on logs partly submerged in marsh. Larvae are associated with decaying wood and sap. June to October, peaking in July.

Xylota jakutorum Bagachanova, 1980   Pl. 9, fig. 9
Xylota coeruleiventris Stubbs & Falk, 1983,   Map: Ball & Morris p. 148
misident.

The existence of this species in Britain was first recognised during the preparation of the first edition of this book, when *coeruleiventris* was the appropriate name. Recent revision (Mutin & Gilbert, 1999) resulted in our species being called *jakutorum*, originally thought to be confined to the eastern Palaearctic (the true *coeruleiventris* is a northern boreal species and its listing in that paper as occurring in Britain would seem to be in error). *X. jakutorum* shares with *florum* the spotted pattern on the tergites and the fact that the basal third of the hind tibia is pale. However, the abdomen is somewhat shorter than in *florum* resulting in an appearance like a large *abiens*. The key illustrates significant differences in the shape of tergite 2 and its markings, also the differences in the hind femur. In the female the dust spots on the frons normally join in the middle, or the gap is very narrow, but to avoid doubt the hind femur should also be examined. The possible occurrence of *X. meigeniana* is discussed under *florum*. Wing length 7.5–8 mm.

Museum collections contain numbers of specimens taken in the Scottish Highlands from about the 1890s to the 1900s. Thus *jakutorum* seems to have been relatively common and widespread in the main Caledonian forests with pine and birch. It is currently widespread in northern and western Britain (and old '*florum*' records in the literature suggest that *jakutorum* has been in northern England for a long time), with a scatter of records extending to the south coast, including the East Anglian Brecks and plantations on southern heathlands. There is also an old

Irish specimen and it has recently been found to be widely scattered but infrequent in Ireland. The larvae have been found in sap-filled tunnels of the bark weevil *Hylobius abietis* and there is a clear association with conifer woodlands and plantations. Conditions appear to be particularly suitable a couple of years after felling when the stumps offer abundant breeding habitat and the hoverfly can be very numerous in clear-fell areas in this stage of the management cycle. It probably spread southwards into plantations as these reached a sufficient age for the cycle of felling and replanting to provide this habitat. It is of interest that adults have been found to visit buttercup flowers along tracks and clearings, an unusual habit for members of this genus. May to October, peaking in July.

Xylota segnis (Linnaeus, 1758)　　　　　　　　　　　　　　　Pl. 9, fig. 6
Map: Ball & Morris p. 149
Larva: Rotheray Pl. 11f

The orange or reddish-orange belt lacks any trace of darkening at the hind edge of tergite 2 (compare with *tarda*). The male has a long spur on the underside of the hind trochanter (unlike other species) and the hind femur in both sexes has strong isolated erect black spines ventrally for most of its length (unlike other species where spines are weak or confined to the distal half). *Brachypalpoides lentus* differs in having entirely black legs. Wing length 7–9.5 mm.

A further European species resembling *segnis* could occur in Britain. *X. ignava* (Panzer, 1798) has the hind tarsus entirely orange (except for segment 5) and the distal end of the hind tibia is yellow (as well as the base). The hind femur in side view is somewhat concave beneath, especially in the male, and the ventral spines are not as conspicuous (more like *tarda* in the latter respect). The male hind trochanter only has a short projection. Conifer plantations would probably provide suitable habitat.

Throughout Britain and Ireland *segnis* is a familiar hoverfly to be found sunbathing on or running over leaves, or on logs about woods, hedgerows and sometimes even the garden. Whilst rotten dead wood can be a breeding site, the frequency of *segnis* seemingly owes much to its use of wet sawdust, very wet decomposing silage and no doubt various other types of rotting vegetable material. The adult has been seen at buttercup flowers (McLean, 1982; Iliff, 1999), but such observations are comparatively infrequent. April to November, peaking in June and July.

Xylota sylvarum (Linnaeus, 1758)　　　　　　　　　　　　　Pl. 9, fig. 12
Map: Ball & Morris p. 149
Larva: Rotheray Pl. 12a

The dense covering of adpressed golden hairs on tergite 4 makes this a conspicuous and attractive hoverfly. There are normally small side patches of such hairs on tergite 3; occasionally the golden hairs on tergite 4 are reduced to side patches. The distal half of the hind tibia is darkened, but it is often necessary to view from various angles before such darkening is obvious due to effects of the overlying short golden hairs (see comments under *xanthocnema*). Wing length 7–12 mm.

This species is frequent in wooded districts in the south of Britain and Ireland, but becomes less abundant in northern England. It has proved to be widely but thinly distributed in Scotland, mainly south of the Highlands but including north Aberdeenshire. Adults are usually seen running over or sunbathing on foliage along woodland edges, or sitting on logs. Quantities of larvae have been found in wet, decaying roots of beech stumps; however, many of its sites lack beech, so oak and birch are also considered to be strong candidates for usage. Puparia from under bark and other drier situations are interpreted as resulting from larvae moving up from underground to pupate (Rotheray, 1990b). Larvae have also been found in a rot-hole, so are not exclusively subterranean. May to October, peaking in late June and July.

Xylota tarda Meigen, 1822   Pl. 9, fig. 7
                                                      Map: Ball & Morris p. 150
                                                        Larva: Rotheray Pl. 12b

There is a close resemblance to a small *segnis*. The abdomen is not parallel-sided but is bulbous towards the apex, more markedly so in the female. There is normally a distinct narrow dark fringe along the posterior margin of tergite 2 and a greater inclination towards the development of a dark median stripe on tergites 2 and 3, though this is variable (but a useful field clue where it does exist). The male hind trochanter only has a short projection. The hind femur has numerous very short black spines below (not like the longer isolated erect spines of *segnis*, especially in the basal half). Wing length 5.5–8.5 mm.

Records are mainly from the Scottish Highlands, the Midlands and southern England. It has also been found at a single locality in County Clare in western Ireland (Speight *et al.*, 1979). It is a very local and scarce species, usually occurring on the edge of wet woods or near streams. Larvae and puparia have been found in a sap run at the base of aspen (Rotheray, 1991) and a specific association with this tree and the closely related grey poplar is becoming apparent, accounting for the very localised occurrence of this species. April to September, peaking in July.

Xylota xanthocnema Collin, 1939   Pl. 9, fig. 11
                                                      Map: Ball & Morris p. 150

This species is very similar to *sylvarum* and was not separated from it until 1939. It is a smaller species, still having the golden adpressed hairs, but faint pairs of reddish spots are often also present on tergites 2 and 3, those of tergite 3 being overlain by patches of pale adpressed hairs that are usually more extensive than those found on *sylvarum*. The hind tibia is entirely yellow (but take care because the darkened apical half on *sylvarum* only shows up from certain angles). Tergite 5 (= pre-genital segment in the male) usually has gold hairs in *xanthocnema* (black hairs occasionally present), but black hairs in *sylvarum*. Wing length 7–10 mm.

This is a rare species with most records from southern England but extending as far north as North Yorkshire. It has not been recorded from Ireland. Larvae have been found in the exudate and rot-holes of yews and also in small rot-holes in oak. May to October, peaking in July.

CHAPTER 10

SUBFAMILY MICRODONTINAE

In the past the genus *Microdon* has been treated in various ways. Coe (1953a) placed it in its own subfamily, the 1976 check list regarded it as a tribe within the Milesiinae, whilst the Afro-tropical check list (= sub-Saharan Africa) placed it in a separate family, as do Speight *et al.* (2001). Certainly it is a very peculiar hoverfly; indeed it does not hover.

These are very odd-looking flies. The adults are very dumpy with a humped abdomen. The antennae are elongate and porrect, projecting well in front of the face, with a basal arista (as in *Chrysotoxum*). The wing venation is unusual in having an extra partial cross-vein which largely divides cell r_5 into two. The adults spend most of their time sitting. There is no courtship: Brigden (1998) reports observing that a female (of '*mutabilis*') walking over short grass was dived on at great speed by a male and the two grappled in the grass for a few seconds.

It is the larva which is really bizarre. Even up to early in the 20th century a succession of people had described it as a type of mollusc new to science, since it resembles a hunched-up slug. Such errors were not surprising since the visible segments one would expect in an arthropod larva are lacking and it creeps very slowly on a flat sole. However, the larva lacks the tentacles of a slug, it is not slimy and the dorsal surface is covered with a peculiar reticulate pattern of tiny ridges (not well developed in some species). To a dipterist there should be no problem in recognising the true place of this unlikely creature since the characteristic posterior syphon of a syrphid larva is readily apparent.

One may correctly anticipate that such an unusual larva must have an unusual way of life, for it lives in ants' nests. It was said to be adapted to eating the minute bits of food discarded by the ants as buccal pellets (Donisthorpe, 1927), but more recent studies (Barr, 1995) have demonstrated that at least two of our species are predatory on the eggs and larvae of formicine ants as follows. The mouthparts are adapted to grasp an ant larva and quickly tuck the prey underneath the head before the ants can retaliate. In the case of *M. analis*, its larvae waited till the very early hours of the morning when the ants had become less vigilant, then made a 50 mm dash in less than 3 minutes to the ant eggs on which it fed for 3 to 15 minutes before returning to its resting site. The longer feeding times resulted from the ants becoming alert and placing themselves between the larva and the ant eggs (in which case there was a pause for things to calm down), or removing the ant eggs. It appeared that the retreat of the satiated hoverfly larva deterred the ants from moving the eggs to another site. However, in the case of *M. 'mutabilis'* larvae placed within an observation nest of *Myrmica ruginodis*, the ants made no attempt to move their brood, though they occasionally succeeded in rescuing their larvae from the clutches of the *Microdon*.

Barr calculated that *Microdon* larvae can cause considerable mortality within ant broods. An average nest of *Formica lemani* contained 5 or 6 *Microdon* larvae, capable of eating 700 ant larvae between them. Competition between larvae was the probable cause of considerable variation in size, and it seemed that the habit of a larva stationing itself in a tunnel entering the brood chamber served to block the entry of competing *Microdon* larvae.

The ants only attack and eat the larva if it rolls onto its back to expose the soft sole. Somehow the flies emerge from the ants' nests without harm; indeed the ants are said to lick the hairs of newly emerged adults (which sounds like a free preening service!). Donisthorpe (1927) remains one of the best references to the biology of *Microdon*. He reports success in rearing larvae in observation nests. If puparia are found by searching just before the emergence period, then there is no problem in hatching them out (the presence of ants is not essential at this stage).

With growing refinement in taxonomic and biological studies, it is clear that although the species look very similar as adults, larval characters and ant associations deserve closer scrutiny. Thus the study of '*mutabilis*' larvae in ants nests from two different subfamilies, Formicinae and Myrmicinae, led to the recognition that two exceedingly similar species of hoverflies were involved. However, host ants may move their nest, a convenient way for getting away from nest predators, and abandoned nests may then be colonised by other types of ant; thus interpretation of ant relationships needs caution (Schönrogge *et al.*, 2002).

The most recent revision of the central European fauna was by Doczkal & Schmid (1999) which included the three long-standing British species. The only non-British species is *miki* Doczkal & Schmid (a new name for the former *latifrons* Loew) which has been included in both adult and larval keys in this book. Subsequently, *mutabilis* has been split, adding a fourth species to the British fauna, *myrmicae* (Schönrogge *et al.*, 2002).

Genus MICRODON

The distinctive features have already been described above. In general appearance the four species are very similar. They are inconspicuous, of a dark brownish colour with faint ill-defined silvery reflections on the humped abdomen.

Whilst most specimens can readily be identified, problem specimens can cause difficulty. Special care should be taken if the habitat and distribution data do not match up with the species identification, and advice should then be sought.

Adults are not easy to find, being easily overlooked, and tend to be very local in occurrence. They sit in a docile manner near their breeding sites and only fly a short distance. Sweeping is as likely to yield specimens as searching.

One method of recording is to search for larvae and puparia in ants' nests, so a key to larvae and puparia is included in this book (p. 163). Rotheray (1993) includes colour photographs. It is invaluable to ascertain which ant species are host to the various species, so accurate ant identification is obviously critical; reference may be made to Collingwood (1964) or Bolton & Collingwood (1975) or assistance may be sought from the Bees, Wasps and Ants Recording Scheme (address via the Biological Records Centre). There is some evidence that certain *Microdon* species are using different ant species in different parts of their range.

Microdon analis (Macquart, 1842)   Pl. 9, fig. 4
Microdon eggeri Mik, 1897   Map: Ball & Morris p. 94
                                                                   Larva: Rotheray Pl. 3c

Having checked that the scutellum is black, it is necessary to view the thoracic dorsum from various angles to make sure that the hairs are entirely pale or golden yellow. Further comments are made under *devius*. However, it is necessary to note that *analis* (formerly *eggeri* of the British list) has been split: thus the key includes *miki* Doczkal & Schmid, which potentially could occur in Britain. Wing length 6.75–8.25 mm.

There is a disjunct distribution, *analis* occurring in heathy woods in some of the valleys in the Central Highlands of Scotland, in open situations on Mull and also on the heathlands of the London Basin, the western Weald, the New Forest and east Dorset. Open heathy woodland would be a more accurate habitat description and in the Weald the species occurs occasionally in woodland rides on well drained clay or more rarely chalk grassland at the margins of woodland. There are a few other southern districts where the habitat is apparently woodland. In Surrey puparia have been found in nests of *Lasius niger* under the bark of logs and stumps of pine and birch, usually in a sunny situation at the edge of woodland (see also Syms, 1935), however the recent split of *L. niger*, which entails segregation of *L. platythorax* which also nests in wood, suggests that the ant associations of *analis* need checking (see Blacker & Collingwood (2002) for an updated key to *Lasius*). On one Surrey heath, adults occur where there are very few trees, only old stumps, so it is the presence of dead wood rather than woodland edge which is important. The species has also been found in south-west Ireland where puparia were found under stones in association with *Lasius niger* (Breen, 1977). Speight *et al.* (1975) refer to the hosts being ants of the *Formica rufa* group (this may be so in Scotland (Speight, *pers. comm.*)). May to August, peaking in June.

Microdon devius (Linnaeus, 1761)   Map: Ball & Morris p. 94
                                                                  Larva: Rotheray Pl. 3d

Of the two species with a black scutellum, *devius* has a pair of black patches of hair on top of the thorax a little in front of the scutellum. These black patches are easily overlooked amidst the yellowish hairs, but they usually show up well by looking along the top of the thorax from in front or behind. The scutellum bears a pair of tiny spines on its hind edge; in *devius* the space between the spines is concave (straight in *analis*). There are various other features of some relevance to identification, but most of them seem too variable or too imprecise. For instance, nearly all *devius* have the hind metatarsus at least three times as long as broad when seen from above, but there is one specimen with a shorter squat hind metatarsus (as is normal in *analis*). Wing length 6.25–9.25 mm.

Chalk grassland is the habitat which most frequently yields this uncommon species. The hoverfly is difficult to locate and is usually encountered as a single individual whilst sweeping. The North Downs of Kent and Surrey, as well as the Chilterns, are favoured areas, but there are scattered records elsewhere involving calcareous grassland or perhaps other habitats; normally there is some scrub present, in preference to very exposed situations. It has not been recorded from Ireland. Larvae have been found in partially shaded (by dewberry) nests of the mound-building ant *Lasius flavus*, but are very hard to detect since they are covered by adhering soil particles except on the white 'sole' (Rotheray, 1991). May to July, peaking in mid to late June.

Microdon mutabilis (Linnaeus, 1758)
  Note: this is not typical *mutabilis* of
  Stubbs & Falk, 1983

Though *mutabilis* has been a well recognised species on the British list, recent studies have revealed that two almost identical species stood under this name, and both occur in Britain. Distinct identities have been recognised as a result of differences in biology as well as larval and puparial characters, but adults cannot be separated with any confidence. The description of *myrmicae* gives some minor differences in comparative measurements which are difficult to apply, requiring graticule optics on a microscope, but even these are not definitive. For example, the ratio of the distance between the two blunt spines on the hind margin of the scutellum and the maximum length of the scutellum is about 0.87 in *mutabilis* and 0.66 in *myrmicae*. More pragmatically, true *mutabilis* tend to be larger, especially in the female. The male genital capsule at the end of the abdomen is duller orange than *myrmicae*; in this sex the strongly chitinised portion of the hind margin of sternite 4 is deeply emarginated (curved inwards) but some *myrmicae* approach this condition and further investigation of the variability of this character is required. Body length up to 10 mm, wing length 6.5–9 mm.

Though adults look so like *myrmicae*, the habitat and ecology of *mutabilis* are very different. It occupies dry well-drained sites, including limestone pavements. In Britain the main host ant is *Formica lemani*, a widespread species in the north and west, but it is still unclear why the hoverfly should be so choosy over which sites are suitable. As yet it has been confirmed to occupy two areas in Scotland (Mull and near Inverness), and six sites in south-west Ireland (mainly the famous limestone district in The Burren) (Schönrogge *et al.*, 2002). There is some additional information. There is a very large specimen from Gaitbarrows in the Liverpool Museum collection that almost certainly belongs to this species; the locality is well known for its limestone pavement and it is probable that similar low-level sites around Morecambe Bay, north-west England, are suitable. Also, Donisthorpe (1927: pp. 125-6) refers to the discovery in mid April of many larvae, and a puparium, found on the underside of a stone over a *Formica fusca* nest at Porlock, coastal west Somerset; the Natural History Museum in London has his bred material, including empty puparia, the latter agreeing with the description of *mutabilis* as now understood. Donisthorpe mentions larvae being found in the nest of *Formica fusca* at Kendal (not far from Gaitbarrows) (*n.b.* at the time of Donisthorpe's work the distinction between *F. fusca* and *lemani* was poorly defined and he makes no mention of the latter species). The cited report of puparia in the nest of *Lasius niger* in the stump of an old tree in Ayrshire is open to re-assessment. He mentions placing a larva from a *Formica fusca* nest into the nest of *Myrmica ruginodis*, which was devoured by these ants, but that larvac of a similar source placed in *F. fusca* nests completed their life-cycle (in retrospect, we now know that only *M. myrmicae* are adapted to *Myrmica* ants). May and June.

Microdon myrmicae Schönrogge, Barr, Wardlaw, Napper, Gardner, Breen,   Pl. 9, fig. 5
Elmes & Thomas, 2002
This corresponds to *mutabilis* of   Map: Ball & Morris p. 95
Stubbs & Falk, 1983   Larva: Rotheray Pl. 3e

Following the split of *mutabilis*, this newly described species corresponds to the best known and 'typical' British material. Unfortunately, the male genitalia are almost identical to those of *mutabilis* and slight differences are blurred by variation within the species. The main features of *myrmicae* are its smaller average size and, in the male, the bright orange genital capsule but there are no definitive characters; as yet only the puparium can be identified with certainty. It would seem that the shape of sternite 4 of the male may be different, being less emarginated in *myrmicae*, but the difference is slight in some specimens. Body length not more than 8 mm, wing length 6–7.5 mm.

It is a very localised species occurring principally on wet heaths in Surrey, the New Forest and east Dorset, and on wet heaths and poor wet grasslands in south-west England. Additionally, there are scattered records for Wales and the west side of England, extending as far as south-west Scotland. The host ant is now known to be *Myrmica scabrinodis* (nationally, a common ant) where ant colonies occur in tussocks about 10-30 cm tall in otherwise waterlogged conditions. Two rather different situations are utilised, *Sphagnum* bogs in acid heathland (as in Surrey), and ungrazed neutral grassland dominated by rushes (as in some Culm grasslands in Devon). May to early July, peaking in late May and early June.

CHAPTER 11

CHECK LIST

Since the publication of the original edition in 1983, it has been advocated that the nomenclature should be maintained consistently, without constantly changing names according to new and possibly controversial ideas. Despite advice to maintain stability of names, some revised names for records have been appearing elsewhere with unseemly haste. Patience is rewarded, since in a number of cases the new names have been retracted in favour of returning to the familiar ones. However, a new benchmark has emerged with the publication of a new check list (Chandler, 1998).

Opinion on the allocation of genera to subfamilies and tribes is still is a state of flux. Hence, the 1998 check list simply listed genera in alphabetic order (Chandler, 1998). In this revision, the original arrangement of subfamilies and tribes has been retained as a pragmatic solution which is, for the most part, helpful in grouping together similar genera. See Rotheray & Gilbert (1989, 1999) for discussion of the issues involved in higher classification, and Peck (1988) and Thompson & Rotheray (1998) for other recent arrangements.

The changes in names since the 1983 edition are listed below (apart from minor gender changes):

Current name

Bacchini

Baccha elongata (Fabricius, 1775)	includes *obscuripennis*
Platycheirus amplus Curran, 1927	New
P. aurolateralis Stubbs, 2002	New
P. europaeus Goeldlin de Tiefenau, Maibach & Speight, 1990	New
P. granditarsus (Forster, 1771)	*Pyrophaena*
P. nielseni Vockeroth, 1990	New (species A, 1986)
P. occultus Goeldlin de Tiefenau, Maibach & Speight, 1990	New
P. ramsarensis Goeldlin de Tiefenau, Maibach & Speight, 1990	New
P. rosarum (Fabricius, 1787)	*Pyrophaena*
P. splendidus Rotheray, 1998	New

Paragini

Paragus constrictus Šimić, 1986	New

Syrphini

Dasysyrphus pinastri (De Geer, 1776)	*lunulatus*
Doros profuges (Harris, 1780)	*conopseus*
Epistrophe melanostoma (Zetterstedt, 1843)	New
E. ochrostoma (Zetterstedt, 1849)	New
Eriozona erratica (Linnaeus, 1758)	*Megasyrphus annulipes*
Eupeodes	*Metasyrphus*
E. bucculatus (Rondani, 1857)	*Metasyrphus latilunulatus*

343

E. lundbecki (Soot-Ryen, 1946)	New
E. species B	New
E. species C	New
Meligramma	s.g. *Meligramma*
Meligramma euchromum (Kowarz, 1885)	*Epistrophe* (*Epistrophella*)
	euchroma
Sphaerophoria bankowskae Goeldlin de Tiefenau, 1989	New
S. fatarum Goeldlin de Tiefenau, 1989	*abbreviata*
S. interrupta (Fabricius, 1805)	*menthastri*
S. potentillae Claussen, 1984	New
S. species B	New
Syrphus rectus Osten Sacken, 1875	New

Callicerini

Callicera aurata (Rossi, 1790)	*aenea*

Cheilosiini

Cheilosia ahenea (von Roser, 1840)	*laskai*
C. fraterna (Meigen, 1830)	includes species C
C. lasiopa Kowarz, 1885	*honesta*
C. latifrons (Zetterstedt, 1843)	*intonsa*
C. proxima (Zetterstedt, 1843)	species D + E
C. psilophthalma Becker, 1894	New
C. ranunculi Doczkal, 2000	New
C. urbana (Meigen, 1822)	*praecox*
	[including *globulipes*]
C. uviformis (Becker, 1894) [= *argentifrons* Hellén, 1914]	species A (?)
C. vicina (Zetterstedt, 1849)	*nasutula*

Chrysogastrini

Chrysogaster cemiteriorum (Linnaeus, 1758)	*chalybeata*
Lejogaster tarsata (Megerle in Meigen, 1822)	*splendida*
Melanogaster aerosa (Loew, 1843)	*Chrysogaster macquarti*
M. hirtella (Loew, 1843)	*Chrysogaster*
Myolepta dubia (Fabricius, 1805)	*luteola*
Orthonevra nobilis (Fallén, 1817)	(includes species A, 1996)
Riponnensia splendens (Meigen, 1822)	*Orthonevra*
Sphegina elegans Schummel, 1843	*kimakowiczi*
S. sibirica Stackelberg, 1953	New

Eristalini

Eristalis interruptus (Poda, 1761)	*nemorum*
E. similis (Fallén, 1817) [= *pratorum* Meigen, 1822]	New
Helophilus affinis Wahlberg, 1844	New

Merodontini

Eumerus funeralis Meigen, 1822	*tuberculatus*

Pipizini

Heringia senilis Sack, 1938	New
Heringia s.g. *Neocnemodon*	*Neocnemodon*
Pipizella viduata (Linnaeus, 1758)	*varipes*

Sericomyiini
Arctophila superbiens (Müller, 1776)   *fulva*
Xylotini
Xylota jakutorum Bagachanova, 1980   *coeruleiventris*
Microdontini
Microdon analis (Macquart, 1842)   *eggeri*
M. myrmicae Schönrogge, Barr, Wardlaw, Napper, Gardner,   New (this is *mutabilis* of the
Breen, Elmes & Thomas, 2002   first edition)

The names used in the check list follow Chandler (1998) and subsequent updates and amendments published in Dipterists Digest to June 2002 (Chandler 1999a, 1999b, 2000a, 2000b, 2001a, 2001b, & 2002).

SYRPHIDAE

SYRPHINAE

BACCHINI [incorporating
MELANOSTOMATINI]

BACCHA Fabricius, 1805
elongata (Fabricius, 1775)
   obscuripennis Meigen, 1822

MELANOSTOMA Schiner, 1860
dubium (Zetterstedt, 1838) [as in Verrall,
   1901, incorrect var. in Coe, 1953a]
mellinum (Linnaeus, 1758)
scalare (Fabricius, 1794)
form A *sensu* Stubbs & Falk, 1983

PLATYCHEIRUS Lepeletier & Serville,
1828
S. PACHYSPHYRIA Enderlein, 1938
ambiguus (Fallén, 1817)

S. PLATYCHEIRUS s.s.
albimanus (Fabricius, 1781)
   cyaneus (Walker, 1851)
amplus Curran, 1927
angustatus (Zetterstedt, 1843)
aurolateralis Stubbs, 2002
clypeatus (Meigen, 1822)
discimanus Loew, 1871

europaeus Goeldlin, Maibach & Speight,
   1990
fulviventris (Macquart, 1829)
immarginatus (Zetterstedt, 1849)
manicatus (Meigen, 1822)
melanopsis Loew, 1856
nielseni Vockeroth, 1990
   species A *sensu* Stubbs, 1986
occultus Goeldlin, Maibach & Speight,
   1990
peltatus (Meigen, 1822)
perpallidus Verrall, 1901
podagratus (Zetterstedt, 1838)
ramsarensis Goeldlin, Maibach & Speight,
   1990
scambus (Staeger, 1843)
scutatus (Meigen, 1822)
splendidus Rotheray, 1998
sticticus (Meigen, 1822)
tarsalis (Schummel, 1836)

S. PYROPHAENA Schiner, 1860
granditarsus (Forster, 1771)
rosarum (Fabricius, 1787)

XANTHANDRUS Verrall, 1901
comtus (Harris, 1780)

PARAGINI

PARAGUS Latreille, 1804
S. PANDASYOPTHALMUS Stuckenberg, 1954
constrictus Šimić, 1986 (Ireland only)
haemorrhous Meigen, 1822
   [*tibialis* of Coe, 1953a, part]
tibialis (Fallén, 1817)

S. PARAGUS s.s.
albifrons (Fallén, 1817)
   bicolor (Fabricius, 1794) of Coe, 1953a,
      misident.

SYRPHINI [incorporating CHRYSOTOXINI]

CHRYSOTOXUM Meigen, 1803
arcuatum (Linnaeus, 1758)
   fasciatum (Müller, 1764) of some recent
      authors; substitution overruled
bicinctum (Linnaeus, 1758)
cautum (Harris, 1776)
elegans Loew, 1841
   latilimbatum Collin, 1940 [not a
      separate species]
festivum (Linnaeus, 1758)
   arcuatum (Linnaeus, 1758) of some
      recent authors; substitution overruled
octomaculatum Curtis, 1837
vernale Loew, 1841
verralli Collin, 1940

DASYSYRPHUS Enderlein, 1938
albostriatus (Fallén, 1817)
friuliensis van der Goot, 1960
[*hilaris* (Zetterstedt, 1843)] ? = var. of
   venustus in GB
pinastri (De Geer, 1776)
   lunulatus (Meigen, 1822)
tricinctus (Fallén, 1817)
venustus (Meigen, 1822)

DIDEA Macquart, 1834
alneti (Fallén, 1817)
fasciata Macquart, 1834
intermedia Loew, 1854

DOROS Meigen, 1803
profuges (Harris, 1780)
   conopseus (Fabricius, 1776)

EPISTROPHE Walker, 1852
diaphana (Zetterstedt, 1843)
eligans (Harris, 1780)
grossulariae (Meigen, 1822)
melanostoma (Zetterstedt, 1843)
nitidicollis (Meigen, 1822)
ochrostoma (Zetterstedt, 1849)

EPISYRPHUS Matsumura & Adachi, 1917
balteatus (De Geer, 1776)

ERIOZONA Schiner, 1860
S. ERIOZONA s.s
syrphoides (Fallén, 1817)

S. MEGASYRPHUS Dušek & Láska, 1967
erratica (Linnaeus, 1758)
   annulipes (Zetterstedt, 1838)

EUPEODES Osten Sacken, 1877
   METASYRPHUS Matsumura, 1917
S. EUPEODES s.s.
bucculatus (Rondani, 1857)
   latilunulatus (Collin, 1931)
   form X *sensu* Stubbs & Falk, 2002
   form Y *sensu* Stubbs & Falk, 2002
corollae (Fabricius, 1794)
latifasciatus (Macquart, 1829)
lundbecki (Soot-Ryen, 1946)
luniger (Meigen, 1822)
nielseni (Dušek & Láska, 1976)
   arcuatus (Fallén, 1817) of Coe, 1953a,
      misident.
nitens (Zetterstedt, 1843)
species B *sensu* Stubbs & Falk, 2002
species C *sensu* Stubbs & Falk, 2002

S. LAPPOSYRPHUS Dušek & Láska, 1967
lapponicus (Zetterstedt, 1838)
species A *sensu* Stubbs & Falk, 1983

LEUCOZONA Schiner, 1860
S. ISCHYROSYRPHUS Bigot, 1882
glaucia (Linnaeus, 1758)
laternaria (Muller, 1776)

S. LEUCOZONA s.s.
lucorum (Linnaeus, 1758)

MELANGYNA Verrall, 1901
arctica (Zetterstedt, 1838)
barbifrons (Fallén, 1817)
cincta (Fallén, 1817)
compositarum (Verrall, 1873)
ericarum (Collin, 1946)
labiatarum (Verrall, 1901)
lasiophthalma (Zetterstedt, 1843)
quadrimaculata (Verrall, 1873)
umbellatarum (Fabricius, 1794)

MELIGRAMMA Frey, 1946
euchromum (Kowarz, 1885)
guttatum (Fallén, 1817)
trianguliferum (Zetterstedt, 1843)

MELISCAEVA Frey, 1946
auricollis (Meigen, 1822)
   v. *maculicornis* (Zetterstedt, 1843)
cinctella (Zetterstedt, 1843)

PARASYRPHUS Matsumura, 1917
annulatus (Zetterstedt, 1838)
lineola (Zetterstedt, 1843)
malinellus (Collin, 1952)
nigritarsis (Zetterstedt, 1843)
punctulatus (Verrall, 1873)
vittiger (Zetterstedt, 1843)

SCAEVA Fabricius, 1805
albomaculata (Macquart, 1842)
mecogramma (Bigot, 1860)

pyrastri (Linnaeus, 1758)
selenitica (Meigen, 1822)

SPHAEROPHORIA Lepeletier & Serville,
1828
bankowskae Goeldin, 1989
batava Goeldin, 1974
fatarum Goeldin, 1989
   abbreviata authors, misident.
interrupta (Fabricius, 1805)
   menthastri (Linnaeus, 1758) *sensu*
      Vockeroth, 1963
loewi Zetterstedt, 1843
philanthus (Meigen, 1822)
potentillae Claussen, 1984
rueppellii (Wiedemann, 1830)
scripta (Linnaeus, 1758)
taeniata (Meigen, 1822)
virgata Goeldin, 1974
form A (var. of *fatarum?*)
species B *sensu* Stubbs, 1995

SYRPHUS Fabricius, 1775
rectus Osten Sacken, 1875
ribesii (Linnaeus, 1758)
torvus Osten Sacken, 1875
vitripennis Meigen, 1822

XANTHOGRAMMA Schiner, 1860
citrofasciatum (De Geer, 1776)
   festivum (Linnaeus, 1758) of some
      recent authors, overruled
pedissequum (Harris, 1776)
   v. *flavipleura* Coe, 1957

MILESIINAE

CALLICERINI

CALLICERA Panzer, 1809
aurata (Rossi, 1790)
   aenea authors, misident.
rufa Schummel, 1841
spinolae Rondani, 1844

CHEILOSIINI

CHEILOSIA Meigen, 1822
ahenea (von Roser, 1840)
   laskai Speight, 1978
albipila Meigen, 1838
albitarsis (Meigen, 1822)
antiqua (Meigen, 1822)
barbata Loew, 1857
bergenstammi Becker, 1894
carbonaria Egger, 1860
chrysocoma (Meigen, 1822)
cynocephala Loew, 1840
fraterna (Meigen, 1830)
   includes species C *sensu* Stubbs & Falk,
   1983
griseiventris Loew, 1857
grossa (Fallén, 1817)
illustrata (Harris, 1780)
impressa Loew, 1840
lasiopa Kowarz, 1885
   honesta: Verrall, 1901, misident.
latifrons (Zetterstedt, 1843)
   intonsa Loew, 1857
longula (Zetterstedt, 1838)
mutabilis (Fallén, 1817)
nebulosa Verrall, 1871
nigripes (Meigen, 1822)
pagana (Meigen, 1822)
proxima (Zetterstedt, 1843)
   includes species D & E *sensu* Stubbs &
   Falk, 1983
psilophthalma Becker, 1894
pubera (Zetterstedt, 1838)
ranunculi Doczkal, 2000
sahlbergi Becker, 1894
scutellata (Fallén, 1817)
semifasciata Becker, 1894
   fasciata Schiner & Egger, 1853 of Coe,
   1953a, misident.
soror (Zetterstedt, 1843)
urbana (Meigen, 1822)
   praecox (Zetterstedt, 1843)
   globulipes Becker, 1894
uviformis Becker, 1894

argentifrons Hellén, 1914
   species A *sensu* Stubbs & Falk, 1983
variabilis (Panzer, 1798)
velutina Loew, 1840
vernalis (Fallén, 1817)
vicina (Zetterstedt, 1849)
   nasutula Becker, 1894
vulpina (Meigen, 1822)
species B *sensu* Stubbs & Falk, 1983 [?=
   gigantea (Zetterstedt, 1838) or *ingerae*
   Nielsen & Claussen, 2001]

FERDINANDEA Rondani, 1844
cuprea (Scopoli, 1763)
ruficornis (Fabricius, 1775)

PORTEVINIA Goffe, 1944
maculata (Fallén, 1817)

RHINGIA Scopoli, 1763
campestris Meigen, 1822
rostrata (Linnaeus, 1758)

CHRYSOGASTRINI

BRACHYOPA Meigen, 1822
bicolor (Fallén, 1817)
insensilis Collin, 1939
pilosa Collin, 1939
scutellaris Robineau-Desvoidy, 1844

CHRYSOGASTER Meigen, 1803
cemiteriorum (Linnaeus, 1758)
   chalybeata Meigen, 1822
solstitialis (Fallén, 1817)
virescens Loew, 1854

HAMMERSCHMIDTIA Schummel, 1834
ferruginea (Fallén, 1817)

LEJOGASTER Rondani, 1857
   LIOGASTER Verrall, 1901, emend.
metallina (Fabricius, 1777)
tarsata (Megerle in Meigen, 1822)
   splendida (Meigen, 1822)

MELANOGASTER Rondani, 1857
aerosa (Loew, 1843)
   macquarti (Loew, 1843)
hirtella (Loew, 1843)

MYOLEPTA Newman, 1838
dubia (Fabricius, 1805)
   luteola (Gmelin, 1788), preoccupied
potens (Harris, 1780)

NEOASCIA Williston, 1886
geniculata (Meigen, 1822)
interrupta (Meigen, 1822)
meticulosa (Scopoli, 1763)
   aenea (Meigen, 1822) of Collin, 1940 &
     Coe, 1953a
obliqua Coe, 1940
podagrica (Fabricius, 1775)
tenur (Harris, 1780)
   dispar (Meigen, 1822) of Collin, 1940
     & Coe, 1953a

ORTHONEVRA Macquart, 1829
brevicornis (Loew, 1843)
geniculata (Meigen, 1830)
nobilis (Fallén, 1817)
   species A *sensu* Stubbs, 1996

RIPONNENSIA Maibach, Goeldlin &
Speight, 1994
splendens (Meigen, 1822)

SPHEGINA Meigen, 1822
S. **ASIOSPHEGINA** Stackelberg, 1975
sibirica Stackelberg, 1953

S. **SPHEGINA** s.s.
clunipes (Fallén, 1816)
elegans Schummel, 1843
   kimakowiczi Strobl, 1897
verecunda Collin, 1937

ERISTALINI

ANASIMYIA Schiner, 1864
contracta Claussen & Torp, 1980
interpuncta (Harris, 1776)
lineata (Fabricius, 1787)
lunulata (Meigen, 1822)
transfuga (Linnaeus, 1758)

ERISTALINUS Rondani, 1845
aeneus (Scopoli, 1763)
sepulchralis (Linnaeus, 1758)

ERISTALIS Latreille, 1804
S. **EOSERISTALIS** Kanervo, 1938
abusivus Collin, 1931
arbustorum (Linnaeus, 1758)
cryptarum (Fabricius, 1794)
horticola (De Geer, 1776)
   lineatus (Harris, 1776)
interruptus (Poda, 1761)
   nemorum (Linnaeus, 1758)
intricarius (Linnaeus, 1758)
pertinax (Scopoli, 1763)
rupium Fabricius, 1805
similis (Fallén, 1817)
   pratorum Meigen, 1822

S. **ERISTALIS** s.s.
tenax (Linnaeus, 1758)

HELOPHILUS Meigen, 1822
affinis Wahlberg, 1844
groenlandicus (Fabricius, 1780)
hybridus Loew, 1846
pendulus (Linnaeus, 1758)
trivittatus (Fabricius, 1805)
   parallelus (Harris, 1776) of Coe, 1953a,
     but incorrect synonymy

LEJOPS Rondani, 1857
vittatus (Meigen, 1822)

MALLOTA Meigen, 1822
cimbiciformis (Fallén, 1817)

MYATHROPA Rondani, 1845
   MYIATROPA Scudder, 1882, emend.
florea (Linnaeus, 1758)

PARHELOPHILUS Girschner, 1897
consimilis (Malm, 1863)
frutetorum (Fabricius, 1775)
versicolor (Fabricius, 1794)

MERODONTINI [incorporating
EUMERINI]

EUMERUS Meigen, 1822
funeralis Meigen, 1822
   tuberculatus Rondani, 1857
ornatus Meigen, 1822
sabulonum (Fallén, 1817)
strigatus (Fallén, 1817)

MERODON Meigen, 1803
equestris (Fabricius, 1794)
   f. *narcissi* (Fabricius, 1805)
   f. *transversalis* Meigen, 1822
   f. *validus* Meigen, 1822

PSILOTA Meigen, 1822
anthracina Meigen, 1822

PELECOCERINI

CHAMAESYRPHUS Mik, 1895
caledonicus Collin, 1940
scaevoides (Fallén, 1817)

PELECOCERA Meigen, 1822
tricincta Meigen, 1822

PIPIZINI

HERINGIA Rondani, 1856
S. HERINGIA s.s.
heringi (Zetterstedt, 1843)
senilis Sack, 1938

S. NEOCNEMODON Goffe, 1944
   CNEMODON Egger, 1865
brevidens (Egger, 1865)
latitarsis (Egger, 1865)
pubescens (Delucchi & Pschorn-Walcher,
   1955)
verrucula (Collin, 1931)
vitripennis (Meigen, 1822)

PIPIZA Fallén, 1810
austriaca Meigen, 1822
bimaculata Meigen, 1822
fenestrata Meigen, 1822
lugubris (Fabricius, 1775)
luteitarsis Zetterstedt, 1843
noctiluca (Linnaeus, 1758)
   form A *sensu* Stubbs & Falk, 1983
   form B *sensu* Stubbs & Falk, 1983
   form C *sensu* Stubbs & Falk, 1983
   form D *sensu* Stubbs & Falk, 1983
   form E *sensu* Stubbs & Falk, 1983
   form F *sensu* Stubbs & Falk, 1983

PIPIZELLA Rondani, 1856
maculipennis (Meigen, 1822)
viduata (Linnaeus, 1758)
   varipes (Meigen, 1822)
virens (Fabricius, 1805)

TRICHOPSOMYIA Williston, 1888
   PARAPENIUM Collin, 1952
flavitarsis (Meigen, 1822)

TRIGLYPHUS Loew, 1840
primus Loew, 1840

SERICOMYIINI

ARCTOPHILA Schiner, 1860
superbiens (Müller, 1776)
   fulva (Harris, 1780)

SERICOMYIA Meigen, 1803
lappona (Linnaeus, 1758)
silentis (Harris, 1776)

VOLUCELLINI

VOLUCELLA Geoffroy, 1762
bombylans (Linnaeus, 1758)
    f. *plumata* (De Geer, 1776)
inanis (Linnaeus, 1758)
inflata (Fabricius, 1794)
pellucens (Linnaeus, 1758)
zonaria (Poda, 1761)

XYLOTINI

BLERA Billberg, 1820
    CYNORHINA Williston, 1887
    CYNORRHINA Verrall, 1901, emend.
fallax (Linnaeus, 1758)

BRACHYPALPOIDES Hippa, 1978
lentus (Meigen, 1822)

BRACHYPALPUS Macquart, 1834
laphriformis (Fallén, 1816)
    bimaculatus (Macquart, 1829)

CALIPROBOLA Rondani, 1844
speciosa (Rossi, 1790)

CHALCOSYRPHUS Curran, 1925
S. XYLOTINA Hippa, 1978
    XYLOTOMIMA Shannon, 1926 in
    1976 check list
nemorum (Fabricius, 1805)

S. XYLOTODES Hippa, 1978
eunotus (Loew, 1873)

CRIORHINA Meigen, 1822
asilica (Fallén, 1816)
berberina (Fabricius, 1805)
    f. *oxyacanthae* (Meigen, 1822)
floccosa (Meigen, 1822)
ranunculi (Panzer, 1804)

POCOTA Lepeletier & Serville, 1828
personata (Harris, 1780)

SYRITTA Lepeletier & Serville, 1828
pipiens (Linnaeus, 1758)

TROPIDIA Meigen, 1822
scita (Harris, 1780)

XYLOTA Meigen, 1822
abiens Meigen, 1822
florum (Fabricius, 1805)
jakutorum Bagachanova, 1980
    coeruleiventris authors, misident.
segnis (Linnaeus, 1758)
sylvarum (Linnaeus, 1758)
tarda Meigen, 1822
xanthocnema Collin, 1939

MICRODONTINAE

MICRODON Meigen, 1803
analis (Macquart, 1842)
    eggeri Mik, 1897
devius (Linnaeus, 1761)
mutabilis (Linnaeus, 1758)
myrmicae Schönrogge, Barr, Wardlaw,
    Napper, Gardner, Breen, Elmes &
    Thomas, 2002

TOTALS

	2002	*1983*
Named species	271	250
Unnamed species	5	6
	276	256
Forms of uncertain status	11	9

CHAPTER 12

THE LITERATURE

For those who wish to follow up on the literature, the notes below are intended to give a lead to the main useful sources, these in turn providing references to many important smaller publications. This chapter is also a historical review of the literature, but this has had to be very selective in its coverage.

The first major review on the British hoverfly fauna was published by Verrall (1901) and reprinted by E.W. Classey in 1969. This gives extensive species descriptions and summarises the records known at that time. It is necessary to bear in mind that a large number of species have been split or added since Verrall's time, but the work remains one of great interest.

The Danish fauna was the subject of a monograph by Lundbeck (1916). This is now so out-of-date as to be only of limited interest. A review of the Palaearctic fauna was compiled by Sack (1932), written in German. The keys and long species descriptions remain a major reference to the European fauna, although of course the number of described species in Europe is now much larger. The distribution statements are incredibly brief.

Verrall's nephew, J.E. Collin, added substantially to our knowledge of British hoverflies, a numbered series of papers between 1931 and 1940 being of particular importance, but he subsequently added further British species. His review of the Pipizini in 1952 was drawn upon by Coe. A British check list was published by Kloet & Hincks (1945), which is helpful in making sense of many of the old names used in locality lists and other publications. Between Verrall (1901) and this check list many additions to the British fauna had been made, not only by Collin but also by Coe, Morley and Wainwright.

European attention returned to Britain with the publication of a Royal Entomological Society Handbook by Coe in 1953 which included a number of additional species. Controversies over classification and names instigated by Goffe (1952) and others were taken into account, with quite a lot of new names brought into use. This work stabilised the classification of hoverflies for some time in Europe since it became widely adopted as the modern work. Parmenter (1954) published a revised check list based on the Handbook.

The French fauna was the subject of a monograph by Séguy (1961), although the treatment of each species is sparse. It was based on Sack (1932) and includes a number of species occurring outside France. This work is more readily obtainable than Sack (1932) and is convenient for those who can understand French better than German. The Polish fauna was reviewed by Bańkowska (1963) and the fauna of the European part of the USSR by Stackelberg (1970). These two works are in the respective national languages but the structure of the keys and the illustrations are helpful.

During the 1950s and 1960s there was a series of notes and locality lists by Parmenter and other British dipterists, continuing into the 1970s and beyond. Locality lists of importance include Malham Tarn, Yorkshire (Flint, 1963); Bookham Common, Surrey (Parmenter, 1950b, 1960 and 1966); Monks Wood NNR (Davis, 1973), Hayley Wood (Gilbert & Perry, 1982), Wicken Fen (Friday & Harley, 2000), Cambridgeshire; Wharncliffe Wood, Yorkshire (Brackenbury & Whiteley, 1981); Clowes Wood, Warwickshire (Pugh, 1977); Rhum NNR (Wormell, 1982); Epping Forest (Hanson, 1985); Sandwell Valley, Staffordshire (Bloxham, 1988) and from a garden in Leicester (Owen, 1991; 91 species over a 15-year period, including many casuals). Many of these papers include new ecological information as well as distribution data.

Though there were earlier county lists, many new ones have appeared, some as duplicated reports: Bedfordshire (Janes, 1985, 110 species); Dorset (Levy *et al.*, 1989, 1992, about 200 species); Essex (R.M. Payne, 1974a; R.G. Payne, 1989, 161 species + 13 pre-1970); the Isle of Man (Moore, 1985, 91 species); Leicestershire (Owen, 1979); Kent (Chandler, 1969); Northumberland (Parrack, 2000, 2001a, 2001b); Staffordshire (Emley, 1988, 1992, 160 species); Somerset (Levy & Levy, 1998, 200 species); Surrey (Morris, 1998b, 214 species); Warwickshire (Wright, 1988d, 173 species); Ceredigion (Fowles, 1986, 117 species); Carmarthenshire (Morgan, 1990, 143 species); Clwyd and Gwynedd (Hughes, 1990a, 73 and 83 species respectively); and Merionethshire (Morgan, 1994, 119 species including some unconfirmed species). Additionally there are a number of major area and locality lists: Sheffield and North Derbyshire (Whiteley, 1987, 169 species); Watford area (Godfrey, 1989b, 84 species): the London area (Plant, 1990b, 204 species of which 178 are recent); part of NE & SE Yorkshire (Grayson, 1993, 138 species); and the Wrexham area (Formstone, 1994, 114 species). The Scottish Islands have received more attention, the whole of *Dipterists Digest* no. 14 being devoted to the Western Isles (Whiteley, 1994; MacGowan, 1994a; Whiteley, Garland and Hancock, 1994; Skidmore, 1994), and there is now a list for Orkney (Andrew & Watt, 1993) and papers on Shetland (Burbidge, Owen, & Fowler, 1988; Pennington, 1999 and 2001).

A feature of more recent years has been the publication of distribution maps covering Great Britain (Ball & Morris, 2000) as well as a number of counties: Staffordshire (Rotheray, 1979a), Essex (Payne, 1989), Dorset (Levy *et al.*, 1992), Somerset (Levy & Levy, 1998), Surrey (Morris, 1998b) and Northumberland (Parrack, 2000, 2001a, 2001b).

A list for Ireland was published by Speight, Chandler & Nash (1975) supplemented in later papers by Speight, most recently by Speight (2000c) which includes detailed data sheets for each species and distribution maps (at a resolution of the 50 km squares of the UTM grid).

In the 1970s we entered an era when revisionary work in Britain and various European countries showed that the classification of hoverflies needed a major overhaul. The stability of the post-Coe era was shattered and we are yet to get clear of the present period of flux. Looking back, among the major revisionary papers which heralded a major re-think were a review of the use of genitalia in the classification of European Syrphini by Hippa (1968a), and a revised generic classification of the Syrphini by Vockeroth (1969). Since then more and more species groups and genera have been found to be in need of revision, including the application of names. Some of the main papers are in the bibliography here. A valuable service has been carried out by Speight in revising the British fauna in accord with new continental work as well as publishing revisions of his own. Needless to say the revised Kloet and Hincks check list (1976) had numerous name changes compared with the 1945 edition and with Coe (1953a). Stubbs (1995b

& 2000) reviews the dates of additions to the British fauna since Verrall (1901), and in Stubbs (2001) he gives a revised histogram of additions. This helps interpret the data in old collections and the literature since the dates of recognition of splits can be taken into account. In 1998, a new check list for British Diptera was edited by Peter Chandler and published by the Royal Entomological Society as the first of a new series of check lists for British Insects. Revisions to the check list for hoverflies and regular updates are published in Dipterists Digest (Chandler 1999a, 1999b, 2000a, 2000b, 2001a, 2001b, 2002).

Perhaps the most significant advance has been in the study of larval taxonomy and ecology, including the key work by Rotheray (1993) which contains a much fuller list of references in this field. In the course of such studies it has become possible to gain a new insight into the evolutionary relationships of the genera (Rotheray & Gilbert, 1989, 1999; Rotheray, 1993).

Many new biological data have been published, especially in Europe. Speight *et al.* (2001) includes much information on the biology and habitat associations of over 500 species occurring in the Atlantic, Northern and Central zones of the European Community. There is a good deal of interesting work in progress, including some in Britain, so some very useful papers can be expected over the coming years. It is perhaps worth specifically mentioning the use of trapping as a survey and research technique, the papers by Owen (*e.g.* 1981) applying to studies in Britain. Gilbert (1986, 1993) has published a popular introduction to hoverflies that includes much useful biological information, together with ideas for observing and studying these flies. The main papers on early stages are mentioned in Chapter 5.

The surge in the active study of the European fauna in recent years has led to the publication of key works, atlases and faunal revisions, as well as European reviews of genera and the European fauna more broadly. A work on the hoverflies of the Benelux countries includes 473 species found in north-west Europe and European Russia (van der Goot, 1981). It is illustrated and, although written in Dutch, the keys (based on Stackelberg, 1970) are not unduly difficult to translate. The revised edition of the Danish book on hoverflies (Torp, 1994) has good photographic plates of large numbers of our species as well as some species that may yet be found in Britain. The distribution maps and ecological notes (English summaries) are of interest (the keys are in Danish). A book on the hoverflies of Belgium (Verlinden, 1994) gives a review with keys in French and is also relevant to the fauna of northern France (an earlier Dutch edition (Verlinden, 1991) has keys that include all Dutch species). The book on the Dutch fauna (van der Goot, 1981) is now out of print, and an atlas was published in 1998 (Nederlandse Jeugdbond voor Natuurstudie, 1998). Bothe (1994) gives a key in German. Nielsen (1999) produced a check list and distribution maps for Norway, and Bartsch (2001) gives the distribution of species in Sweden by province. Hence there are now modern works covering the fauna of many of the adjacent areas of Europe which assist understanding of identification and distribution of species that we should be searching for in Britain. See also Speight (1988c, 1991a, 1991b and 2000b) for reviews of potential extra British species.

Two major publications dealing with hoverflies of the Palaearctic region are the catalogue compiled by Peck (1988) and the chapter by Thompson & Rotheray (1998) in the series *Contributions to a Manual of Palaearctic Diptera*, which includes a key to genera for adults and for those larvae that have been described, as well as a detailed diagnosis of the family and summaries of literature sources on topics such morphology, biology and behaviour.

356

In the references and selected bibliography below, journal titles largely follow the abbreviations in *Serial Publications in the British Museum* (*Natural History*) *Library*, 1980.

ALDERSON, E.M., 1909. *Melangyna quadrimaculata* Verr. *Entomologist's mon. Mag.* **45**: 166.

ALDERSON, E.M., 1910. A further note on *Melangyna quadrimaculata* Verr. *Entomologist's mon. Mag.* **46**: 193.

ALDRIDGE, M.C., 1998. *Volucella zonaria* (Dipt., Syrphidae) – a recent northward extension of range into Hertfordshire. *Entomologist's mon. Mag.* **134**: 292.

ALFORD, D.V., 1975. *Bumblebees*. xii+352pp. Davis-Poynter, London.

ALLEN, A.A., 1982-3. Further notable Diptera from Windsor Forest. *Entomologist's Rec. & J. Var.* **94**: 191-194, 229-232; **95**: 24-28.

ALLEN, A.A., 1985a. A colony of *Anasimyia interpuncta* Harris (Dipt.: Syrphidae) on the Thames Marshes. *Entomologist's Rec. & J. Var.* **97**: 85-86.

ALLEN, A.A., 1985b. *Xylota segnis* (L.) (Dipt., Syrphidae) feeding at buddleia flowers. *Entomologist's mon. Mag.* **121**: 205.

ALLEN, A.A., 1987a. *Sphegina kimakowiczi* Strobl (Dipt.: Syrphidae) in W. Kent and S. Essex. *Entomologist's Rec. & J. Var.* **99**: 250.

ALLEN, A.A., 1987b. *Melangyna guttata* Fall. (Dipt.: Syrphidae), etc., at Charlton, S.E. London. *Entomologist's Rec. & J. Var.* **99**: 267.

ALLEN, A.A., 1988. Notes on *Agrilus pannonicus* Pill. & Mitt. (Col.: Buprestidae) in 1985. *Entomologist's Rec. & J. Var.* **100**: 25-28.

ALLEN, A.A., 1989. *Cheilosia variabilis* Panz. (Dipt.: Syrphidae) and figwort. *Entomologist's Rec. & J. Var.* **101**: 18.

ALLEN, A.A., 1992. Some notable Diptera from Oxleas Wood SSSI, Shooters Hill, N.W. Kent. *Entomologist's Rec. & J. Var.* **104**: 265-271.

ALLEN, A.A., 1998. *Didea fasciata* Macq. (Dipt., Syrphidae) in a south-east London garden. *Entomologist's mon. Mag.* **134**: 270.

ANDERSON, R., 1987a. Rare hoverflies (Diptera: Syrphidae) in South Down, including *Brachypalpoides lenta* (Meigen). *Ir. Nat. J.* **22**: 210.

ANDERSON, R., 1987b. *Neoascia obliqua* Coe, a hoverfly (Diptera: Syrphidae) new to Ireland. *Ir. Nat. J.* **22**: 211.

ANDERSON, R., 1987c. Some local woodland hoverflies (Diptera: Syrphidae) including *Parasyrphus lineolus* (Zett.) from the Lagan Valley, Belfast. *Ir. Nat. J.* **22**: 258.

ANDERSON, R., 1988. An interesting faunal association including *Anasimyia transfuga* (L.) (Diptera: Syrphidae) at Aughnadarragh Lough, Co Down. *Ir. Nat. J.* **22**: 452.

ANDERSSON, H., 1970a. Notes on the morphology of "melanoid females" in Syrphidae (Diptera). *Ent. scand.* **1**: 120-122.

ANDERSSON, H., 1970b. Taxonomic notes on the genera *Platycheirus* and *Melanostoma* (Dipt., Syrphidae) with lectotype designations. *Ent. scand.* **1**: 236-240.

ANDERSSON, H., 1970c. The *Sphaerophoria* species described by J.W. Zetterstedt (Dipt., Syrphidae). *Ent. scand.* **1**: 297-300.

ANDERSSON, H., 1988. [The Swedish Xylotini species (Diptera, Syrphidae).] *Ent. Tidskr.* **109**: 129-137. [In Swedish]

ANDREW, R.H. & WATT, K.R., 1993. Orkney hoverflies (Dipt. Syrphidae). *Bull. Orkney Field Club* **1993**: 41-45.

ANDREWES, C.H., 1957. A note on the female of *Brachyopa pilosa* Collin and on the occurrence of all four British species of *Brachyopa* (Dipt., Syrphidae) near London. *Entomologist's mon. Mag.* **93**: 20.

ANDREWS, H.W., 1903. Syrphidae in North Kent. *Entomologist's mon. Mag.* **39**: 38.

ANDREWS, H.W., 1944. *Chilosia albipila* Mg. (Diptera, Syrphidae) bred. *Entomologist's Rec. & J. Var.* **56**: 71.

APPLETON, D., 1987. *Eriozona syrphoides* (Fallén) (Dipt., Syrphidae) new to Hampshire. *Entomologist's mon. Mag.* **123**: 14.

ASHER, J., WARREN, M., FOX, R., HARDING, P., JEFFCOATE, G. & JEFFCOATE, S., 2001. *The Millennium Atlas of Butterflies in Britain and Ireland*. xx+433pp. Oxford University Press, Oxford.

ASTON, A., 1996a. *Callicera aenea* (Fabr.) (Dip.: Syrphidae) in North Hampshire. *Entomologist's Rec. & J. Var.* **108**: 48.

ASTON, A., 1996b. The golden hoverfly *Callicera spinolae* Rondani. *Suffolk Natural History* **32**: 28-29.

ASTON, A., 1997. Recurrence of *Callicera aurata* Rossi (= *aenea* Fabr.) (Dip.: Syrphidae) in North Hampshire. *Entomologist's Rec. & J. Var.* **109**: 143.

AUBERT, J., AUBERT, J.-J. & GOELDLIN DE TIEFENAU, P., 1976. Douze ans de captures systématiques de Syrphides (Diptères) au col de Bretolet (Alpes valaisannes). *Mitt. schweiz. ent. Ges.* **49**: 115-142.

AUBERTIN, D., 1928. The larva of *Pocota apiformis* Schrank. *Entomologist* **61**: 151-152.

AUBERTIN, D. & DIVER, C., 1933. *Triglyphus primus* Lw. (Syrphidae) taken in London. *Entomologist's mon. Mag.* **69**: 188-189.

AUDCENT, H.L.F., 1950. Midnight flies. *Entomologist's mon. Mag.* **87**: 133.

BADMIN. J., 1994. Hoverfly (Dipt., Syrphidae) predators of the hellebore aphid *Macrosiphum hellebori* Theobald & Walton (Hem., Aphididae). *Entomologist's mon. Mag.* **130**: 238.

BAGACHANOVA, A.K., 1990. [*The fauna and ecology of the syrphids* (Diptera, Syrphidae) *of Yakutia.*] 164pp. Yakutsk Nauchnye Tsentr SO SSSR, Yakutsk. [In Russian]

BALL, S.G. & MORRIS, R.K.A., 1992. Progress report 1, March 1992. *Hoverfly Newsletter* no. 14: 1-12.

BALL, S.G. & MORRIS, R.K.A., 2000. *Provisional atlas of British hoverflies* (*Diptera, Syrphidae*). 167pp. Biological Records Centre, Huntingdon.

BAŃKOWSKA, R., 1963. [*Keys for identification of Polish Insects* **28**, Diptera. Part 34 Syrphidae.] 236pp. Państowe Wydawnictwo Naukowe, Warsaw. [In Polish]

BAŃKOWSKA, R., 1980. Fly communities of the family Syrphidae in natural and anthropogenic habitats of Poland. *Memorabilia Zoologica* **33**: 1-94.

BANKS, C.J., 1959. Experiments with suction traps to assess the abundance of Syrphidae (Diptera), with special reference to aphidophagous species. *Ent. exp. appl.* **2**: 110-124.

BARENDREGT, A., 1980. The identification of the females in the genus *Parhelophilus* Girschner, 1897 (Diptera, Syrphidae). *Ent. Berichten, Amst.* **40**: 113-114.

BARENDREGT, A., 1981. The distribution of four species of the genus *Anasimyia* in the Netherlands (Diptera, Syrphidae). *Newsbrief European Invert. Surv. – Nederland.* **10**: 99-102.

BARENDREGT, A., 1982. *Zweefvliegentabel* (zevende druk). 82pp. Jeugdbondsuitgeverij, 'S Graveland, Amsterdam. [In Dutch]

BARENDREGT, A., 1983. *Syrphus nitidifrons* Becker, 1921, from the Netherlands, with description of the male, and a key to the European species (Diptera: Syrphidae). *Ent. Berichten, Amst.* **43**: 59-64.

BARKALOV, A.V. & STAHLS, G., 1997. Revision of the Palaearctic bare-eyed and black-legged species of the genus *Cheilosia* Meigen (Diptera, Syrphidae). *Acta Zoologica Fennica* **208**: 1-74.

BARKEMEYER, W. & CLAUSSEN, C., 1986. Zur Identität von *Neoascia unifasciata* (Strobl 1898) – mit einem Schlüssel für die in der Bundesrepublik Deutschland nachgewiesenen Arten der Gattung *Neoascia* Williston 1886 (Diptera: Syrphidae). *Bonn. zool. Beitr.* **37**: 229-239. [In German]

BARNETT, R.J., 1992. Records of *Volucella zonaria* (Poda) (Dipt., Syrphidae) in Bristol. *Entomologist's mon. Mag.* **128**: 206.

BARR, B., 1995. Feeding behaviour and mouthpart structure of larvae of *Microdon eggeri* and *Microdon mutabilis* (Diptera, Syrphidae). *Dipterists Digest* (second series) **2**: 31-36.

BARR, B., 1996a. *Mallota cimbiciformis* (Diptera, Syrphidae) in Lanarkshire. *Dipterists Digest* (second series) **3**: 4.

BARR, B., 1996b. *Cheilosia chrysocoma* (Diptera, Syrphidae) in Argyll. *Dipterists Digest* (second series) **3**: 48.

BARTSCH, H.D., 2001. Swedish province catalogue for hoverflies (Diptera, Syrphidae). *Ent. Tidskr.* **122**: 189-215.

BASTIAN, O., 1986. *Schwebfliegen.* 168pp. A. Ziemsen, Wittenberg Lutherstadt.

BEUK, P.L.T., 1990. A hoverfly of the genus *Epistrophe* (Dipt., Syrphidae) new to Britain. *Entomologist's mon. Mag.* **126**: 167-170.

358

BIRKETT, N.L., 1959. Some records of hoverflies (Dipt., Syrphidae) at mercury-vapour light. *Entomologist's mon. Mag.* **95**: 63.

BIRKETT, N.L., 1989a. A record of *Sphegina elegans* (Schummel, 1843) (=*kimakowiczi*) (Diptera: Syrphidae) in Cumbria (VC69). *Dipterists Digest* (first series) **2**: 35.

BIRKETT, N.L., 1989b. Another record of *Brachypalpus laphriformis* (Fallén) (Diptera: Syrphidae). *Entomologist's Rec. & J. Var.* **101**: 59-60.

BIRKETT, N.L., 1990. Polyandry in *Merodon equestris* (Fab.) (Syrphidae). *Dipterists Digest* (first series) **6**: 6.

BIRKETT, N., 2000. *Chrysotoxum cautum* (Harris) (Diptera, Syrphidae) in north Lancashire (V.C.69). *Dipterists Digest* (second series) **7**: 4.

BLACKER, N.C. & COLLINGWOOD, C.A., 2002. Some significant new records of ants (Hymenoptera: Formicidae) from the Salisbury area, South Wiltshire, England, with a key to the British species of *Lasius*. *British Journal of Entomology and Natural History* **15**: 25-46.

BLACKITH, R.E. & BLACKITH, R.M., 1989. Diptera reared from decaying potatoes in Ireland. *Ir. Nat. J.* **23**: 71-72.

BLACKITH, R.E., BLACKITH, R.M., SPEIGHT, M.C.D. & COURCY WILLIAMS, M. DE, 1991. A first list of Diptera from Murrough, Co. Wicklow, Ireland, including 663 species and 140 breeding records. *Bull. Ir. biogeog. Soc.* **14**: 185-253.

BLAIR, K.G., 1948. Some recent additions to the British Insect Fauna. *Entomologist's mon. Mag.* **84**: 51-52.

BLAND, K. & ROTHERAY, G.E., 1999. *Xanthandrus comtus* (Harris) (Diptera, Syrphidae) apparently resident in Scotland. *Dipterists Digest* (second series) **5**: 17.

BLOOMFIELD, E.N., 1897. Habits of *Sericomyia borealis* Fln. *Entomologist's mon. Mag.* **33**: 222-223.

BLOXHAM, M.G., 1988. The Diptera (Syrphidae) of the Sandwell Valley. *Entomologist's Rec. & J. Var.* **100**: 11-19.

BLOXHAM, M.G., 2001. Hoverflies as primary woodland indicator species in the Sandwell Valley. *Sandnats* **23**: 33-44.

BOLTON, B. & COLLINGWOOD, C.A., 1975. Hymenoptera, Formicidae. *Handbk Ident. Br. Insects* **6** (3c): 1-33.

BOTHE, G., 1994. *Schwebfliegen.* 123pp. Deutscher Jugendbund für Naturbeobachtung, Hamburg. [In German]

BOWDEN, J., 1997. *Didea fasciata* Macquart and *Pipizella maculipennis* Meigen (Diptera, Syrphidae) rediscovered in N.E. Essex. *Entomologist's mon. Mag.* **133**: 204.

BOWDREY, J.P., 1987. Aphid galls and hoverflies. *Cecidology* **2**: 45.

BRACKENBURY A., 1998. *Eristalis pratorum* a new & rare hoverfly for Derbyshire. *Derbyshire & Notttinghamshire Entomological Society Quarterly Journal* no. 131: 27.

BRACKENBURY A. & WHITELEY, D., 1981. Hoverflies (Diptera, Syrphidae) of Wharncliffe Wood. *Sorby Record* **19**: 4-17.

BRANQUART, E., HEMPTINNE, J.L., BAUFFE, C. & BENFEKIH, L., 1997. Cannibalism in *Episyrphus balteatus* (Dipt.: Syrphidae). *Entomophaga* **42**: 145-152.

BRAUNS, A., 1953. Beiträge zur Ökologie und wirtschaftlichen Bedeutung der aphidivoren Syrphidenarten. *Beitr. Ent.* **3**: 279-303. [In German]

BRAUNS, A., 1954. Untersuchungen zur Angewandten Bodenbiologie. 1. Terricole Dipterenlarven. 179pp. 2. Puppen terricoler Dipterenlarven. 156pp. Musterschmidt, Göttingen. [In German]

BREEN, J.A.G., 1977. A note on the species of *Microdon* (Diptera, Syrphidae) in Ireland. *Entomologist's Gaz.* **28**: 243-244.

BRIAN, M.C., 1987. *Xanthandrus comtus* (Harris) (Diptera: Syrphidae) new to Staffordshire (VC 39). *Entomologist's Rec. & J. Var.* **99**: 131.

BRIAN, M.C., 1995a. Diptera notes from Staffordshire - hibernating hoverflies? *Dipterists Digest* (second series) **2**: 40.

BRIAN, M.C., 1995b. Diptera notes from Staffordshire - *Pocota personata* Harris (Diptera - Syrphidae) in Staffordshire. *Dipterists Digest* (second series) **2**: 40.

BRIGDEN, B., 1997. *Microdon mutabilis*: a case of sexual aggression. *Hoverfly Newsletter* no. 24: 5-6.

BRITTEN, H., 1916. *Mallota cimbiciformis* Fln., bred from rotten wood. *Trans. ent. Soc. Lond.* (*Proc.*) **1916**: lxxxiii-lxxxiv.

BRITTEN, H., 1951. A list of Staffordshire Diptera. *Trans. N. Staffs. Field Club* **85**: 31-47.

BROADBENT, B., 1925. Notes on the life history of the lesser bulb-fly *Eumerus strigatus* Fallén. *J. econ. Ent.* **18**: 141-143.

BROWN, A.J. & SEARLE, C.A., 1974. Syrphidae (Diptera) in Dorset. *Entomologist's Gaz.* **25**: 111-123.

BROWN, E.S., 1951. Variation and polymorphism in *Lampetia equestris* (F.) (Dipt., Syrphidae) and other British mimetic insects. *Entomologist's mon. Mag.* **87**: 16-18.

BRUNEL, E. & CADOU, D., 1994. Syrphid larvae (Diptera: Syrphidae) mining the roots of artichoke (*Cynara scolymus* L.) in Brittany. *Dipterists Digest* (second series) **1**: 69-71.

BRYAN, M.D., 1987. Island interludes – Guernsey and the Isle of Mull in 1986. *Entomologist's Rec. & J. Var.* **99**: 125-128.

BUCKTON, G.B., 1895. *The natural history of* Eristalis tenax. 88pp. London.

BUNN, D.S., 1988. Observations on the foraging habits of the hornet *Vespa crabro* L. (Hym., Vespidae). *Entomologist's mon. Mag.* **124**: 187-193.

BURBIDGE, A., OWEN, J. & FOWLER, J.A., 1988. Some records of hoverflies (Dipt., Syrphidae) in Shetland. *Entomologist's mon. Mag.* **124**: 44.

CAMPAN, M., 1973. [Preliminary observations of the influence of meteorological factors on the rhythm of activity of female *Eristalis tenax* on the oviposition site.] *Rev. Comport. anim.* **3**: 69-76. [In French]

CARPENTER, G.H., 1913. Injurious insects and other animals observed in Ireland during the year 1912. *Econ. Proc. Dublin Soc.* **2** (6): 79-104.

CHAMBERS, R.L. & ADAMS, T.H.L., 1986. Quantification of the impact of hoverflies (Diptera: Syrphidae) on cereal aphids in winter wheat: an analysis of field populations. *J. appl. Ecol.* **23**: 895-904.

CHAMBERS, R.L., SUNDERLAND, K.D., STACEY, D.L., & WYATT, I.J., 1986. Control of cereal aphids in winter wheat by natural enemies: aphid specific predators, parasitoids and pathogenic fungi. *Ann. appl. Biol.* **108**: 219-231.

CHANDLER A.E.F., 1968a. The relationship between aphid infestations and oviposition by aphidophagous Syrphidae (Diptera). *Ann. appl Biol.* **61**: 425-434.

CHANDLER, A.E.F., 1968b. Some factors influencing the site and occurrence of ovipositing by aphidophagous Syrphidae (Diptera). *Ann. appl Biol.* **61**: 435-446.

CHANDLER, A.E.F., 1968c. A preliminary key to the eggs of some of the commoner aphidophagous Syrphidae (Diptera) occurring in Britain. *Trans. R. ent. Soc. Lond.* **120**: 199-218.

CHANDLER, P.J., 1969. The hover-flies of Kent. *Trans. Kent Field Club* **3**: 139-202.

CHANDLER, P.J., 1998. Checklists of insects of the British Isles (New Series) part 1: Diptera. *Handbk Ident. Br. Insects* **12** (1): 1-234.

CHANDLER, P.J., 1999a. Corrections and changes to the Diptera Checklist (1). *Dipterists Digest* (second series) **6**: 57-61.

CHANDLER, P.J., 1999b. Corrections and changes to the Diptera Checklist (2) - Editor. *Dipterists Digest* (second series) **6**: 112-113.

CHANDLER, P.J., 2000a. Corrections and changes to the Diptera Checklist (3) - Editor. *Dipterists Digest* (second series) **7**: 50-52.

CHANDLER, P.J., 2000b. Corrections and changes to the Diptera Checklist (4) - Editor. *Dipterists Digest* (second series) **7**: 81-82.

CHANDLER, P.J., 2001a. Corrections and changes to the Diptera Checklist (5) - Editor. *Dipterists Digest* (second series) **8**: 67-70.

CHANDLER, P.J., 2001b. Corrections and changes to the Diptera Checklist (6) - Editor. *Dipterists Digest* (second series) **8**: 126-127.

CHANDLER, P.J., 2002. Corrections and changes to the Diptera Checklist (7) - Editor. *Dipterists Digest* (second series) **9**: 84-86.

CHAPMAN, T.A., 1905. Some observations on *Hastula hyerana* Mill. *Entomologist's mon. Mag.* **41**: 149-157.

CHAPMAN, T.A., 1906. Food and habits of *Xanthandrus comtus* Harris. *Entomologist's mon. Mag.* **42**: 14-16.

CHOI, D.-S. & HAN, Y., 1999. A taxonomic study of the genus *Platycheirus* Lepeletier et Serville (Diptera: Syrphidae) in Korea. *Korean J. ent.* **29**: 165-176.

CLAUSSEN, C., 1980. Die Schwebfliegenfauna des Landesteils Schleswig in Schleswig-Holstein (Diptera, Syrphidae). *Faun. Ökol. Mitt., Suppl., Kiel* **1**: 3-79. [In German]

CLAUSSEN, L. & KASSEBEER, C., 1993. Eine neue Art der Gattung *Cheilosia* Meigen 1822 aus den Pyrenäen (Diptera: Syrphidae). *Entomol. Z.*, **103**: 409-428. [In German]

CLAUSSEN, L. & TORP, E., 1980. Untersuchungen über vier europäische Arten der Gattung *Anasimyia* Schiner 1864 (Insecta, Diptera, Syrphidae). *Mitt. Zool. Mus. Univ. Kiel.* **1**: 1-11. [In German]

CLEMENTS, D.K., 1987a. *Eristalis rupium* F. (Diptera: Syrphidae) in Derbyshire. *Entomologist's mon. Mag.* **123**: 68.

CLEMENTS, D.K., 1987b. *Criorhina asilica* (Fallén) (Dipt., Syrphidae) new to Wales. *Entomologist's mon. Mag.* **123**: 96.

CLEMENTS, D.K., 1987c. An unusual aberration of leg structure in *Cheilosia albitarsis* Meigen (Dipt., Syrphidae). *Entomologist's mon. Mag.* **123**: 107-108.

CLEMENTS, D.K., 1988. *Dasysyrphus friuliensis* van der Goot (Dipt., Syrphidae) in Northumberland. *Entomologist's mon. Mag.* **124**: 144.

CLEMENTS, D.K. & ALEXANDER, K.N.A., 1987. *Ctenophora* species (Dipt., Tipulidae) in Hereford and Worcestershire. *Entomologist's mon. Mag.* **123**: 140.

CLEMONS, L., 2000. *Psilota anthracina* Mg. (Dip.: Syrphidae) and *Melanochaeta capreolus* (Haliday) (Dip.: Chloropidae): two enigmatic species found together at a site in East Kent. *Entomologist's Rec. & J. Var.* **112**: 180-181.

COE, R.L., 1938. Rediscovery of *Callicera yerburyi* Verrall (Diptera: Syrphidae); its breeding-habits, with a description of the larva. *Entomologist* **71**: 97-102.

COE, R.L., 1939a. Description of the female of *Xylota xanthocnema* Collin (Diptera: Syrphidae). *Entomologist's mon. Mag.* **75**: 224.

COE, R.L., 1939b. A second British record of *Rhingia rostrata* L. (Dipt., Syrphidae); its distinctions from *R. campestris* Meigen. *Entomologist's mon. Mag.* **75**: 225-227.

COE, R.L., 1939c. *Callicera yerburyi* Verrall (Diptera: Syrphidae) a synonym of *C. rufa* Schummel; further details of its life-history, with a description of the puparium. *Entomologist* **72**: 228-231.

COE, R.L., 1940. A new British species of the genus *Neoascia* Williston (Diptera: Syrphidae). *Entomologist's mon. Mag.* **76**: 18-19.

COE, R.L., 1941a. Distribution of *Eristalis abusivus* Collin (Dipt., Syrphidae) in the British Isles, with notes on the female. *Entomologist's mon. Mag.* **77**: 130-131.

COE, R.L., 1941b. *Callicera rufa* Schummel (Diptera: Syrphidae); colour-variation of abdominal hairs in the adult, with a note on longevity of the larva. *Entomologist* **74**: 131-132.

COE, R.L., 1941c. *Chrysochlamys ruficornis* F. (Dipt., Syrphidae): its distinctions from *C. cuprea* Scop. *Entomologist's mon. Mag.* **77**: 165-167.

COE, R.L., 1941d. *Brachypalpus eunotus* Loew (Dipt., Syrphidae) new to Britain; its distinctions from *B. bimaculatus* Macquart; and notes on synonymy in the genus. *Entomologist's mon. Mag.* **77**: 193-197.

COE, R.L., 1942. *Rhingia campestris* Meigen (Dipt., Syrphidae): an account of its life-history and descriptions of the early stages. *Entomologist's mon. Mag.* **78**: 121-130.

COE, R.L., 1943. *Callicera spinolae* Rond. (Dipt., Syrphidae) taken in Britain; its redescription, with notes on *C. aenea* Fabr. and *C. rufa* Schumm. *Entomologist* **76**: 155-158.

COE, R.L., 1950. *Criorrhina oxyacanthae* Meig. a variety of *C. berberina* F. (Dipt., Syrphidae). *Entomologist's mon. Mag.* **86**: 124-126.

COE, R.L., 1953a. Diptera. Family Syrphidae. *Handbk Ident. Br. Insects* **10** (1): 1-98.

COE, R.L., 1953b. *Mallota cimbiciformis* Fallén (Diptera: Syrphidae) breeding in Hyde Park, London. *Entomologist's Gaz.* **4**: 282-286.

COE, R.L., 1957. Some new Syrphidae (Diptera) from Yugoslavia. *Proc. R. ent. Soc. Lond.* (*B*) **26**: 60-62.

COE, R.L., 1961. Massed occurrence of the rare syrphid fly, *Rhingia rostrata* Linnaeus, at Selsdon Woods in Surrey. *Entomologist* **94**: 257.

COLDWELL, J.D., 1985. Some interesting insects in a Barnsley Wood. *Sorby Record* **23**: 82-83.

COLDWELL, J.D., 1992. Three flies new to Yorkshire in 1991. *Dipterists Digest* **11**: 41-42.

COLENUTT. S., 1992. Observation of a migration at West High Down, the Needles, Isle of Wight. *Entomologist's Rec. & J. Var.* **104**: 46.

COLLETT, T.S. & LAND, M.F., 1975a. Visual control of flight behaviour in the hoverfly *Syritta pipiens*. *J. comp. Physiol.* **99**: 1-66.

COLLETT, T.S. & LAND, M.F., 1975b. Visual spatial memory in hoverflies. *J. comp. Physiol.* **100**: 59-84.

COLLETT, T.S. & LAND, M.F., 1978. How hoverflies compute interception courses. *J. comp. Physiol.* **125**: 191-204.

COLLIN, J.E., 1918. A Dipteron new to the British List. *Trans. ent. Soc. Lond.* (*Proc.*) **1918**: lxxvii.

COLLIN, J.E., 1931a. Notes on some Syrphidae. *Entomologist's mon. Mag.* **67**: 153-159.

COLLIN, J.E., 1931b. Notes on some Syrphidae. *Entomologist's mon. Mag.* **67**: 177-182.

COLLIN, J.E., 1931c. The Oxford University Expedition to Greenland, 1928—Diptera (Orthorrhapha, Brachycera and Cyclorrhapha) from Greenland. *Ann. Mag. nat. Hist.* (10) **7**: 67-91.

COLLIN, J.E., 1937. Notes on Syrphidae (Diptera), II. *Entomologist's mon. Mag.* **73**: 182-185.

COLLIN, J.E., 1939. Notes on Syrphidae (Diptera), III. *Entomologist's mon. Mag.* **75**: 104-109.

COLLIN, J.E., 1940. Notes on Syrphidae (Diptera), IV. *Entomologist's mon. Mag.* **76**: 150-158.

COLLIN, J.E., 1946a. A redescription of *Syrphus mecogramma* Bigot, and a note on the occurrence of probably the same species in Scotland. *Proc. R. ent. Soc. Lond.* (B) **15**: 11-12.

COLLIN, J.E., 1946b. *Syrphus ericarum* sp. n. *Entomologist's Rec. & J. Var.* **58**: 117-119.

COLLIN, J.E., 1950. A second British species of *Myolepta*. *J. Soc. Br. Ent.* **3**: 133-137.

COLLIN, J.E., 1952a. *Syrphus malinellus* sp. n. *Proc. R. ent. Soc. Lond.* (B) **21**: 35-36.

COLLIN, J.E., 1952b. On the subdivisions of the genus *Pipizella* Rond., and an additional British species. *J. Soc. Brit. Ent.* **4**: 85-88.

COLLIN, J.E., 1960. A fourth species of *Cnemodon* (Diptera, Syrphidae) in Britain. *Entomologist* **93**: 144-145.

COLLINGWOOD, C.A., 1964. The identification and distribution of British ants, 1. A revised key to the species found in Britain. *Trans. Soc. Br. Ent.* **16**: 93-114.

COLYER, C.N. & HAMMOND, C.O., 1951. *Flies of the British Isles*. (First edition). 383pp. Warne, London.

COLYER, C.N. & HAMMOND, C.O., 1968. *Flies of the British Isles*. (Second edition). 384pp. Warne, London.

CONN, D.L.T., 1972. The genetics of mimetic colour polymorphism in the large narcissus bulb fly, *Merodon equestris* Fabr. (Diptera: Syrphidae). *Phil. Trans. R. Soc. B* **264**: 353-402.

CONN, D.L.T., 1976a. Estimates of population size and longevity of adult *Narcissus* bulb fly, *Merodon equestris* Fabricius (Diptera, Syrphidae). *J. appl. Ecol.* **13**: 429-434.

CONN, D.L.T., 1976b. Evidence of restricted mimetic colour polymorphism in the Pyrenees. *Heredity* **36**: 185-189.

CONN, D.L.T., 1976c. Rearing the large narcissus bulb fly in captivity. *Bull. amat. Ent. Soc.* **35**: 20-21.

COOKSON, H. A. & OLDROYD, H., 1937. Intestinal infestation by larvae of a Drone Fly. *Lancet* **233**: 804-805.

COOTER, J., 1979. Some uncommon insects on Deeside. *Entomologist's mon. Mag.* **113** (1977): 202.

COWGILL, S.E., WRATTEN, S.D. & SOTHERTON, N.W., 1993. The effects of weeds on the numbers of hoverfly (Diptera: Syrphidae) adults and the distribution and composition of their eggs in winter wheat. *Ann. appl. Biol.* **123**: 499-515.

COWLEY, J., 1949a. Clythiidae, Dorilaidae and Syrphidae (Diptera) collected by E. and H. Drabble. *J. Soc. Br. Ent.* **3**: 98-101.

COWLEY, J., 1949b. Some Diptera from Surrey and the South-west of England. *J. Soc. Br. Ent.* **3**: 101-118.

CROSSLEY, R., 1965. *Eristalis abusivus* Collin (Dipt., Syrphidae) in Northern England. *Entomologist* **98**: 174.

CROSSLEY, R., 1967. Some notes on the Syrphidae (Diptera) of a Yorkshire clough. *Entomologist* **100**: 73-74.

CROSSLEY, R., 1980. *Eriozona syrphoides* (Fallén) (Dipt., Syrphidae) in Yorkshire. *Entomologist's mon. Mag.* **115** (1979): 200.

CROW, P., 1969. *Eriozona syrphoides* Fal. (Diptera, Syrphidae) in North Wales: a new British species and genus. *Entomologist's Rec. & J. Var.* **81**: 237-238.

CROW, P., 1974. *Eriozona syrphoides* Fallén (Dipt., Syrphidae) in North Wales. *Entomologist's mon. Mag.* **110**: 202.

CROW, P., 1983. *Eriozona syrphoides* (Fallén) (Dipt., Syrphidae) at Morfa Harlech, Merioneth, North Wales and the earliest date for Great Britain. *Entomologist's mon. Mag.* **119**: 79.

CROW, P., 1987. *Didea alneti* (Fallén) (Dipt., Syrphidae) in Wales and its colour change after death. *Entomologist's mon. Mag.* **123**: 34.

DAVIS, B.N.K., 1965. A preliminary list of hoverflies (Diptera: Syrphidae) from Huntingdonshire with special reference to Monks Wood National Nature Reserve. *Entomologist's Gaz.* **16**: 89-93.

DAVIS, B.N.K., 1973. Syrphidae. pp. 169-176. **In:** Steele, R.C. & Welch, R.C. (Eds) *Monks Wood a nature reserve record.* xiv+337pp. The Nature Conservancy, Huntingdon.

DAWE, G. & McGLASHAN, S., 1987. The ecology of urban hoverflies in relation to spontaneous and managed vegetation. *Bulletin of the British Ecological Society* **18**: 168-171.

DECLEER, K. & ROTHERAY, G.E., 1990. The puparium and larval habitat of the hoverfly *Tropidia scita* (Diptera: Syrphidae). *Entomologist's Gaz.* **41**: 157-160.

DECLEER, K., VERLINDEN, L. & ZWÖLFER, H., 1991. A standard method for site evaluation and indication of 'Red Data Book' species, using distribution data of invertebrates. An example based on the hoverfly fauna (Diptera, Syrphidae) of Belgium. pp. 115-132. **In:** van Goethem, J.L. & Grootaert, P. (Eds) *Faunal inventories of sites for cartography and nature conservation.* Proceedings of the 8th International Colloquium of the European Invertebrate Survey, Brussels, 9-10 September 1991. European Invertebrate Survey, Brussels.

DELUCCHI, V. & PSCHORN-WALCHER, H., 1955. Les espèces du genre *Cnemodon* Egger (Diptera, Syrphidae) prédatrices de *Dreyfusia* (*Adelges*) *piceae* Ratz. (Hem. Adelgidae). **1**: Révision systématique et répartition géographique des espèces du genre *Cnemodon* Egger. *Z. angew. Ent.* **37**: 492-506. [In French]

DELUCCHI, V. & PSCHORN-WALCHER, H., 1957. *Cnemodon*-Arten (Syrphidae) als Räuber von *Dreyfusia piceae* Ratz. (Adelgidae). **2**: Morphologie und Biologie von *Cnemodon dreyfusiae* D. & P.-W. nebst Beobachtungen über *C. latitarsis* Egger. *Z. angew. Ent.* **41**: 246-259. [In German]

DELY-DRASKOVITS, A. & BABOS, M., 1993. Flies (Diptera) in macrofungi species in Hungary. *Folia Entomologica Hungarica* **54**: 17-45.

DENTON, J.S. & FRY, R.M., 1998. Recent records of scarce and notable hoverflies (Dipt., Syrphidae) in England. *Entomologist's mon. Mag.* **134**: 327-328.

DICKER, G.H.L., 1979. A migration of syrphids (Dipt., Syrphidae) in East Sussex. *Entomologist's mon. Mag.* **113** (1977): 212.

DINKEL, T. & LUNAU, K. 2001. How drone flies (*Eristalis tenax* L., Syrphidae, Diptera) use floral guides to locate food sources. *Journal of Insect Physiology* **47**: 1111-1118.

DISNEY, R.H.L., ERZINCLIOGLU, Y.Z., HENSHAW, D.J. DE C., HOWSE, D., UNWIN, D.M., WITHERS, P. & WOODS, A., (1982). Collecting methods and the adequacy of attempted faunal surveys, with reference to the Diptera. *Field Studies* **5**: 607-621.

DITTRICH, W., GILBERT, F., GREEN, P., McGREGOR, P. & GREWCOCK, D., 1994. Imperfect mimicry: a pigeon's perspective. *Proc. R. Soc. Lond. B* **251**: 195-200.

DIXON, T.J., 1959. Studies on the oviposition behaviour of Syrphidae (Diptera). *Trans. R. ent. Soc. Lond.* **111**: 57-80.

DIXON, T.J., 1960. Key to and descriptions of the third instar larvae of some species of Syrphidae (Diptera) occurring in Britain. *Trans. R. ent. Soc. Lond.* **112**: 345-379.

DOBSON, J.R., 1997a. Oviposition in *Epistrophe diaphana* (Syrphidae). *Dipterists Digest* (second series) **4**: 47.

DOBSON, J.R., 1997b. An early record of *Scaeva selenitica* (Meigen) (Syrphidae) from the Brent Reservoir, Middlesex. *Dipterists Digest* (second series) **4**: 64.

DOCZKAL, D., 1998. *Leucozona lucorum* (Linnaeus) – a species complex? (Diptera, Syrphidae). *Volucella* **3**: 27-49.

DOCZKAL, D., 2000a. Description of *Cheilosia ranunculi* spec. nov. from Europe, a sibling species of *C. albitarsis* Meigen (Diptera, Syrphidae). *Volucella* **5**: 63-78.

DOCZKAL, D., 2000b. Redescription of *Leucozona nigripila* Mik and description of *Leucozona inopinata* spec. nov. (Diptera, Syrphidae). *Volucella* **5**: 115-127.

DOCZKAL, D. & SCHMID, U., 1994. Drei neue Arten der Gattung *Epistrophe* (Diptera: Syrphidae), mit einem Bestimmungsschlüssel für die deutschen Arten *Stuttgarter Beitr. Naturk.* (*A*) no. **507**: 1-32. [In German]

DOCZKAL, D. & SCHMID, U., 1999. Revision der mitteleuropäischen Arten der Gattung *Microdon* Meigen (Diptera, Syrphidae). *Volucella* **4**: 45-68. [In German]

DOLEZIL, Z., 1972. Developmental stages of the tribe Eristalini (Diptera, Syrphidae). *Čas. české. Spol. ent.* **69**: 339-350.

DONISTHORPE, H., 1927. The guests of British ants, their habits and life-histories. 244pp. Routledge & Sons, London.

DONISTHORPE, H., 1928. The bionomics of *Pocota apiformis* Schrank. *Entomologist* **61**: 150-151.

DONISTHORPE, H., 1932. *Psilota anthracina* Meigen, a rare Dipteron taken in Windsor Forest. *Entomologist's Rec. & J. Var.* **44**: 93.

DRABBLE, E. & DRABBLE, H., 1917. The syrphid visitors to certain flowers. *New Phytol.* **16**: 105-109.

DRABBLE, E. & DRABBLE, H., 1927. Some flowers and their dipteran visitors. *New Phytol.* **26**: 115-123.

DRAKE, C.M., 1988. Diptera from the Gwent Levels, South Wales. *Entomologist's mon. Mag.* **124**: 37-44.

DUNCAN, A.B., 1982a. *Tropidia scita* (Harris, M.) (Dipt., Syrphidae) in Dumfriesshire. *Entomologist's mon. Mag.* **118**: 30.

DUNCAN, A.B., 1982b. *Criorhina ranunculi* (Panzer) (Dipt., Syrphidae) in Dumfriesshire. *Entomologist's mon. Mag.* **118**: 165.

DUNCAN, A.B., 1983. *Xanthogramma pedissequum* (Harris) (Dipt., Syrphidae) in Dumfriesshire. *Entomologist's mon. Mag.* **119**: 244.

DUNN, J.A., 1949. The parasites and predators of potato Aphids. *Bull. ent. Res.* **40**: 97-122.

DUŠEK, J., 1962. Beitrag zur Kenntnis von Larven der Gattung *Cheilosia* Meigen (Diptera, Syrphidae). *Čas. české. Spol. ent.* **59**: 68-73.

DUŠEK, J. & KŘÍSTEK, J., 1967. Zur Kenntnis der Schwebfliegenlarven (Diptera, Syrphidae) in den Gallen der Pappelblattläuse (Hemiptera, Pemphigidae). *Z. angew. Ent.* **60**: 124-136. [In German]

DUŠEK, J. & LÁSKA, P., 1964. A contribution to distinguishing the European species of the subgenus *Syrphus* Fabricius (Syrphidae, Diptera) according to male genitalia and larvae. *Čas. české. Spol. ent.* **61**: 58-70.

DUŠEK, J. & LÁSKA, P., 1967. Versuch zum Aufbau eines natürlichen Systems mitteleuropäischer Arten der Unterfamilie Syrphinae (Diptera). *Přírodov. Pr. Česk. Acad Ved.* **1**: 349-390.

DUŠEK, J. & LÁSKA, P., 1974a. Overwintering and spring emergence of some common species of aphidophagous syrphids (Syrphidae, Diptera). *Folia přírod. Fak. Univ. Purkyne.* **15**: 71-75. [In German]

DUŠEK, J. & LÁSKA, P., 1974b. Influence of temperature during pupal development on the colour of syrphid adults (Syrphidae, Diptera). *Folia přírod. Fak. Univ. Purkyne.* **15**: 77-81.

DUŠEK, J. & LÁSKA, P., 1976. European species of *Metasyrphus*: key, descriptions and notes (Dipt., Syrphidae). *Acta ent. bohemoslovaca* **73**: 263-282.

DUSSAIX, C., 1996. *Callicera spinolae* (Diptera, Syrphidae) reared in France. *Dipterists Digest* (second series) **3**: 44.

DUSSAIX, C., 1997. *Myolepta vara* (Diptera, Syrphidae) reared in France (Dép. Sarthe). *Dipterists Digest* (second series) **4**: 18-19.

EDWARDS, R., 1980. *Social Wasps*. 398pp. Rentokil, East Grinstead.

ELLIS, E.A., 1937. *Eristalis tenax* hibernating, clustered in crevice of exposed chalk in November. *Trans. Norfolk Norwich Nat. Soc.* **14**: 189.

ELMES, G.W., BARR, B., THOMAS, J.A. & CLARKE, R.T., 1999. Extreme host specificity by *Microdon mutabilis* (Diptera: Syrphidae), a social parasite of ants. *Proc. R. Soc. Lond. B* **266**: 447-453.

ELSE, G.R., 1976. Uncommon Diptera recorded from Oxenbourne Downs, Hampshire in 1972-74. *Entomologist's mon. Mag.* **111** (1975): 114.

EMLEY, D.W., 1988. *Staffordshire hoverflies*. 12pp. Staffordshire Biological Records Centre. City Museum, Stoke-on-Trent.

364

EMLEY, D.W., 1992. *Staffordshire flies*. 139pp. Staffordshire Biological Records Scheme, Publ. no. 15. City Museum, Stoke-on-Trent.

ENTWISTLE, P.F., 1978. Twenty years of *Eriozona syrphoides* (Fallén) (Diptera, Syrphidae) in Britain. *Entomologist's mon. Mag.* **113** (1977): 146.

ENTWISTLE, P.F., 1980. *Criorhina ranunculi* (Panz.) (Dipt., Syrphidae) in N.E. Scotland. *Entomologist's mon. Mag.* **115** (1979): 256.

ENTWISTLE, P.F., 1982. *Dasysyrphus friuliensis* v. d. Goot (Dipt. Syrphidae) in Welsh coniferous forests. *Entomologist's mon. Mag.* **118**: 245.

ENTWISTLE, P.F., 1995a. Hoverflies north of Inverness. *Hoverfly Newsletter* no. 20: 2-5.

ENTWISTLE, P.F., 1995b. *Eriozona syrphoides* (Fallén) (Dipt., Syrphidae) in Sutherland, Scotland. *Entomologist's mon. Mag.* **131**: 40.

ENTWISTLE, P.F. & STUBBS, A.E., 1983. *Preliminary atlas of the hoverflies* (*Diptera*: *Syrphidae*) *of the British Isles*. 30pp. Biological Records Centre, Huntingdon.

EVENHUIS, H.H., 1959. *Cnemodon vitripennis* (Meig.) als roofvijand van de appelbloedluis, *Eriosoma lanigerum* (Hausm.) (Dipt., Hemipt.). *Ent. Berichten, Amst.* **19**: 238-240. [In Dutch]

EVENHUIS, H.H., 1978. *Didea intermedia* (Dipt., Syrphidae) als predator van *Schizolachnus pineti* (Hemipt., Aphididae) en over prooi-specialisatie van andere bladluisvretende zweefvlieglarven. *Ent. Berichten, Amst.* **38**: 129-131. [In Dutch]

FALK, S.J., 1990. *Eristalis pratorum* (Meigen, 1822): a new British hoverfly. *British Journal of Entomology and Natural History* **3**: 139-141.

FALK, S.J., 1991a. *Scaeva selenitica* (Meigen) recorded in March with discussion on the overwintering status of *Scaeva* species in Britain. *Dipterists Digest* (first series) **8**: 36-37.

FALK, S.J., 1991b. A review of the scarce and threatened flies of Great Britain. *Research and Survey in Nature Conservation* no. 39. 194pp. Nature Conservancy Council, Peterborough.

FALK, S.J., 1992. *Parasyrphus nigritarsis* (Zetterstedt) and some other scarce flies recorded from Malham Tarn, N.W. Yorkshire. *Dipterists Digest* (first series) **11**: 40.

FALK, S.J., 1998. Individual Species Impact Assessments: A standardised technique for describing the impact of development proposals on critical invertebrate species. *British Journal of Entomology and Natural History* **11**: 19-29.

FALK, S.J. & STUBBS, A.E., 1991. Further records and observations of *Platycheirus* species (Syrphidae) recently added to the British list, with discussion on the identification of *P. ramsarensis*. *Dipterists Digest* (first series) **10**: 40-45.

FALK, S.J., SMITH, D.A. & STUBBS, A.E., 1981. *Neoascia interrupta* (Meigen, 1822) (Diptera: Syrphidae) new to Britain. *Proc. Trans. Br. ent. nat. Hist. Soc.* **14**: 12-14.

FELTON, J.C., 1975. Insects on Hothfield local Nature Reserve. *Trans. Kent Field Club* **5**: 150-174.

FELTON, J.C., 1980. Further notes on the insects of Hothfield local Nature Reserve. *Trans. Kent Field Club* **8**:91-99.

FERGUSSON, N.D.M., 1980. A revision of the British species of *Dendrocerus* Ratzeberg (Hymenoptera: Ceraphronoidea) with a review of their biology as aphid hyperparasites. *Bull. Br. Mus. nat. Hist.* (*Ent.*) **41**: 255-314.

FINCH, S., COLLIER, R.H. & ELLIOTT, 1990. Biological studies associated with forecasting the time of attacks by the large narcissus fly, *Merodon equestris*. *Brighton Crop Protection Conference – Pests and Diseases 1990* **1**: 111-116.

FITTON, M.G. & ROTHERAY, G.E., 1982. A key to the European genera of diplazontine ichneumon-flies with notes on the British fauna. *Syst. Ent.* **7**: 311-320.

FITZPATRICK, S.M. & WELLINGTON, W.G., 1981. Insect territoriality. *Can. J. Zool.* **61**: 471-486.

FITZPATRICK, S.M. & WELLINGTON, W.G., 1983. Contrasts in the territorial behaviour of three species of hoverflies. *Can. Ent.* **115**: 559-566.

FLINT, J.H., (Ed.) 1963. Insects of the Malham Tarn area. *Leeds Phil. Lit. Soc.* (*Sci. Sect.*) **9**: 15-91.

FORMSTONE, B., 1994. Hoverflies recorded in the Wrexham area of Denbighshire V.C. 50 1990-93. *North Wales Invertebrate Group Newsletter* **9**: 6-8.

FOSTER, A.P., 1987a. *Xanthogramma pedissequum* (Harris) (Dipt.: Syrphidae) bred from a *Lasius niger* (L.) (Hym. Formicidae) nest. *Entomologist's Rec. & J. Var.* **99**: 44-45.

FOSTER, A.P., 1987b. *Agrilus pannonicus* (Piller & Mitterpacher, 1783) (Col.: Buprestidae) and other noteworthy insects recorded from Hampstead Heath in 1984. *Entomologist's Rec. & J. Var.* **99**: 153-155.

FOWLES, A.P., 1986. *Hoverfly recording in Ceredigion.* 24pp. Nature Conservancy Council, Dyfed-Powys Region, Aberystwyth.

FRASER, F.C., 1946. Breeding of *Volucella* larvae in nest of *Vespula vulgaris. Entomologist's mon. Mag.* **82**: 158.

FRIDAY, L. & HARLEY, B., (Eds) 2000. *Checklist of the flora and fauna of Wicken Fen.* xiv+112pp. Harley Books, Colchester.

FRYER, J.C.F., 1914. Narcissus flies. *J. Bd. Agric. Fish.* **21**: 136-141.

FRYER, J.C.F., 1915. The food-plant of *Chilosia variabilis* Panzer. *Entomologist's mon. Mag.* **51**: 193-194.

GARDINER, B.O.C., 1991. *Volucella zonaria* in Cambridge. *Bull. amat. Ent. Soc.* **50**: 285.

GARLAND, S.P., GIBBS, D., LEE, J. & WHITELEY, D., 1985. Some interesting Coleoptera, Hymenoptera and Diptera from Ford Valley, Derbyshire. *Entomologist's mon. Mag.* **121**: 54.

GAULD, I.D., 1979. An analysis of the classification of the *Ophion* genus-group (Ichneumonidae). *Syst. Ent.* **5**:59-82.

GEORGE, R.S., 1991. *Volucella zonaria* in Christchurch. *Bull. amat. Ent. Soc.* **50**: 287.

GEORGE, W.S., 1960. A plague of hover flies. *Trans. Suffolk Nat. Soc.* **11**: 418.

GEORGE, W.S., 1971. The hover-flies (Syrphidae) of Gromford Meadow, Snape. *Suffolk Natural History* **15**: 389-390.

GEORGE, W.S. & ASTON, A.E., 1960. The Diptera of Suffolk. *Trans. Suffolk Nat. Soc.* **11**: 314-320, 403-411.

GIBBS, D., 1987. Some interesting insects from the Kennet Valley. *Entomologist's mon. Mag.* **123**: 242.

GIBBS, D., 1992. Flies of the Essex coast. *Dipterists Digest* (first series) **11**: 4-16.

GIBBS, D., 2002. Scarcer Diptera found in the Bristol Region in 1999, 2000 and 2001. *Dipterists Digest* (second series) **9**: 1-13.

GIBBS, D.A. & PLANT, C.W., 2001. *Cheilosia ranunculi* Doczkal (Dip.: Syrphidae) in Britain. *Entomologist's Rec. & J. Var.* **113**: 65-68.

GILBERT, F.S., 1980. Flower visiting by hoverflies (Syrphidae). *J. Biol. Education* **14**: 70-74.

GILBERT, F.S., 1981. Foraging ecology of hoverflies: morphology of mouthparts in relation to feeding on nectar and pollen in some common urban species. *Ecol. Ent.* **6**: 245-262.

GILBERT, F.S., 1984. Thermoregulation and structure of swarms in *Syrphus ribesii* (*Syrphidae*). *Oikos* **42**: 249-255.

GILBERT, F.S., 1985a. Diurnal activity patterns in hoverflies (Diptera, Syrphidae). *Ecol. Ent.* **10**: 385-392.

GILBERT, F.S., 1985b. Morphometric patterns in hoverflies (Diptera, Syrphidae). *Proc. R. Soc. Lond. B* **224**: 79-90.

GILBERT, F.S., 1985c. Ecomorphogical relationships in hoverflies (Diptera, Syrphidae). *Proc. R. Soc. Lond. B* **224**: 91-105.

GILBERT, F.S., 1985d. Size and shape in *Syrphus ribesii* (Diptera, Syrphidae). *Proc. R. Soc. Lond. B* **224**: 107-114.

GILBERT, F., 1986. *Hoverflies.* Naturalists' Handbooks **5**. (First edition). vi+66pp. Cambridge University Press, Cambridge.

GILBERT, F., 1993. *Hoverflies.* Naturalists' Handbooks **5**. (Second edition). 67pp. Richmond Publishing Co. Ltd., Richmond.

GILBERT, F. & OWEN, J., 1990. Size, shape, competition and community structure in hoverflies (Diptera: Syrphidae). *J. Anim. Ecol.* **59**: 21-39.

GILBERT, F.S. & PERRY, I., 1982. The hoverflies (Diptera: Syrphidae) of Hayley Wood. *Nature in Cambridgeshire* no. **25**: 41-45.

GILBERT, F.S., HARDING, E.F., LINE, J.M. & PERRY, I., 1985. Morphological approaches to community structure in hoverflies (Diptera, Syrphidae). *Proc. R. Soc. Lond. B* **224**: 115-130.

GIRSCHNER, E., 1884. Beschreibung der Puppe von *Spilomyia* (*Calliprobola*) *speciosa* Rossi. *Wien. ent. Ztg.* **3**: 199. [In German]

GODFREY, A., 1989a. Local Diptera in Darenth Wood. *Trans. Kent Field Club* **11**: 44-45.

GODFREY, A., 1989b. Diptera - Syrphidae (Hoverflies) – in the Watford area 1985-1988. *Trans. Herts. nat. Hist. Soc.* **30**: 213-218.

GODFREY, A., 1991. A survey of Diptera at Blackburn Meadows. *Sorby Record* **28**: 34-46.

GODFREY, A., 1998. The Diptera of Moccas Park National Nature Reserve. *Dipterists Digest* (second series) **5**: 44-48.

GOELDLIN DE TIEFENAU, P., 1974. Contribution à l'étude systématique et écologique des Syrphidae (Dipt.) de la Suisse occidentale. *Mitt. Schweiz. ent. Ges.* **47**: 151-252.

GOELDLIN DE TIEFENAU, P., 1996. Sur plusieurs nouvelles espèces européennes de *Syrphus* (Diptera, Syrphidae) et clé des espèces paléarctiques du genre. *Mitt. Schweiz. ent. Ges.* **69**: 157-171.

GOELDLIN DE TIEFENAU, P., 1997. Le genre *Trichopsomyia* Williston, 1888 (Diptera: Syrphidae) in Europe avec description d'une nouvelle espèce, connue depuis longtemps. *Mitt. Schweiz. ent. Ges.* **70**: 191-201.

GOELDLIN DE TIEFENAU, P., MAIBACH, A. & SPEIGHT, M.C.D., 1990. Sur quelques espèces de *Platycheirus* (Diptera, Syrphidae) nouvelles ou méconnues. *Dipterists Digest* (first series) **5**: 19-43.

GOFFE, E.R., 1934. *Epistrophe balteata* de Geer, on wing in February. *J. Soc. Br. Ent.* **1**: 47-48.

GOFFE, E.R., 1944a. *Volucella zonaria* Poda (Dipt, Syrphidae), two further British records. *J. Soc. Br. Ent.* **2**: 173-174.

GOFFE, E.R., 1944b. Removal of *Cerioides conop(s)oides* Linn. (Dipt., Syrphidae) from the list of British Diptera. *J. Soc. Br. Ent.* **2**: 176-178.

GOFFE, E.R., 1944c. *Brachyopa scutellaris* Rob.–Desv., 1844 (Dipt., Syrphidae) in a cottage garden. *J. Soc. Br. Ent.* **2**: 225.

GOFFE, E.R., 1944d. *Tubifera* (*Eristalis*) *vitripennis* Strobl 1893, a species of Syrphidae (Diptera) new to Britain. *J. Soc. Br. Ent.* **2**: 226-228.

GOFFE, E.R., 1944e. The genus *Blera* Billberg, 1820 (Dipt., Syrphidae). *J. Soc. Br. Ent.* **2**: 229-231.

GOFFE, E.R., 1945. *Volucella zonaria* (Poda, 1761) (Dipt., Syrphidae) in Britain. *Entomologist's mon. Mag.* **81**: 159-162.

GOFFE, E.R., 1949. Some further records of *Triglyphus primus* Loew (Diptera, Syrphidae) and the finding of the larva in Belgium. *J. Soc. Br. Ent.*, **3**: 62-63.

GOFFE, E.R., 1950. *Syrphidis lapponica* Ztsdt., 1838, recorded from South Devonshire. *J. Soc. Br. Ent.* **3**: 149-150.

GOFFE, E.R., 1952. An outline of a revised classification of the Syrphidae (Diptera) on phylogenetic lines. *Trans. Soc. Br. Ent.* **11**: 97-124.

GOOT, V.S. VAN DER, 1970. *Cheilosia semifasciata* Becker (Diptera, Syrphidae) in Britain. *Entomologist's mon. Mag.* **105** (1969): 215.

GOOT, V.S. VAN DER, 1981. De zweefvliegen van Noordwest-Europa en Europees Rusland, in het bijzonder van de Benelux. 275pp. Koninklijke Nederlandse Natuurhistorische Vereniging, Amsterdam. [In Dutch]

GOOT, V.S. VAN DER, 1982. Het determinatiekenmerk voor de wijfjes van de twee Nederlandse Baccha-soorten onbetrouwbaar? (Diptera: Syrphidae). *Ent. Berichten, Amst.* **42**: 17-19. [In Dutch]

GOOT, V.S. VAN DER & GRABANDT, R.A.J., 1970. Some species of the genera *Melanostoma*, *Platycheirus* and *Pyrophaena* (Diptera, Syrphidae) and their relation to flowers. *Ent. Berichten, Amst.* **30**: 135-143.

GOOT, V.S. VAN DER & VERLINDEN, L., 1982. *Eriozona syrphoides* (Fallén) (Diptera, Syrphidae) in the Low Countries. *Entomologist's mon. Mag.* **118**: 248.

GOOT, V.S. VAN DER & VERLINDEN, L., 1986. Translation of Violovitch, N.A., 1983. Siberian Syrphidae (Diptera). *Verslagen en Technische Gegevens* no. 43. Institute voor Taxonomische Zoölogie, University of Amsterdam. [English translation of Russian original]

GORMAN, L. 1996. Some field observations on three uncommon hoverflies – *Doros profuges* (Harris), *Microdon mutabilis* (L.) and *Cheilosia chrysocoma* (Mg.) (Dip.: Syrphidae) in Lancashire, 1991-1996. *Entomologist's Rec. & J. Var.* **108**: 311-312.

GRAYSON, A., 1988. Some rarities and new records for Yorkshire. *Bull. amat. Ent. Soc.* **47**: 224.

GRAYSON, A., 1993. Hoverflies recorded between 1987 and 1991 inclusive. *Bull. amat. Ent. Soc.* **52**: 31-41.

GRAYSON, A., 2002. *Platycheirus amplus* Curran, 1927 (Diptera, Syrphidae) new to England. *Dipterists Digest* (second series) **9**: 15-16.

GREENWOOD, S., 1989. Feeding behaviour of *Panorpa communis* (L.) (Mecopt., Panorpidae). *Entomologist's mon. Mag.* **125**: 36.

GREIG, C., 1989. Overwintering behaviour of the larva of *Myathropa florea* (L.) (Diptera: Syrphidae). *Dipterists Digest* (first series) **2**: 11-16.

GRIFFITHS, G.C.D., 1954. On gynandromorphs in *Melanostoma ambiguum* (Fallén) (Dipt., Syrphidae). *Entomologist* **87**: 136-139.

GRIMSHAW, P.H., 1898. Lincolnshire Diptera: a preliminary list. *Naturalist* **1898**: 157-170.

GROVE, S.J., 1990. Old forest insects noted from some Berkshire parklands. *British Journal of Entomology and Natural History* **3**: 97-101.

GOULSON, D. & WRIGHT, N.P., 1998. Flower constancy in the hoverflies *Episyrphus balteatus* (Degeer) and *Syrphus ribesii* (L.) (Syrphidae). *Behavioural Ecology* **9**: 213-219.

HALFPENNY, G., 1989. Occurrence of *Callicera aenea* (Fabricius) (Diptera: Syrphidae) in Staffordshire. *Entomologist's Gaz.* **40**: 182.

HALSTEAD, A.J, 1999. A new prey record for *Meliscaeva auricollis* (Meigen) (Diptera, Syrphidae). *Dipterists Digest* (second series) **6**: 21.

HAMM, A.H., 1941. *Volucella inanis* L. taken in entrance to nest of *Vespa vulgaris*. *Entomologist's Rec. & J. Var.* **53**: 44.

HAMMOND, C.O., 1967. *Volucella zonaria* Poda (Diptera, Syrphidae) in Wood Green, London. *Entomologist's Rec. & J. Var.* **79**: 24-25.

HAMMOND, C.O., 1973. *Callicera spinolae* Rondani – extended range. *Entomologist's Rec. & J. Var.* **85**: 22-24.

HAMMOND, P.M., SMITH, K.G.V., ELSE, G.R. & ALLEN, G.W., 1989. Some recent additions to the British insect fauna. *Entomologist's mon. Mag.* **125**: 95-102.

HANCOCK, E.G. & ROTHERAY, G.E., 1990. *Molophilus lackschewitzianus* Alexander and *Brachypalpoides lenta* (Meigen) (Dipt., Tipulidae and Syrphidae) in Scotland. *Entomologist's mon. Mag.* **126**: 212.

HANSON, M., 1985. A provisional list of larger Brachycera, Syrphidae and Conopidae of the Epping Forest area. *Proc. Trans. Br. Ent. nat. Hist. Soc.* **18**: 37-48.

HART, A.J. & BALE, J.S., 1997a. A method of mass-rearing the hoverfly *Episyrphus balteatus* (Diptera, Syrphidae). *Dipterists Digest* (second series) **4**: 1-3.

HART, A.J. & BALE, J.S., 1997b. Cold tolerance of the aphid predator *Episyrphus balteatus* (De Geer) (Diptera, Syrphidae). *Physiological Entomology* **22**: 332-338.

HART, A.J. & BALE, J.S., 1997c. Factors affecting the freeze tolerance of the hoverfly *Syrphus ribesii* (Diptera: Syrphidae). *Journal of Insect Physiology* **44**: 21-29.

HART, A.J., BALE, J.S. & FENLON, J.S., 1997. Developmental threshold, day-degree requirements and voltinism of the aphid predator *Episyrphus balteatus* (Diptera: Syrphidae). *Ann. appl. Biol.* **130**: 427-437.

HARTLEY, J.C., 1958. The root-piercing spiracles of the larva of *Chrysogaster hirtella* Loew (Diptera: Syrphidae). *Proc. R. ent. Soc. Lond.* (*A*) **33**: 81-87.

HARTLEY, J.C., 1961. A taxonomic account of the larvae of some British Syrphidae. *Proc. Zool. Soc. Lond.* **136**: 505-573.

HARTLEY, J.C., 1963. The cephalopharyngeal apparatus of syrphid larvae and its relationship to other Diptera. *Proc. Zool. Soc. Lond.* **141**: 261-280.

HASLETT, J.R., 1983. A photographic account of pollen digestion by adult hoverflies. *Physiol. Ent.* **8**: 167-171.

HASLETT, J.R., 1988. Assessing the quality of alpine habitat: hoverflies (Diptera, Syrphidae) as bio-indicators of skiing pressure on alpine meadows in Austria. *Zool. Anz.* **220**: 179-184.

HASLETT, J., 1989a. Interpreting patterns of resource utilisation; randomness and selectivity in pollen feeding by adult hoverflies. *Oecologica* **78**: 422-433.

HASLETT, J., 1989b. Adult feeding by holometabolous insects: pollen and nectar as complementary nutrient sources for *Rhingia campestris* (Diptera: Syrphidae). *Oecologica* **81**: 361-363.

HASLETT, J.R. & ENTWISTLE, P.F., 1980. Further notes on *Eriozona syrphoides* (Fall.) (Dipt., Syrphidae) in Hafren Forest, mid-Wales. *Entomologist's mon. Mag.* **116**: 36.

HAWKINS, R.D., 1995. *Metasyrphus latilunulatus* (Collin), a rare hoverfly found near Sheffield. *Sorby Record* **31**: 79.

HAYHOW, S.J., 1999. *Doros profuges* Harris (Diptera: Syrphidae) in north Lancashire. *Journal of the Lancashire & Cheshire Entomological Society* **121-123**: 53-54.

HEAL, J., 1979a. Colour patterns of Syrphidae: I. Genetic variation in the dronefly *Eristalis tenax*. *Heredity* **42**: 223-236.

HEAL, J., 1979b. Colour patterns of Syrphidae. II. *Eristalis intricarius*. *Heredity* **43**: 229-238.

HEAL, J., 1981. Colour patterns of Syrphidae. III. Sexual dimorphism in *Eristalis arbustorum*. *Ecol. Ent.* **6**: 119-127.

HEAL, J., 1982. Colour patterns of Syrphidae. IV. Mimicry and variation in natural populations of *Eristalis tenax*. *Heredity* **49**: 95-110.

HEAL, J., 1989a. Behavioural ecology of hoverflies. *Dipterists Digest* (first series) **2**: 8-10.

HEAL, J., 1989b. Variation and seasonal changes in hoverfly species: interactions between temperature, age and genotype. *Biol. J. Linn. Soc.* **36**: 251-269.

HEAL, J., 1990. Eggs and egg-laying: some details about hoverflies. *Dipterists Digest* (first series) **6**: 27-29.

HEAVER, D., 1990. *Epistrophe ochrostoma*: new to Britain. *Hoverfly Newsletter* no. 10: 8.

HEINRICH, B. & PANTLE, C., 1975. Thermoregulation in small flies (*Syrphus* spp.); basking and shivering. *J. exp. Biol.* **62**: 599-610.

HEMPTINNE, J.L., DIXON, A.F.G., DOUCET, J.L. & PETERSEN, J.E., 1993. Optimal foraging by hoverflies (Dept.: Syrphidae) and ladybirds (Coleoptera: Coccinellidae): mechanisms. *European J. Ent.* **90**: 451-455.

HERBERT, B., 1920. Diptera in South Shropshire. *Entomologist's mon. Mag.* **56**: 249-256.

HINCKS, W.D., 1953. xii. Diptera. **In**: Butler, P.M. & Hincks, W.D. (Eds) *The entomology of Spurn Peninsula. Naturalist* **1953**: 159-167.

HIPPA, H., 1968a. A generic revision of the genus *Syrphus* and allied genera (Diptera, Syrphidae) in the Palearctic region, with descriptions of the male genitalia. *Acta ent. fenn.* **25**: 1-94.

HIPPA, H., 1968b. Classification of the palearctic species of the genera *Xylota* Meigen and *Xylotomima* Shannon (Dipt., Syrphidae). *Ann. ent. fenn.* **34**: 179-197.

HIPPA, H., 1978. Classification of Xylotini (Diptera, Syrphidae). *Acta zool. Fenn.* **156**: 1-153.

HIPPA, H., 1986. Morphology and taxonomic value of the female external genitalia of Syrphidae and some other Diptera by new methodology. *Ann. zool. Fenn.* **23**: 307-320.

HIPPA, H., NIELSEN, T.R. & STEENIS, J. van, 2001. The West Palaearctic species of the genus *Eristalis* Latreille (Diptera, Syrphidae). *Norw. J. Entomol.* **48**: 289-327.

HOBBY, B.M., 1940. *Pocota personata* (Harris, 1776) (= *apiformis* (Schrank, 1781)) (Dipt., Syrphidae): occurrence in Britain. *Entomologist's mon. Mag.* **76**: 238-244.

HOBBY, B.M., 1946. What is the present status of *Volucella zonaria* Poda (Dipt., Syrphidae) in Britain? *Proc. R. ent. Soc. Lond.* (*A*) **21**: 1-2.

HODSON, W.E.H., 1927. The bionomics of the lesser bulb flies, *Eumerus strigatus* Fall. and *Eumerus tuberculatus* Rond., in South-west England. *Bull. ent. Res.* **17**: 373-384.

HODSON, W.E.H., 1931. A comparison of the immature stages of *Eumerus tuberculatus* Rond. and *Syritta pipiens* Linn. (Syrphidae). *Bull. ent. Res.* **22**: 55-58.

HODSON, W.E.H., 1932a. A comparison of the larvae of *Eumerus strigatus* Fln., and *Eumerus tuberculatus* Rond., (Syrphidae). *Bull. ent. Res.* **23**: 247-249.

HODSON, W.E.H., 1932b. The large narcissus bulb fly, *Merodon equestris* Fab. (Syrphidae). *Bull. ent. Res.* **23**: 429-448.

HÖLLDOBLER, K., 1929. Über die Entwicklung der Schwirrfliege *Xanthogramma citrofasciatum* im Neste von *Lasius alienus* und *niger*. *Zool. Anzeig.* **82**: 171-176. [In German]

HOLLOWAY, B.A., 1976. Pollen feeding in hoverflies. *New Zealand J. Zool.* **3**: 339-350.

HOLLOWAY, G.J. & McCAFFERY, A.R., 1990. Habitat utilisation and dispersion in *Eristalis pertinax* (Diptera: Syrphidae). *Entomologist* **109**: 116-124.

HOLLOWAY, G.J., MARRIOTT, C.G. & CROCKER, H.J., 1997. Phenotypic plasticity in hoverflies: the relationship between colour pattern and season in *Episyrphus balteatus* and other Syrphidae. *Ecological Entomology* **22**: 425-432.

HOWARTH, B., CLEE, C. & EDMUNDS, M., 2000. The mimicry between British Syrphidae (Diptera) and Aculeate Hymenoptera. *British Journal of Entomology and Natural History* **13**: 1-39.

HOWARTH, B. & EDMUNDS, M., 2000. The phenology of Syrphidae (Diptera): are they Batesian mimics of Hymenoptera? *Biol. J. Linn. Soc.* **71**: 437-457.

HOWE, M.A. & HOWE, E.A., 2001. A review of the Dipterists Forum summer field meeting at Abergavenny, 1997. *Dipterists Digest* (second series) **8**: 31-48.

HOWE, M.A., PARKER, M.J. & HOWE, E.A., 2000. *Dorset Field Meeting 27 June to 4 July 1998*. Dipterists Forum Occasional Publication no. 1. 167pp. Dipterists Forum, Bangor.

HUGHES, M.O., 1990a. Some observations on the Syrphidae (Diptera) of the counties of Clwyd and Gwynedd, Wales. *Bull. amat. Ent. Soc.* **49**: 165-171.

HUGHES, M.O., 1990b. An uncommon syrphid, *Didea fasciata*, in Gwynedd. *Bull. amat. Ent. Soc.* **49**: 270.

HUGHES, M.O., 1993. Uncommon syrphid found in Gwynedd, Wales. *Bull. amat. Ent. Soc.* **52**: 280-281.

HULL, F.M., 1949. The morphology and inter-relationship of the genera of syrphid flies, recent and fossil. *Trans. Zool. Soc. Lond.* **26**: 257-408.

HURKMANS, W. & HAYAT, R., 1997. Ethology and ecology of *Merodon* (Diptera, Syrphidae) in Turkey II: descriptions of new species and notes on other syrphid flies. *Dipterists Digest* (second series) **3**: 62-78.

ILIFF, D., 1996. *Chalcosyrphus eunotus* (Diptera, Syrphidae) female found in Gloucestershire. *Dipterists Digest* (second series) **2**: 95-96.

ILIFF, D., 1999. *Xylota segnis* on buttercups: not unusual at all (apparently). *Hoverfly Newsletter* no. 28: 9.

ILSE, D., 1949. Colour discrimination in the dronefly, *Eristalis tenax*. *Nature, Lond.* **163**: 255-256.

IMHOF, G., 1979. Arthropod communities connected with *Phragmites*. *Monographia biol.* **37**: 389-405.

JANES, N.F., 1985. Hoverflies (Diptera-Syrphidae). Report of the recorder. *Bedfordshire Nat.* **38**: 61-64.

JEFFERIES, M.G., 1976. The distribution of *Triglyphus primus* Loew (Dipt., Syrphidae) in Britain. *Entomologist mon. Mag.* **111** (1975): 61.

JOHNSON, C.G., 1961. Syrphid (Dipt.) migration on the Norfolk coast in August 1960. *Entomologist's mon. Mag.* **96**: 196-7.

JOHNSON, C.G., 1969. Migration and dispersal of insects by flight. 763pp. Methuen, London.

JOHNSON, W.F., 1922. Diptera and Hymenoptera at Poyntzpass, in 1921. *Ir. Nat.* **31**: 66-70.

JONES, A.W., 1953. Notes on the drone-flies (Syrphidae, Diptera) of Wimbledon Common. *London Nat.* **33**: 83-88.

JONES, A.W., 1954. Drone-fly visitors to the flowers of the city bombed sites. *London Nat.* **34**: 154-157.

JONES, R., 1977. Observations on *Doros conopseus*. *Bull. amat. Ent. Soc.* **36**: 90-91.

JONES, R., 1978. Some interesting Diptera taken in 1976 in Sussex. *Entomologist's mon. Mag.* **113** (1977): 124.

JONES, R.A., 1988. *Pelecocera tricincta* (Meig.) (Diptera: Syrphidae) in the Isle of Wight. *British Journal of Entomology and Natural History* **1**: 188.

JONES, R.A., 1991. *Xylota xanthocnema* Collin (Diptera: Syrphidae) in Kent. *British Journal of Entomology and Natural History* **4**: 66.

JONES, R.A., 2000a. *Callicera aurata* (Rossi) (Diptera, Syrphidae) and *Paraclusia tigrina* (Fallén) (Diptera, Clusiidae) in south-east London. *Dipterists Digest* (second series) **7**: 108.

JONES, R.A., 2000b. Extreme size variation in *Episyrphus balteatus* (Degeer) (Dip.: Syrphidae). *Entomologist's Rec. & J. Var.* **112**: 224.

JONES, R.A., 2002. *Heringia senilis* Sack (Diptera, Syrphidae): a hoverfly new to Britain. *British Journal of Entomology and Natural History* **14** (2001): 185-194.

KASSEBEER, C., MAIBACH, A. & ROTHERAY, G.E., 1998. The third (= final) stage larva of *Psilota anthracina* Meigen and *Psilota decessa* (Hutton) (Dipt., Syrphidae). *Entomologist's mon. Mag.* **134**: 39-43.

KAY, Q.O.N., 1976. Preferential pollination of yellow-flowered morphs of *Raphanus raphanistrum* by *Pieris* and *Eristalis*. *Nature* **261**: 230-232.

KEELER, C.E., 1926. Recent work by Gabritchevsky on the inheritance of colour varieties in *Volucella bombylans*. *Psyche* **33**: 22-27.

KENDALL, D.A. & STRADLING, D.J., 1972. Some observations on the overwintering of the drone-fly, *Eristalis tenax*. *Entomologist* **105**: 229-230.

370

KHALIL, Z., WHALLEY, W.M. & SULLIVAN, M.S., 1997. Some bacteria, fungi and yeast isolated from free-living *Episyrphus balteatus* (Diptera, Syrphidae). *Dipterists Digest* (second series) **3**: 56-58.

KIDD, L.N., 1964. *The Diptera of Lancashire and Cheshire*, part 1 (supplement). Lancashire & Cheshire Fauna Committee. Publication no. 46: 1-6.

KIDD, L.N., 1971. *The Diptera of Lancashire and Cheshire*. Lancashire & Cheshire Fauna Committee. Publication no. 59: 18-23.

KIDD, L.N. & BRINDLE, A., 1959. *The Diptera of Lancashire and Cheshire*. Lancashire & Cheshire Fauna Committee. 136pp. T. Buncle & Co., Arbroath.

KLOET, G.S. & HINCKS, W.D., 1945. *A check list of British insects*. (First edition). 483pp. Kloet & Hincks, Stockport.

KLOET, G.S. & HINCKS, W.D., 1976. A checklist of British insects. (Second edition). Diptera and Siphonaptera. *Handbk Ident. Br. Insects* **11**: 1-139.

KLUGER, H., 1970. [The flower visits of the drone fly *Eristalis tenax*.] *Z. vergl. Physiol.* **32**: 328-347. [In German]

KNIGHT, G.T., 1989. *Callicera aenea* in Wolverhampton. *Dipterists Digest* (first series) **2**: 33.

KNUTSON, L. V., 1973. Taxonomic revision of the aphid-killing flies of the genus *Sphaerophoria* in the Western Hemisphere (Syrphidae). *Publs. ent. Soc. Am.* **9**: 1-50.

KORMANN, K., 1988. *Schwebfliegen Mitteleuropas*. 176pp. Ecomed, München.

KULA, E., 1983. The larva and puparium of *Eriozona syrphoides* (Fallén) (Diptera, Syrphidae). *Acta. ent. bohemoslovaca* **30**: 71-73.

KURIR, A., 1963. [On the biology of two aphidophagous syrphids (Diptera, Syrphidae), *Heringia heringii* Zett. and *Pipiza festiva* Meigen in the galls of the late leaf-petiole-gall poplar aphid (*Pemphigus spirothecae* Passerini) on the Lombardy poplar.] *Z. angew. Ent.* **52**: 61-83. [In German]

LAMB, C.G., 1911. The habitat of *Eristalis aeneus* Scop. *Entomologist's mon. Mag.* **47**: 215-216.

LÁSKA, P. & BIČÍK, V., 1996. On the problems of the species *Dasysyrphus venustus* (Zetterstedt) and *D. hilaris* (Meigen) (Diptera, Syrphidae). *Entomologist's mon. Mag.* **132**: 305-309.

LAURENCE, B.R., 1950. Syrphidae (Diptera) in Bedfordshire. *Entomologist's mon. Mag.* **86**: 351-353.

LAURENCE, B.R., 1991. Syrphidae in the Northern Isles. *Dipterists Digest* (first series) **8**: 15-16.

LAURENCE, B.R., 1996. Beyond the Red Data Book. *Dipterists Digest* (second series) **2**: 85-89.

LAURENCE, B.R., 1997. Flies from ancient coppiced woodland in Suffolk. *Dipterists Digest* (second series) **4**: 78-91.

LE QUESNE, W.J., 1978. Evidence for a mass movement of Syrphidae (Diptera) in Jersey. *Entomologist's mon. Mag.* **113** (1977): 176.

LEVY, E.T., LEVY, D.A. & DEAN, W.F., 1989. Dorset Syrphidae 1989. *Proc. Dorset nat. Hist. & archaeol. Soc.* **111**: 137-138.

LEVY, E.T., LEVY, D.A. & DEAN, W.F., 1992. *Dorset hoverflies*. 73pp. Dorset Environmental Record Centre, Dorchester.

LEVY, E.T. & LEVY, D.A., 1994. *Eoseristalis cryptarum* (Diptera, Syrphidae) - on Dartmoor. *Dipterists Digest* (second series) **1**: 86.

LEVY, E.T. & LEVY, D.A., 1998. *Somerset hoverflies*. 74pp. E.T. & D.A. Levy, Yeovil.

LITTLE, C., PAYNE, R.M., AALDHOUS, A. & SCOTT, P., 1988. The insect fauna of saltmarshes in the Severn Estuary; a preliminary survey. *Entomologist's Gaz.* **39**: 235-246.

LUCAS, J.A.W., 1976. New species of the genus *Pipizella* Rondani, 1856 (Diptera, Syrphidae). *Publ. nat. hist. Genootschap Limb.* **26**: 5-13.

LUFF, M.L. & SELMAN, B.J., 1977. The Diptera of Castle Eden Dene. *Vasculum* **62**: 32-40.

LUNAU, K. & WACHT, S., 1997. [Innate flower recognition in the hoverfly *Eristalis tenax* L.] *Mitteilungen der Deutschen Gesellschaft für Allgemeine und Angewandte Entomologie.* **11**: 481-484. [In German]

LUNDBECK, W., 1916. *Diptera Danica*. **5**. (Lonchopteridae, Syrphidae). ii+603pp. Gad, Copenhagen.

LYSZKOWSKI, R.M., MacGOWAN, I. & ROTHERAY, G.E., 1992. The goat moth (*Cossus cossus* (L.) Lep., Cossidae) and associated insects in Scotland. *Entomologist's mon. Mag.* **128**: 24.

MacGOWAN, I., 1981. *Eriozona syrphoides* (Fallén) (Dipt., Syrphidae) in Angus. *Entomologist's mon. Mag.* **117**: 124

371

MacGOWAN, I., 1985. Notes on the Diptera of the Western Isles. *Entomologist's mon. Mag.* **121**: 24.

MacGOWAN, I., 1986. *Sciapus contristans* (Wied.) (Dolichopodidae) in Scotland and other Diptera new to the Western Isles. *Entomologist's mon. Mag.* **122**: 213.

MacGOWAN, I., 1994a. Additions to the list of Diptera from the Western Isles. *Dipterists Digest* (first series) **14**: 28-31.

MacGOWAN, I., 1994b. Creating breeding sites for *Callicera rufa* Schummel (Diptera, Syrphidae) and a further host tree. *Dipterists Digest* (second series) **1**: 6-8.

MacGOWAN, I., GILBERT, F.S. & ROTHERAY, G.E., 1997. The status of *Melanostoma dubium* (Diptera, Syrphidae). *Dipterists Digest* (second series) **3**: 79-87.

MacGOWAN, I. & WATT, K., 1994. A further record of *Parasyrphus nigritarsis* (Zetterstedt, 1843) (Diptera: Syrphidae), with a review of its known distribution in Britain. *Dipterists Digest* (second series) **1**: 26-29.

MAIBACH, A. & GOELDLIN DE TIEFENAU, P., 1989. *Mallota cimbiciformis* (Fallén) nouvelle pour la faune de Suisse: morphologie du dernier stade larvaire, de la pupe et notes biologiques (Diptera, Syrphidae). *Mitt. Schweiz. Ent. Ges.*, **62**: 67-78. [In French]

MAIBACH, A. & GOELDLIN DE TIEFENAU, P., 1991. Note biologique et description des larve et pupe d' *Eristalis* (*Eoseristalis*) *rupium* F. (Diptera, Syrphidae). *Mitt. Schweiz. ent. Ges.* **64**: 321-330. [In French]

MAIBACH, A. & GOELDLIN DE TIEFENAU, P., 1993. Description et clé de détermination des stades immatures de plusieurs espèces du genre *Neoascia* Williston de la région paléarctique occidentale (Diptera, Syrphidae). *Mitt. Schweiz. Ent. Ges.* **66**: 337-357. [In French]

MAIBACH, A. & GOELDLIN DE TIEFENAU, P., 1995. *Chrysogaster rondanii* sp.n. from Western and Central Europe (Diptera: Syrphidae). *Mitt. Schweiz. ent. Ges.* **68**: 459-464.

MAIBACH, A., GOELDLIN DE TIEFENAU, P. & SPEIGHT. M.C.D., 1994a. Limites generiques et caracteristiques taxonomiques de plusieurs genres de la tribu Chrysogasterini (Diptera: Syrphidae). I. Diagnoses generiques et description de *Riponnensia* gen. nov. *Ann. Soc. ent. Fr.* (*ICS.*) **30**: 217-247. [In French]

MAIBACH, A., GOELDLIN DE TIEFENAU, P. & SPEIGHT, M.C.D., 1994b. Limites generiques et caracteristiques taxonomiques de plusieurs genres de la tribu Chrysogasterini (Diptera: Syrphidae). II. Statut taxonomique de plusieurs des espèces etudiées et analyse du complexe *Melanogaster macquarti* (Loew). *Ann. Soc. ent. Fr.* (*ICS.*) **30**: 253-271. [In French]

MAIBACH, A., GOELDLIN DE TIEFENAU, P. & SPEIGHT, M.C.D., 1994c. Limites generiques et caracteristiques taxonomiques de plusieurs genres de la tribu Chrysogasterini (Diptera: Syrphidae). III. Description des stades immatures de plusieurs espèces ouest-paléarctiques. *Rev. Suisse Zool.* **101**: 369-411. [In French]

MAIER, C. T. & WALDBAUER, G. P., 1979. Dual mate-seeking strategies in male syrphid flies (Diptera: Syrphidae). *Ann. ent. Soc. Am.* **72**: 54-61.

MARCOS-GARCÍA, A. & LÁSKA, P. 1983. Description of *Metasyrphus lucasi* sp. n. (Diptera, Syrphidae). *Nouv. Revue ent.* **13**: 113-116.

MAZÁNEK, L., BIČÍK, V. & LÁSKA, P., 1998. Redescription and reinstatement of *Eupeodes bucculatus* (Rondani, 1857) and its synonymy (Dipt., Syrphidae). *Act Univ. Palacki. Olomuc. Fac. rer. nat.*, *Biol.* **36**: 27-38.

MAZÁNEK, L., LÁSKA, P. & BIČÍK, V., 1999a. Key to males of Norwegian species of *Eupeodes* (Diptera: Syrphidae). *Dipt. bohemoslav.* **9**: 143-152.

MAZÁNEK, L., LÁSKA, P. & BIČÍK, V., 1999b. Two new Palaearctic species of *Eupeodes* similar to *E. bucculatus* (Diptera, Syrphidae). *Volucella* **4**: 1-9.

McCULLOCH, A. & WAKEHAM-DAWSON, A., 2001. Hoverfly records from North Uist and the Monach Islands, Scotland – July 1999. *British Journal of Entomology and Natural History* **13**: 196.

McLEAN, I.F.G., 1982. *Xylota segnis* (L.) (Dipt., Syrphidae) observed feeding at flowers. *Entomologist's mon. Mag.* **118**: 193.

McLEAN, I.F.G., 1986. *Pipizella maculipennis* (Meigen) (Dipt., Syrphidae) found in Gloucestershire. *Entomologist's mon. Mag.* **122**: 50.

McLEAN, I.F.G., 2000. *Volucella inanis* (Linnaeus) (Diptera, Syrphidae) new to Cambridgeshire. *Dipterists Digest* (second series) **7**: 8.

McLEAN, I.F.G. & STUBBS, A.E., 1990. The breeding site of *Brachyopa pilosa* (Diptera; Syrphidae). *Dipterists Digest* (first series) **3**: 40.

MEASDAY, V., 1992. *Xylota florum* Fab. (Dipt., Syrphidae) new to Kent. *Entomologist's Rec. & J. Var.* **104**: 157.

MILES, P.M., 1951. The Small Bulb Fly, *Paragopsis* (=*Eumerus*) *strigatus* Fall., bred from onion in Wales. *Entomologist's mon. Mag.* **87**: 192.

MOORE, A., 1985. Hoverflies of the Isle of Man. *Peregrine* **6**: 45-47.

MOORE, L., 1999. *Didea fasciata* (Macquart) in Coventry. *Proceedings of the Coventry and District Natural History Society* **7**: 132.

MORGAN, I.K., 1990. *An annotated list of the hoverflies of Carmarthenshire*. Nature Conservancy Council, Dyfed-Powys Region, Aberystwyth. [Unpublished report]

MORGAN, J., 1994. Peter Crow's Merioneth syrphids (Diptera, Syrphidae). *Dipterists Digest* (second series) **1**: 51-55.

MORLEY, C., 1910. Oviposition of *Baccha*. *Entomologist's mon. Mag.* **46**: 192-193.

MORLEY, C., 1940. The hover-fly, *Eristalis cryptarum* Fab., in Britain. *Entomologist* **73**: 118-119.

MORLEY, C., 1941. *Eristalis aeneus* clustered under steel helmet. *Trans. Suffolk Nat. Soc.* **4**: 272-273.

MORLEY, C., 1942. Golden hoverer-fly new to Britain. *Trans. Suffolk Nat. Soc.* **5**: 14-15.

MORLEY, C., 1947. The second Golden Hoverer. *Trans. Suffolk Nat. Soc.* **6**: 149-150.

MORRIS, R.K.A., 1998a. Flies and wasps at an Insect-o-cutor. *Entomologist's Rec. & J. Var.* **110**: 246.

MORRIS, R.K.A., 1998b. *Hoverflies of Surrey*. 244pp. Surrey Wildlife Trust, Pirbright.

MORRIS, R.K.A., 2000. Shifts in the phenology of hoverflies in Surrey: do these reflect the effects of global warming? *Dipterists Digest* (second series) **7**: 103-108.

MORSE, D.A., 1981. Interactions among syrphid flies and bumblebees on flowers. *Ecology* **62**: 81-88.

MOYLE, J.L. & JEPSON, P.C., 1993. Short-term risk predictions for *Episyrphus balteatus* (Dipt., Syrphidae) larvae exposed to pyrethroids on winter wheat. *Science of the Total Environment* **1993** (supplement part 1): 791-797.

MUNK, T., 2000. Svirrefluen *Eumerus sabulonum* (Fallén, 1817) (Syrphidae, Diptera) yngler i blåmunke (*Jasione montana*). *Flora og Fauna* **106**: 19-22. [In Danish]

MUTIN, V. & GILBERT. F., 1999. Phylogeny of the genus *Xylota* (Diptera, Syrphidae), with descriptions of new taxa. *Dipteron* **2**: 45-68.

NASH, R., 1975. *Parasyrphus vittiger* (Zetterstedt) (Diptera: Syrphidae) confirmed as an Irish species. *Ir. Nat. J.* **18**: 229-230.

NASH, R., 1997. Species inventory for Northern Ireland: hoverflies (Diptera: Syrphidae). *Environment and Heritage Service Research and Development Series* **97**: 1-23.

NASH, R. & SPEIGHT, M.C.D., 1976. Records of, and notes on, some rare Irish hoverflies (Dipt., Syrphidae), including a first Irish record of *Criorhina ranunculi*. *Ir. Nat. J.* **18**: 351-156.

NEDERLANDSE JEUGDBOND VOOR NATUURSTUDIE, 1998. Voorlopige atlas van de Nederlandse zweefvliegen (Syrphidae). 182pp. European Invertebrate Survey Nederland, Leiden, & Nederlandse Jeugdbond voor Natuurstudie, Graveland. [In Dutch]

NELSON, B., 1988. Records of uncommon hoverflies (Diptera: Syrphidae) from Northern Ireland. *Ir. Nat. J.* **22**: 453.

NEWSTEAD, R., 1891. Insects, etc., taken in the nests of British Vespidae. *Entomologist's mon. Mag.* **27**: 39-41.

NIELSEN, T.R., 1966. Species of the genus *Helophilus* (Dipt., Syrphidae) found on Jaeren, Rogaland. *Norsk ent. Tidsskr.* **13**: 427-439.

NIELSEN, T.R., 1969. Population studies of *Helophilus hybridus* Loew and *Sericomyia silentis* (Harris) (Dipt., Syrphidae) on Jaeren, S.W. Norway. *Norsk ent. Tidsskr.* **16**: 33-38.

NIELSEN, T.R., 1970. *Cheilosia sootryeni* nov. sp. (Dipt. Syrphidae), a Norwegian species resembling *C. vernalis* Fal. *Norsk ent. Tidsskr.* **17**: 115-118.

NIELSEN, T.R., 1971. Syrphidae (Dipt.) from Jaeren, Norway, 1. With description of two new species. *Norsk ent. Tidsskr.* **18**: 53-73.

NIELSEN, T.R., 1974. Notes on two northern species of the genus *Platycheirus* St.-Farg. et Serv. (Dipt., Syrphidae). *Norsk ent. Tidsskr.* **21**: 167-172.

NIELSEN, T.R., 1980. *Melangyna lucifera* n. sp. from southern Norway. *Ent. scand.* **11**: 310-312.

NIELSEN, T.R., 1997. The hoverfly genera *Anasimyia* Schiner, *Helophilus* Meigen, *Parhelophilus* Girschner and *Sericomyia* Meigen in Norway (Diptera, Syrphidae). *Fauna norv.*, *Ser. B* **44**: 107-122.

NIELSEN, T.R., 1999. Check-list and distribution maps of Norwegian hoverflies with description of *Platycheirus laskai* nov. sp. (Diptera, Syrphidae). *NINA Fagrapport* 035: 1-99.

NIELSEN, T.R. & CLAUSSEN, C., 2001. On *Cheilosia ingerae* spec. nov. (Diptera, Syrphidae) from northern Fennoscandia. *Dipteron* **4**: 43-46.

NIXON, G.E.J., 1934. Two notes on the behaviour of *Volucella pellucens* in its association with the wasps *Vespa vulgaris* Linn. and *Vespa germanica* Fab. *Entomologist's mon. Mag.* **70**: 17-18.

NOTTON, D.G., 1991. Some Diptera host records for species of *Basalys* and *Trichopria* (Hym., Diapriidae). *Entomologist's mon. Mag.* **127**: 123-126.

NURSE, C.G., 1910a. Notes regarding the breeding of *Chilosia grossa*. *Entomologist* **43**: 313-314.

NURSE, C.G., 1910b. Further notes regarding the breeding of *Chilosia grossa*. *Entomologist* **43**: 349-350.

OATES, M., 1987. Some late sightings of butterflies and other insects in and around Hampshire during the mild autumn of 1986. *Entomologist's Rec. & J. Var.* **99**: 222-224.

OSBORNE, P. J., 1956. Insects other than Lepidoptera at a mercury-vapour light trap. *Entomologist's mon. Mag.* **92**: 19.

OTTENHEIM, M.M., VOLMER, A.D. & HOLLOWAY, G.J., 1996. The genetics of phenotypic plasticity in adult abdominal colour pattern of *Eristalis arbustorum* (Diptera: Syrphidae). *Heredity* **77**: 493-499.

OTTENHEIM, M.M., WALLER, G.E. & HOLLOWAY, G.J., 1995. The influence of the development rates of immature stages of *Eristalis arbustorum* (Diptera: Syrphidae) on adult abdominal colour pattern. *Physiological Entomology* **20**: 343-348.

OWEN, J., 1979. Hoverflies (Diptera: Syrphidae) of Leicestershire: an annotated checklist. *Trans. Leicester lit. phil. Soc.* **73**: 13-31.

OWEN, J., 1981. Trophic variety and abundance of hoverflies (Diptera, Syrphidae) in an English suburban garden. *Holarct. Ecol.* **4**: 221-228.

OWEN, J., 1983. The most neglected wildlife habitat of all. *New Scientist* **1983**: 9-11.

OWEN, J., 1988. *Sericomyia silentis* (Harris) (Diptera: Syrphidae): the 44,834th hoverfly. *Entomologist's Rec. & J. Var.* **100**: 43-44.

OWEN, J., 1991. *The ecology of a garden: the first fifteen years*. 403pp. Cambridge University Press, Cambridge.

OWEN, J. & GILBERT, F.S., 1989. On the abundance of hoverflies (Diptera: Syrphidae). *Oecologica* **55**: 183-193.

PALMER, C., 1988. Some notes on the hoverflies of the North Merseyside coastal dune system. *Dipterists Digest* (first series) **1**: 41-42.

PALMER, C., 1996. A further record of *Scaeva albomaculata* in Britain and a note on the K.G. Blair collection of British Diptera. *Dipterists Digest* (second series) **2**: 97-99.

PALMER, C., 1997a. *Parasyrphus nigritarsis* (Diptera, Syrphidae) in Hampshire. *Dipterists Digest* (second series) **4**: 60.

PALMER, C., 1997b. *Epistrophe melanostoma* (Diptera, Syrphidae) in Hampshire. *Dipterists Digest* (second series) **4**: 71.

PARKER, J.B., 1999. *Callicera aurata* (Rossi) (Diptera, Syrphidae) in the Lake District. *Dipterists Digest* (second series) **6**: 120.

PARKER, M.J., 2001. *Cheilosia ahenea* von Roser (Diptera, Syrphidae) new to Great Britain. *Dipterists Digest* (second series) **8**: 24-26.

PARMENTER, L., 1944. Collecting Diptera on the Norfolk Broads. *J. Soc. Br. Ent.* **2**: 208-213.

PARMENTER, L., 1950a. *Doros conopseus* F. (Dipt., Syrphidae) in Surrey. *Entomologist's mon. Mag.* **86**: 256.

PARMENTER, L., 1950b. The Diptera of Bookham Common. *Lond. Nat.* **29**: 98-133.

PARMENTER, L., 1951. Flies visiting fennel, *Foeniculum vulgare* Miller, (Umbelliferae). *J. Soc. Brit. Ent.* **4**: 41-42.

PARMENTER, L., 1953a. City bombed sites survey. The flies of the Cripplegate bombed site, City of London. *Lond. Nat.* **33**: 89-100.

PARMENTER, L., 1953b. The hoverflies (Syrphidae). *Entomologist's Rec. & J. Var.* **65**: 122-126, 154-159, 185-190, 234-238.

PARMENTER, L., 1954. A list of the species of Syrphidae (Diptera) of the British Isles. *Entomologist's Gaz.* **5**: 135-144.

PARMENTER, L., 1955. Flies visiting the bluebell *Endymion non-scriptus* (L.) Garcke. *Entomologist's Rec. & J. Var.* **67**: 89-90.

PARMENTER, L., 1956a. On *Syritta pipiens* L. (Syrphidae) and its habits. *Entomologist's Rec. & J. Var.* **68**:211-214.

PARMENTER, L., 1956b. Flies and the selection of the flowers they visit. *Entomologist's Rec. & J. Var.* **68**: 242-243.

PARMENTER, L., 1957. Flies (Diptera) and their relations with plants. *Lond. Nat.* **37**: 115-125.

PARMENTER, L., 1959. The Diptera about Dale Fort Field Centre, Pembrokeshire. *Entomologist's Rec. & J. Var.* **71**: 1-11.

PARMENTER, L., 1960. A further list of the Diptera of Bookham Common. *Lond. Nat.* **39**: 66-76.

PARMENTER, L., 1961. Flies visiting the flowers of wood spurge, *Euphorbia amygdaloides* L. (Euphorbiaceae). *Entomologist's Rec. & J. Var.* **73**: 48-49.

PARMENTER, L., 1966. Some additions to the list of flies (Diptera) of Bookham Common. *Lond Nat.* **45**: 56-59.

PARMENTER, L., 1968. More flies of the Cripplegate bombed site, City of London. *Lond. Nat.* **47**: 81-86.

PARRACK, J.D. 2000. Hoverflies of Northumberland - Part 1 (Syrphidae, Syrphinae, Syrphini). *Vasculum* **85**(4): 1-33.

PARRACK, J.D. 2001a. Hoverflies of Northumberland - Part 2 Syrphinae (Bachini, Paragini), Milesiinae (Cheilosiini, Chrysogastrini). *Vasculum* **86**(1): 1-32.

PARRACK, J.D. 2001b. Hoverflies of Northumberland - Part 3 Milesiinae (Eristalini, Merodontini, Pipizini, Sericomyiini, Volucellini and Xylotini). *Vasculum* **86**(2): 2-36.

PASTON, S., 2000. *Volucella inanis* (Linnaeus) (Diptera, Syrphidae) new to Norfolk. *Dipterists Digest* (second series) **7**: 7.

PAVETT, P.M., 1989. Hoverflies and other Diptera in south Wales during 1988. *Bull. amat. Ent. Soc.* **48**: 227.

PAVETT, P.M., 1990. Diptera recorded in 1989. *Bull. amat. Ent. Soc.* **49**: 225.

PAYNE, R.G., 1982. *Hoverflies of Essex: provisional maps*. 8pp. Southend Museum Biological Records Centre, Southend.

PAYNE, R.G., 1989. *Provisional atlas of the hoverflies* (*Diptera: Syrphidae*) *of Essex*. 31pp. Essex Biological Records Centre Publication no. 7. Southend Museum Service, Southend.

PAYNE, R.G., 1996. Some notable hoverflies found in Essex since 1990. *Essex Naturalist* **13**: 20-22.

PAYNE, R.M., 1974a. The hover-flies of Essex. *Essex Naturalist* **33**: 79-103.

PAYNE, R.M., 1974b. Insects at the flowers of *Inula crithmoides* L. (Compositae). *Entomologist's mon. Mag.* **110**: 202.

PAYNE, R.M., 1979. Insects attracted to Alexanders (*Smyrnium olusatrum* L.). *Entomologist's mon. Mag.* **113** (1977): 233.

PAYNE, R.M., 1981. Insects on flowers of *Senecio fluviatilis* Wallr. *Entomologist's mon. Mag.* **117**: 98.

PECK, L.V., 1988. Family Syrphidae. Vol. 8. pp. 11-230. **In**: Soós, Á. & Papp, L. (Eds) *Catalogue of Palaearctic Diptera. Syrphidae-Conopidae*. Elsevier Science Publishing, Amsterdam.

PEDERSEN, E.T., 1971. De danske arten of slaegten *Neoascia* Williston (Dipt. Syrphidae). *Ent. Meddr.* **39**: 51-62. [In Danish]

PENNINGTON, M.G., 1999. The status of hoverflies (Diptera, Syrphidae) in Shetland. *Dipterists Digest* (second series) **6**: 93-104.

PENNINGTON, M.G., 2001. *Xanthandrus comtus* (Dip.: Syrphidae) new to Shetland. *Entomologist's Rec. & J. Var.* **113**: 38-39.

PENNINGTON, T.H., 1989. Thirty years of *Eriozona syrphoides* (Fallén) (Dipt., Syrphidae) in Britain. *Entomologist's mon. Mag.* **125**: 132.

PERRY, I., 1997. *Callicera aurata* in Suffolk found breeding in birch. *Dipterists Digest* (second series) **3**: 53.

PERRY, I., 1998. *Sphegina sibirica* Stackelberg (Diptera, Syrphidae) in the Central Highlands of Scotland. *Dipterists Digest* (second series) **5**: 8-9.

PICKARD, R.S., 1975. Relative abundance of syrphid species in a nest of the wasp *Ectemnius cavifrons* compared with that in the surrounding habitat. *Entomophaga* **20**: 143-151.

PLANT, C.W., 1986a. A working list of the hoverflies (Diptera: Syrphidae) of the London area. *Lond. Nat.* **65**: 109-117.

PLANT, C.W., 1986b. A further colony of *Anasimyia interpuncta* Harris (Dipt.: Syrphidae) in the Thames Estuary area. *Entomologist's Rec. & J. Var.* **98**: 22-24.

PLANT, C.W., 1988. *Sphaerophoria virgata* (Dipt., Syrphidae) in the Wyre Forest, Worcestershire, with notes on other *Sphaerophoria* at this locality. *Entomologist's Rec. & J. Var.* **100**: 73-74.

PLANT, C.W., 1990a. *Sphaerophoria bankowskae* Goeldlin, 1989 (Syrphidae) recorded in mainland Britain. *Dipterists Digest* (first series) **3**: 32-33.

PLANT, C.W., 1990b. Hoverflies (Diptera: Syrphidae) in the London Area: progress report and selected distribution maps. *Lond. Nat.* **69**: 53-65.

PLANT, C.W., 1991. [Exhibit at BENHS indoor meeting, 13 June 1990.] *British Journal of Entomology and Natural History* **4**: 48.

PLANT, C.W., 1994. Three hoverflies (Dipt., Syrphidae) new to Hertfordshire, with notes on others. *Entomologist's mon. Mag.* **130**: 253-254.

PLANT, C.W., 1998. More on *Didea fasciata* Macquart (Dipt., Syrphidae) in Essex and nearby. *Entomologist's mon. Mag.* **134**: 270.

PLANT, C.W., 2000. The wasp hoverfly *Doros profuges* (Harris): Report of the 1999 survey. *English Nature Research Reports* no. 352. 49pp. English Nature, Peterborough.

PLANT, C.W., 2001. Hoverflies (Diptera: Syrphidae) in Buckingham Palace garden. *Suppl. Lond. Nat.* **80**: 259-268.

POLLARD, E., 1971. Hedges. VI. Habitat diversity and crop pests: a study of *Brevicoryne brassicae* and its syrphid predators. *J. appl. Ecol.* **8**: 751-780.

POLLARD, E., 1977. A method for assessing the abundance of butterflies. *Biol. Conserv.* **12**: 115-134.

PONTIN, A.J., 1960. Some records of predators and parasites adapted to attack aphids attended by ants. *Entomologist's mon. Mag.* **95**: 154-155.

PROCTOR, M. & YEO, P.F., 1973. *The pollination of flowers*. 418pp. Collins New Naturalist, London.

PROCTOR, M., YEO, P.F. & LACK, A., 1996. *The Natural History of Pollination*. 479pp. Collins New Naturalist, London.

PUGH, M.N., 1977. The hoverflies of Clowes Wood nature reserve, Warwickshire (Diptera, Aschiza-Syrphidae). *Proc. Birmingham Nat. Hist. Soc.* **23**: 264-266.

RAVENSCROFT, N.O.M. & BARBOUR, D.A., 1992. *Doros conopseus* (Diptera: Syrphidae) on the Isle of Mull, Scotland. *Entomologist's Gaz.* **43**: 72-73.

RAVENSCROFT, N.O.M., FAULKNER, C.G.N., OXLEY, J.R., PUMPHREY, C.J., ROGERS, L.M. & THOMAS, J.L., 1991. Some hoverflies (Diptera: Syrphidae) of Rhum National Nature Reserve, Western Scotland. *Dipterists Digest* (first series) **8**: 25-28.

REEMER, M., 1999. Faunistiek en Ecologie van het Zweefvliegengenus *Epistrophe* in Nederland (Diptera: Syrphidae). *Nederlandse Faunistische Mededelingen* **8**: 33-54. [In Dutch]

REEMER, M. 2000. A new species of *Parhelophilus* Girschner, 1897 (Diptera, Syrphidae). *Dipteron* **3**: 1-6.

RIZZA, A., CAMPOBASSO, G., DUNN, P.H. & STAZI, M., 1988. *Cheilosia corydon* (Dipt.: Syrphidae), a candidate for the biological control of musk thistle in North America. *Ann. ent. Soc. Am.* **81**: 225-232.

ROBERTS, M.J., 1970. The structure of the mouthparts of syrphid larvae (Diptera) in relation to feeding habits. *Acta zool. Stockh.* **51**: 43-65.

ROBERTSON, D.M., 1986. Some hoverfly (Dipt., Syrphidae) records from Scotland. *Entomologist's mon. Mag.* **122**: 208.

ROBERTSON, I., 1953. The hypopus of *Hericia hericia*. *Proc. Zool. Soc. Lond.* **123**: 267-271.

ROJO, S., PÉREZ-BAÑÓN, C. & MARCOS-GARCÍA, M.A., 1999. First observations on the biology of *Scaeva mecogramma* (Bigot, 1860) (Diptera, Syrphidae) and notes on some other syrphids preying on psyllids (Hemiptera, Aphalaridae and Triozidae). *Volucella* **4**: 105-111.

376

ROPER, P., 1992. Notes on Greenwich Park, S.E. London. *Entomologist's Rec. & J. Var.* **104**: 221-222.

ROTHERAY, G.E., 1979a. Atlas of the Diptera of Staffordshire, part 1 Hoverflies, Syrphidae. Staffordshire Biological Recording Scheme Publication 5. 49pp. City Museum, Stoke-on-Trent.

ROTHERAY, G.E., 1979b. *Biological studies on some parasitoids of aphidophagous Syrphidae (Diptera)*. Unpublished Ph.D. Thesis, University of Wales.

ROTHERAY, G.E., 1979c. The biology and host-searching behaviour of a cynipoid parasite of aphidophagous syrphid larvae. *Ecol. Ent.* **4**: 75-82.

ROTHERAY, G.E., 1981. Host searching and oviposition behaviour of some parasitoids of aphidophagous Syrphidae. *Ecol. Ent.* **6**: 79-87.

ROTHERAY, G.E., 1983. Feeding behaviour of *Syrphus ribesii* and *Melanostoma scalare* on *Aphis fabae*. *Ent. exp. & appl.* **34**: 148-154.

ROTHERAY, G.E., 1984. Host relations, life cycles and multiparasitism in some parasitoids of aphidophagous Syrphidae (Diptera). *Ecol. Ent.* **9**: 303-310.

ROTHERAY, G.E., 1985. Arrested development of *Syrphus ribesii* (L.) larvae (Diptera: Syrphidae) caused by the encyrtid *Bothriothorax clavicornis* (Dalman) (Hymenoptera). *Entomologist's Gaz.* **36**: 51-53.

ROTHERAY, G.E., 1986a. The larva and puparium of *Epistrophe grossulariae* (Meigen) (Dipt., Syrphidae) with a note on overwintering behaviour. *Entomologist's mon. Mag.* **122**: 215-218.

ROTHERAY, G.E., 1986b. Colour, shape and defence in aphidophagous syrphid larvae (Diptera). *Zool. J. Linn. Soc.* **86**: 201-216.

ROTHERAY, G.E., 1987a. The larvae and puparia of five species of aphidophagous Syrphidae (Diptera). *Entomologist's mon. Mag.* **123**: 121-125.

ROTHERAY, G.E., 1987b. The ever-so-helpful hooverfly. *BBC Wildlife* **5**: 340-345.

ROTHERAY, G.E., 1987c. More on attachment – saliva sticks syrphids to plants. *Antenna* **11**: 5-7.

ROTHERAY, G.E., 1988a. Larval morphology and feeding patterns of four *Cheilosia* species (Dipt., Syrphidae) associated with *Cirsium palustre* (L.) Scopoli (Compositae) in Scotland. *J. nat. Hist.* **22**: 17-25.

ROTHERAY, G.E., 1988b. Morphology and feeding behaviour of the leaf-mining larva of *Cheilosia semifasciata* (Diptera: Syphidae). *J. nat. Hist.* **22**: 865-873.

ROTHERAY, G.E., 1988c. Third stage larvae of six species of aphidophagous Syrphidae (Diptera). *Entomologist's Gaz.* **39**: 153-159.

ROTHERAY, G.E., 1989. *Aphid predators*. Naturalists' Handbooks 11. 77pp. Richmond Publishing Co. Ltd., Slough.

ROTHERAY, G.E., 1990a. An old specimen of a new European *Platycheirus* species (Dipt., Syrphidae). *Entomologist's mon. Mag.* **126**: 204.

ROTHERAY, G.E., 1990b. Larval and puparial records of some hoverflies associated with dead wood (Diptera, Syrphidae). *Dipterists Digest* (first series) **7**: 2-7.

ROTHERAY, G.E., 1990c. The relationship between feeding mode and morphology in *Cheilosia* larvae (Diptera: Syrphidae). *J. nat. Hist.* **24**: 7-19.

ROTHERAY, G.E., 1990d. A new species of *Bioblapsis* (Hymenoptera, Ichneumonidae) from Scotland parasitising a mycophagous hoverfly, *Cheilosia longula* (Diptera: Syrphidae). *Ent. scand.* **21**: 277-280.

ROTHERAY, G.E., 1991. Larval stages of 17 rare and poorly known British hoverflies (Diptera: Syrphidae). *J. nat. Hist.* **25**: 945-969.

ROTHERAY, G.E., 1993. Colour guide to hoverfly larvae (Diptera, Syrphidae) in Britain and Europe. *Dipterists Digest* (first series) **9**: 1-155.

ROTHERAY, G.E., 1996. The larva of *Brachyopa scutellaris* Robineau-Desvoidy (Diptera: Syrphidae), with a key to and notes on the larvae of British *Brachyopa* species. *Entomologist's Gaz.* **47**: 199-205.

ROTHERAY, G.E., 1997a. J.W. Yerbury's contribution to the study of Scottish Diptera. *Dipterists Digest* (second series) **4**: 92-99.

ROTHERAY, G.E., 1997b. Larval stages of the predatory hoverflies *Trichopsomyia flavitarsis* (Meigen), *Platycheirus melanopsis* Loew and *Parasyrphus nigritarsis* (Zetterstedt) (Diptera: Syrphidae). *Entomologist's Gaz.* **48**: 127-134.

ROTHERAY, G.E., 1998. *Platycheirus splendidus* sp. n. from Britain formerly confused with *Platycheirus scutatus* (Diptera: Syrphidae). *Entomologist's Gaz.* **49**: 271-276.

ROTHERAY, G.E., 1999a. Description and a key to the larval and puparial stages of north-west European *Volucella* (Diptera, Syrphidae). *Studia Dipterologica* **6**: 103-116.

ROTHERAY, G.E., 1999b. The early stages of *Cheilosia illustrata* (Harris) (Diptera, Syrphidae). *Dipterists Digest* (second series) **6**: 107-111.

ROTHERAY, G.E. & BLAND, K.P., 1992. *Xanthandrus comtus* (Harris) (Dipt., Syrphidae) breeding in Scotland. *Entomologist's mon. Mag.* **128**: 57-58.

ROTHERAY, G.E. & DOBSON, J., 1987. Aphidophagy and the larval and pupal stages of the syrphid *Platycheirus fulviventris* (Macquart). *Entomologist's Gaz.* **38**: 245-251.

ROTHERAY, G.E. & GILBERT, F.S., 1989. The phylogeny and systematics of European predacious Syrphidae (Diptera) based on larval and puparial stages. *Zool. J. Linn. Soc.* **95**: 29-70.

ROTHERAY, G.E. & GILBERT, F.S., 1999. Phylogeny of Palaearctic Syrphidae (Diptera): evidence from larval stages. *Zool. J. Linn. Soc.* **127**: 1-112.

ROTHERAY, G.E. & HEWITT, S.M., 1999. Northern records of *Parasyrphus nigritarsis* (Zetterstedt) (Syrphidae). *Dipterists Digest* (second series) **6**: 106.

ROTHERAY, G.E. & MacGOWAN, I., 1990. Re-evaluation of the status of *Callicera rufa* Schummel (Diptera: Syrphidae) in the British Isles. *Entomologist* **109**: 35-42.

ROTHERAY, G.E. & MacGOWAN, I., 2000. Status and breeding sites of three presumed endangered Scottish saproxylic syrphids (Diptera, Syrphidae). *Journal of Insect Conservation* **4**: 215-223.

ROTHERAY, G.E. & MARTINAT, P., 1984. Searching behaviour in relation to starvation in *Syrphus ribesii*. *Ent. exp. appl.* **36**: 17-21.

ROTHERAY, G.E. & PERRY, I., 1994. The larva of *Callicera spinolae* with a key to the larvae of British *Callicera* species (Diptera, Syrphidae). *Entomologist* **113**: 205-210.

ROTHERAY, G.E. & STUKE, J.H., 1998. Third stage larvae of four species of saproxylic Syrphidae (Diptera), with a key to the larvae of British *Criorhina* species. *Entomologist's Gaz.* **49**: 209-217.

ROTHERAY, G.E., BARR, B. & HEWITT, S.M., 1996. The myrmecophilous larvae of *Chrysotoxum arcuatum*, *Pipizella varipes* and *Xanthogramma pedissequum* from Europe and *Platycheirus milleri* from New Zealand (Dip.: Syrphidae). *Entomologist's Rec. & J. Var.* **108**: 257-265.

ROTHERAY, G.E., HANCOCK, G., HEWITT, S., HORSEFIELD, D. & MacGOWAN, I., 2001. The biodiversity and conservation of saproxylic Diptera in Scotland. *Journal of Insect Conservation* **5**: 77-85.

SACK, P., 1932. Syrphidae. **In**: Lindner, E. (Ed.) *Die Fliegen der Palaearktischen Region* **4** (6). 451pp. E. Schweizerbart'sche Verlagsbuchhandlung, Stuttgart. [In German]

SANKEY, J., 1977. *Doros conopseus* (F.) (Dipt., Syrphidae) in mid-Surrey. *Entomologist's mon. Mag.* **113**: 18.

SAUNT, J.W., 1940. Diptera in the Tile Hill nature reserve. *Proc. Coventry nat. Hist. Scient. Soc.* **2**: 15-20.

SAUNT, J.W., 1945. Migration of Syrphidae. *Entomologist's mon. Mag.* **81**: 131.

SCHIEMENZ, H., 1957. Vergleichende funktionellanatomische Untersuchungen der Kopfmuskulatur von *Theobaldia* und *Eristalis* (Dipt. Culicid. und Syrphid.). *Deut. ent. Zeitschr.* **4**: 268-331. [In German]

SCHMID, U., 1999a. *Syrphus obscuripes* Strobl, 1910: ein älteres Synonym von *Epistrophe similis* Doczkal & Schmid, 1994 (Diptera, Syrphidae). *Volucella* **4**: 103-104. [In German]

SCHMID, U., 1999b. Die Larve von *Cheilosia impressa* Loew, 1840 (Diptera, Syrphidae). *Volucella* **4**: 113-119. [In German]

SCHMID, U. & GROSSMAN, A., 1996. Eiablage von *Cheilosia latifrons* (Zetterstedt, 1843) (Diptera, Syrphidae) an *Leontodon autumnalis* L. Volucella **2**: 86-87. [In German]

SCHNEIDER, F., 1953. *Syrphus nigritarsis* Zett., ein Ei- and Larvenräuber von *Melasoma* (Chrysom., Col.). *Tijdschr. Plantenziekten* **59**: 192-194. [In German]

378

SCHNEIDER, F., 1958. Künstliche Blumen zum Nachweis von Winterquartieren, Futterpflanzen und Tageswanderungen von *Lasiopticus pyrastri* (L.) und andern Schwebfliegen (Syrphidae Dipt.). *Mitt. schweiz. ent. Ges.* **31**: 1-24. [In German]

SCHNEIDER, F., 1969. Bionomics and physiology of aphidophagous Syrphidae. *Ann. Rev. Ent.* **14**: 103-124.

SCHÖNROGGE, K., BARR, B., WARDLAW, J.C., NAPPER, E., GARDNER, M.G., BREEN, J., ELMES, G.W. & THOMAS, J.A., 2002. When rare species become endangered: cryptic speciation in myrmecophilous hoverflies. *Biol. J. Linn. Soc.* **75**: 291-300.

SCHUHMACHER, H. & HOFFMAN, H., 1982. Zur funktion der Mundwerkzeuge von Schwebfliegen bei der Nahrungsaufnahme (Diptera: Syrphidae). *Entomologia generalis* **7**: 327-342. [In German]

SCOTT, E.I., 1939. An account of the developmental stages of some aphidophagous Syrphidae (Dipt.) and their parasites (Hymenopt.). *Ann. appl Biol.* **26**: 509-532.

SCOTT, H., 1923. A genuine British specimen of *Volucella zonaria* Poda. *Entomologist's mon. Mag.* **59**: 260.

SEDLAG, U., 1967. [*Triglyphus primus*, a widely overlooked hoverfly.] *Ent. Ber., Berlin* **1966**: 88-90. [In German]

SÉGUY, E., 1961. Diptères Syrphides de l'Europe occidentale. *Mém. Mus. natn. Hist. nat. Paris* **23**: 1-248.

SHARP, D., 1903. *Chamaesyrphus lusitanicus* Mik: a new British Syrphid fly. *Entomologist's mon. Mag.* **39**: 197-198.

SHAW, M.R. & ROTHERAY, G.E., 1990. *Xanthandrus comtus* (Harris) (Dipt., Syrphidae) reared. *Entomologist's mon. Mag.* **126**: 258.

SHILLITO, J.F., 1947. *Pocota personata* (Harris, M.) (Dipt., Syrphidae) from Epping Forest. *Entomologist's mon. Mag.* **83**: 180-181.

SHIRT, D.B., (Ed.), 1987. *British Red Data Books: 2. Insects.* xliv+402pp. Nature Conservancy Council, Peterborough.

SKIDMORE, P., 1985. Diptera report: 1977-84. *Naturalist* **110**: 111-117.

SKIDMORE, P., 1994. Composite list of Diptera collected in South Uist, Benbecula and North Uist in August 1989. *Dipterists Digest* (first series) **14**: 44-52.

SKUFJIN, K.V., 1980. A review of the genus *Sphaerophoria* Lepeletier et Serville (Diptera, Syrphidae) in the fauna of the USSR. *Ent. Rev. Wash.* **59**: 134-142.

SMITH, A.P.L. & SMITH, K.G.V., 1991. Some insect records from Tanera More, Summer Isles, Ross, (Scotland). *Entomologist's mon. Mag.* **127**: 34.

SMITH, K.G.V., 1955. Notes on the egg and first instar larva of *Volucella bombylans. Entomologist's mon. Mag.* **91**: 52-54.

SMITH, K.G.V., 1974. Changes in the British dipterous fauna. pp. 371-391. **In**: Hawksworth, D.L. (Ed.) *The changing flora and fauna of Britain.* Academic Press, London.

SMITH, K.G.V., 1979. The larva and puparium of *Cheilosia bergenstammi* Becker (Diptera: Syrphidae) with a summary of the known biology of the genus in Europe. *Entomologist's Rec & J. Var.* **91**: 190-194.

SMITH, K.G.V., 1989. An introduction to the immature stages of British flies . *Handbk Ident. Br. Insects* **10** (14): 1-280.

SMITH, K.G.V., 1991. *Brachyopa insensilis* Collin (Dipt., Syrphidae) in North London (Middlesex). *Entomologist's mon. Mag.* **127**: 208.

SMITH, K.G.V., 1997. *Didea fasciata* Macq., (Dipt., Syrphidae) in North London (Middlesex). *Entomologist's mon. Mag.* **133**: 204.

SØNDERUP, H. P. S., 1941. Insektfund fra 1939-40. *Flora og Fauna* **47**: 63-68. [In Danish]

SØRENSEN, K.L. & GILBERT, F.S., 1996. The Hoverflies (Diptera, Syrphidae) of Białowieża Primeval Forest. *Dipterists Digest* (second series) **2**: 92-94.

SPEIGHT, M.C.D., 1973. British species of *Sphaerophoria* (Dipt., Syrphidae) confused with *S. menthastri* (L.), including a key to the males of the seven species of *Sphaerophoria* found in the British Isles. *Entomologist* **106**: 228-233.

SPEIGHT, M.C.D., 1974a. *Bombus lapponicus, Parasyrphus lineola* and *Phaonia exoleta*: insects new to Ireland. *Ir. Nat. J.* **18**: 123-124.

SPEIGHT, M.C.D., 1974b. *Cheilosia sahlbergi* (Diptera: Syrphidae) in Britain. *Entomologist's Rec. & J. Var.* **86**: 193-194 + 1 plate.

379

SPEIGHT, M.C.D., 1976a. *Agonum livens*, *Asemum striatum* and *Xylota coeruleiventris*: insects new to Ireland. *Ir. Nat. J.* **18**: 274-275.

SPEIGHT, M.C.D., 1976b. *Sphaerophoria rueppellii* (Dipt., Syrphidae) new to Ireland, with figures of its surstyli. *Ir. Nat. J.* **18**: 332-334.

SPEIGHT, M.C.D., 1976c. The puparium of *Chrysotoxum festivum* (L.) (Diptera: Syrphidae). *Entomologist's Rec. & J. Var.* **88**: 51-52.

SPEIGHT, M.C.D., 1976d. *Sphaerophoria virgata* Goeldlin (Dipt.: Syrphidae) new to the British Isles. *Entomologist's Rec. & J. Var.* **88**: 300-302.

SPEIGHT, M.C.D., 1977a. Athlone field meeting: insects collected on and near the shores of Loch Ree. *Bull. Ir. biogeog. Soc.* **1**: 27-36.

SPEIGHT, M.C.D., 1977b. *Metasyrphus nielseni* D. & L. (Dipt.: Syrphidae) in the British Isles. *Entomologist's Rec. & J. Var.* **89**: 154-155.

SPEIGHT, M.C.D., 1978a. A check list of Irish Syrphidae (Diptera). *Bull. Ir. biogeog. Soc.* **2**: 26-31.

SPEIGHT, M.C.D., 1978b. *Cheilosia laskai* sp. n. (Diptera: Syrphidae) from western Ireland. *Ir. Nat. J.* **19**: 217-222.

SPEIGHT, M.C.D., 1978c. The genus *Paragus* (Dipt.: Syrphidae) in the British Isles, including a key to known and possible British Isles species. *Entomologist's Rec. & J. Var.* **90**: 100-107.

SPEIGHT, M.C.D., 1978d. *Melanostoma dubium* (Dipt. Syrphidae) in Britain and a key to the British Isles *Melanostoma* species. *Entomologist's Rec. & J. Var.* **90**: 226-230.

SPEIGHT, M.C.D., 1980. The *Chrysogaster* species (Dipt. Syrphidae) known in Great Britain and Ireland. *Entomologist's Rec. & J. Var.* **92**: 145-150.

SPEIGHT, M.C.D., 1981a. A Key to the Xylotini (*sensu* Hippa) known in Great Britain and Ireland, plus *Xylota ignava* (Dipt., Syrphidae). *Entomologist's Rec. & J. Var.* **93**: 25-27.

SPEIGHT, M.C.D., 1981b. The Irish *Anasimyia* species including a key and first records of *A. contracta* (Diptera: Syrphidae). *Ir. Nat. J.* **20**: 229-234.

SPEIGHT, M.C.D., 1985. Adjustments to the Irish hoverfly list (Diptera., Syrphidae). *Ir. Nat. J.* **21**: 385-391.

SPEIGHT, M.C.D., 1986a. *Portevinia maculata* (Fal.): last instar larva and puparium, with notes on the relationship between this hoverfly and its larval host-plant, *Allium ursinum* (Diptera, Syrphidae). *Nouv. Revue ent.* **3**: 37-43.

SPEIGHT, M.C.D., 1986b. *Cheilosia nasutula*, *Neocnemodon vitripennis* and *Parasyrphus nigritarsis* (Diptera: Syrphidae) new to Ireland. *Ir. Nat. J.* **22**: 149-152.

SPEIGHT, M.C.D., 1986c. *Cheilosia argentifrons* (Diptera: Syrphidae) new to Ireland: *Donacia cinerea* (Coleoptera: Chrysomelidae) and *Palloptera muliebris* (Diptera: Pallopteridae), presence confirmed in Ireland. *Ir. Nat. J.* **22**: 159-160.

SPEIGHT, M.C.D., 1987. External morphology of adult Syrphidae (Diptera). *Tijdschr. Ent.* **130**: 141-175.

SPEIGHT, M.C.D., 1988a. *Neoascia podagrica* (Diptera: Syrphidae) in Ireland, with a key to distinguish it from related European species. *Ir. Nat. J.* **22**: 447-452.

SPEIGHT, M.C.D., 1988b. *Platycheirus amplus*: an insect new to Ireland not previously recorded from Europe (Diptera: Syrphidae). *Ir. Nat. J.* **22**: 518-521.

SPEIGHT, M.C.D., 1988c. Syrphidae known from temperate Western Europe: potential additions to the fauna of Great Britain and Ireland and a provisional species list for N. France. *Dipterists Digest* (first series) **1**: 2-35.

SPEIGHT, M.C.D., 1988d. *Doros destillatorius*, espèce nouvelle pour la France, avec désignation des types des deux espèces européennes du genre *Doros*, description de leurs pupes et clés de détermination des adultes et des pupes. *Bull. Soc. ent. Fr.* **92**(5-6): 193-200. [In French]

SPEIGHT, M.C.D., 1989a. *Sphaerophoria fatarum* in the British Isles (Syrphidae). *Dipterists Digest* (first series) **2**: 34.

SPEIGHT, M.C.D., 1989b. *Saproxylic invertebrates and their conservation.* Nature and Environment Series no 42. 81pp. Council of Europe, Strasbourg.

SPEIGHT, M.C.D., 1990a. A tale of two texts. *Dipterists Digest* (first series) **5**: 2-4.

SPEIGHT, M.C.D., 1990b. *Platycheirus occultus* and *P. ramsarensis* in Ireland and correct citation of the original descriptions of these species and the original description of *P. europaeus* (Diptera, Syrphidae). *Ir. Nat. J.* **23**: 276-277.

SPEIGHT, M.C.D., 1990c. The puparia of *Xanthogramma festivum* and *Xanthogramma pedissequum* (Syrphidae). *Dipterists Digest* (first series) **6**: 29-31.

SPEIGHT, M.C.D., 1990d. *Hippodamia 13-punctata* (Coleoptera: Coccinellidae) and other insects from All Saint's Bog, Co. Offaly, Ireland. *Bull. Ir. biogeog. Soc.* **13**: 200-212.

SPEIGHT, M.C.D., 1991a. A key to W. European *Parasyrphus* species (Syrphidae). *Dipterists Digest* (first series) **8**: 3-5.

SPEIGHT, M.C.D., 1991b. *Callicera aenea, C. aurata, C. fagesii* and *C. macquartii* redefined, with a key to and notes on the European *Callicera* species (Diptera: Syrphidae). *Dipterists Digest* (first series) **10**: 1-25.

SPEIGHT, M.C.D., 1993a. Liechtenstein Syrphidae (Diptera): records of seven extra species. *Ber. Bot.-Zool. Ges. Liechtenstein-Sargans-Werdenberg* **20**: 211-216.

SPEIGHT, M.C.D., 1993b. Révision des syrphes de la fauna de France: I. - List alphabétique des espèces de la sous-famille des Syrphinae (Diptera, Syrphidae). *Bull. Soc. ent. France* **98**: 35-46. [In French]

SPEIGHT, M.C.D., 1994. Révision des syrphes de la fauna de France: II. - Les Microdontidae et les Syrphidae Milesiinae (in part) (Diptera, Syrphoidea). *Bull. Soc. ent. France* **99**: 35-46. [In French]

SPEIGHT, M.C.D., 1996a. *Cheilosia psilophthalma* and *Odinia boletina*: insects new to Ireland and *Sapromyza sexpunctata* confirmed as an Irish species. *Ir. Nat. J.* **25**: 178-182.

SPEIGHT, M.C.D., 1996b. A mass migration of *Episyrphus balteatus* and *Eupeodes corollae* arriving in the south-west and remarks on other migrant hoverflies (Diptera, Syrphidae) in Ireland. *Ir. Nat. J.* **25**: 182-183.

SPEIGHT, M.C.D., 1998. *Eriozona syrphoides* (Diptera: Syrphidae); an insect new to Ireland. *Ir. Nat. J.* **26**: 114-116.

SPEIGHT, M.C.D., 1999a. The puparia of *Xanthogramma festivum* and *X. pedissequum* (Syrphidae). *Dipterists Digest* (second series) **6**: 29-31.

SPEIGHT, M.C.D., 1999b. *Syrphus rectus* Osten Sacken and its potential implications to the recording of *Syrphus* species. *Dipterists Digest* (second series) **6**: 85-91.

SPEIGHT, M.C.D., 1999c. A key to the European Xylotini (Dip.: Syrphidae). *Entomologist's Rec. & J. Var.* **111**: 211-217.

SPEIGHT, M.C.D., 2000a. Hoverflies (Dip.: Syrphidae) with a drinking habit. *Entomologist's Rec. & J. Var.* **112**: 107-113.

SPEIGHT, M.C.D., 2000b. The syrphid fauna of western temperate Europe revisited (Diptera, Syrphidae). *Dipterists Digest* (second series) **7**: 89-99.

SPEIGHT, M.C.D., 2000c. Irish Syrphidae (Diptera), Pt.1: species accounts and distribution maps. **In**: SPEIGHT, M.C.D., CASTELLA, E., OBRDLIK, P. & BALL, S. (Eds) Syrph the Net, the database of European Syrphidae , vol. 18, 215 pp., Syrph the Net publications, Dublin.

SPEIGHT, M.C.D. & CHANDLER, P.J., 1995. *Paragus constrictus, Pteromicra pectorosa* & *Stegana similis*: insects new to Ireland and *Stegana coleoptrata*, presence in Ireland confirmed. *Ir. Nat. J.* **25**: 28-32.

SPEIGHT, M. C. D. & CLAUSSEN, C., 1987. Redefinition of *Cheilosia ahenea* and *Cheilosia argentifrons* with records extending the known range of these species in Western Europe (Diptera, Syrphidae). *Ann. Soc. ent. Fr.* (*ICS.*) **23**: 299-308.

SPEIGHT, M.C.D. & GOELDLIN DE TIEFENAU, P., 1990. Keys to distinguish *Platycheirus angustipes, P. europaeus, P. occultus* and *P. ramsarensis* (Dipt., Syrphidae) from other *clypeatus* group species known in Europe. *Dipterists Digest* (first series) **5**: 5-18.

SPEIGHT, M.C.D. & IRWIN, A.G., 1978. Irish *Paragus* (Diptera: Syrphidae), including a key to British Isles species. *Ir. Nat. J.* **19**: 198-199.

SPEIGHT, M.C.D. & LUCAS, J.A.W., 1992. Liechtenstein Syrphidae (Diptera). *Ber. Bot.-Zool. Ges. Liechtenstein-Sargans-Werdenberg* **19**: 327-463.

SPEIGHT, M.C.D. & NASH, R., 1993. *Chrysotoxum cautum, Ctenophora ornata, C. pectinicornis, Helophilus trivittatus* and *Mesembrina mystacea* (Diptera), insects new to Ireland. *Ir. Nat. J.* **24**: 231-236.

SPEIGHT, M.C.D. & SMITH, K.G.V., 1975. A key to males of the British species of *Neocnemodon* Goffe (Dipt.: Syrphidae). *Entomologist's Rec. & J. Var.* **87**: 150-154.

SPEIGHT, M.C.D. & VOCKEROTH, J.R., 1988. *Platycheirus amplus*: an insect new to Ireland not previously recorded from Europe (Diptera, Syrphidae). *Ir. Nat. J.* **22**: 518-521.

SPEIGHT, M.C.D., CASTELLA, E., OBRDLIK, P. & BALL, S., 2001. *Syrph the Net on CD*. Syrph the Net Publications, Dublin.

SPEIGHT, M.C.D., CHANDLER, P.J. & NASH, R., 1975. Irish Syrphidae (Diptera): notes on the species and an account of their known distribution. *Proc. R. Ir. Acad. (B)* **75**: 1-80.

SPEIGHT, M.C.D., WILLIAMS, M. de C. & LEGRAND, J., 1986. *Scaeva dignota* et *S. mecogramma* nouveaux pour la France et clé de détermination des espèces du genre (Diptera, Syrphidae). *l'Entomologiste* **42**: 359-364. [In French]

SPEIGHT, M.C.D., WILLIAMS, M. de C. & WITHERS, P., 1979. *Pachygaster minutissima, Psacadina zernyi* and *Xylota tarda*: insects new to Ireland. *Ir. Nat. J.* **19**: 354-355.

SRINIVASAN, M.R. & GUY, R.G., 1990. Spectral properties of movement perception in the dronefly *Eristalis*. *J. comp. Physiol. A* **166**: 287-295.

SSYMANK, A. & GILBERT, F., 1993. Anemophilous pollen in the diet of syrphid flies with special reference to the leaf feeding strategy in Xylotini (Diptera, Syrphidae). *Deut. ent. Zeitschr.* **40**: 245-258.

STACE, C., 1997. *New Flora of the British Isles*. (Second edition). xxx+1130pp. Cambridge University Press, Cambridge.

STACKELBERG, A.A., 1970. *Syrphidae*. pp. 11-96. **In**: Bei-Bienko, G, Y., Classification key to the insects of the European part of USSR **5**(2). *Opredeliteli po Faune SSSR* **103**. Leningrad. [In Russian] (1988: English translation published by Smithsonian Institution Library and The National Science Foundation, Washington D.C.)

STEENIS, J. VAN & GOELDLIN DE TIEFENAU, P., 1998. Description of and key to the European females of the *Platycheirus peltatus* sub-group (Diptera, Syrphidae), with a description of the male and female of *P. islandicus* Ringdahl, 1930, stat. n. *Mitt. Schweiz. ent. Ges.* **71**: 187-199.

STELLEMAN, P., 1978. The possible role of insect visits in pollination of reputedly anemophilous plants, exemplified by *Plantago lanceolata* and syrphid flies. pp. 41-46. **In**: Richards, A.J. (Ed.) *Pollination of Flowers by Insects*. Linnean Society Symposium Series **6**. 213pp. Academic Press, London.

STELLEMAN, P., 1981. Anthecological relations between reputedly anemophilous flowers and syrphid flies. V. Some special aspects of the visiting of *Plantago media* and *P. lanceolata* by insects. *Beiträge zur Biologie der Pflanzen* **55**: 157-167.

STELLEMAN, P. & MEEUSE, A.D.J., 1976. Anthecological relations between reputedly anemophilous flowers and syrphid flies. I . The possible role of syrphid flies as pollinators of *Plantago*. *Tijdschrift voor Entomologie* **119**: 15-31.

STUBBS, A.E., 1980a. The rearing of *Cheilosia pagana* and *C. fraterna* (Diptera: Syrphidae). *Entomologist's Rec. & J. Var.* **92**: 114-117.

STUBBS, A.E., 1980b. *Neocnemodon brevidens* (Egger, 1865) (Syrphidae) New to Britain. *Entomologist's Rec. & J. Var.* **92**: 45-46.

STUBBS, A.E., 1981a. *Anasimyia contracta* Claussen & Torp, 1980 and *A. interpuncta* (Harris, 1776) (Diptera: Syrphidae) in Britain. *Proc. Trans. Br. ent. nat. Hist. Soc.* **14**: 10-11.

STUBBS, A.E., 1981b. Cyril Oswald Hammond. *Proc. Trans. Br. ent. nat. Hist. Soc.* **14**: 40-43.

STUBBS, A.E., 1982. Hoverflies as primary woodland indicators with reference to Wharncliffe Wood. *Sorby Record* no. **20**: 62-67.

STUBBS, A.E., 1986. *Appendix to reprint of British Hoverflies*. 15pp. British Entomological and Natural History Society, London.

STUBBS, A.E., 1989a. An additional British *Sphaerophoria* discovered in Devon. *Dipterists Digest* (first series) **2**: 34-35.

STUBBS, A.E., 1989b. Dual courtship strategies in *Criorhina asilica* (Syrphidae). *Dipterists Digest* (first series) **2**: 43.

STUBBS, A.E., 1991. A method of monitoring garden hoverflies. *Dipterists Digest* (first series) **10**: 26-39.

382

STUBBS, A.E., 1994. *Sphegina* (*Asiosphegina*) *sibirica* Stackelberg, 1953, a new species and subgenus of hoverfly (Diptera, Syrphidae) in Britain. *Dipterists Digest* (second series) **1**: 23-25.

STUBBS, A.E., 1995a. *Sphaerophoria* species B, a hoverfly (Diptera, Syrphidae) previously unrecognised in Britain. *Dipterists Digest* (second series) **2**: 6-7.

STUBBS, A.E., 1995b. Advances to the British hoverfly list: 1901 to 1990. *Dipterists Digest* (second series) **2**: 13-23.

STUBBS, A.E., 1996a. *British Hoverflies. Second* (*Revised and Enlarged*) *Supplement.* 55pp. British Entomological and Natural History Society, Reading.

STUBBS, A.E., 1996b. On the major peaks in hoverfly numbers during August 1991 at Peterborough. *Dipterists Digest* (second series) **2**: 82-84.

STUBBS, A.E., 1997. Observations on the ecology and oviposition of *Eumerus sabulonum* (Syrphidae) and *Acrosathe annulata* (Therevidae) (Diptera). *Dipterists Digest* (second series) **3**: 54-55.

STUBBS, A.E., 1998a. The separation of *Pipizella maculipennis* and *Pipizella virens*. *Hoverfly Newsletter* no. 25: 6-7.

STUBBS, A.E., 1998b. Territorial hovering by *Platycheirus scutatus*. *Hoverfly Newsletter* no. 25: 10.

STUBBS, A.E., 1998c. Summer migration peak of hoverflies at Peterborough in 1997. *Hoverfly Newsletter* no. 25: 10-11.

STUBBS, A.E., 2000. An update on the British hoverfly list. *British Journal of Entomology and Natural History* **13**: 127-133.

STUBBS, A.E., 2001. Flies. pp. 239-261. **In**: Hawksworth, D.L. (Ed.) *The Changing Wildlife of Great Britain and Ireland.* Systematics Association special volume **62**. Taylor & Francis, London.

STUBBS, A.E., 2002. Advances in the understanding of the *Platycheirus scutatus* complex in Britain, including the addition of *Platycheirus aurolateralis* sp. nov. (Diptera, Syrphidae). *Dipterists Digest* (second series) **9**: 75-80.

STUBBS, A.E. & CHANDLER, P.J., 1978. A Dipterist's Handbook. *The Amateur Entomologist* **15**: 1-255.

STUBBS, A.E. & FALK, S.J., 1983. *British Hoverflies: an illustrated identification guide.* 253pp. British Entomological and Natural History Society, London.

STUBBS, A.E. & FALK, S.J., 2000. *British Hoverflies: an illustrated identification guide, including the 1996 Second Supplement and an update to the British List.* 315pp. British Entomological and Natural History Society, Reading.

STUKE, J.-H., 1996. *Helophilus affinis* new to the British Isles (Diptera, Syrphidae). *Dipterists Digest* (second series) **3**: 45-46.

STUKE, J.-H., 2000. Phylogenetische Rekonstruktion der Verwandtschaftsbeziehungen innerhalb der Gattung *Cheilosia* Meigen, 1882 anhand der Larvenstadien (Diptera: Syrphidae). *Studia Dipterologica Supplement* **8**: 1-118. [In German]

STUKE, J.-H., 2002 (In prep.). The larval biology of the genus *Cheilosia* Meigen, 1820: an overview about the available information (Diptera: Syrphidae). Internet site: www.schwebfliegen.de

STUKE, J.-H. & CARSTENSEN, L.B., 2000. Biologie und Morphologie des dritten Larvenstadiums von *Cheilosia lasiopa* Kowarz, 1885 (Diptera, Syrphidae). *Volucella* **5**: 95-101. [In German]

SUTHERLAND, J.P., 1997. The hoverflies (Diptera, Syrphidae) of Rostherne Mere, Cheshire. *Dipterists Digest* (second series) **4**: 35-40.

SUTHERLAND, J.P., 1999. A record of an entomoparasitic nematode in *Syrphus vitripennis* (Diptera, Syrphidae). *Dipterists Digest* (second series) **6**: 28.

SUTHERLAND, J.P., SULLIVAN, M.S. & POPPY, G.M., 2001. Oviposition behaviour and host colony size discrimination in *Episyrphus balteatus* (Diptera: Syrphidae). *Bull. ent. Res.* **91**: 411-417.

SUTTON, S.L., 1969. A migration of Syrphid flies at Spurn. *Naturalist* no. **909**: 51-53.

SVENSSON, B.G. & JANSON, L.A., 1984. Why does the hoverfly *Metasyrphus corollae* migrate? *Ecol. Ent.* **9**: 329-335.

SYMS, E.E., 1935. Notes on the biology of *Microdon eggeri* Mik. *Trans. Soc. Br. Ent.* **2**: 163-165.

THOMPSON, F.C., 1972. A contribution to a generic revision of the Neotropical Milesinae (Diptera: Syrphidae). *Archos. Zool. S. Paulo* **23**: 73-213.

THOMPSON, F.C., 1980. The problems of old names as illustrated by *Brachyopa* "conica" Panzer", with a synopsis of palaearctic *Brachyopa* Meigen (Diptera: Syrphidae). *Ent. scand.* **11**: 209-216.

THOMPSON, F.C., 1981. Nomenclature of the European species of *Neoascia* Williston (Diptera: Syrphidae). *Ent. scand.* **12**: 470-478.

THOMPSON, F.C. & ROTHERAY, G., 1998. Family Syrphidae. pp. 81-139. **In**: Papp, L. & Darvas, B. (Eds) *Contributions to a Manual of Palaearctic Diptera.* **3**. Science Herald, Budapest.

THOMPSON, F.C. & TORP, E., 1986. Synopsis of the European species of *Sphegina* Meigen (Diptera: Syrphidae). *Ent. scand.* **17**: 235-269.

THOMPSON, F.C., VOCKEROTH, J.R. & SPEIGHT, M.C.D., 1982. The Linnean species of flower flies (Diptera: Syrphidae). *Mem. ent. Soc. Wash.* **10**: 150-165.

THORPE, E., 1988. Another look at flowers. *Derbyshire Entomological Society Quarterly Journal* no. 92: 7-12.

TIMMS, C., 1946. Hibernation of *Tubifera tenax* L. *Entomologist's Rec. & J. Var.* **58**: 39.

TIMMS, C., 1956. *Sericomyia silentis* Harris (Dipt., Syrphidae) at light. *Entomologist's Rec. & J. Var.* **68**: 78.

TORP, E., 1984. De danske svirrefluer (Diptera: Syrphidae). *Danmarks Dyreliv* Bind 1. 300pp. Fauna Bøger, Copenhagen. [In Danish]

TORP, E., 1994. Danmarks svirrefluer (Diptera: Syrphidae). *Danmarks Dyreliv* **6**. 490pp. Apollo Books, Stenstrup. [In Danish]

TRUSCOTT, L., 2000. *Callicera aurata* (Rossi, 1790) (Diptera, Syrphidae) new to Cornwall. *Dipterists Digest* (second series) **7**: 70.

UK BIODIVERSITY GROUP, 1998. *Tranche 2 Action Plans.* English Nature, Peterborough.

VARLEY, G.C., 1935. A new Syrphid larva and some other aquatic insect larvae which obtain their oxygen from plant roots. *Proc. R. ent. Soc. Lond.* (*A*) **10**: 30-31.

VARLEY, G. C., 1937. Aquatic insect larvae which obtain their oxygen from the roots of plants. *Proc. R. ent. Soc. Lond.* (*A*) **12**: 55-60.

VERDCOURT, B., 1996. *Callicera aenea* (F.) (Dipt., Syrphidae) at Maidenhead, Berkshire. *Entomologist's mon. Mag.* **132**: 47.

VERLINDEN, L., 1991. *Fauna van Belgie: Zweefvliegen (Syrphidae).* 298pp. Royal Belgian Institute for Natural Sciences, Brussels. [In Dutch]

VERLINDEN, L., 1994. *Faune de Belgique. Syrphides (Syrphidae).* Royal Belgian Institute for Natural Sciences, Brussels. [In French]

VERLINDEN, L. & DECLEER, K., 1987. The hoverflies (Diptera, Syrphidae) of Belgium and their faunistics: frequency, distribution, phenology. *Documents de Travail* nr 39. 170pp. Institut Royal des Sciences Naturelles de Belgique, Bruxelles.

VERRALL, G.H., 1901. *British Flies* **8**. *Syrphidae etc.* 691pp. Gurney and Jackson, London.

VIOLOVICH, N.A., 1981. Review of Siberian species of the genus *Pipizella* Rondani, 1856 (Diptera, Syrphidae). pp. 57-78. **In**: Cherepanov, A.I. (Ed.) *Insects and Acari of Siberia* **20**. *New and little known species of the fauna of Siberia.*

VOCKEROTH, J.R., 1963. The specific status of *Sphaerophoria taeniata* (Meigen) (Dipt., Syrphidae). *Entomologist's mon. Mag.* **99**: 32-33.

VOCKEROTH, J.R., 1969. A revision of the genera of the Syrphini (Diptera: Syrphidae). *Mem. ent. Soc. Can.* **62**: 1-176.

VOCKEROTH, J.R., 1973. The identity of some genera of Syrphini (Diptera: Syrphidae) described by Matsumura. *Can. Ent.* **105**: 1075-1079.

VOCKEROTH, J.R., 1980. A review of the Nearctic species of *Melangyna* (*Meligramma*) Frey (Diptera: Syrphidae). *Can. Ent.* **122**: 775-778.

VOCKEROTH, J.R., 1986a. Revision of the New World species of *Paragus* Latreille (Diptera: Syrphidae). *Can. Ent.* **118**: 183-198.

VOCKEROTH, J.R., 1986b. Nomenclatural notes on Nearctic *Eupeodes* (including *Metasyrphus*) and *Dasysyrphus* (Diptera: Syrphidae). *Can. Ent.* **118**: 199-204.

VOCKEROTH, J.R., 1990. Revision of the Nearctic species of *Platycheirus* (Diptera, Syrphidae). *Can. Ent.* **122**: 659-766.

VOCKEROTH, J.R., 1992. *The Flower Flies of the Subfamily Syrphinae of Canada, Alaska and Greenland.* The Insects and Arachnids of Canada Part 18. 456pp. Agriculture Canada, Ottawa.

VOCKEROTH, J.R. & THOMPSON, F.C., 1987. 52. Syrphidae. **In**: McAlpine, J.F. *et al.* (Eds). *Manual of Nearctic Diptera* **2**: 713-743.

VUJIĆ, A., 1997. The genus *Pipizella* (Diptera, Syrphidae) on the Balkan Peninsula and a description of *Pipizella zloti* sp. n. *Dipterists Digest* (second series) **4**: 51-60.

VUJIĆ, A. & MILANKOV, V., 1999. New data for the tribes Milesini and Xylotini (Diptera, Syrphidae) on the Balkan Peninsula. *Dipteron* **2**: 113-132.

VUJIĆ, A., REDENKOVIĆ, S. & ŠIMIĆ, S., 1996. *Merodon albonigrum*, a new European species related to *Merodon geniculatus* Strobl, 1909. *Dipterists Digest* (second series) **2**: 72-79.

WACHT, S., LUNAU, K. & HANSEN, K. 1996. Optical and chemical stimuli control pollen feeding in the hoverfly *Eristalis tenax. Ent. exp. appl.* **80**: 50-53

WAINWRIGHT, C.J., 1942. A new British Syrphid: *Lasiophthicus* (*Catabomba*) *albomaculata* Macq. (*gemellarii* Rond.). *Entomologist's mon. Mag.* **78**: 3-4.

WAINWRIGHT, C.J., 1944. *Hammerschmidtia ferruginea* Fall. in Scotland. *Entomologist's mon. Mag.* **80**: 8-9.

WALDBAUER, G.P. & SHELDON, J.K., 1971. Phenological relationships of some aculeate Hymenoptera, their Dipteran mimics and insectivorous birds. *Evolution* **25**: 371-382.

WALKER, F., 1864. On the late swarms of Syrphini in the Isle of Wight. *Entomologist's mon. Mag.* **1**: 134-140.

WATT, K.R. & ROBERTSON, D.M., 1990. *Eupeodes lundbecki* (Soot-Ryen) (Diptera: Syrphidae) new to Britain and its separation from related species. *Dipterists Digest* (first series) **6**: 23-27.

WAY, M.J., MURDIE, G. & GALLEY, D.J., 1969. Experiments on integration of chemical and biological control of aphids on brussel sprouts. *Ann. appl. Biol.* **63**: 459-475.

WELLINGTON, W.G., 1976. Applying behavioural studies in entomological problems. pp. 87-97. **In**: Anderson, J.F. & Kaya, H.K. (Eds) *Perspectives in forest entomology.* Academic Press, New York.

WELLINGTON, W.G. & FITZPATRICK, S.M., 1981. Territoriality in the drone fly, *Eristalis tenax* (Diptera: Syrphidae). *Can. Ent.* **113**: 695-704.

WHITELEY, D., (Ed.) 1985. *The natural history of the Sheffield area and the Peak District.* 256pp. Sorby Natural History Society, Sheffield.

WHITELEY, D., 1987. Hoverflies of the Sheffield area and north Derbyshire. *Sorby Record*, Special Series **6**: 1-56.

WHITELEY, D., 1988a. Hoverflies on urban derelict land in Sheffield. *Sorby Record* **25**: 45-48.

WHITELEY, D., 1988b. Hoverflies and other notable insects at Tinsley Sewage Farm. *Sorby Record* **25**: 94-98.

WHITELEY, D., 1988c. Hoverfly report for 1987. *Derbyshire Entomological Society Quarterly Journal* no. 91: 10-15.

WHITELEY, D., 1988d. *Cheilosia argentifrons* Hellén – a hoverfly new to Derbyshire and Great Britain. *Derbyshire Entomological Society Quarterly Journal* no. 93:5.

WHITELEY, D., 1989a. Hoverfly report for the Matlock area and some limestone dales 1988. *Derbyshire Entomological Society Quarterly Journal* no. 96: 13-15.

WHITELEY, D., 1989b. The hoverfly *Chrysogaster virescens* in Derbyshire. *Derbyshire Entomological Society Quarterly Journal* no. 97: 10.

WHITELEY, D., 1989c. The hoverfly *Platycheirus perpallidus* in Derbyshire. *Derbyshire Entomological Society Quarterly Journal* no. 97: 11.

WHITELEY, D., 1989d. The hoverfly *Cheilosia pubera* in Derbyshire. *Derbyshire Entomological Society Quarterly Journal* no. 97: 11.

WHITELEY, D., 1989e. The hoverfly *Platycheirus* 'species A' in Derbyshire. *Derbyshire Entomological Society Quarterly Journal* no. 98: 19.

WHITELEY, D., 1990. Hoverfly report for 1988 and 1989. *Derbyshire Entomological Society Quarterly Journal* no. 99: 8-17.

WHITELEY, D., 1993. Hoverfly recorder's report for 1993. *Sorby Record* **30**: 25-31.

WHITELEY, D., (Ed.) 1994. A survey of Diptera on the Isle of Rum – 1990. *Dipterists Digest* (first series) **14**: 2-27.

WHITELEY, D., 1995. Using Diptera for assessment of local wetlands. *Sorby Record* **31**: 82-83.

WHITELEY, D., 1996. *Xylota tarda* - a remarkable hoverfly new to Derbyshire. *Derbyshire Entomological Society Quarterly Journal* no. 124: 10.

WHITELEY, D., 1997. *Melangyna barbifrons* - a hoverfly new to Derbyshire. *Derbyshire Entomological Society Quarterly Journal* no. 129: 10.

WHITELEY, D., 1998a. The hoverfly *Brachyopa insensilis* in Derbyshire and Nottinghamshire. *Derbyshire & Nottinghamshire Entomological Society Quarterly Journal* no. 132: 16.

WHITELEY, D., 1998b. *Pocota personata* - a remarkable new hoverfly for Derbyshire. *Derbyshire & Nottinghamshire Entomological Society Quarterly Journal* no. 134: 7.

WHITELEY, D., 2001a. The hoverfly *Brachyopa insensilis* in north Derbyshire. *Derbyshire & Nottinghamshire Entomological Society Quarterly Journal* no. 144: 10.

WHITELEY, D., 2001b. *Heringia vitripennis* - a hoverfly new to Derbyshire. *Derbyshire & Nottinghamshire Entomological Society Quarterly Journal* no. 145: 13.

WHITELEY, D., GARLAND, S.P. & HANCOCK, E.G., 1994. A survey of Diptera on South Uist and adjacent Outer Hebridean Islands. *Dipterists Digest* (first series) **14**: 32-43.

WILLS, H.J., 1968. Diptera from Monks Wood National Nature Reserve. *Entomologist's Rec. & J. Var.* **80**: 115-119, 137-140.

WINDER, L., HIRST, D.J., CARTER, N., WRATTEN, S.D. & SOPP, P.I., 1994. Estimating predation of the grain aphid *Sitobion avenae* by polyphagous predators. *J. appl. Ecol.* **31**: 1-12.

WITHERS, P., 1983. Recent records of some rare British Syrphidae (Diptera). *Entomologist's mon. Mag.* **119**: 11-12.

WORMELL, P., 1982. The entomology of the Isle of Rhum National Nature Reserve. *Biol. J. Linn. Soc.* **18**: 291-401.

WRIGHT, A., 1988a. Hoverflies in a city environment: experiences in Coventry. *Dipterists Digest* (first series) **1**: 37-40.

WRIGHT, A., 1988b. The hoverflies of Brandon Wood, Warwickshire. *Coventry nat. Hist. & Sci. Soc.* **6**: 65-68.

WRIGHT, A., 1988c. *Xylota xanthocnema* Collin and other notable Syrphidae (Dipt.) in Warwickshire. *Entomologist's mon. Mag.* **124**: 105.

WRIGHT, A., 1988d. *Provisional atlas of the hoverflies (Diptera: Syrphidae) of Warwickshire*. 9pp. Herbert Art Gallery & Museum, Coventry. [Duplicated report]

WRIGHT, A., 1990. *Psilota anthracina* Meigen and other scarce Diptera in Warwickshire (VC38). *British Journal of Entomology and Natural History* **3**: 103-105.

WYNNE, I.R., 1993. Recent records of hoverflies (Dipt., Syrphidae) in Hertfordshire. *Entomologist's mon. Mag.* **129**: 251-252.

WYNNE, I.R., 2000. *Helophilus trivittatus* (F.) (Dipt., Syrphidae) unusually common in North Wales. *Entomologist's mon. Mag.* **136**: 246.

ZWÖLFER, V.H., 1958. Zur Systematik, Biologie and Ökologie unterirdisch lebender Aphiden (Homoptera, Aphidoidea) (Anoeciinae, Tetraneurini, Pemphigini and Fordinae). *Z. angew. Ent.* **43**: 1-52. [In German]

THE PLATES

PLATE A

Cheilosia male genitalia: an explanation of the views and terms used in Plates B – N.

The genital capsule is illustrated in its correct orientation, although *in situ* on the male fly it is folded under the end of the abdomen and is therefore the other way up. It is divided into two main parts which are articulated. The **epandrium** (a highly modified tergite 9) bears the **cerci** and paired claspers called **surstyli** (= *paralobes*) which can provide a useful character through their varied shape. These may have ridges on their outer surface called **carina.** Joined to the base of the **epandrium** is the **hypandrium** (a highly modified sternite 9) which consists of a membranous body termed the **theca**, which gives rise to another smaller pair of clasping organs called the **superior lobes** (= *parameres*) which flank the **aedeagus**. The aedeagus has a long **apodeme** that passes back into the theca and acts as a muscle attachment. In most species the aedeagus bears a pair of lateral processes referred to as **lateral flaps**, although these are missing in the fungus feeders and *Nigrocheilosia* groups.

The most useful feature in critical identification of many species of *Cheilosia* is the shape of the superior lobes of the hypandrium. Viewed from the side, these have a **ventral process** which is long and upcurved in most species (but not in the *Nigrocheilosia* group or *C. scutellata*), and a **dorsal process**, which is usually shorter and often diagnostically shaped. There may also be a small **median process** between the two. The shape and size of the aedeagus, theca and surstyli can also be useful.

All lateral views are drawn from the right unless otherwise stated. The figures of the epandrium are usually drawn at 50% of the scale of those of the hypandrium for the same species, and without showing the hairs in most cases. The magnification varies between species so that larger species such as *illustrata* are less magnified than small ones such as *pagana*.

It should be noted that the genitalia do not differ appreciably between all *Cheilosia* species, *e.g. nigripes* and *vicina*, *latifrons* and *griseiventris* and some of the species allied to *bergenstammi* and *vernalis*. However, there can be appreciable differences between some otherwise similar species, *e.g. urbana* and *psilophthalma*, and *longula* and *scutellata*.

Species are arranged in five groups so that those with similar genitalia appear close together. They are then, with a few exceptions, arranged alphabetically within these groups.

Drawn by S.J.Falk

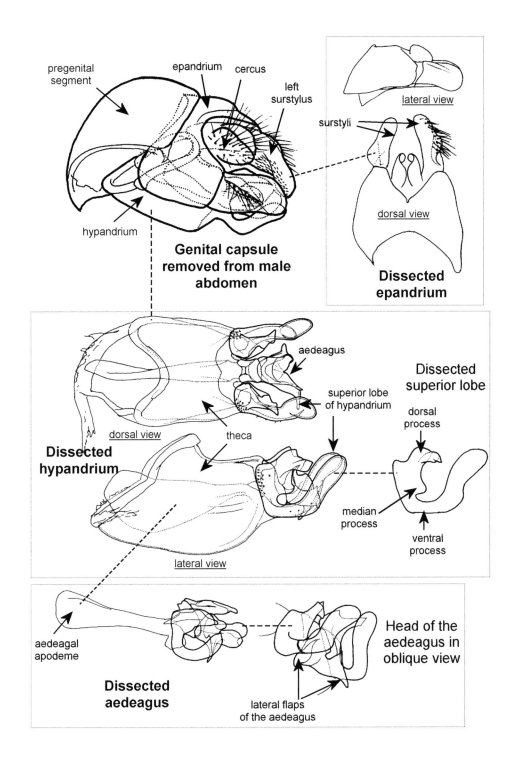

pregenital segment

epandrium

cercus

left surstylus

lateral view

surstyli

dorsal view

Genital capsule removed from male abdomen

hypandrium

Dissected epandrium

aedeagus

Dissected superior lobe

superior lobe of hypandrium

dorsal process

dorsal view

theca

Dissected hypandrium

median process

ventral process

lateral view

aedeagal apodeme

Head of the aedeagus in oblique view

Dissected aedeagus

lateral flaps of the aedeagus

PLATE B

NIGROCHEILOSIA **GROUP.** A distinct group, which deserves at least subgeneric rank, containing all the black-legged, bare-eyed species. The superior lobes have a short ventral process and a hood-like dorsal one. The aedeagus is large and slung low, and bears a pair of small apical processes. The theca is quite narrow. Overall, the genitalia more closely resemble *Portevinia, Ferdinandea* and *Rhingia* than other *Cheilosia*, suggesting that this is a primitive group. Barkalov & Stahls (1997) review the Palaearctic species of this large and difficult group.

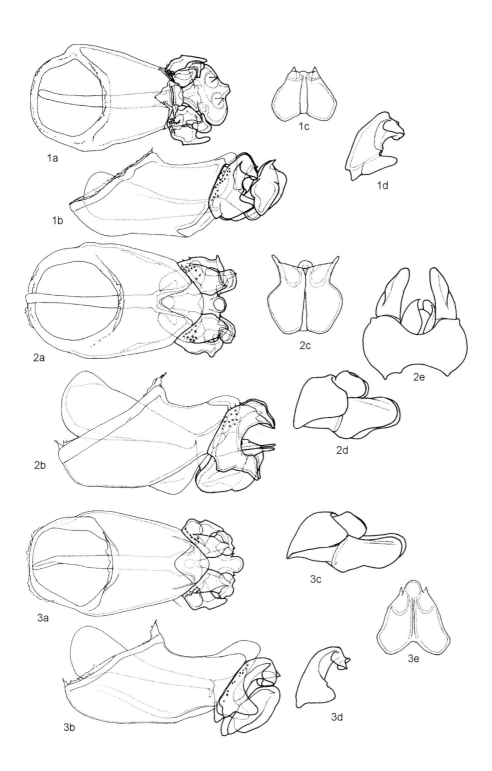

1a

1b

1c

1d

2a

2b

2c

2d

2e

3a

3b

3c

3d

3e

PLATE C

NIGROCHEILOSIA GROUP (*continued*)

1. **Cheilosia pubera** – the ventral process of the superior lobe is pointed and the ventral edge is angled about halfway along. The dorsal process has a particularly 'shallow' hood. The aedeagus, viewed ventrally, is rather rounded. The surstyli are more strongly narrowed towards their tip than in other *Nigrocheilosia*. (*a* dorsal view of hypandrium, *b* lateral view of hypandrium, *c* dorsal view of epandrium, *d* lateral view of another superior lobe, *e* lateral view of epandrium, *f* ventral view of aedeagus).
2. **C. sahlbergi** – very similar to *nigripes*, *vicina* and *ahenea*, but the ventral process of the superior lobe rather broad in the single specimen dissected. The surstyli are broader than in *nigripes* and *vicina* (as in *ahenea*). (*a* dorsal view of hypandrium, *b* lateral view of hypandrium, *c* ventral view of aedeagus, *d* lateral view of epandrium).
3. **C. vicina** – possibly not distinguishable from *nigripes* and prone to some variation. (*a* dorsal view of hypandrium, *b* lateral view of hypandrium, *c* dorsal view of epandrium, *d* ventral view of aedeagus, *e* lateral view of epandrium, *f* lateral view of another superior lobe, *g* lateral view of another superior lobe and the head of the aedeagus).

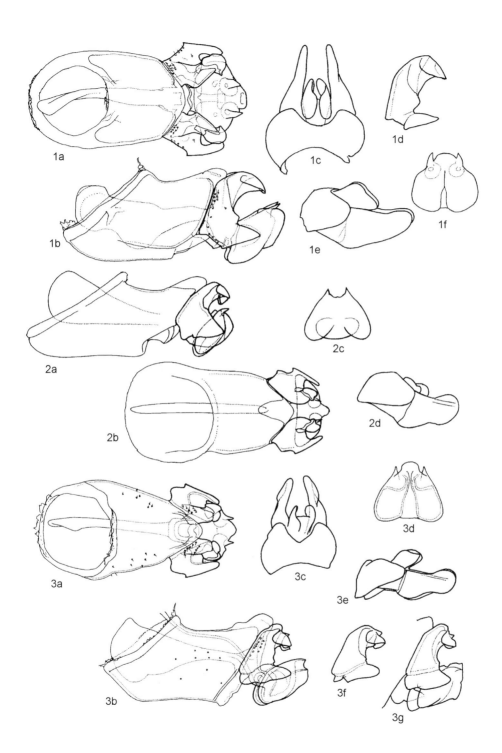

1a

1b

1c

1d

1e

1f

2a

2b

2c

2d

3a

3b

3c

3d

3e

3f

3g

394

PLATE D

THE FUNGUS-FEEDERS. Bare-eyed with fused antennal pits like the previous group (all subsequent groups have separated antennal pits). The aedeagus is long and rather cylindrical and lacks any obvious processes. The superior lobes of *longula* and *soror* are typical of this group (considered on a World basis) with a long, inwardly curved ventral process and a short, *Nigrocheilosia*-type dorsal one, but in *scutellata* the dorsal process becomes massively enlarged and downcurved and the ventral process reduced.

1. **Cheilosia longula** – superior lobe with dorsal process very small and ventral process long and narrow. Theca rather short. (*a* dorsal view of hypandrium, *b* lateral view of hypandrium, *c* lateral view of epandrium (left), *d* lateral view of epandrium (right), *e* oblique view of superior lobes and the head of the aedeagus). *p. 253*
2. **C. scutellata** – quite unmistakeable, the superior lobes with a huge downcurved dorsal process and relatively short and narrow ventral process. (*a* dorsal view of hypandrium, *b* lateral view of hypandrium, *c* oblique view of the head of the hypandrium, *d* posterior view of hypandrium, *e* lateral view of epandrium (showing chaetotaxy), *f* dorsal view of epandrium (showing chaetotaxy)). *p. 258*
3. **C. soror** – resembling *longula* but dorsal process larger, ventral process shorter, aedeagus smaller and theca longer. (*a* dorsal view of hypandrium, *b* lateral view of hypandrium, *c* lateral view of another hypandrium, *d* lateral view of epandrium, *e* oblique view of the head of the hypandrium). *p. 260*

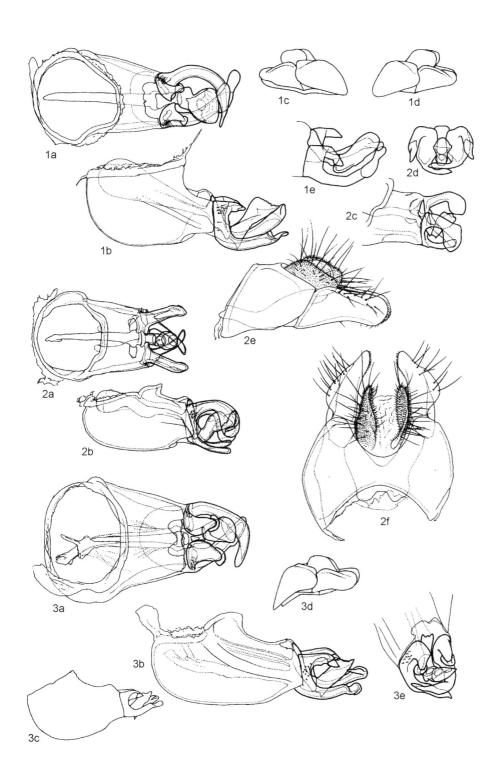

1a

1b

1c

1d

1e

2a

2b

2c

2d

2e

2f

3a

3b

3c

3d

3e

PLATE E

THE *CHRYSOCOMA* GROUP. An intermediate stage between previous groups and subsequent ones, characterised by the distinct hollowing out of the inner face of the ventral process of the superior lobes (which are long and upcurved as in subsequent groups) and the distinct ventral flap of the aedeagus. In *illustrata* and *chrysocoma*, this is augmented by a pair of blunt lateral flaps (missing in *semifasciata*)

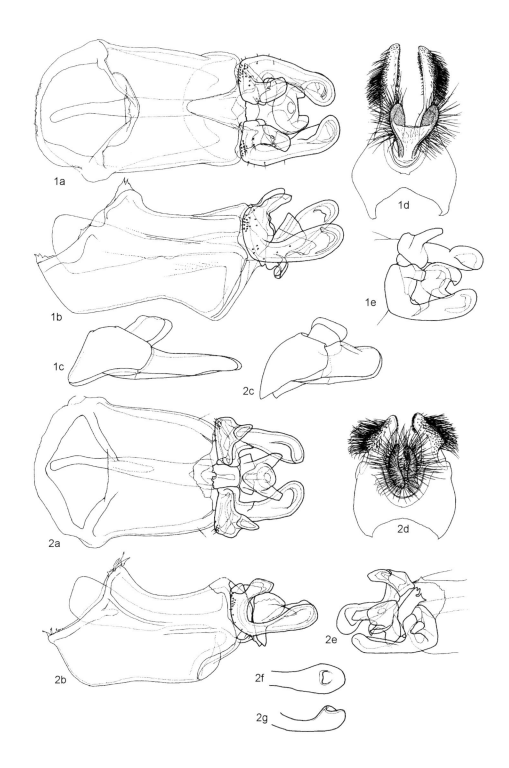

1a

1b

1c

1d

1e

2a

2b

2c

2d

2e

2f

2g

PLATE F

THE *CHRYSOCOMA* **GROUP** (*continued*).

1. **Cheilosia semifasciata** – superior lobes with a tiny dorsal process. The long ventral process is hollowed on its inner surface and no sign of a median process is present. The aedeagus bears a large ventral flap, but no lateral flaps are present. The theca is relatively short and broad. The surstyli are very distinctly triangular in lateral view. (*a* dorsal view of hypandrium, *b* lateral view of hypandrium, *c* dorsal view of the epandrium, *d* oblique view of the head of the hypandrium, *e* lateral view of the epandrium (right), *f* lateral view of the epandrium (right)). *p. 259*

DASYCHEILOSIA **GROUP.** This group has genitalia closely resembling the final group, but the dorsal process of the superior lobes is long and curved, and the median process is usually double-pointed. The aedeagus lacks the ventral flap of the previous group and has a pair of lateral flaps that end in a single downcurved point. All members of this group have a hairy face, though most hairy-faced species belong to the next group. The theca is always long.

2. **Cheilosia lasiopa** – long and pointed dorsal process on the superior lobe, and a double-pointed median lobe. Theca long and aedeagus symmetrical with lateral flaps bearing a single, downcurved point. (*a* dorsal view of hypandrium, *b* lateral view of hypandrium, *c* lateral view of epandrium). *p. 252*
3. **C. variabilis** – resembling *lasiopa* but dorsal process shorter and narrower. Surstyli with lower margin slightly convex (straight or slightly concave in *lasiopa*). (*a* dorsal view of hypandrium, *b* lateral view of hypandrium, *c* oblique view of the head of the hypandrium from below, *d* lateral view of epandrium, *e* lateral view of another superior lobe). *p. 262*

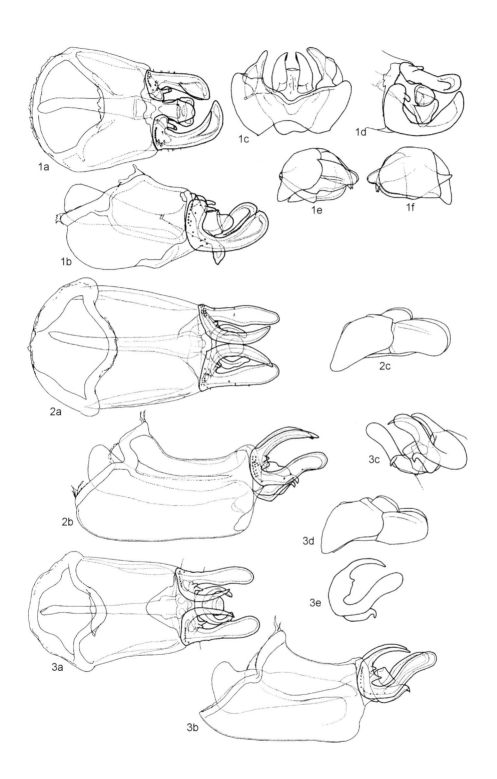

1a

1c

1d

1e

1f

1b

2a

2c

2b

3c

3d

3e

3a

3b

PLATE G

HIGHER *CHEILOSIA* GROUP. This group is characterised by an aedeagus bearing a pair of distinct lateral flaps which usually end in two points, though there is a range of variation from a fairly symmetrical aedeagus where both of the lateral flaps are of a similar shape (*e.g. grossa* and *bergenstammi*) to highly asymmetrical where the right flap becomes greatly elongated and ends in a single point (*e.g. barbata* and *pagana*). The superior lobe always has a long upcurved ventral process and a much smaller dorsal one, the shape of which can provide an important character. There is often a well formed median process between the two. The theca can vary from very long (*vulpina*) to very short (*pagana*). The surstyli can vary in their length and breadth, also the shape of the carina (ridges) they bear on their outer surface. This is a large group and many additional species occur on the near continent.

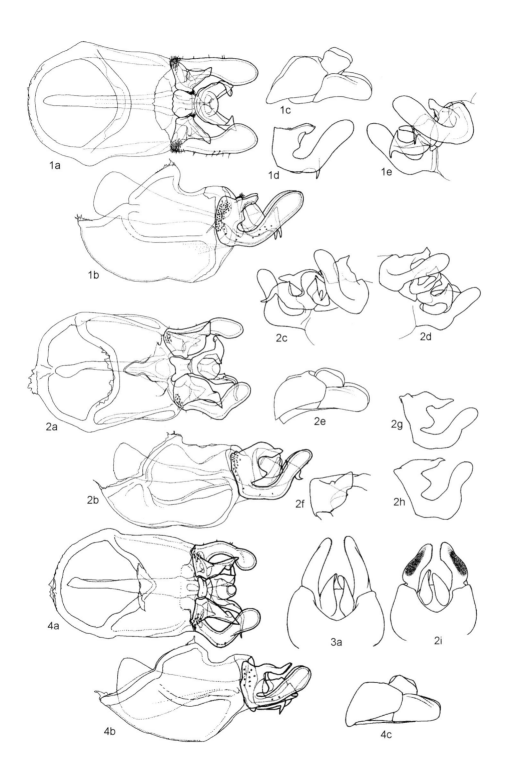

1a

1b

1c

1d

1e

2a

2b

2c

2d

2e

2f

2g

2h

2i

3a

4a

4b

4c

402

PLATE H

HIGHER *CHEILOSIA* GROUP (*continued*).

1. **Cheilosia bergenstammi** – typical of the species with glossy sternites and dark eye hairs (*carbonaria, cynocephala, fraterna* and *vernalis*) and scarcely distinguishable from these. The aedeagus is fairly symmetrical, the superior lobe has a fairly large dorsal process and a distinct median process is present. (*a* dorsal view of hypandrium, *b* lateral view of hypandrium, *c* lateral view of another superior lobe (right)).　　*p. 246*
2. **C. carbonaria** – very similar to *vernalis*. (*a* dorsal view of hypandrium, *b* lateral view of hypandrium, *c* lateral view of epandrium).　　*p. 247*
3. **C. cynocephala** – similar to *vernalis* but superior lobe viewed from side rather more compactly formed, *i.e.* less 'tall'. (*a* dorsal view of hypandrium, *b* lateral view of hypandrium, *c* lateral view of epandrium, *d, e* lateral views of other superior lobes showing variation).　　*p. 248*

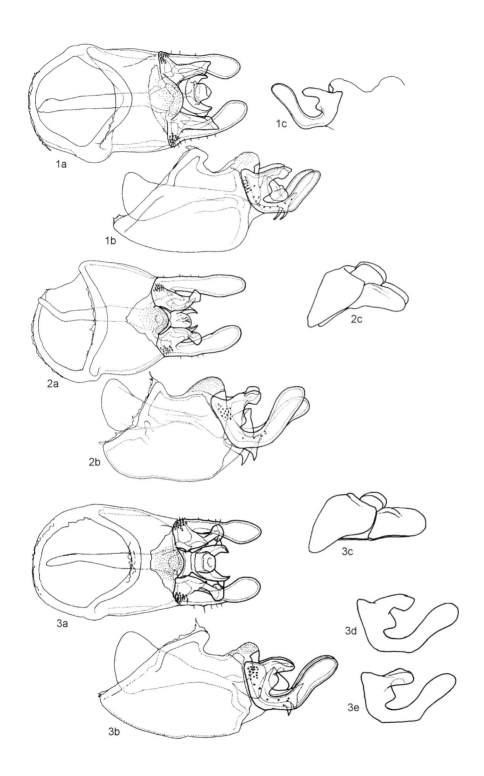

1a

1b

1c

2a

2b

2c

3a

3b

3c

3d

3e

404

PLATE I

HIGHER *CHEILOSIA* GROUP (*continued*).

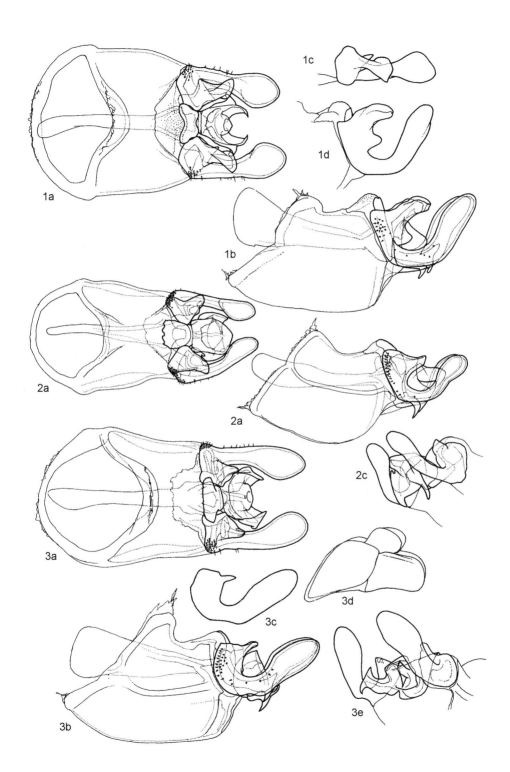

1a

1b

1c

1d

2a

2a

2c

3a

3b

3c

3d

3e

PLATE J

HIGHER *CHEILOSIA* GROUP (*continued*).

1. **Cheilosia impressa** – rather similar to species such as *proxima* and *velutina*, the dorsal process of the superior lobe lacks the domed shape of *albitarsis* and has a dorsal concavity near its base. (*a* dorsal view of hypandrium, *b* lateral view of hypandrium, *c*, *d* oblique views of the tip of the hypandrium from below, *e* lateral view of epandrium, *f*, *g* lateral views of other superior lobes showing variation). *p. 252*

2. **C. latifrons** – quite variable, but not safetly distinguishable from *griseiventris*. The illustrated example is unusual in that the dorsal process has become deflected outwards. (*a* dorsal view of hypandrium, *b* lateral view of hypandrium, *c* lateral view of epandrium, *d* dorsal view of another superior lobe, *e* oblique view of the head of the hypandrium from below, *f*, *g* lateral views of other superior lobes showing variation). *p. 252*

3. **C. mutabilis** – resembling *urbana* due to the rather long and narrow dorsal projection of the superior lobe, though this is less extreme than in *urbana* and there is no pronounced dorsal concavity. Aedeagus similarly weakly asymmetrical. (*a* dorsal view of hypandrium, *b* lateral view of hypandrium, *c* lateral view of epandrium, *d* oblique view of hypandrium and aedeagus, *e*, *f* lateral views of other superior lobes showing variation). *p. 254*

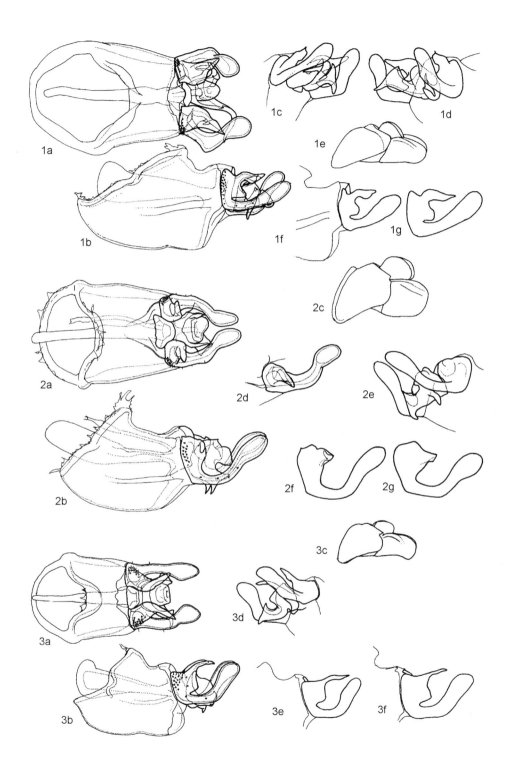

1a

1b

1c

1d

1e

1f

1g

2a

2b

2c

2d

2e

2f

2g

3a

3b

3c

3d

3e

3f

408

PLATE K

HIGHER *CHEILOSIA* GROUP (*continued*).

1. **Cheilosia pagana** – genitalia of the Higher *Cheilosia* type, but with extreme asymmetry of the aedeagal lateral flaps and very short theca. The dorsal process of the superior lobe is quite long and very broad in top view with an extensive transparent web forming its lateral part (unique amongst *Cheilosia*). No median process is present between the ventral and dorsal ones. (*a* dorsal view of hypandrium, *b* lateral view of hypandrium, *c*, *d* oblique views of the head of the hypandrium, *e* lateral view of another superior lobe, *f* posterior view of hypandrium, *g* lateral view of hypandrium with theca removed (right), *h* lateral view of entire genital capsule, *i* lateral view of epandrium).*p. 255*
2. **C. proxima** – the dorsal process of the superior lobe bears a characteristic dorsal projection and a well formed median lobe is present. The aedeagus is strongly asymmetrical. (*a* dorsal view of hypandrium, *b* lateral view of hypandrium, *c* lateral view of epandrium, *d* dorsal view of epandrium, *e*, *f* dorsal views of other superior lobes showing variation, *g*, *h*, *i*, *j*, *k* lateral views of other superior lobes showing variation, *m* oblique view of the head of the hypandrium from below).*p. 256*

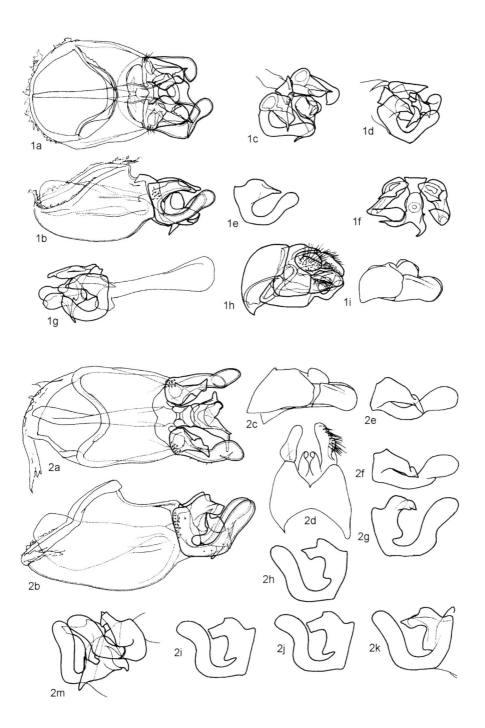

410

PLATE L

HIGHER *CHEILOSIA* GROUP (*continued*).

1. **Cheilosia nebulosa** – generally similar to *albipila* and *grossa*, but most resembling *uviformis* from which it differs in minor details of the superior lobe *e.g.* the more flattened upper margin of the dorsal process. (*a* dorsal view of hypandrium, *b* lateral view of hypandrium, *c* lateral view of epandrium, *d* oblique view of the head of the hypandrium from below, *e* lateral view of superior lobe). *p. 254*
2. **C. psilophthalma** – dorsal process of superior lobe short and its dorsal outline convex and sloped downwards. Theca shorter than *urbana* but aedeagus similarly weakly asymmetrical. (*a* dorsal view of hypandrium, *b* lateral view of hypandrium, *c* oblique view of the head of the hypandrium). *p. 257*
3. **C. urbana** – the very elongate and narrow dorsal process of the superior lobe is very different to *psilophthalma* and could only be confused with *mutabilis* where it is slightly shorter and broader and lacks the dorsal concavity of *urbana*. The aedeagus is weakly asymmetrical. (*a* dorsal view of hypandrium, *b* lateral view of hypandrium, *c*, *d* oblique views of the head of the hypandrium from above and below, *e* dorsal view of another superior lobe, *f*, *g* lateral views of other superior lobes showing variation). *p. 260*

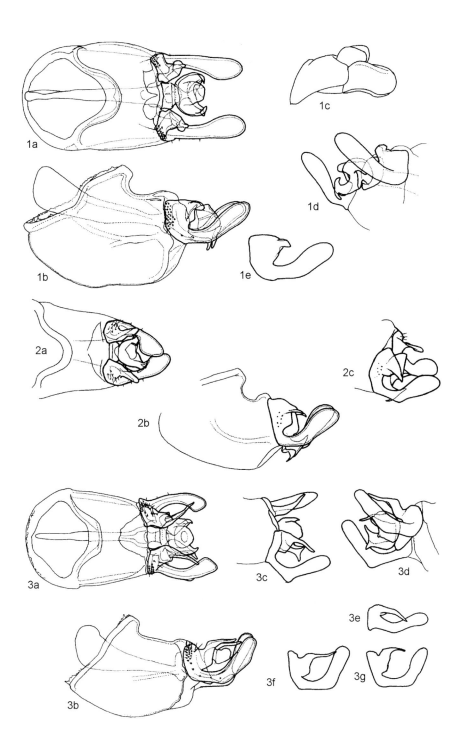

1a

1c

1b

1d

1e

2a

2b

2c

3a

3c

3d

3e

3b

3f

3g

PLATE M

HIGHER *CHEILOSIA* GROUP (*continued*).

1. **Cheilosia uviformis** – resembling *nebulosa*, but the dorsal projection of the superior lobe is slightly longer and narrower and has a slight dorsal concavity (straight or convex in *nebulosa* and *psilophthalma*). (*a* dorsal view of hypandrium, *b* lateral view of hypandrium, *c* oblique view of the head of the hypandrium from above).   *p. 261*
2. **C. velutina** – resembles *proxima* but dorsal process of superior lobe is longer and more pointed and lacks a distinct dorsal projection. (*a* dorsal view of hypandrium, *b* lateral view of hypandrium, *c* lateral view of epandrium, *d, f* lateral views of other superior lobes (right), *e* lateral view of another superior lobe (left), *g* oblique view of the head of the hypandrium from below).   *p. 262*
3. **C. vernalis** – not safely distinguishable from *carbonaria* and *fraterna*, though superior lobes larger than in *cynocephala*. (*a* dorsal view of hypandrium, *b* lateral view of hypandrium, *c* lateral view of epandrium, *d, e* lateral views of other superior lobes showing variation, *f, g* oblique views of the head of the hypandrium from above and below).   *p. 263*

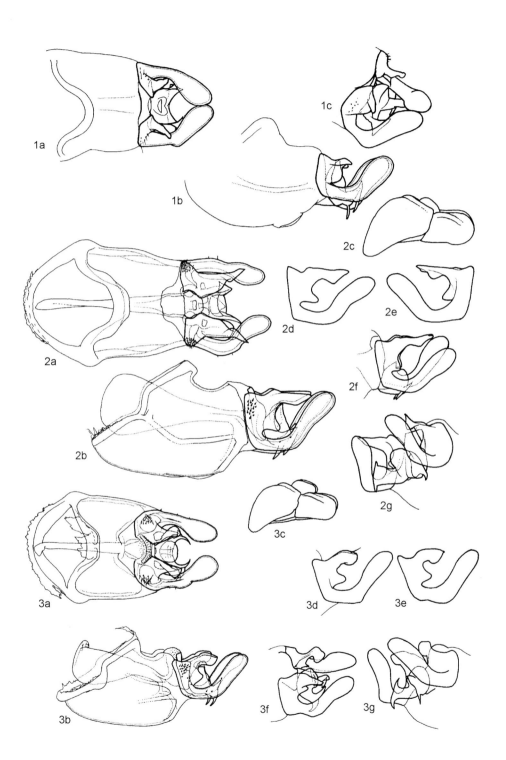

PLATE N

HIGHER *CHEILOSIA* GROUP (*continued*).

1. **Cheilosia vulpina** – Dorsal process of superior lobe quite long and pointed with a triangularly swollen tip and a dorsal projection towards the base. Theca longer than other Higher *Cheilosia* and aedeagus strongly asymmetrical as in *barbata*. (*a* dorsal view of hypandrium, *b* lateral view of hypandrium, *c* lateral view of epandrium, *d* dorsal view of epandrium showing very large carina, *e, f* oblique view of the head of the hypandrium from below right and below left).   *p. 264*

2. **C. species B** – most probably an example of *gigantea* or the recently described Scandinavian *ingerae*, both of which have very similar genitalia. (*a* dorsal view of hypandrium, *b* lateral view of hypandrium, *c* oblique view of the head of the hypandrium from below).   *p. 265*

3. **[C. gigantea]** – rather variable with some specimens being very similar to species B. (*a* dorsal view of hypandrium, *b* lateral view of hypandrium, *c* lateral view of epandrium, *d* dorsal view of surstyli, *e, g* dorsal views of other superior lobes showing variation, *f, h* lateral views of other superior lobes showing variation).

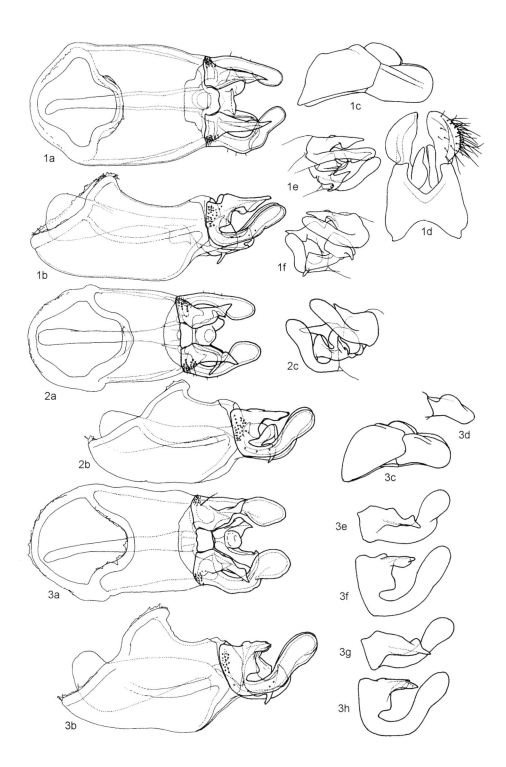

1a

1b

1c

1d

1e

1f

2a

2b

2c

3a

3b

3c

3d

3e

3f

3g

3h

PLATE O

MALE GENITALIA OF *SPHAEROPHORIA.*

Drawn by S.G. Ball

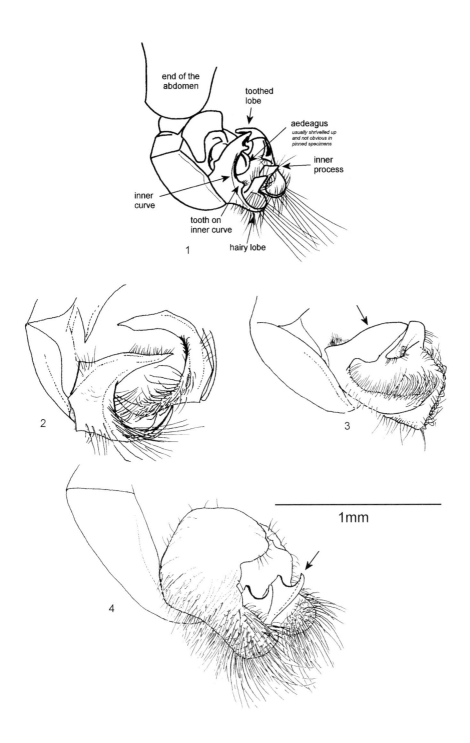

end of the
abdomen

toothed
lobe

aedeagus
*usually shrivelled up
and not obvious in
pinned specimens*

inner
process

inner
curve

tooth on
inner curve

hairy lobe

1

2

3

4

1mm

418

PLATE P

MALE GENITALIA OF *SPHAEROPHORIA* (*continued*).

1. **Sphaerophoria philanthus** – toothed lobe with a very broad 'shoulder'. Inner process long and narrow. *p. 227*
2. **S. potentillae** – hairy lobe very little developed, barely projecting when viewed from below. Inner process long and strap-like. *p. 228*
3. **S. batava** – toothed lobe broadened at base. Inner process very large and prominent. *p. 226*
4. **S. interrupta** – upper tooth of toothed lobe much more strongly developed than the lower. Left and right toothed lobes very strongly asymmetrical (as in some other species). *p. 227*
5. **S. virgata** – toothed lobe with a very strong 'shoulder', but with only a small apical tooth. Inner process long, thin and pointed. *p. 229*

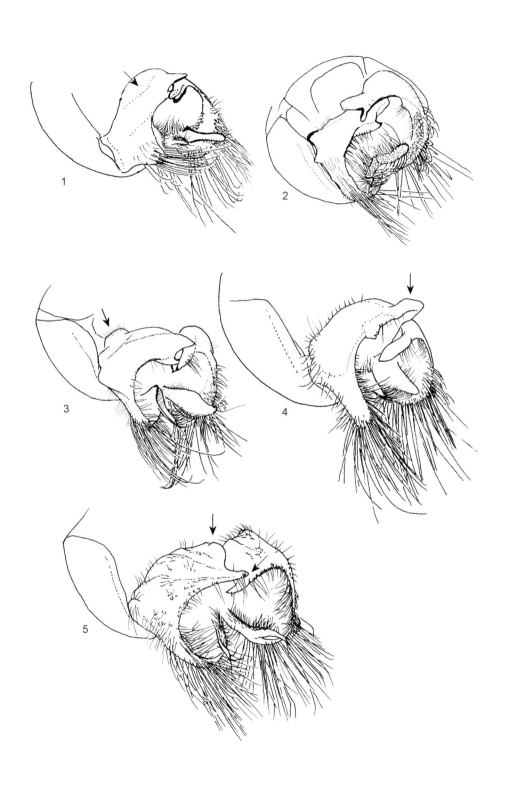

PLATE Q

MALE GENITALIA OF *SPHAEROPHORIA* (*continued*).

1

2

3

4

5

PLATE R

Platycheirus male front legs (figs 1-16), abdomens of Syrphini (figs. 17-19).

1. **P. melanopsis** *p. 179*
2. **P. manicatus** *p. 179*
3. **P. tarsalis** *p. 184*
4. **P. discimanus** *p. 177*
5. **P. peltatus** *p. 181*
6. **P. albimanus** *p. 174*
7. **P. scutatus** *p. 183*
8. **P. podagratus** *p. 182*
9. **P. angustatus** *p. 175*
10. **P. clypeatus** *p. 176*
11. **P. fulviventris** *p. 178*
12. **P. perpallidus** *p. 181*
13. **P. immarginatus** *p. 178*
14. **P. scambus** *p. 182*
15. **P. sticticus** *p. 184*
16. **P. ambiguus** *p. 171*
17. **Sphaerophoria loewi** male *p. 227*
18. **Sphaerophoria loewi** female *p. 227*
19. **Scaeva mecogramma** *p. 223*

Drawn by S.J. Falk.

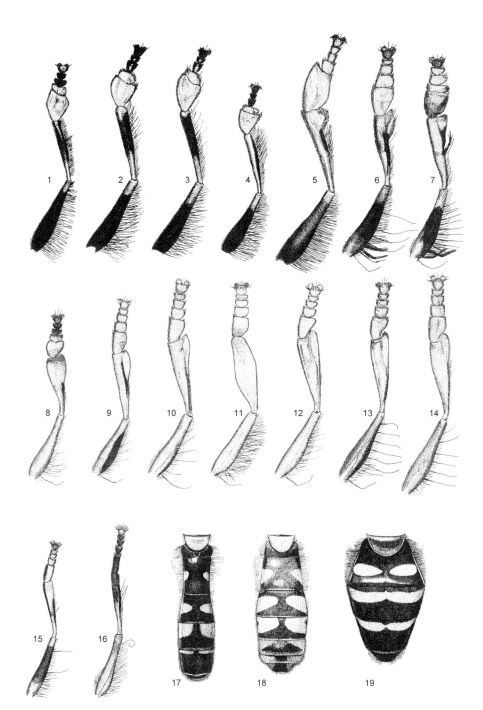

PLATE 1 (3⅓×)

BACCHINI Scutellum black and face black, otherwise often resembling Syrphini on plates 2 & 3.
PARAGINI (*Paragus* only) Tiny compact, mainly black flies. Face partly yellow.

1. **Baccha elongata** This species is distinct in having such a slender abdomen. (♂) p. 168
2. **Melanostoma scalare** Genus has slender front tibiae and tarsi in the male, females with triangular spots of distinctive orientation. Male *scalare* have a very elongate abdomen. (*a* ♂, *b* ♀) p. 170
3. **M. mellinum** Male has a short abdomen; female also rather short, often melanic. (*a* ♂, *b* ♀, *c* melanic ♀) p. 169
4. **Platycheirus (Pyrophaena) granditarsus** Very distinctive reddish-orange species, male pattern like *Xylota segnis* but front tarsi expanded and hind femur slender. (*a* ♂, *b* ♀, *c* intersex) p. 185
5. **P. (Pyrophaena) rosarum** Very distinctive because of yellow spots on tergite 3. Note rather pear-shaped abdomen. (*a* ♂, *b* ♀) p. 185
6. **P. (Platycheirus) albimanus** Largest and commonest grey-spotted species in the genus. (*a* ♂, *b* ♀) p. 174
7. **P. (Pachysphyria) ambiguus** Male front femur with a curled hair at apex, female with grey bands. (*a* ♂, *b* ♀) p. 171
8. **P. (Platycheirus) scutatus** With basic pattern of yellow spots, so compare shapes with other species. Look also at shape of male front feet. (*a* ♂, *b* ♀) p. 183
9. **P. (P.) sticticus** A small very slender grey-spotted species, male front legs almost cylindrical. (*a* ♂, *b* ♀) p. 184
10. **P. (P.) discimanus** Rather like a small *albimanus*, male front tarsi very different. (*a* ♂, *b* ♀) p. 177
11. **P. (P.) podagratus** Male slender, rather like *Melanostoma scalare*, but front legs expanded. Female with rather rounded spots. (*a* ♂, *b* ♀) p. 182
12. **P. (P.) peltatus** Large species, male front tarsus with basal segment large and asymmetrical. (♂) p. 181
13. **P. (P.) manicatus** Male with long rounded spots. (♂) p. 179
14. **P. (P.) melanopsis** Male with very short abdomen, tergite 2 with spots far back. (♂) p. 179
15. **P. (P.) tarsalis** Male tergite 2 with elongate spots, front tarsus with only first two segments expanded (see also 13 & 14). (♂) p. 184
16. **P. (P.) clypeatus** Male with gently tapering front tibia and tarsus (as in 17-21), but note small round spots on tergite 2. Female tergite 2 may have smaller spots than shown. (*a* ♂, *b* ♀) p. 176
17. **P. (P.) angustatus** A very slender species. Female sometimes only with spots on tergite 3. (*a* ♂, *b* ♀) p. 175
18. **P. (P.) fulviventris** Very extensive yellow markings (closely similar to 19-21). (*a* ♂, *b* ♀) p. 178
19. **P. (P.) perpallidus** See key for differences from *fulviventris*. (*a* ♂, *b* ♀) p. 181
20. **P. (P.) immarginatus** Female with hind margin of spots oblique. (*a* ♂, *b* ♀) p. 178
21. **P. (P.) scambus** Tergite 2 with markings more elongate and triangular. (*a* ♂, *b* ♀) p. 182
22. **Xanthandrus comtus** Large like many Syrphini, but scutellum black. Tergite 2 with round spots. Very distinctive. (*a* ♂, *b* ♀) p. 186
23. **Paragus (P.) albifrons** Small compact-bodied species. Face partly yellow, legs partly yellow – useful when comparing with other black-bodied genera. (*a* ♂, *b* ♀) p. 188
24. **P. (Pandasyopthalmus) haemorrhous** Abdomen slightly waisted (as in *tibialis*), otherwise like *albifrons*. (*a* ♂, *b* ♀) p. 187

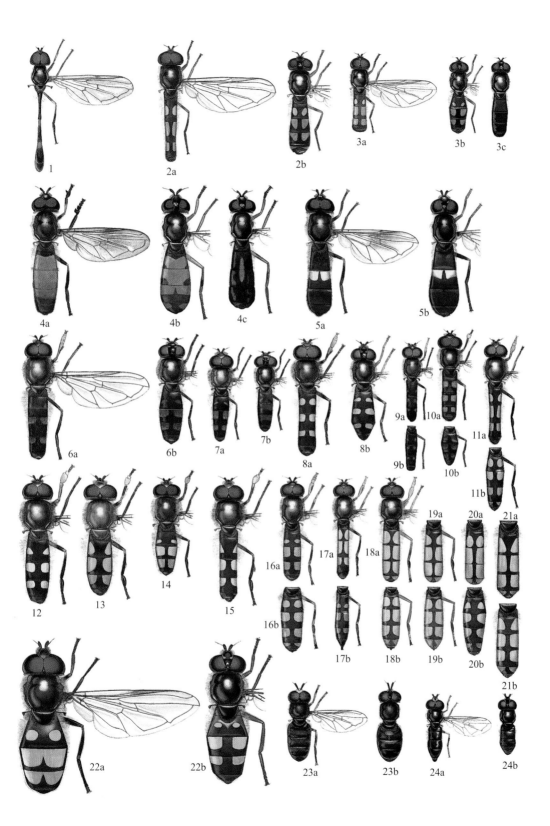

PLATE 2 (3⅓×)

SYRPHINI Scutellum yellow, abdomen with bold yellow markings.

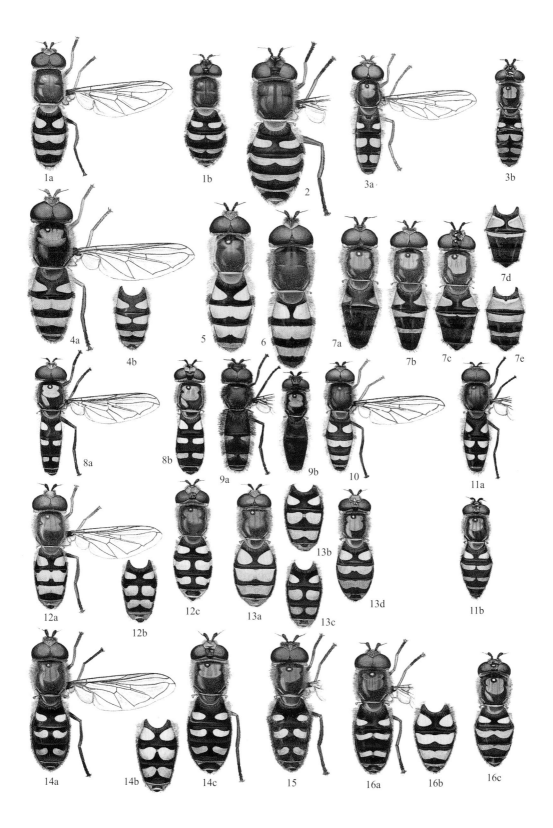

1a   1b   2   3a   3b

4a   4b   5   6   7a   7b   7c   7d   7e

8a   8b   9a   9b   10   11a

12a   12b   12c   13a   13b   13c   13d   11b

14a   14b   14c   15   16a   16b   16c

PLATE 3 (3⅓×)

SYRPHINI (cont.) Scutellum yellow, abdomen with bold yellow markings. This plate includes Syrphini which have wing vein R₄₊₅ dipped (*Eupeodes s.g. Lapposyrphus, Didea, Eriozona erratica*) or fairly dipped (*Scaeva*) – see also *Chrysotoxum* on plate 4.

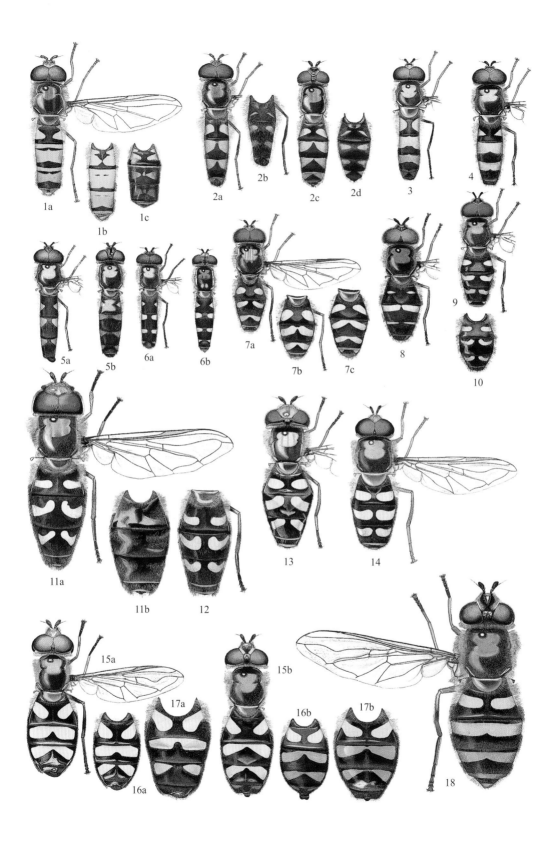

PLATE 4 (3⅓×)

SYRPHINI (cont.) Scutellum yellow, abdomen usually with bold markings. Species with largest markings on tergite 2 (*Leucozona*), or a bumblebee mimic (*Eriozona syrphoides*), or with yellow markings on pleura and conspicuously yellow at sides of thoracic dorsum (*Xanthogramma, Chrysotoxum, Doros, Sphaerophoria*).

1. **Leucozona (Leucozona) lucorum** Dark patch on wing, tergite 2 mainly whitish or pale yellow. Male sometimes with tergite 2 darker, (*a* typical ♂, *b* dark ♀) — *p. 211*
2. **Leucozona (Ischyrosyrphus) glaucia** Wing with dark stigma. Markings on tergite 2 large, especially in male. Scutellum yellow; front legs mainly yellow. (*a* ♂, *b* ♀) — *p. 211*
3. **L. (I.) laternaria** Scutellum only yellow at apex; front legs mainly black. (♂) — *p. 211*
4. **Xanthogramma pedissequum** Thorax with strong yellow side stripes. Tergite 2 with broadly triangular markings; wings partly dark in front. (♂) — *p. 234*
5. **X. citrofasciatum** Tergite 2 with narrow wedges; wings clearer. (♂) — *p. 234*
6. **Chrysotoxum bicinctum** Strong bars or bands on tergites 2 and 4 only. Genus has long antennae. (♂) — *p. 190*
7. **C. festivum** Abdomen black with three pairs of bars; bars are rather curved and do not reach side margins. (♂) — *p. 192*
8. **C. vernale** Abdomen as *festivum*, but bars straighter. (♂) — *p. 193*
9. **C. cautum** A large species with very straight black bars. (♂) — *p. 190*
10. **C. elegans** A fairly large species with markings of variable extent. (typical ♂) — *p. 191*
11. **C. arcuatum** Small compact species (eyes with dense dark hairs). (♂) — *p. 190*
12. **C. octomaculatum** Black at front edge of tergites 3 and 4 interrupted before margin, but actual margin black. (♂) — *p. 192*
13. **C. verralli** Tergite 2 with front black margin straight rather than arcuate. (♂) — *p. 193*
14. **Doros profuges** Large species with elongate waisted abdomen; front margin of wing darkened. (♂) — *p. 199*
15. **Eriozona syrphoides** Furry bumblebee mimic with yellow scutellum, dark patch on wing and ground colour at tip of abdomen red. (♂) — *p. 203*
16. **Sphaerophoria scripta** Genus of small slender flies with yellow stripe at side of thoracic dorsum. Unlike other species, *scripta* males have the abdomen much longer than the wings. (*a & b* ♂, *c* ♀) — *p. 228*
17. **S. interrupta** A common but variable species. (♂) — *p. 227*
18. **S. taeniata** Rather larger and brighter than other species. (♂) — *p. 229*
19. **S. philanthus** A small dark species. (♂) — *p. 227*
20. **S. rueppellii** Small species with yellow at side of thorax not a complete stripe. Male with abdomen waisted. Antennae usually pale (unlike *loewi*). (♂) — *p. 228*

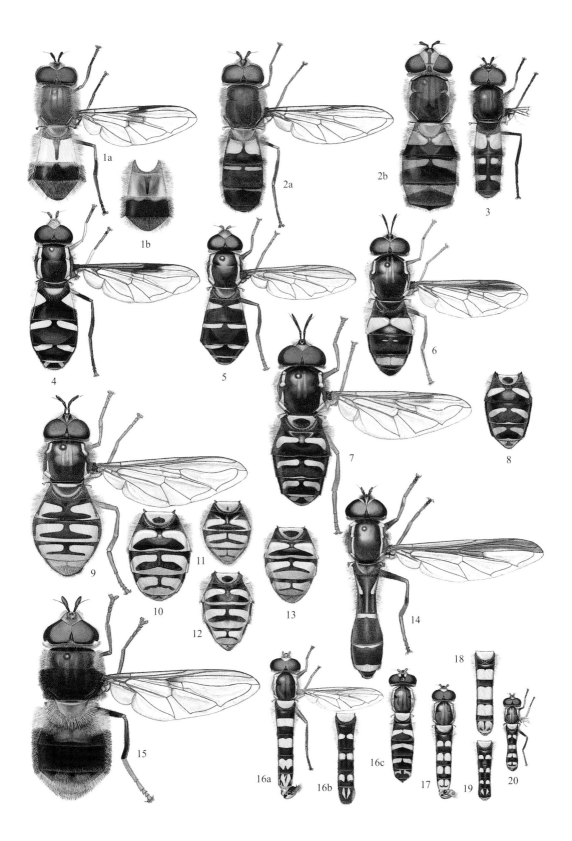

PLATE 5 (4×)

CHEILOSIINI Distinctive genera *Ferdinandea*, *Rhingia*, *Portevinia* (figs. 1, 2, 4-6)
MERODONTINI *Psilota*, resembling Pipizini (fig. 3).
PIPIZINI Mainly black species, flat hairy face (figs. 7-17).
PELECOCERINI Lower half of face expanded, third antennal segment large and with short thick arista (figs. 18-20)

1. **Ferdinandea cuprea** Thorax with grey stripes, legs orange, abdomen brassy. (♂) — *p. 266*
2. **F. ruficornis** A blacker species. Thoracic dorsum with lateral bristles (generic character), abdomen black. (♂) — *p. 266*
3. **Psilota anthracina** Dumpy bluish-black species, wings strongly yellowish in front. (♂) — *p. 305*
4. **Rhingia campestris** Face with long snout, orange abdomen often black on centre line, always black on lateral edge (not visible). (♂) — *p. 268*
5. **R. rostrata** Snout slightly shorter. Abdomen entirely orange except sometimes on centre line of tergite 2 (as shown). (♂) — *p. 268*
6. **Portevinia maculata** Grey spots, build much more robust than *Platycheirus* (Pl. 1, fig. 6). (♂) — *p. 267*
7. **Pipizella viduata** Upper outer cross-vein fairly upright, third antennal segment elongate (not very apparent in illustration), hind tibia with pale fringe of hairs anteriorly. Compact build. (♂) — *p. 319*
8. **P. virens** More elongate, somewhat brassy coloured. (♂) — *p. 319*
9. **Trichopsomyia flavitarsis** Upper outer cross-vein fairly upright. Hind tibia with black fringe of hairs on anterior surface. Female with spots on tergite 2. (*a* ♂, *b* ♀) — *p. 320*
10. **Heringia (Heringia) heringi** Upper outer cross-vein strongly oblique. Third antennal segment oval and partly pale beneath. (♂) — *p. 308*
11. **Heringia (Neocnemodon) vitripennis** Differs from subgenus *Heringia* in having a spur beneath hind coxae in male and third antennal segment often round. (♂) — *p. 311*
12. **Triglyphus primus** Usually only three tergites visible, tergite 4 not apparent or only very short. (*a* ♂, *b* ♀) — *p. 320*
13. **Pipiza noctiluca** Genus with oblique upper outer cross-vein, antennae black, third antennal segment often semi-rhomboid. Presence or absence of spots varies within species more than illustrated. *P. noctiluca* is typical, being the commonest species. (*a* ♂, *b* ♀) — *p. 315*
14. **P. luteitarsis** The front tarsus is extensively yellow. (♂) — *p. 315*
15. **P. fenestrata** Typically a rather large species. The male can have one or two pairs of spots, or is completely black. (♀) — *p. 314*
16. **P. lugubris** There is a strong sharply defined wing patch. (♀) — *p. 314*
17. **P. austriaca** The hind femur is strongly swollen. (♂) — *p. 313*
18. **Pelecocera tricincta** Like a tiny *Meliscaeva cinctella* (Pl. 3, fig. 3), but scutellum black. (*a* ♂, *b* ♀) — *p. 307*
19. **Chamaesyrphus scaevoides** Like *Platycheirus* but front leg cylindrical in the male and the face is partly yellow. *Melangyna* has a yellow scutellum. (*a* ♂, *b* ♀) — *p. 307*
20. **C. caledonicus** Spots are much reduced and greyish. (♀) — *p. 306*

1

2

3

4

5

6

7

8

9a

9b

10

11

12a

12b

13a

13b

14

15

16

17

18a

18b

19a

19b

20

PLATE 6 (4×)

CHEILOSIINI — *Cheilosia*. The illustrations give a general view of the appearance of this large genus and are of limited use in identifying species. There is often considerable sexual dimorphism.

PLATE 7 (4×)

CHRYSOGASTRINI Wing with cross-vein r-m near base of discal cell. Face often concave, at least in female.

MERODONTINI *Eumerus:* flat hairy face, upper outer cross-vein re-entrant.

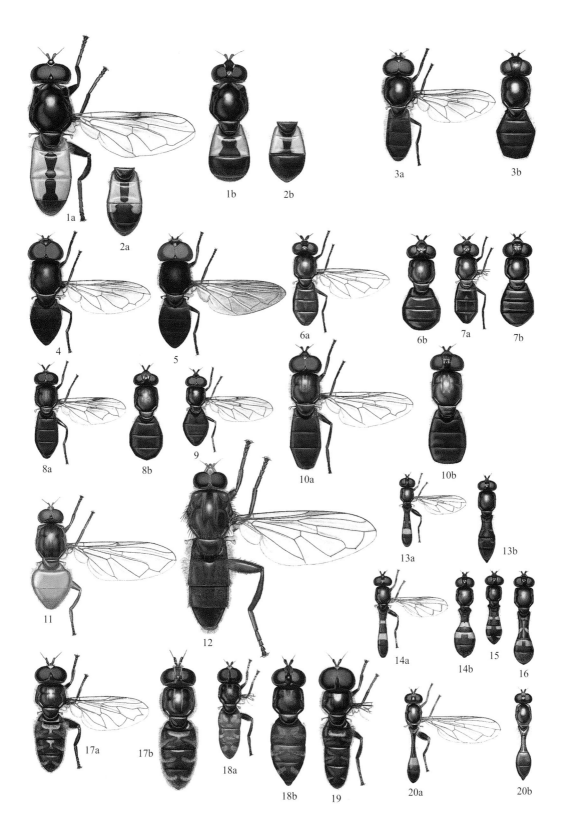

1a 2a 1b 2b 3a 3b

4 5 6a 6b 7a 7b

8a 8b 9 10a 10b

11 12 13a 13b

14a 14b 15 16

17a 17b 18a 18b 19 20a 20b

PLATE 8 (2⅔×)

VOLUCELLINI Upper outer cross-vein re-entrant.
SERICOMYIINI Upper outer cross-vein not re-entrant.
These are large robust flies with a plumose arista (note that because of their size, they are drawn only at 2⅔×)

1. **Volucella bombylans** A bumblebee mimic, the only one with a re-entrant outer cross-vein. The typical form has a red-haired tail and var. *plumata* a white-haired tail. A rare variety has extensively pale hairs. (*a* var. *plumata* ♂, *b* typical form ♂, *c* pale-haired variety ♀) *p. 323*
2. **V. pellucens** Tergite 2 is mainly white. (♂) *p. 324*
3. **V. inflata** Like *pellucens* but tergite 2 is orange and the thoracic dorsum has orange sides. (♀) *p. 324*
4. **V. inanis** All tergites have similar yellow markings. (♂) *p. 323*
5. **V. zonaria** Like *inanis* but larger and tergite 2 has chestnut-brown markings. (♀) *p. 324*
6. **Sericomyia lappona** The tergites have narrow bars which are whitish in life though often becoming yellowish in a collection. (♂) *p. 321*
7. **S. silentis** A larger species with broader wedge-shaped yellow bars. (♂) *p. 322*
8. **Arctophila superbiens** A bumblebee mimic with uniformly brown (or grey) hairs and a dark wing cloud. (♂) *p. 321*

1a

1b

1c

2

3

4

5

6

7

8

PLATE 9 (3⅓×)

CALLICERINI (*Callicera* only) Long antennae with a terminal arista.

MICRODONTINAE (*Microdon* only) Long antennae with a dorsal arista, extra incomplete cross-vein in cell r_5.

XYLOTINI *Xylota* and allies, with rather parallel-sided abdomen, a swollen hind femur and characteristic patterns.

1. **Callicera spinolae** Bands of golden hairs across bronze abdomen and darkening near wing tip. (♀)   *p. 239*
2. **C. aurata** Like *spinolae*, but lacking distinct bands of golden hairs and wing clear of darkening near apex. (♀)   *p. 238*
3. **C. rufa** A reddish-haired species. (♀)   *p. 239*
4. **Microdon analis** Scutellum dark, as in *devius*. (♂)   *p. 338*
5. **M. myrmicae** Scutellum orange. (♀)   *p. 340*
6. **Xylota segnis** Orange-red-belted abdomen, legs partly pale. (♂)   *p. 335*
7. **X. tarda** As *segnis*, but hind margin of tergite 2 faintly darkened and abdomen slightly bulbous, especially in the female. (*a* ♂, *b* ♀)   *p. 336*
8. **X. florum** Rather elongate species with paired spots. (*a* ♂, *b* ♀)   *p. 334*
9. **X. jakutorum** Shorter abdomen than *florum* and male spots not elongate. (*a* ♂, *b* ♀)   *p. 334*
10. **X. abiens** The hind tibia is only narrowly pale at the base (thus compare with *C. nemorum* rather than *X. florum* or *jakutorum*). (*a* ♂, *b* ♀)   *p. 333*
11. **X. xanthocnema** Tergite 4 with adpressed golden hairs, hind tibia entirely yellow from all view points. (♂)   *p. 335*
12. **X. sylvarum** As *xanthocnema* but often larger and with the hind tibia dark in the distal half from some angles of view. (♂)   *p. 335*
13. **Chalcosyrphus (Xylotina) nemorum** A very short-bodied species with the hind tibia mostly dark, and very swollen hind femora. (*a* ♂, *b* ♀)   *p. 328*
14. **Brachypalpoides lentus** Differs from *X. segnis* in that the belt is blood-red (may become dull in collections) and the legs are entirely black. (♂)   *p. 326*

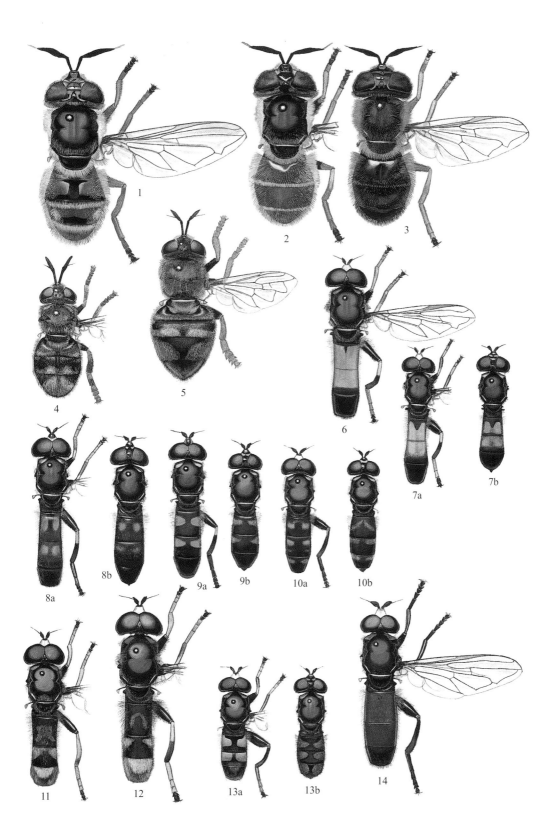

1
2
3
4
5
6
7a
7b
8a
8b
9a
9b
10a
10b
11
12
13a
13b
14

PLATE 10 (3⅓×)

XYLOTINI (cont.) Varied but distinctive genera. Wing with cross-vein r-m beyond middle of discal cell (except in some *Syritta*).

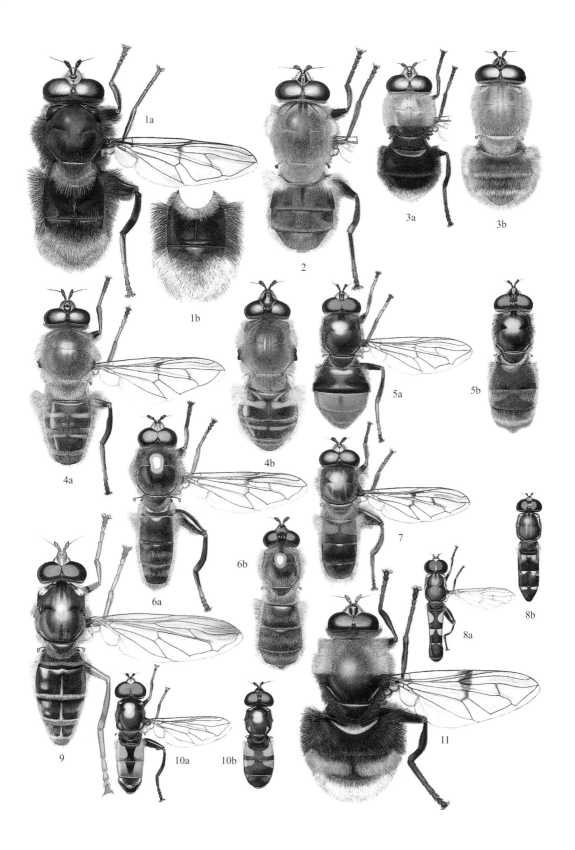

1a

1b

2

3a

3b

4a

4b

5a

5b

6a

6b

7

8a

8b

9

10a

10b

11

PLATE 11 (2⅔×)

ERISTALINI Deep loop in wing vein R_{4+5}, upper and lower outer cross-veins form a virtually continuous vein parallel with the wing margin.

1a

1b

1c

2

3

4a

4b

4c

5

6a

6b

7

8

9

10

11

12

PLATE 12 (3⅓×)

ERISTALINI (cont.) Species usually with a striped thorax.
MERODONTINI (cont.) Wings as in Eristalini but with re-entrant upper outer cross-vein.

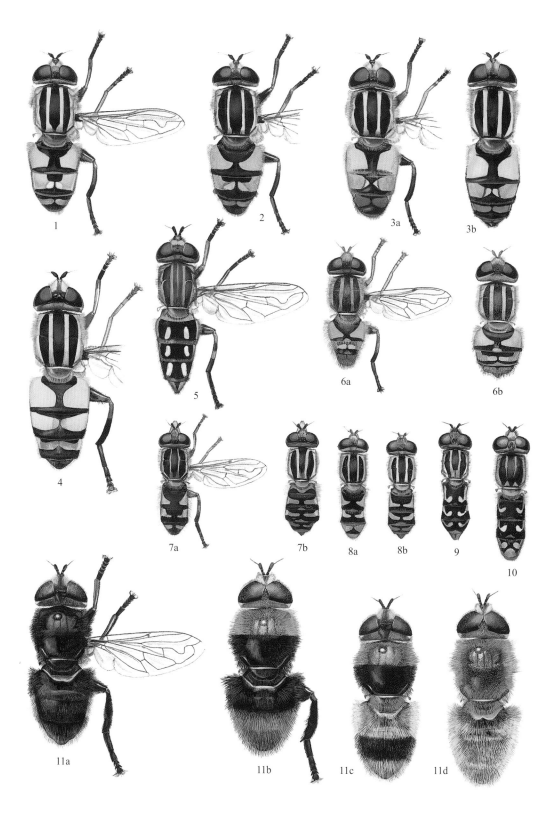

1　2　3a　3b　4　5　6a　6b　7a　7b　8a　8b　9　10　11a　11b　11c　11d

INDEXES

List of plant names used in the text

The names of plants follow Stace (1997). Dipterists usually refer to plants by their English names and, where these can only be related to genera, the most likely species are given here.

Alder   *Alnus glutinosa* (L.) Gaertn.
Alder Buckthorn   *Frangula Alnus* Mill.
Alpine Bistort   *Polygonum viviparum* L.
Angelica   *Angelica sylvestris* L.
Apple   *Malus* spp.
Ash   *Fraxinus excelsior* L.
Aspen   *Populus tremula* L.
Autumn Hawkbit   *Leontodon autumnalis* L.

Balsam Poplar   *Populus balsamifera* L. [not native]
Barberry   *Berberis* spp.
Bedstraws   *Galium* spp.
Beech   *Fagus sylvatica* L.
Birch   *Betula* [*pendula* Roth. and *pubescens* Ehrh.]
Bird Cherry   *Prunus padus* L.
Black Currant   *Ribes nigrum* L.
Black Poplar   *Populus nigra* L. [scarce native]; usually applied to *Populus x canadensis* 'Serotina'
Blackthorn   *Prunus spinosa* L.
Bluebell   *Hyacinthoides non-scripta* (L.) Chouard ex Rothm.
Bog Asphodel   *Narthecium ossifragrum* (L.) Huds.
Bogbean   *Menyanthes trifoliate* L.
Bottle Sedge   *Carex rostrata* Stokes
Bramble   *Rubus fruticosus* L. agg.
Broom   *Cytisus scoparius* (L.) Link
Buckthorn   *Rhamnus cathartica* L.
Buddleia   *Buddleja davidii* Franch. [not native]
Bugle   *Ajuga reptans* L.
Bulbous Buttercup   *Ranunculus bulbosus* L.
Bulrush   *Typha* [usually *latifolia* L.]
Burnet-saxifrage   *Pimpinella saxifraga* L.
Bur-reeds   *Sparganium* spp.
Butterbur   *Petasites hybridus* (L.) P. Gaertn., B. Mey. & Scherb.
Buttercups   *Ranunculus* spp.

Cabbage Thistle	*Cirsium oleraceum* (L.) Scop.
Cat's-ears	*Hypochoeris* spp.
Cherry Laurel	*Prunus laurocerasus* L. [non-native, widely planted]
Colt's-foot	*Tussilago farfara* L.
Common Figwort	*Scrophularia nodosa* L.
Common Fleabane	*Pulicaria dysenterica* (L.) Bernh.
Common Lady's Mantle	*Alchemilla vulgaris* L.
Common Mouse-ear	*Cerastium fontanum* Baumg.
Common Ragwort	*Senecio jacobaea* L.
Common Reed	*Phragmites australis* (Cav.) Trin. ex Steud.
Composites	Asteraceae (= Compositae)
Cow Parsley	*Anthriscus sylvestris* (L.) Hoffm.
Creeping Buttercup	*Ranunculus repens* L.
Creeping Thistle	*Cirsium arvense* (L.) Scop.
Creeping Willow	*Salix repens* L.
Cross-leaved Heath	*Erica tetralix* L.
Crosswort	*Cruciata laevipes* Opiz
Daffodils	*Narcissus* spp.
Daisy	*Bellis perennis* L.
Dandelions	*Taraxacum* spp.
Devil's-bit scabious	*Succisa pratensis* Moench
Dewberry	*Rubus caesius* L.
Docks	*Rumex* spp.
Dog's Mercury	*Mercurialis perennis* L.
Douglas Fir	*Pseudotsuga menziesii* (Mirb.) Franco [non-native, planted in forestry]
Elm	*Ulmus* spp.
English Elm	*Ulmus procera* Salisb.
European Silver-fir	*Abies alba* Mill. [non-native]
Field Maple	*Acer campestre* L.
Figworts	*Scrophularia* spp.
Fir	*Abies* spp. [not native, commonly planted in forestry]
Fool's-water-cress	*Apium nodiflorum* (L.) Lag.
Forget-me-nots	*Myosotis* spp.
Foxglove	*Digitalis purpurea* L.
Garlic Mustard	*Alliaria petiolata* (M. Bieb.) Cavara & Grande
Globe Artichoke	*Cynara scolymus* L. [cultivated]
Globeflower	*Trollius europaeus* L.
Goat Willow	*Salix caprea* L.
Goatsbeard	*Tragopogon pratensis* L.
Goosefoots	*Chenopodium* spp.
Great Willowherb	*Epilobium hirsutum* L.

Navelwort	*Umbilicus rupestris* (Salisb.) Dandy
Nettles	*Urtica* spp.
Northern Dock	*Rumex longifolius* DC.
Norway spruce	*Picea abies* (L.) H. Karst. [not native, commonly planted in forestry]
Oak	*Quercus robur* L., *Q. petraea* (Matt.) Liebl. and various non-native *Quercus* spp.
Onion	*Allium cepa* L. [cultivated]
Orpine	*Sedum telephium* L.
Oxeye Daisy	*Leucanthemum vulgare* Lam.
Oxlip	*Primula elatior* (L.) Hill
Parsnip	*Pastinaca sativa* L. var. *hortensis* Gaudin [cultivated]
Pignut	*Conopodium majus* (Gouan) Loret
Pines	*Pinus* spp. [native *sylvestris* and various non-native species commonly planted in forestry]
Plantains	*Plantago* spp.
Poplars	*Populus* spp.
Potato	*Solanum tuberosum* L. [cultivated]
Primrose	*Primula vulgaris* Huds.
Primulas	*Primula* spp. [cultivated]
Purple Moor-grass	*Molinia caerulea* (L.) Moench
Ragworts	*Senecio* spp.
Ramsons	*Allium ursinum* L.
Raspberry	*Rubus idaeus* L.
Red Campion	*Silene dioica* (L.) Clairv.
Redshank	*Persicaria maculosa* Gray
Reed Canary-grass	*Phalaris arundinacea* L.
Reed Sweet-grass	*Glyceria maxima* (Hartm.) Holumb.
Ribwort Plantain	*Plantago lanceolata* L.
Rose	*Rosa* spp.
Rosebay Willowherb	*Chamerion angustifolium* (L.) Holub
Rowan	*Sorbus aucuparia* L.
Rushes	*Juncus* spp.
Sallow	*Salix cinerea* L., *caprea* L. and other broad-leaved willows
Sanicle	*Sanicula europaea* L.
Saxifrage	*Saxifraga* spp.
Scented Mayweed	*Matricaria recutita* L. (= *chamomilla* L.)
Scentless Mayweed	*Tripleurospermum inodorum*(L.) Sch. Bip.
Scotch Thistle	*Onopordum acanthium* L.
Scots Pine	*Pinus sylvestris* L.
Scottish Dock	*Rumex aquaticus* L.
Sea Club-rush	*Bolboschoenus maritimus* (L.) Palla (= *Scirpus maritimus* L.)

Index to names other than hoverflies

Index to hoverfly names

All species mentioned are indexed. The currently accepted names of British hoverflies are shown in plain text and names in *italic face* are either synonyms or are non-British species. Page numbers for the main species account are in **bold face**, those for names appearing in the keys are in *italic face*, whilst remaining entries are in plain text. The reference list is not indexed. Otherwise the species epithets and genera are fully indexed except in the species accounts where cross-references between species in the same genus have been omitted.